NEWSWEEK CONDENSED BOOKS

CALVIN TRILLIN

RICHARD M. COHEN and JULES WITCOVER

WALTER McQUADE and ANN AIKMAN

CHARLES NEIDER

AMERICAN FRIED
ADVENTURES OF A HAPPY EATER

A HEARTBEAT AWAY
THE INVESTIGATION AND RESIGNATION OF
VICE PRESIDENT SPIRO T. AGNEW

STRESS
WHAT IT IS, WHAT IT CAN DO TO YOUR
HEALTH, HOW TO FIGHT BACK

EDGE OF THE WORLD
ROSS ISLAND, ANTARCTICA

NEWSWEEK BOOKS, New York

NEWSWEEK CONDENSED BOOKS

Kermit Lansner, Editor

NEWSWEEK BOOKS

Joseph L. Gardner, Editor
Janet Czarnetzki, Art Director
Barbara Graustark, Copy Editor
Susan S. Gombocz, Picture Researcher

S. Arthur Dembner, President

CONTENTS

AMERICAN FRIED

ADVENTURES OF
A HAPPY EATER

A condensation of the book by
CALVIN TRILLIN

The best restaurants in the world are, of course, in Kansas City. Not all of them; only the top four or five. Anyone who has visited Kansas City and still doubts that statement has my sympathy: He never made it to the right places. Being in a traveling trade myself, I know the problem of asking someone in a strange city for the best restaurant in town and being led to some purple palace that serves "Continental cuisine" and has as its chief creative employee a menu-writer rather than a chef. I have sat in those places, an innocent wayfarer, reading a three-paragraph description of what the trout is wrapped in, how long it has been sautéed, what province its sauce comes from, and what it is likely to sound like sizzling on my platter—a description lacking only the information that before the poor trout went through that process it had been frozen for eight and a half months.

In American cities the size of Kansas City, a careful traveling man has to observe the rule that any restaurant the executive secretary of the chamber of commerce is particularly proud of is almost certainly not worth eating in. Its name will be something like La Maison de la Casa

House, Continental cuisine; its food will sound European but taste as if the continent they had in mind was Australia. Lately, a loyal chamber man in practically any city is likely to recommend one of those restaurants that have sprouted in the past several years on the tops of bank buildings, all of them encased in glass and some of them revolving—offering the diner not only Continental cuisine and a twenty-thousand-word menu but a spectacular view of other restaurants spinning around on the top of other bank buildings. "No, thank you," I finally said to the twelfth gracious host who invited me to one of those. "I never eat in a restaurant that's over a hundred feet off the ground and won't stand still."

What is saddest about a visitor's sitting in the Continental cuisine palace chewing on what an honest menu would have identified as Frozen Duck à l'Orange Soda Pop is that he is likely to have passed a spectacular restaurant on the way over. Despite the best efforts of forward-looking bankers and mad-dog franchisers, there is still great food all over the country, but the struggle to wring information from the locals about where it is served can sometimes leave a traveler too exhausted to eat. I often manage to press on with a seemingly hopeless interrogation only because of my certain knowledge that the information is available—discussed openly by the residents in their own homes, the way that French villagers might have discussed what they really thought of the occupation troops they had been polite to in the shops. As it happens, I grew up in Kansas City and spent hours of my youth talking about where a person could find the best fried chicken, barbecued ribs or hamburgers in the world—all, by chance, available at that time within the city limits of Kansas City, Missouri. I grew up among the kind of people whose response some years later to a preposterous claim about Little Rock's having a place that served better spareribs than the ones served by Arthur Bryant's Barbecue at Eighteenth and Brooklyn was to fly to Little Rock, sample the ribs, sneer, and fly back to Kansas City.

Knowing that the information exists does make me impatient if some civic booster in, say, one of the middle-sized cities of the Southwest is keeping me from dinner by answering my simple questions about restaurants with a lot of talk about the wine cellar of some palace that has inlaid wallpaper chosen personally by a man who is supposed to be the third best interior decorator in San Francisco. As the booster goes on about the onion soup with croutons and the sophisticated headwaiter named Jean-Pierre, my mind sometimes wanders off into a fantasy in which my interrogation of the booster is taking place in the presence of one of those ominous blond Germans from the World War II films—the ones with the steel-blue eyes and the small scars who sat silently in the corner while the relatively civilized German line officer asked the downed Allied flyer for military information. "I do hope you will now agree to tell me if there's any Mexican food worth eating around here and quit talking about the glories to be found in La Maison de la Casa House, Continental cuisine," I tell the booster. "If not, I'm afraid Herr Mueller here has his methods."

It is common for an American city to be vaguely embarrassed about its true delights. In the fifties, a European visitor to New Orleans who insisted on hearing some jazz was routinely taken to hear a group of very respectable-looking white businessmen play Dixieland. A few years ago, I suspect, an Eastern visitor to Nashville who asked a local banker if there was any interesting music in town might have been taken—by a circuitous route, in order to avoid overhearing any of the crude twanging coming out of the Grand Old Opry or the country recording studios—to the home of a prominent dermatologist who had some friends around every Friday night for chamber music. In most American cities, a booster is likely to insist on defending the place to outsiders in terms of what he thinks of as the sophisticated standards of New York—a city, he makes clear at the start, he would not consider living in even if the alternative were moving with his family and belongings to Yakutsk, Siberia, U.S.S.R. A visitor, particularly a visitor from the East, is invariably subjected to a thirty-minute commercial about the improvement in the local philharmonic, a list of Broadway plays (well, musicals) that have been through in the past year, and some comments like "We happen to have an *excellent* French restaurant here now." The short answer to that one, of course, would be "No you don't." An American city's supply of even competent French restaurants is limited by the number of residents willing to patronize them steadily, and, given the difficulty of finding or importing ingredients and capturing a serious chef and attracting a clientele sufficiently critical to keep the chef from spending most of his time playing the commodities market out of boredom, "an *excellent* French restaurant" will arrive in Tulsa or Omaha at about the time those places near the waterfront in Marseilles start turning out quality pan-fried chicken.

"I don't suppose your friends took you to Mary-Mac's on Ponce de Leon for a bowl of pot likker, did they?" I once said to a friend of mine who had just returned from her first visit to Atlanta. Naturally not. No civic-minded residents of Atlanta—which advertises itself as the World's

Next Great City—would take an out-of-town guest to Mary-Mac's. Their idea of a regional eating attraction is more likely to be some place built to look like one of the charming antebellum houses that Atlanta once had practically none of—having been, before Sherman got there, an almost new railroad terminus that had all the antebellum charm of Parsons, Kansas. Pot likker, I told my friend, is the liquid left in the bottom of the greens pot, is eaten like a soup, after crumbling some corn bread into it, and is what a Great City would advertise instead of a lot of golf courses.

"They took me to a very nice French restaurant," she said, gamely claiming that it was almost as good as the one she can go to for lunch on days she doesn't feel like walking far enough to get to the decent places.

Since "No you don't" would be considered an impolite reply to the usual boast about a city's having a three-star French restaurant, I have, in the past, stooped to such responses as "French food makes me break out." I love French food. (In fairness, I should say that I can't think of a nation whose food I don't love, although in Ethiopia I was put off a bit by the appearance of the bread, which looks like a material that has dozens of practical uses, not including being eaten as food.) But who wants to hear a skin doctor saw away at the cello when Johnny Cash is right down the street? Lately, when the local booster informs me—as the city ordinance apparently requires him to do within ten minutes of meeting anyone who lives in New York—that he would never live in New York himself, I say something like, "Well, it's not easy of course. There's no barbecue to speak of. That's because of a shortage of hickory wood, I think, although I haven't checked out that theory with Arthur Bryant. We don't really have any Mexican restaurants—I mean the kind you find in Texas, say. Oh, we have Mexican restaurants run by maybe a guy from the East Side who picked up a few recipes while he was down in San Miguel de Allende thinking about becoming a painter, but no Mexican family restaurants. No señora in the kitchen. No Coors beer. No Lone Star. I wouldn't claim that you can live in New York and expect to drink Lone Star. There's a shortage of Chicago-style pizza south of Fourteenth Street. They don't know much about boiling crabs in New York. It's only since the soul-food places opened that we've been able to get any fried chicken, and we still don't have those family-style fried-chicken places with the fresh vegetables and the picked watermelon rind on the table. Sure we've got problems. Grits are a problem. I'd be the last one to say living in New York is easy."

Somehow, people have listened to my entire speech and then suggested that I forget my troubles with some fine Continental cuisine at

La Maison de la Casa House. I'm then forced into playing the restaurant section of the Yellow Pages—trying one system after another, like a thoroughly addicted horse-player who would rather take his chances with a palpably bad system than give up the game altogether. I go with small listings for a while—no place that says anything like "See Advertisement Page 253 of this section." Then places called by someone's first name. Then places not called by someone's first name. For a while, I tried a complicated formula having to do with the number of specialties claimed in relation to the size of the entry, but I could never remember whether the formula called for me to multiply or divide.

There are some types of food that do lend themselves to sophisticated techniques of interrogation. When an Italian restaurant is suggested, for instance, I always say, "Who controls the city council here?" I suppose a good Italian restaurant could exist in a city that doesn't have enough Italians to constitute at least a powerful minority in city politics, but a man in town for only two or three meals has to go with the percentages. It is axiomatic that good barbecue is almost never served in an obviously redecorated restaurant—the reason being, according to my favorite theory on the subject, that walls covered with that slick precut paneling let the flavor slide away.

Some time ago, I found myself in Muskogee, Oklahoma, with dinnertime approaching, and I asked some people I was having a drink with if they knew of any good barbecue places. Through a system of what amounted to ethnic elimination, I had arrived at barbecue as the food most likely to see me through the evening. There is, I am relieved to say, no Continental cuisine in Muskogee, Oklahoma. The people I was having a drink with were trying to be helpful, perhaps because the liquor laws of Oklahoma see to it that citizens who are taking a Bourbon in public feel so much like criminals—having skulked in through an unmarked back door and flashed some patently phony membership cards—that we had developed the closeness of conspirators. (Even states that allow grown-ups to drink in public with comparative ease expect a traveler to observe some bizarre liquor laws, of course, including at least one I approve of—the Vermont statute that makes it illegal for a customer to carry a drink from one table to another. I have found that a man who picks up his drink and moves to your table is invariably a man who is going to talk at length about how many miles his car gets to the gallon.) One barbecue place was mentioned, but something about the way it was mentioned made me suspicious.

"They have plates there?" I asked.

"What do you mean 'plates'?" one of my fellow criminal-boozers asked me.

"You know—plates you eat off of," I said.

"Of course they have plates," he said.

"You have any other barbecue restaurants around here?" I asked.

"Well," my partner in crime began, "there's an old colored fellow out on the highway who—"

"Tell me how to get there," I said.

It turned out to be a small diner, and if it had been a half-mile closer I might have been able to locate it unassisted by following the perfume of burning hickory logs. There were, as it happened, no plates. The proprietor's version of the formal restaurant custom of including a dinner plate on top of a larger plate at each place setting was to put down a piece of butcher paper and then a piece of waxed paper and then the barbecue—first-class barbecue. It would have been a thoroughly satisfying meal except that my success in finding the place caused me to ponder all through dinner on how much happier traveling would be if only I could think of a workable formula for finding fried-chicken restaurants.

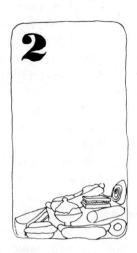

I know a radical from Texas who holds the stock market in contempt but refuses to give up his seven shares of Dr. Pepper. He says that Dr. Pepper, like the late President Eisenhower, is above politics. I have personally acted as a courier in bringing desperately craved burnt-almond chocolate ice cream from Will Wright's in Los Angeles to a friend who survived a Beverly Hills childhood and now lives in New York—living like a Spanish Civil War refugee who hates the regime but would give his arm for a decent bowl of *gazpacho*. I have also, in the dark of night, slipped into a sophisticated apartment in upper Manhattan and left an unmarked paper bag containing a powdered substance called Ranch Dressing —available, my client believes, only in certain supermarkets in the state of Oklahoma. I once knew someone from Alabama who, in moments of melancholy or stress or drunkenness, would gain strength merely by staring up at some imaginary storekeeper and saying, in the accent of an Alabama road-gang worker on his five-minute morning break, "Jes gimme an R.C. and a moon pah."

Because I happened to grow up in Kansas City and now live in New York, there may be, I realize, a temptation to confuse my assessment of Kansas City restaurants with the hallucinations people all over the country suffer when gripped by the fever of Hometown Food Nostalgia. I am aware of the theory held by Bill Vaughan, the humor columnist of the Kansas City *Star,* that millions of pounds of hometown goodies are constantly crisscrossing the country by U.S. mail in search of desperate expatriates—a theory he developed, I believe, while standing in the post office line in Kansas City holding a package of Wolferman's buns that he was about to send off to his son in Virginia. I do not have to be told that there is a tendency among a lot of otherwise sensible adults to believe that the best hamburgers in the world are served in the hamburger stands of their childhood. A friend of mine named William Edgett Smith, after all, a man of good judgment in most matters, clings to the bizarre notion that the best hamburgers in the world are served at Bob's Big Boy— Glendale, California, branch—rather than at Winstead's Drive-in in Kansas City. He has, over the years, stubbornly rejected my acute analysis of the Big Boy as a gimmick burger with a redundant middle bun, a run-of-the-mill triple-decker that is not easily distinguishable from a Howard Johnson's 3-D.

"It has a sesame seed bun," Smith would say, as we sat in some midtown Manhattan bar eating second-rate cheeseburgers at a dollar seventy-five a throw—two expatriates from the land of serious hamburger-eaters.

"Don't talk to me about seeds on buns," I'd say to Smith. "I had a Big Boy in Phoenix and it is not in any way a class burger."

"Phoenix is not Glendale," Smith would say, full of blind stubbornness.

Smith has never been to Winstead's, although he often flies to

California to visit his family (in Glendale, it goes without saying) and I have reminded him that he could lay over in Kansas City for a couple of hours for little extra fare. He has never been able to understand the monumental purity of the Winstead's hamburger—no seeds planted on the buns, no strong sauce that might keep the exquisite flavor of the meat from dominating, no showy meat-thickness that is the downfall of most hamburgers. Winstead's has concentrated so hard on hamburgers that for a number of years it served just about nothing else. Its policy is stated plainly on the menu I have framed on the kitchen wall for inspiration: "We grind U.S. Graded Choice Steak daily for the sandwich and broil on a greaseless grill." That is the only claim Winstead's makes, except "Your drinks are served in sterilized glasses."

I can end any suspicion of hometown bias on my part by recounting the kind of conversation I used to have with my wife, Alice, an Easterner, before I took her back to Kansas City to meet my family and get her something decent to eat. Imagine that we are sitting at some glossy road stop on the Long Island Expressway, pausing for a bite to eat on our way to a fashionable traffic jam:

ME: Anybody who served a milkshake like this in Kansas City would be put in jail.

ALICE: You promised not to indulge in any of that hometown nostalgia while I'm eating. You know it gives me indigestion.

ME: What nostalgia? Facts are facts. The kind of milkshake that I personally consumed six hundred gallons of at the Country Club Dairy is a historical fact in three flavors. Your indigestion is not from listening to my fair-minded remarks on the food of a particular American city. It's from drinking that gray skim milk this bandit is trying to pass off as a milkshake.

ALICE: I suppose it wasn't you who told me that anybody who didn't think the best hamburger place in the world was in his hometown is a sissy.

ME: But don't you see that one of those places actually *is* the best hamburger place in the world? Somebody has to be telling the truth, and it happens to be me.

Alice has now been to Kansas City many times. If she is asked where the best hamburgers in the world are served, she will unhesitatingly answer, from the results of her own extensive quality testing, that they are served at Winstead's. By the time our first child was three, she had already been to Winstead's a few times, and as an assessor of hamburgers, she is, I'm proud to say, her father's daughter. Once, I asked her what I could bring her from a trip to Kansas City. "Bring me a hamburger," she said. I did. I now realize what kind of satisfaction it must have given my father when I, at about the age of ten, finally agreed with him that *Gunga Din* was the greatest movie ever made.

I once went to Kansas City for the express purpose of making a grand tour of its great restaurants. Almost by coincidence, I found myself on the same plane with Fats Goldberg, the New York pizza baron, who grew up in Kansas City and was going back to visit his family and get something decent to eat. Fats, whose real name is Larry, got his nickname when he weighed about three hundred pounds. Some years ago, he got thin, and he has managed to remain at less than one hundred sixty ever since by subjecting himself to a horrifyingly rigid eating schedule. In New York, Fats eats virtually the same thing every day of his life. But he knows that even a man with his legendary will power—a man who can spend every evening of the week in a Goldberg's Pizzeria without tasting—could never diet in Kansas City, so he lets himself go a couple of times a year while he is within the city limits. For Fats, Kansas City is the DMZ. He currently holds the world's record for getting from the airport to Winstead's.

Fats seemed a bit nervous about what we would find at Winstead's. For as long as I can remember, everyone in Kansas City has been saying that Winstead's is going downhill. Even in New York, where there has always been obsessive discussion of Winstead's among people from Kansas City, the Cassandras in our ranks have often talked as if the next double-with-everything-and-grilled-onions I order at Winstead's will come out tasting like something a drugstore counterman has produced by peeling some morbid-looking patty from waxed paper and tossing it on some grease-caked grill—a prophecy that has always proved absolutely false. I can hardly blame a Kansas City emigré for being pessimistic. We have all received letters about Winstead's decline for years—in the way people who grew up in other parts of the country receive letters telling them that the fresh trout they used to love to eat now tastes like turpentine because of the lumber mill upstream or that their favorite picnic meadow has become a trailer park. When Winstead's began serving French-fried potatoes several years ago, there was talk of defection in New York. The price of purity is purists. The French fries did turn out to be unspectacular—a lesson, I thought, that craftsmen should stick to their craft. The going-downhill talk was strong a few years later when Winstead's introduced something called an eggburger. My

17

sister has actually eaten an eggburger—she has always had rather exotic tastes—but I found the idea so embarrassing that I avoided William Edgett Smith for days, until I realized he had no way of knowing about it. Fats told me on the plane that there had been a lot of going-downhill talk since Winstead's sold out to a larger company. He seemed personally hurt by the rumors.

"How can people talk that way?" he said, as we were about to land in Kansas City.

"Don't let it bother you, Fats," I said. "People in Paris are probably always going around saying the Louvre doesn't have any decent pictures any more. It's human nature for the locals to bad-mouth the nearest national monument."

"You'll go to Zarda's Dairy for the banana split, of course," Fats said, apparently trying to cheer himself up by pitching in with some advice for the grand tour. "Also the Toddle House for hash browns. Then you'll have to go to Kresge's for a chili dog."

"Hold it, Fats," I said. "Get control of yourself." He was beginning to look wild. "I'm not sure a grand tour would include Kresge's chili dogs. Naturally, I'll try to get to the Toddle House for hash browns; they're renowned."

I gave Fats a ride from the airport. As we started out, I told him I was supposed to meet my sister and my grandfather at Mario's— a place that had opened a few years before featuring a special sandwich my sister wanted me to try. Mario cuts off the end of a small Italian loaf, gouges out the bread in the middle, puts in meatballs or sausages and cheese, closes everything in by turning around the end he had cut off and using it as a plug, and bakes the whole thing. He says the patent is applied for.

"Mario's!" Fats said. "What Mario's? When I come into town, I go to Winstead's from the airport."

"My grandfather is waiting, Fats," I said. "He's eighty-eight years old. My sister will scream at me if we're late."

"We could go by the North Kansas City Winstead's branch from here, get a couple to go, and eat them on the way to whatzisname's," Fats said. He looked desperate. I realized he had been looking forward to a Winstead's hamburger since his last trip to Kansas City five or six months before—five or six months he had endured without eating anything worth talking about.

That is how Fats and I came to start the grand tour riding toward Mario's clutching Winstead's hamburgers that we would release only long enough to snatch up our Winstead's Frosty Malts ("The Drink You Eat

With a Spoon"), and discussing the quality of the topmeat, no-gimmick burger that Winstead's continued to put out. By the time we approached Mario's, I felt that nothing could spoil my day, even if my sister screamed at me for being late.

"There's LaMar's Do-Nuts," Fats said, pulling at the steering wheel. "They do a sugar doughnut that's dynamite."

"But my grandfather . . ." I said.

"Just pull over for a second," Fats said. "We'll split a couple."

I can now recount a conversation I would like to have had with the "free-lance food and travel writer" who, according to the Kansas City *Star,* spent a few days in town and then called Mario's sandwich "the single best thing I've ever had to eat in Kansas City." I mean no disrespect to Mario, whose sandwich might be good enough to be the single best thing in a lot of cities. I hope he gets his patent.

ME: I guess if that's the best thing you've ever had to eat in Kansas City you must have got lost trying to find Winstead's. Also, I'm surprised at the implication that a fancy free-lance food and travel writer like you was not allowed into Arthur Bryant's Barbecue, which is only the single best restaurant in the world.

FREE-LANCE FOOD AND TRAVEL WRITER: I happen to like Italian food. It's very Continental.

ME: There are no Italians in Kansas City. It's one of the town's few weaknesses.

FLFTW: Of course there are Italians in Kansas City. There's a huge Italian neighborhood on the northeast side.

ME: In my high school we had one guy we called Guinea Gessler, but he kept insisting he was Swiss. I finally decided he really *was* Swiss. Anyway, he's not running any restaurants. He's in the finance business.

FLFTW: Your high school is not the whole city. I can show you statistics.

ME: Don't tell me about this town, buddy. I was born here.

"Actually, there probably *are* a lot of good restaurants there, because of the stockyards," New Yorkers say—swollen with condescension—when I inform them that the best restaurants in the world are in Kansas City. But, as a matter of fact, there are *not* a lot of good steak restaurants in Kansas City; American restaurants do not automatically take advantage of proximity to the ingredients, as anyone who has ever tried to find a fresh piece of fish on the Florida Coast does not need to be told. The best steak restaurant in the world, Jess & Jim's, does happen to be in Kansas

City, but it gets its meat from the stockyards in St. Joe, fifty miles away. The most expensive steak on the menu is Jess & Jim's Kansas City Strip Sirloin. When I arrived on the first evening of my tour, it was selling for $6.50, including salad and the best cottage-fried potatoes in the tri-state area. They are probably also the best cottage-fried potatoes in the world, but I don't have wide enough experience in eating cottage fries to make a definitive judgment.

Jess & Jim's is a sort of roadhouse, decorated simply with bowling trophies and illuminated beer signs. But if the proprietor saw one of his waitresses emerge from the kitchen with a steak that was no better than the kind you pay twelve dollars for in New York—in one of those steak houses that also charge for the parsley and the fork and a couple of dollars extra if you want ice in your water—he would probably close up forever from the shame of it all. I thought I might be unable to manage a Jess & Jim's strip sirloin. Normally, I'm not a ferocious steak-eater— a condition I trace to my memories of constant field trips to the stockyards when I was in grade school. (I distinctly remember having gone to the stockyards so many days in a row that I finally said, "Please, teacher, can we have some arithmetic?" But my sister, who went to the same school at the same time, says we never went to the stockyards—which just goes to show how a person's memory can play tricks on her.) As it turned out, I was able to finish my entire Jess & Jim's Kansas City Strip Sirloin—even though I had felt rather full when I sat down at the table. I had eaten a rather large lunch at Winstead's, Mario's, and the doughnut place. I had spent the intervening hours listening to my sister tell me about a place on Independence Avenue where the taxi drivers eat breakfast and a place called Laura's Fudge Shop, where you can buy peanut-butter fudge if you're that kind of person, and a place that serves spaghetti in a bucket. My sister has always been interested in that sort of thing—spaghetti in a bucket, chicken in a basket, pig in a blanket. She's really not an eater; she's a container freak.

It has long been acknowledged that the single best restaurant in the world is Arthur Bryant's Barbecue at Eighteenth and Brooklyn in Kansas City—known to practically everybody in town as Charlie Bryant's, after Arthur's brother, who left the business in 1946. The day after my Jess & Jim's Kansas City Strip Sirloin had been consumed, I went to Bryant's with Marvin Rich, an eater I know in Kansas City who practices law on the side. Marvin happens to number among his clients the company that bought Winstead's—the equivalent, in our circle, of a Bronx stickballer having grown up to find himself house counsel to the Yankees. Marvin eats a lot of everything—on the way to Bryant's, for instance, he brought me up-to-date on the local chili-parlor situation with great precision—but I have always thought of him as a barbecue specialist. He even attempts his own barbecue at home—dispatching his wife to buy hickory logs, picking out his own meat, and covering up any mistakes with Arthur Bryant's barbecue sauce, which he keeps in a huge jug in his garage in defiance of the local fire ordinances.

Bryant's specializes in barbecued spareribs and barbecued beef—the beef sliced from briskets of steer that have been cooked over a hickory fire for thirteen hours. When I'm away from Kansas City and depressed, I try to envision someone walking up to the counterman at Bryant's and ordering a beef sandwich to go—for me. The counterman tosses a couple of pieces of bread onto the counter, grabs a half-pound of beef from the pile next to him, slaps it onto the bread, brushes on some sauce in almost the same motion, and then wraps it all up in two thicknesses of butcher paper in a futile attempt to keep the customer's hand dry as he carries off his prize. When I'm in Kansas City and depressed, I go to Bryant's. I get a platter full of beef and ham and short ribs. Then I get a plate full of what are undoubtedly the best French-fried potatoes in the world. ("I get fresh potatoes and I cook them in pure lard," Arthur Bryant has said. "Pure lard is expensive. But if you want to do a job, you do a job.") Then I get a frozen mug full of cold beer—cold enough so that ice has begun to form on the surface. But all of those are really side dishes to me. The main course at Bryant's, as far as I'm concerned, is something that is given away free— the burned edges of the brisket. The counterman just pushes them over to the side as he slices the beef, and anyone who wants them helps himself. I dream of those burned edges. Sometimes, when I'm in some awful, overpriced restaurant in some strange town—all of my restaurant-finding techniques having failed, so that I'm left to choke down something that costs seven dollars and tastes like a medium-rare sponge— a blank look comes over my face: I have just realized that at that very moment someone in Kansas City is being given those burned edges free.

Marvin and I had lunch with a young lawyer in his firm. (I could tell he was a comer: He had spotted a hamburger place at Seventy-fifth and Troost that Marvin thought nobody knew about.) We had a long discussion about a breakfast place called Joe's. "I would have to say that the hash browns at Joe's are the equivalent of the Toddle browns," Marvin said judiciously. "On the other hand, the cream pie at the Toddle

House far surpasses Joe's cream pie." I reassured Marvin that I wouldn't think of leaving town without having lunch at Snead's Bar-B-Q. Snead's cuts the burned edges off the brisket with a little more meat attached and puts them on the menu as "brownies." They do the same thing with ham. A mixed plate of ham and beef brownies makes a stupendous meal—particularly in conjunction with a coleslaw that is so superior to the soured confetti they serve in the East that Alice, who has been under the impression that she didn't like coleslaw, was forced to admit that she had never really tasted the true article until she showed up, at an advanced age, at Snead's. Marvin, a man who has never been able to rise above a deep and irrational prejudice against chicken, said nothing about Stroud's, although he must have been aware of local reports that the pan-fried chicken there had so moved the New York gourmet Roy Andries de Groot that he could only respond to his dinner by stopping at the cash register and giving Mrs. Stroud a kiss on the forehead.

After an hour or so of eating, the young lawyer went back to the office ("He's a nice guy," Marvin said, "but I think that theory of his about the banana-cream pie at the airport coffee shop is way off base"), and Marvin and I had a talk with Arthur Bryant himself, who is still pretty affable, even after being called Charlie for twenty-five years. When we mentioned that we had been customers since the early Fifties, it occurred to me that when we first started going to Bryant's it must have been the only integrated restaurant in town. It has always been run by black people, and white people have never been able to stay away. Bryant said that was true. In fact, he said, when mixed groups of soldiers came through Kansas City in those days, they were sent to Bryant's to eat. A vision flashed through my mind:

A white soldier and a black soldier become friends at Fort Riley, Kansas. "We'll stick together when we get to Kansas City," the white soldier says. "We're buddies." They arrive in Kansas City, prepared to go with the rest of the platoon to one of the overpriced and under-seasoned restaurants that line the downtown streets. But the lady at the U.S.O. tells them they'll have to go to "a little place in colored town." They troop toward Bryant's—the white soldier wondering, as the neighborhood grows less and less like the kind of neighborhood he associates with good restaurants, if what his father told him about not paying any attention to the color of a man's skin was such good advice after all. When they get to Bryant's—a storefront with five huge, dusty jugs of barbecue sauce sitting in the window as the only decoration—the white soldier flirts for a moment with the idea of deserting his friend. But they had promised to stick together. He stiffens his resolve, and walks into Bryant's with his friend. He is in THE SINGLE BEST RESTAURANT IN THE WORLD. All of the other guys in the platoon are at some all-white cafeteria eating tasteless mashed potatoes. For perhaps the only time in the history of the Republic, virtue has been rewarded.

Bryant told us that he and his brother learned everything they knew about barbecue from a man named Henry Perry, who originated barbecue in Kansas City. "He was the greatest barbecue man in the world," Bryant said, "but he was a mean outfit." Perry used to enjoy watching his customers take their first bite of a sauce that he made too hot for any human being to eat without eight or ten years of working up to it. What Bryant said about Henry Perry, the master, only corroborated my theory that a good barbecue man is likely to tend toward the sullen—a theory I had felt wilting a bit in the face of Bryant's friendliness. (A man who tends briskets over a hickory fire all night, I figure, is bound to stir up some dark thoughts by morning.) I'm certain, at least, of my theory that a good barbecue man—or a good cook of any kind, for that matter—is not likely to be a promoter or a back-slapper. Once, while my wife and I were waiting to try out the fried clams at a small diner on the Atlantic Coast, I asked the proprietor if he had any lemon. "No, but I'll just make a note of that and I'll have some by the next time you come in," he said, turning on his best smile as he made the note. "You have to keep on your toes in this kind of business." We looked around and noticed, for the first time, a flashy new paint job and a wall plaque signifying some kind of good-citizen award. "Watch it," my wife whispered to me, "we're in for a stinker." We were. The redecoration job must have included reinforcing the tables so they would be able to support the weight of the fried clams.

When Arthur Bryant took over the place that had originally been called Perry's #2, he calmed the sauce down, since the sight that made him happiest was not a customer screaming but a customer returning. He eventually introduced French fries, although the barbecued sweet potatoes that Perry used to serve do not sound as if they were the source of a lot of customer complaints. Arthur Bryant is proud that he was the one who built up the business. But he still uses Perry's basic recipe for the sauce ("Twice a year I make me up about twenty-five hundred gallons of it") and Perry's method of barbecuing, and he acknowledges his debt to the master. "It's all Perry," he says. "Everything I'm doing is his." He keeps jugs of barbecue sauce in the window because that was Henry Perry's trademark. I immediately thought of a conversation I would like to have with the mayor and the city council of Kansas City:

ME: Have you ever heard of Henry Perry?

MAYOR AND CITY COUNCIL (In unison): Is that Commodore Perry?

ME: No, that is Henry Perry, who brought barbecue to Kansas City from Mississippi and therefore is the man who should be recognized as the one towering figure of our culture.

MAYOR AND CITY COUNCIL: Well, we believe that all of our citizens, regardless of their color or national origin—

ME: What I can't understand is why this town is full of statues of the farmers who came out to steal land from the Indians and full of statues of the businessmen who stole the land from the farmers but doesn't even have a three-dollar plaque somewhere for Henry Perry.

MAYOR AND CITY COUNCIL: Well, we certainly think—

ME: As you politicians are always saying, we have got to re-order our priorities.

Some time after my grand tour of Kansas City restaurants, I managed to get to the Glendale, California, branch of Bob's for a Big Boy. Since I had to be in Los Angeles anyway, I decided to take the opportunity to end the debate with Smith once and for all, and also to check out a place called Cassell's Patio, which some people in Los Angeles have claimed has the best hamburgers in the world. (Mr. Cassell ostentatiously grinds his beef right in front of one's very eyes, but then he uses too much of it for each hamburger patty. I suspect that Cassell's hamburger probably is the best one available in Los Angeles, but among Kansas City specialists it would be considered a very crude burger indeed.)

"The game is just about up, Smith," I informed William Edgett Smith before I left for California. "You won't be able to get away with any of that 'Phoenix is not Glendale' stuff any more."

"Be sure to go to the original branch, across from Bob's international headquarters on Colorado," Smith said.

The Big Boy at Bob's on Colorado Avenue tasted like the Big Boy at Bob's in Phoenix—only slightly superior, in other words, to a McDonald's Big Mac anywhere. I was not surprised. Smith knows nothing about food. He once dragged us to a kind of Women's Lib restaurant he had thought was glorious, and it only required one course for anyone except Smith to realize that the point of the restaurant was to demonstrate, at enormous damage to the customers, that women are not necessarily good cooks. I have been at family-style dinners in Szechuan Chinese restaurants with Smith when his persistence about including Lobster Cantonese in the order has forced the rest of us to threaten him with exile to a table of his own. I long ago decided that the one perceptive remark he ever made about food—the observation that it is C.C. Brown's in Hollywood rather than Will Wright's that has the best hot fudge sundae in Southern California—was a fluke, an eyes-shut home run by a .200 hitter.

"It's all over, Smith," I said to him when I returned to New York. "I had one and I can tell you that Glendale is Phoenix."

"You went to the original, you're sure, on Colorado?" Smith asked.

"Right across from Bob's international headquarters," I said.

"And you did ask for extra sliced tomatoes?" he said.

I paused for a long time, trying to remain calm. "You didn't say anything about extra sliced tomatoes," I said.

"But the whole taste is dependent on extra sliced tomatoes," he said. "The waitress would have been happy to bring you some. Bob prides himself on their friendliness."

"You realize, of course," I said, "that it's only a matter of time before I get back to Glendale and ask for extra sliced tomatoes and call this shameless bluff."

"I'm surprised you didn't ask for sliced tomatoes," Smith said. "It's the sliced tomatoes that really set it off."

3

My friend Fats Goldberg, the pizza baron, has been slim enough to be called Larry for years, of course, but I still think of him as Fats Goldberg. So does he. Although he has "been down," as he puts it, for fourteen years, after twenty-five years of exceptional fatness, he sees himself not as a man who weighs one hundred and sixty but as a man who is constantly in danger of weighing three hundred and twenty. "Inside, I'm still a fat man," he sometimes says. When Fats and I were boys in Kansas City, he was already renowned for his corpulence—though I can't say I was ever approached about posing for Refugee Relief ads in those days myself. During college, at the University of Missouri, he reached three hundred pounds and became known as both Fats Goldberg and Three Cases Goldberg—Columbia, Missouri, having been, through a derivation process that must still puzzle students of the language, the only place in the country where anybody recognized a one-hundred-pound unit of measurement called the case. I occasionally saw him when I visited Columbia, where he was one of a number of storied eaters. According to one tale, when a restaurant near the campus instituted a policy of giving customers all they wanted to eat on Sunday nights for a dollar thirty-five, a fraternity brother of Fats's called Hog Silverman, who weighed less than two and a half cases, went over one Sunday and put it out of business. Fats was known not only for that kind of single-sitting tour de force but for the fact that he never stopped eating. When he talks about those days, a lot of his sentences begin with phrases like "Then on the way to lunch I'd stop off at the Tastee-Freez . . ."

Although Fats has never cared much for salad, he used to eat just about anything else within reach. He had a catholicity of taste comparable to that of a southern eater I once heard mentioned as being happy to eat "just about everything except Coke bottles." His specialty, though, was always junk food. "I did not get fat on *coq au vin*," he once told me. Candy bars. Lunch-meat sandwiches on white bread. Sweet rolls. Hamburgers. Chili dogs. Cake. Fats loves cake, and I suspect he likes it even better when it comes in a package. When he was visiting our house one day, long after he had forbidden himself to eat cake in New York, we wondered why he kept wandering in and out of the kitchen; then Alice remembered that there was a cake on the kitchen counter. Fats had been prowling back and forth in front of it, like a tiger circling a tethered goat. At Missouri, Fats often brightened up the late afternoon with something called a Boston sundae, which is, more or less, a milkshake with a floating sundae on top—a floating chocolate sundae with bananas if Fats happened to be the customer. I don't mean to imply that Fats was completely undiscriminating. There are good chili dogs and bad chili dogs. The only food that Fats still finds almost literally irresistible is, of course, a double cheeseburger with everything but onions at Winstead's, and our afflictions differ only in that I prefer the double hamburger with everything and grilled onions. For a number of years, Fats was in the habit of reading the latest diet book at Winstead's—holding the book in one hand and a double cheeseburger with everything but onions in the other.

I didn't see Fats for ten years after college, and when I did see him I didn't recognize him. It was a Sunday morning in New York, and I was at Ratner's on Second Avenue. I was having eggs scrambled with lox and onions, trying to ignore the scoop of mashed potatoes that Ratner's, for some reason, always includes on the plate—perhaps as a way of reminding the customer what less fortunate people may be eating in London, or wherever it's late enough for gentiles to be having dinner. I was glancing around constantly, as I tend to do at Ratner's, to see if some other table was being given a roll basket with more of my favorite kind of onion rolls than our roll basket had. Fats didn't even look familiar. In fact, if we hadn't had some intimate discussions since then about Winstead's hamburgers and Arthur Bryant's barbecued spareribs, I might even now suspect him of being an imposter. Fats later told me that on the morning of May 1, 1959, while employed as a three-hundred-and-twenty-pound salesman of newspaper advertising space in Chicago, he had decided to lose weight. Naturally, he had made similar decisions several dozen times in the past, and he still doesn't know why he was finally able to stop eating. He can't remember any single incident's having set him on his course—no humiliation by some secretary who called him fat stuff, no particularly embarrassing experience buying trousers or trying to tie his shoelace. He is certain that it was not fear for his health that stiffened his will power; several years before, his reaction to a serious warning by a doctor in Kansas City was to think about it over three Winstead's cheeseburgers, a fresh-lime Coke, and a Frosty Malt. On May 1, 1959, Fats started losing weight. He didn't use pills or gimmick diets. "It was cold turkey," he says now, referring to the method rather than the food. "I suffered." In a year, Fats weighed one ninety. Then, gradually, he went down to one sixty. In other words, by the time I saw him at Ratner's the Fats Goldberg I had known was half gone.

Fats was still selling advertising space then, but he wasn't happy in his work. He believed that his true calling was stand-up comedy. After he moved to New York, he and a young woman he knew formed a nightclub comedy act called Berkowitz and Goldberg. Their first public performance was at the Bitter End, in the Village, which has what amounts to an amateur night on Tuesdays, but they got on so late that the audience consisted of only four people, all of them grim-faced. Berkowitz later discovered that none of them spoke English. As it turned out, a knowledge of the language did not vary the audience response. I never saw the act, but I think I have a pretty good idea of what it was like from a chance remark Fats once made while we were reminiscing about our show-business careers. (At Southwest High School, I had a comedy act with a partner who specialized in foreign dialects and took great advantage, I realized some years later, of the fact that none of the people we performed for had ever met any foreigners.) "We were called Berkowitz and Goldberg but we didn't do Jewish humor," Fats told me during that talk of lost opportunities. "That was one of the jokes."

After having inspired audiences all over town to puzzled silence, Berkowitz and Goldberg finally folded. Fortunately, Fats had one joke left; he opened a restaurant called Goldberg's Pizzeria. He was armed not only with the gimmick of having a Jewish pizza parlor but with the recipe for an excellent version of what the connoisseurs call a Chicago pizza—characterized by a thick, crispy, and particularly fattening crust. I have only an occasional craving for pizza—a craving that I used to nurture carefully, like a small trust fund, at the Spot in New Haven, Connecticut—but I have eaten enough of it to know that Fats serves superior Chicago pizza. Almost as soon as Goldberg's Pizzeria had opened, Fats had what every comic dreams of—a lot of free publicity, critical acclaim, and "exposure" on the *Tonight Show*. (Actually, it was the pizza that was exposed rather than Goldberg; one was given away to a member of the audience who named a tune the band couldn't play.) Fats himself became so celebrated that he was able to publish a pizza cookbook—a volume that may add little to the literature of food but seems at least to have provided a resting place for some old jokes from the Berkowitz and Goldberg days. (One chapter is called "The Goldberg Variations, or How to Make Johann Sebastian Roll Over on His Bach.") Within a few years, there were three Goldberg's Pizzerias, and Fats was getting feelers from conglomerates.

Although Fats enjoys the trappings of a pizza barony, he realizes that his most notable accomplishment is not having created a successful business but having stayed thin. Among his pizza customers are some experts in obesity, and they have informed him that any fat man who remains slim for fourteen years can safely consider himself a medical phenomenon. (Since all Goldberg's Pizzerias display poster-size pictures of Fats when he weighed three cases, the subject of fatness often comes up, particularly on Sunday night, a traditional time for eating pizza and making diet resolutions.) Fats has been told that specialists can always make fat people thin through a variety of hospital treatments—treatments that a layman would probably summarize as solitary confinement. But once released the patients almost invariably become fat again—meaning that, according to any reasonable assessment of the odds, Fats really is someone constantly in danger of weighing three hundred and twenty pounds.

Someone who has gone without a relapse since 1959 is so rare that one reasearcher from the Rockefeller University asked Fats if he would mind donating some of his fat cells for analysis. Researchers at Rockefeller and at Mt. Sinai Hospital have found that fat people who were fat as children have not only larger fat cells but more of them. When a chronically fat person loses weight, all his fat cells just shrink temporarily, remaining available for re-expansion—or, as someone who apparently enjoys taunting the fatties once put it, "screaming to be refilled." Fat-cell research has led to the depressing speculation that a person who was fat as a child faces horrifying pressure to become fat again and again, no matter how many times he sits in Goldberg's Pizzeria on a Sunday evening and vows that the diet he is going on the following morning will be different. Fats is unenthusiastic about the Rockefeller people's method of studying his fat cells, which would amount to withdrawing a section of tissue from the part of the body in which it is most accessible (or, as Fats sees it, "having three nurses stick an eight-inch needle in my *tushe*") but he sometimes hints that he might be willing to cooperate. The more he thinks about the effort required for a fat man to stay thin, the more he thinks that he is extraordinary enough to be a boon to medical research.

A thin psychologist I know, Stanley Schachter, has done a lot of research at Columbia on obesity, and I once asked him if it was scientifically sound to consider Fats Goldberg truly amazing. After I had described Fats's accomplishments, Schachter seemed filled with admiration. According to Schachter's research, staying thin would be even more difficult for a pizza baron than for a run-of-the-mill fatty. The research indicates that what causes fat people to eat is not the physical sensations that go along with an empty stomach but what Schachter calls "external cues"—the sight of candy in the candy dish or the smell of hamburgers frying or the information that it is dinnertime or, in the case of poor Fats, the constant presence of delicious, aromatic pizza. One of Fats's doctor friends once told him that a remarkably high percentage of the few former fatties who have managed to stay thin had fetched up in businesses having to do with food in one way or the other—tightrope walkers who want to defy the odds a bit more by working in unsnapped galoshes.

Schachter believes that fat people are unable to recognize the physical sensation of hunger—so that they actually eat less than thin people if external cues are missing. When two Columbia doctors, Theodore Van Italie and Sami Hashim, removed virtually all external cues—they allowed people to eat all they wanted of an almost tasteless liquid, but nothing else—the thin people ate about the same number of calories per day that they had eaten of normal food but the fat people ate so little that one of them lost more than two hundred pounds in eight months. Schachter has found that among Jewish college students with roughly the same habits of synagogue attendance the fat ones are more likely to fast on Yom Kippur than the normal-sized ones—and that their fasting is more likely to be helped by staying in the synagogue, where there are few food cues. The normal-sized ones get hungry. Normal people given food in a laboratory will eat less if their stomachs are full or if they're frightened, but if a plate of crackers is put in front of a fat person who has just eaten or who has been led to believe he is about to receive some electric shocks, he is likely to clean the plate anyway—or, in Schachter's terms, to eat until he is out of cues.

After listening to Schachter explain the peculiar eating habits of fat people for a while, it occurred to me that what he had really discovered was that fat people are smarter than other people. For instance, in an experiment to test the hypothesis that fat people are less willing to work for their food than ordinary people, he found that the appeal of a bowl of almonds to normal-sized people who were filling out some meaningless forms he had concocted (Schachter is a very devious researcher) was unaffected by whether or not the almonds had shells on them. But when fat people were given the same test, only one out of twenty ate almonds that had to be shelled and nineteen out of twenty ate almonds that were already shelled. That seems to me a simple matter of intelligence. Who wants to spend his time shelling almonds? Testing the same hypothesis, Schachter and some of his students loitered around Chinese restaurants and found that fat Occidentals are much less likely to try chopsticks than thin Occidentals—the difference being, Schachter assured me, too great to be accounted for by the problem of manipulation inherent in chubby fingers.

"But the fat people behave the way any normal intelligent person would behave, Stanley," I said when I heard about that discovery.

Schachter didn't say anything. Then I began to realize that a lot of the fat-people habits he had talked about applied to me. I have always thought that anyone who sacrifices stuffing power by using chopsticks in a Chinese restaurant must be demented. I would use a tablespoon if I thought I could get away with it, but I know that the people I tend to share my Chinatown meals with, terrified that I would polish off the twice-fried pork before they had a chance to say "Pass the bean curd," would start using tablespoons themselves, and sooner or later we would be off on an escalating instruments race that might end with soup ladles or dory-bailers. Although I may have talked about being hungry from the moment I learned to talk, I am still not sure precisely what physical feeling people have in mind when they describe hunger. The last piece of food I left on my plate—that was in the fall of 1958, as I remember—had a bug on it. I suppose I might be persuaded not to finish a normal helping of Grand Marnier soufflé if a reputable and eloquent person I had every reason to trust insisted that my host had poisoned it, but I really couldn't say for certain until the situation actually came up. Schachter's theories, I decided, must be incorrect.

I tried to prove it to myself the next time I saw Fats by asking him a question in what I knew was a somewhat misleading way.

"Do you ever get hungry, Fats?" I asked.

"You bet your booties I do!" Fats said.

That would show Schachter, I thought. But a few days later, when I asked Fats for an example of a time when it was particularly hard for him to avoid eating, he said, "Tonight when I passed that pizza stand on Eighth Street that has that great frozen custard, it almost killed me." External cue.

My discussion with Fats about hunger began at the Gaiety Delicatessen on Lexington Avenue, where he goes every day for a kind of lunchtime breakfast. Having been terrified by Schachter, I ordered the tunafish-salad plate with double coleslaw, hold the potato salad, and a low-caloric cream soda. Fats ate two scrambled eggs, sausages, a bagel with cream cheese, and four cups of coffee with a total of eight packets of sugar. "A fat man's got to have something to look forward to," Fats said. "When I'm reading in bed late at night, I think about being able to have this bagel and cream cheese the next day." Underlying the Fats Goldberg system of weight control is more or less the same philosophy that led to the great Russian purge trials of the thirties—deviation is treason. His Gaiety meals vary daily only in how the eggs are done. In the evening, he has either a steak or half a chicken, baked in the pizza oven. (He is always careful to cut the chicken in half before baking and to put the unneeded half back in the refrigerator. "You have to pre-plan," he says. "A fat man always cleans his plate.") On Sunday night he permits himself a quarter of a small sausage pizza in place of the steak or chicken, but then he works at the ovens trying to sweat it off. On Monday he cheats to the extent of some bread or maybe a piece of pie. The schedule is maintained only in New York, of course. Kansas City remains a free zone for Fats. He says that in the earlier years of his thinness a week's trip to Kansas City to visit his family would mean gaining seventeen pounds. Lately, restraint has begun to creep into his Kansas City binges. The week's eating he was about to start when I saw him on the Kansas City plane cost him only ten pounds.

A few days after our meeting at the Gaiety, Fats happened to drop by my house. It had been a difficult few days for me: Schachter's theories were still fresh in my mind, and St. Anthony's, my favorite Italian street fair, was being held so close to my house that I had been able to convince myself that I could smell the patently irresistible aroma of frying sausages day and night. I have looked all over the country for a sausage I don't like, trying them all along the way. In the course of my research, I have tested country patties in Mississippi and Cuban *chorizos* in Tampa and bratwurst in Yorkville and Swedish potato sausages in Kansas (yes, Kansas) and garlic sausages in Rumanian restaurants in New York and just about everything else that has ever been through a sausage grinder. So far, I love them all. I even like English bangers. I look on the bright side: With all of that bread in them, they couldn't possible cause heartburn. The number of sausage sandwiches I eat at St. Anthony's— Italian sausages that were fried on a griddle right next to the sliced pepper and onion that always accompanies them—is ordinarily limited only by how many *calzones* and *zeppoles* I eat between sausage booths.

Trying, I think, to keep my mind off my own problems, I mentioned to Fats that a doctor I knew had said that in order to gain even fourteen pounds a week in Kansas City it would be necessary for Fats to consume an additional seventy-two hundred calories a day—or the equivalent of fifteen or twenty Winstead's cheeseburgers.

Fats considered that for a while. He didn't seem shocked.

"Just what *did* you eat on a big day in Kansas City the week you gained seventeen pounds?" I asked. I prepared to make a list.

"Well, for breakfast I'd have two eggs, six biscuits with butter and jelly, half a quart of milk, six link sausages, six strips of bacon, and a couple of homemade cinnamon rolls," Fats said. "Then I'd hit MacLean's Bakery.

They have a kind of fried cinnamon roll I love. Maybe I'd have two or three of them. Then, on the way downtown to have lunch with somebody, I might stop at Kresge's and have two chili dogs and a couple of root beers. Ever had their chili dogs?"

I shook my head.

"Greasiest chili dogs in the world," Fats said. "I love 'em. Then I'd go to lunch. What I really like for lunch is something like a hot beef sandwich or a hot turkey sandwich. Open-faced, loaded with that flour gravy. With mashed potatoes. Then Dutch apple pie. Kansas City is big on Dutch apple pie. Here they call it apple crumb or something. Then, sometimes in the afternoon, I'd pick up a pie—just an ordinary nine-inch pie—and go to my friend Matt Flynn's house, and we'd cut the pie down the middle and put half in a bowl for each of us and then take a quart of ice cream and cut that down the middle and put it on top of the pie. We'd wash it down with Pepsi-Cola. Sometimes Matt couldn't finish his and I'd have to finish it for him. Then that would be it until I stopped at my sister's house. She's very big on crunchy peanut butter. She even has peanut butter and jelly already mixed. They didn't have that when I was a kid. Then for dinner we'd maybe go to Charlie Bryant's or one of the barbecues out on the highway. At the movies I'd always have a bag of corn and a big Coke and knock off a Payday candy bar. Payday is still my favorite candy bar. They're hard to get here, but they have a very big distribution in Kansas City. Then we'd always end up at Winstead's, of course. Two double cheeseburgers with everything but onions, a fresh-lime Coke and a Frosty Malt. If it was before eleven, I'd stop at the Zarda Dairy for one of their forty-nine-cent banana splits. Then when I'd get home maybe some cherry pie and a sixteen ounce Pepsi."

And so to bed. I looked at the list. "To tell you the truth, Fats, I'm afraid to add it all up," I said. I looked at the list again. Something on it had reminded me of sausages. It must have been the mention of Bryant's, which used to have barbecue sausages but quit serving them before I had a chance to try them—a situation that has always made me feel like an archeologist who arrived at the tomb just a few days after the locals began to use the best pot for a football. I decided that I would walk over to the fair later and have just one sausage sandwich with peppers and onions—saving a few calories by having a barbecued rather than a fried sausage. If things got out of hand, I figured, I could always go on one of those diets that allow you as much as you want to eat as long as you eat only Brussels sprouts, quinces, and summer squash. I had mentioned the fair to Fats, but he couldn't go. It wasn't a Monday.

"Is life worth living, Fats?" I asked.

"Well, I figure that in my first twenty-five years I ate enough for four normal lifetimes," Fats said. "So I get along. But there is a lot of pain involved. A lot of pain. I can't stress that enough."

When people in other parts of the country ask me why I live in New York, they expect a specific answer. After all, if I asked one of them why he lives in, say, St. Paul, he wouldn't hesitate to give me a specific answer ("Well, I was born here, and we have a lot of family here, and when I got out of the Army an uncle of mine knew somebody in this window-shade firm that needed a sales representative . . ."). They often try to help me out by saying something like "the cultural life must be exciting of course—the opera and all." The opera has nothing to do with it. I have only been to the opera once in New York, and that is when we were sent tickets by a friend in Kansas City. Early in autumn a few years ago, I finally found the short answer I had been looking for. We had spent the summer in New Mexico, and, during a brief stop in Santa Fe, we had been grilled on why we live in New York by that group of Eastern-refugee remittance men the place specializes in—people who half-retire at forty-two in order to devote themselves to talking about a novel they might write and overseeing the repairs of any cracks that might develop in the adobe walls of their house and discussing the water rights their land carries by virtue of the original Spanish land grant and raising a herd of twelve or fourteen particularly elegant goats. A week or so after our return, Alice and I happened to walk by a Chinese restaurant on Irving Place and we realized we had forgotten about it. I don't mean we had forgotten its name or its exact address; we had forgotten about its existence. The previous spring, we had eaten a spectacular meal there, including a dish that came close to being The Great Dried Beef in the Sky—an oriental grail we had been in search of since we ate an awesome dried-beef dish in a Chinese restaurant in London (across the street from the Golders Green tube station) several years ago. "This is why we live here," I said to Alice. "Where else could you *forget* a restaurant like this?" Now when someone asks me why my family and I choose to live in New York, I don't have to launch into all sorts of complicated and fuzzy explanations. I just say, "We're big eaters."

I once met someone who had collected information about four hundred New York restaurants and stored it in a computer in Cupertino, California. In the context of the conversation we were having at the time, it struck me as a natural enough thing to have done. We were eating dinner at the New York apartment of some friends named Peter and Alessandra Wolf, where the talk often turns to food even before the first course is served. Peter, who grew up in New Orleans, and Alessandra, who is an immigrant from Fort Worth, are basically regional loyalists who eat or prepare other types of food as a kind of casual sideline—the way some tournament-class tennis player might mop up all of the paddle tennis and table tennis competition at the local club if it's too cold to play the real game. Peter is such a discriminating consumer of his hometown cooking that when a trip allows him time for only one or two meals in New Orleans, the one American city most citizens associate with French cuisine, he is likely to take them at Italian restaurants—Italian restaurants that specialize in something like baked oysters and cracked-crab salad, it's true, but still Italian restaurants. Peter once discovered, in an upper Broadway Szechuan restaurant, a dish called Red Soup, which he claimed was the best Chinese dish available in New York for those who like their Chinese food flavored hot, but the claim turned out not to be subject to independent confirmation, since Red Soup was so hot that only someone who had trained on Cajun peppers or Henry Perry's barbecue sauce for twenty or thirty years could eat enough of it to find out what it tasted like.

Alessandra lived in France for quite a while, but she hasn't allowed that to ruin her cooking. She can turn out a first-rate French meal, of course, and she is one of the few Occidentals in New York whose Chinese cooking does not evoke sympathy for the organizers of the Boxer

Rebellion. But an occasion at her house seems particularly special when she serves something called Chili Texas Party Style—a Fort Worth meat delicacy that each guest flavors to taste by adding chopped onions or sour cream or shredded lettuce or Monterey Jack cheese or, in my case, all of the above. (In such situations, I have yet to add anything less than everything. I like everything with everything, and I find people who don't impossible to fathom except as victims of the Puritan Ethic. Failing to add everything, it seems to me, demonstrates not the presence of restraint but the absence of curiosity—the kind of healthy curiosity that impels me to try every single cheese on the cheese board no matter how many times the French waiter with the tight smile emits one of those impatient sighs he practices in the kitchen during slack hours.) I believe it was merely a delicious French meal we were being served by Alessandra when the subject of New York restaurants worked its way into the conversation and I learned that one of the other guests, an investment banker named Anthony Lamport, could summon data on four hundred of them simply by strolling over to a computer terminal he had installed in a small office one flight above his bedroom and punching a few keys—having first dialed a special number in California on the telephone and placed the receiver next to what passes for the machine's ear.

Those who consider Lamport's facilities, well, more than the situation calls for have never developed a serious interest in eating out in New York. On long winter nights, when more responsible citizens are presumably discussing foreign policy or urban mass transit, I have found myself locked in intent conversation about restaurants. Perhaps a fifteen-year-old Spanish restaurant on Staten Island has been rediscovered, like an elderly black blues singer who is plucked out of the Mississippi Delta and brought to New York for a well-received appearance at Town Hall at least once every twenty years. Or there is a new Chinese restaurant on Doyers Street specializing in the dishes of a remote province whose cuisine is so exquisite that those of its residents who have to travel to Szechuan or Hunan traditionally never leave home without packing a lunch. Or there is new word on a chef who moves constantly from restaurant to restaurant, carrying with him not only a grudge against all restaurant proprietors but the Ancient Greek secret of spinach pie.

By eating out I don't mean dining out—showing up at the kind of East Side restaurants that are often mentioned in gossip columns and expense accounts, restaurants that prosper or languish for reasons other than how the food tastes. There is, of course, always plenty of that going on in

Manhattan, and there is also plenty of business for the fast-food operators. McDonalds, which got a late start in the city, is now doing the kind of volume restaurant people speak of in the tones that theater people reserve for discussions of Neil Simon's box office, and lately there has been a spreading rash of Steak 'n Brew outlets, Steak 'n Brew being a chain that has done for steaks what Astroturf did for outfields. (If I ever captured control of City Hall, the first law promulgated would require all of the merchants running establishments with names like Steak 'n Brew or Doodads 'n Things or Birds 'n Bees to spell out all words or be put in the stocks.) Fats Goldberg believes that, the appeal of limited-menu, fast-service operations being what it is in New York, a restaurant entrepreneur could enrich himself by creating a midtown restaurant based on a two-way conveyor belt moving within a building between, say, Forty-fifth and Forty-sixth streets. The customer who entered on Forty-fifth would pay for one of three or four set lunches, sit down at a table on a slow-moving conveyor belt, and, after eating his fill and perusing some discreet advertising displays on the wall and nodding to a few acquaintances who have passed slowly in the other direction, be dumped out on Forty-sixth Street.

People who are serious about eating out in New York have to work a territory way beyond the expense-account joints or fast-food operations. There are in the five boroughs something like twenty-three thousand establishments that serve food of one kind or another, and the devout restaurant-trotter has to consider every single one of them. He might find out, after all, that what looks like an expanded lunch counter actually functions in the evenings as a Syrian family restaurant featuring a minced-lamb dish so fantastic it would tempt a Zionist to change sides. The lunch counter then becomes not merely an enjoyable place to eat but a discovery, almost a personal possession. Although young couples in films set in New York have always seemed very fond of fatherly old Enrico, the man who runs the little red-and-white checkered-tablecloth Italian restaurant they frequent, there is a limit to the kind of success real New Yorkers would wish for old Enrico. What they dread more than rubbery fettucini is a write-up in the *Times*. They believe, of course, that keeping information about Enrico's place on what the Army calls a strict need-to-know basis is all for Enrico's own good. Ever since Craig Claiborne established the restaurant column in the *Times* as the first item of morning business for a confirmed restaurant-trotter, an out-of-the-way place praised by the *Times* can be instantly Claibornized—swollen and perhaps even burst by a sudden infusion of temporary loyalists. If Enrico reacts to a favorable notice in the *Times* by trying to run the kind of place he operated before, he is likely to find the regulars driven away forever as a horde of fickle review-followers manage to turn the chef into a short-order cook before they move on to the West Side Spanish seafood house that has just had its *mariscos* extolled at length. If Enrico proves adaptable enough to exploit the publicity, he will redecorate and raise the prices and eventually open a fancy place in midtown, where his encounters with the waiters' union and the real-estate sharks will drive him into the life insurance business. Who would wish such alternatives on a pal? Shortly after John Hess took over as restaurant critic of the *Times,* he wrote a piece about a modest upstairs trattoria called the Eldorado, which had been in the garment district for years but was about to close. "I would never tell you about the Eldorado if it weren't doomed," Hess's informant said to him. With only a few weeks to go, in other words, the place might as well be Hessed.

A New York restaurant-trotter who remains wary of the *Times* restaurant-column because of some rough handling in the past by a band of Claibornites or a horde of Hessians can now get his restaurant tips from a restaurant newsletter. Premise of a newsletter—the premise that its subscribers will pay well for information not shared with the entire population—is the kind of openly selfish notion easily appreciated by the serious eater in New York. Reading restaurant reviews of any kind, of course, carries the risk of being lectured to about how the texture of the *crème anglaise* in question deviates from the texture *crème anglaise* is supposed to have—an experience that always makes me feel the way a man who takes great joy in his pet basset hound might feel if he found himself trapped in a room with a couple of dog-show types who want to discuss only whether the poor beast has the prescribed depth of chest or the classic markings. When a reviewer starts explaining how the preparation of a quiche Lorraine at the restaurant he has visited differs from the way one prepares a *true* quiche Lorraine, I always want to interrupt. "But did you like it?" I want to shout. "Did it make you happy? Did you clean your plate?" Any chance that I might someday acquire a serious interest in how closely what I ate resembled the true article disappeared one day at a block party near our house while I was eating some homemade *gazpacho* and talking about how it differed from the authentic *gazpacho* one got in Seville. The more I talked about the difference the faster I wolfed down the *gazpacho*—until I realized that one way what I was eating differed from authentic *gazpacho* was that it tasted better.

I now realize, though, that before restaurant newsletters came along we were in the position of people who had to argue about the latest film without having a collection of film critics to cite with approval or dismiss with contempt. Just after one newsletter, *The Restaurant Reporter*, had criticized the prices and service at the Palm steak house, for instance, some zealous *palmistes* I know took Alice and me there and presented an impassioned two-hour defense over dinner—a defense that did not, in fact, include everything they wanted to say on the subject, since their mouths were often too full of steak or home-fried potatoes to permit articulation. At the end of the evening, they remained unpersuaded by my argument that a diner who is presented a bill at a restaurant—such as the Palm—that has no menu and therefore no announced prices has no choice but to negotiate. I still think that if a man tells you for the first time that the lobster you just ate costs eighteen dollars, the only sensible response is to offer him six.

I am now so accustomed to *The Restaurant Reporter* that I would probably subscribe even if I lived in Kansas City, just on the chance that I might fall into a conversation with a visiting machine-tools drummer about Japanese restaurants on the Upper West Side. (The other New York newsletter I have seen, *The Craig Claiborne Journal*, devotes more space to recipes than to restaurants, and is therefore of less use to me, since my cooking skill does not extend past a special way of preparing scrambled eggs so that they always stick to the pan. I do enjoy Claiborne's use of the editorial we, such as "We remember the first time we ever dined at Le Pavilion . . ." It has the effect of making me think that he is eating double portions of everything.) I like *The Restaurant Reporter* for the writing as well as for the tips. The ordinary restaurant reviewer might express his displeasure over a dish of spinach by saying that it was limp or tasteless. *The Restaurant Reporter* described the spinach served at one midtown restaurant as tasting like "new-mown artificial lawn." Reviewing Mr. & Mrs. Foster's Place, a small, expensive restaurant on the East Side, *The Restaurant Reporter* said, "After over-charging 25 patrons twice a night, six nights a week, for a couple of years, Mrs. Foster, the sole proprietor, apparently still cannot afford larger quarters for her establishment, or the elimination of a couple of tables, so that the remaining diners could eat comfortably." Talking about a steak restaurant that had every characteristic of those out-of-the-way, informal little places New York restaurant samplers are always touting for everything except good food, *The Restaurant Reporter* said, "You have heard of a tourist trap? This restaurant is a New Yorker trap."

One spring evening in New York, I happened to run across a friend of mine who was on his way to Chinatown but seemed to lack the look of gleeful anticipation I associate with the beginning of such a journey. What concerned him, I quickly learned, was that an excellent new restaurant he had been patronizing for a while had just been reviewed in the *Times*. We were both familiar with an uptown Chinese restaurant that had been Sokoloved a year or so before—having transformed itself within a few days of being praised in the *Times* by Hess's predecessor, Raymond Sokolov, into an approximation of what might have happened during the more antic phases of the Cultural Revolution if someone had tested out his new authority by ordering every single soldier in the People's Army to eat at the same mess hall. "It was a very good notice," my friend said glumly. It had even mentioned the cold-kidney appetizer, his favorite dish. He admitted that complete lack of publicity also had its perils: He said he had once managed to keep a perfect Chinese restaurant pretty much to himself for six months, until it closed, apparently having maintained an exclusivity that was inconsistent with paying the rent. But as he started off toward his first post-review dinner, I could tell he was haunted by expectations of having a harried waiter bob up from a shoving mass of new customers after a forty-minute delay only to announce that the chef had been forced to turn to canned shrimp for the Shrimp With Brown Sauce and had, regrettably, given up trying to make the cold kidneys altogether.

"Cheer up," I wanted to say. "Maybe they'll be listed in the *Times* tomorrow for a health-code violation." But he seemed inconsolable.

For a chronic restaurant-sampler, one of the rewards of success is being able to take a friend to the new discovery and smile knowingly as he tastes the kind of *bouillabaisse* he thought did not exist more than two hundred yards from the Mediterranean. That kind of moment seems particularly savored by the specialists—New Yorkers who make themselves lay experts in a particular cuisine the way some securities analysts concentrate on keeping completely up-to-date on all aspects of, say, copper mining or the toy industry. Zero Mostel—the actor, painter, and eater—is, for instance, widely known in New York as a specialist in Jewish food, although, like Alessandra Wolf, he is creative about wandering effortlessly from his specialty. During a tour of the Lower East Side I once took with him to observe him in action—I did it in the medieval spirit of an eager novice apprenticing himself to a master glutton—he described an experience of taking an acquaintance of his to a kosher dairy restaurant that used to exist on upper Broadway. At the time, we were standing on Houston Street, having just emerged from the back room of Russ & Daughters appetizer store, where a counterman friend of Mostel's named Herbie Federman had created for us some stupendous sandwiches of Nova Scotia salmon, cream cheese with vegetables in it, sliced onions, and Russ & Daughters' ineffable sturgeon. Mostel, who can speak with Talmudic subtlety for ten minutes on, say, the soured milk with fresh chives that Yonah Shimmel used to serve in the spring, said he had prepared the acquaintance for his first trip to the dairy restaurant by describing some of its specialties, and I could imagine a cab ride to upper Broadway fragrant with Mostel descriptions of *kasha varnishke* and potato *latkes*. "The guy ordered angel-food cake and a glass of milk," Mostel said. He paused to let that sink in. His eyes opened wide, and he seemed to expand. I thought he was going to begin shouting. But he lowered his voice nearly to a whisper. "Angel-food cake and a glass of milk," he repeated, very calmly. "He went into a restaurant like that and ordered angel-food cake and a glass of milk. It's like going into this store and Herbie asks you what he can get you and you say, 'Herbala, open me up a can of tuna.' I said, 'You sure you want angel-food cake and a glass of milk?' He said he wasn't very hungry." Mostel paused again. Suddenly he flung out his arm to point dramatically straight in front of him. "I said, 'GET OUT OF HERE! GET OUT OF THIS RESTAURANT!'" he said, in a voice that caused some motorists on Houston Street to slow down and look in our direction. "ANGEL-FOOD CAKE AND A GLASS OF MILK! THE NERVE!"

Mostel seems to enjoy talking about the restaurants he goes to; the real masters have never been stingy about sharing trade secrets with apprentices. But there are, of course, some people in New York who enjoy knowing about little-known restaurants for the same reason that some people in the White House enjoy knowing national secrets—it makes them feel superior to people who only know what they read in the newspapers. Some people in New York concerned with rank and station attach as much importance to the answer to "Where do you usually go in Chinatown?" as some people in other parts of the country attach to the answer to "Whadaya drive?" When two restaurant-trotters meet, the conversation is often tense. "We happened to run across a little Italian place at Eighteenth and Ninth Avenue last month," one competitor will say. "The sign, for some reason, says something like 'Mantucci's Bolt & Nut Supply,' and you have to call in advance, of course, and the owner doesn't know much English, but he has a dish that starts with these little dumplings—"

"Oh," his opponent will say, in the tone of someone doing his best to be polite while listening to the plot summary of a film he happens to have written. "Is that place still good?"

I admit to having been intrigued by the idea of storing restaurant information in a computer. I could think of a few useful ways to arrange New York restaurants into the kinds of sub-groups computers are always providing—those restaurants that use actual potatoes for their French fries and those that merely fry the icy fingers found in bags of precut Idahos, for instance, or those restaurants that furnish schmaltz on the table and those restaurants that don't furnish schmaltz on the table. As far as I know, only one restaurant in New York has schmaltz (chicken fat) available on the table for those patrons who want to improve on the chef's excesses—the Parkway, a favorite of Mostel's, on Allen Street, includes in its table setting a glass dispenser of schmaltz in the same way some other restaurants furnish a similar dispenser full of half-and-half—but I would welcome any computer that could find another one, since the Parkway is closed on Monday and a schmaltz craving can strike any day of the week. (The Parkway has resisted Sokolovization despite a glowing notice a couple of years ago, possibly because patronage is limited by the fact that one Parkway meal is likely to make most people feel full for a month or two.) I phoned Anthony Lamport and arranged to come around one evening to investigate the computer. I ate first, just in case.

Lamport, as it turned out, is a director of a computer-time-sharing company in California, and had figured that it would be to the company's advantage if he learned to write and use programs such as his restaurant-selection program. I wouldn't argue with that; directors are obviously less likely to cause management a lot of trouble if they're well fed. Lamport finds a number of uses for the computer in his business, and while he was in the market for a brownstone or a co-op apartment, he fed into it all sorts of figures like yearly maintenance and tax-deductible operating expenses in order to determine the real cost of each piece of property—another confirmation of the axiom that computers have no intelligence of their own, since a machine with any brains would have taken one look at a collection of New York real-estate figures and typed out, "MOVE TO ST. PAUL."

Now that Lamport has the restaurant program, if he happens to want to eat, say, medium-priced Italian food within ten blocks of Sixtieth and Third on a Monday, the machine will provide him with a list that varies according to such matters as whether or not he is interested in a place that has live music. I could see from the variables Lamport had included that his machine was of limited use. There was no provision for schmaltz. Nothing was said about French fries. Some variables that he had included—live music or atmosphere or outdoor dining—were of no interest to me. As far as I'm concerned, a place that serves perfect *gnocchi* or soft-clam bellies that taste like the bellies of soft clams can feature a quartet of female tuba players if that's what makes the chef happy. If a New York restaurant figured out how to serve crawfish bisque or the kind of *sopapaillas* available in, say, Española, New Mexico—a *sopapailla* being a sort of pastry that tastes like what might result if some little old lady in New England were inspired by the devil himself to fry her popovers in oil and pour honey on them—I would be happy to eat the special of the day in a small, dark closet. People who attach great importance to the bright lights ought just to go to Radio City Music Hall and pack some sandwiches.

I decided to give the machine at least one try. "Tell the thing to type out the name of a three-star French restaurant with moderate prices and a headwaiter who believes that accepting tips is unethical," I said. Lamport said the computer was not programmed to do that. I hadn't really thought it would be. If Lamport found such a place, he would know better than to say anything about it to a machine.

Having heard a number of people discuss the Last Straw that drove them from the city, I realize that if I didn't leave when Ben's Dairy started closing Sundays I'm probably in New York for good. It was an awful blow. It happened four years ago, and I still remember the details of the morning I discovered it, the way some people remember what they were wearing when they learned of the attack on Pearl Harbor—which also, as I remember it, took place on a Sunday morning. (I mention that without trying to imply any mystic pattern governing catastrophes. I understand that the Spanish Inquisition began late on a Tuesday afternoon.) At about nine-thirty, I had parked brilliantly on Houston Street itself—as the ex-co-editor of a one-issue journal called *Beautiful Spot, A Magazine of Parking*, I find that a perfect spot on Houston Street on Sunday morning can give me almost as much pleasure as a freshly baked bialy—and found myself in front of Yonah Shimmel's Knishery. Restraining myself from having one of Shimmel's legendary potato knishes at that hour of the morning, I had settled for a cheese bagel, figuring a little extra energy might be useful when I faced the counter crowds down the street. At Russ & Daughters, ordinarily my first stop, I was hardly in the door before someone was expertly removing from a succulent-looking Nova Scotia salmon some slices that were going to be my very own. My next move had been established years before. Leaving Russ & Daughters, I would take a quick look into Ben's Dairy, next door, and a quick look into Tanenbaum's Bakery, next door to Ben's—both tiny stores with barely enough room between the counter and the wall for a customer to elbow aside more than one other customer at a time. In either place, there could be an occasional lull in the crowd, the way there is a lull when a group of large men who are breaking down a door with a battering ram back up to get some running room. Making a quick, hard decision about which crowd looked less lethal at the moment, I would plunge into Ben's or Tanenbaum's, stagger back out to Houston Street, and plunge into the other one—emerging at the end carrying Ben's homemade cream cheese with scallions and Tanenbaum's fresh pumpernickel bagels, both of which would be combined with my Russ & Daughters' Nova Scotia to create the single perfect Nova Scotia and cream cheese on bagel available in today's depleted market. Whenever I put the final ingredient in my shopping bag, I felt ecstatic in the way I have always imagined a Manhattan real-estate speculator must feel ecstatic when he finally gets his hands on the last historic brownstone he needs to make up an entire block that can be torn down for a luxury highrise. That Sunday, I shot my customary glance toward Ben's as I moved toward Tanenbaum's, and I saw a steel gate across the storefront. Closed.

I remained calm. In the past, I had often found Ben closed when I expected him to be open. Although his official policy had always been to close only on Saturdays and Jewish holidays, it had long seemed to me that Ben knew about Jewish holidays that had escaped the notice of other observant Jews. Finding Ben closed on Sundays when knishes were pouring out of Yonah Shimmel's and customers were four deep at Russ & Daughters and the open-air discount cubbyholes on Orchard Street, around the corner, were booming, I had got the impression that Ben might sometimes observe, say, the anniversary of the death of some wise and scholarly rabbi whose wisdom did not happen to spread much beyond the boundaries of one small neighborhood in Vitebsk. But my assumption that Ben was closed for religious reasons was destroyed when I looked into Tanenbaum's. Tanenbaum was known on Houston Street to be at least as strict about such matters as Ben. I had always suspected, in fact, that Tanenbaum observed the anniversary of the death of not only great rabbis but maybe cantors as well and maybe some secular heroes and perhaps an ecumenical Methodist or two. Tanenbaum was in his store, dealing out bagels with both hands. I raced back into Russ & Daughters to find out what had happened, and my worst fears were confirmed: Ben had decided to close Sundays.

I had never objected to Tanenbaum and Ben closing on Saturdays. After all, freedom of religion is guaranteed in the Constitution, and, besides, I'm usually busy on Saturday shopping for Italian food. On a Saturday morning, I'm likely to be walking down Bleecker Street making last-minute adjustments to the intricate timing that sometimes allows me to start by buying a pound of prosciuttini at Mario Bosco's, get to Zito's just as the fresh-baked bread is coming up from the basement, and still arrive at the mozzarella store on Sullivan Street before it has been snatched clean of cheese-in-the-basket. (I go to the mozzarella store mainly to buy mozzarella, of course—mozzarella soaked in milk and salt, smoked mozzarella, any kind of mozzarella they are willing to sell me. But I often eat all of it before I've gone two blocks from the store, so if I fail to get cheese-in-the-basket I can arrive home with nothing to show for the trip.) Sometimes I stop in at the bakery on Carmine Street that, on Saturdays only, creates a ring-shaped loaf of bread containing small pieces of cheese and sausage, both of which snuggle into the dough when the loaf is heated. On Saturdays I have things to do. I had never even objected to closings on Jewish holidays that I suspected were known only to two or three senior professors at the Jewish Theological Seminary. But Sundays!

I took it personally. My Sundays had been ruined. The satisfaction of capturing each of the ingredients for the perfect Nova Scotia and cream cheese on bagel was no more. The pleasure of a late breakfast that could be extended to include picking at the small bits of Nova Scotia left on the platter at three-thirty or four was gone. I felt like a baseball manager who, having finally polished a double-play combination to such brillance that it provided the inspiration for the entire team, learns that the second baseman has decided to retire so that he can devote full time to his franchise estate-planning business.

It seemed to me that the reasons for the decision I had heard on Houston Street—that Ben was tired, that Ben had found it impossible to prepare enough cheese for the Sunday rush, that Ben could no longer take the crowds—were unpersuasive. Sunday is by far the busiest day on Houston Street. Closing on the busiest day is the kind of thing I might expect from some stationer in Surrey but not from a cheese merchant on the Lower East Side. I was not myself, of course. I became convinced that Ben, realizing how much I depended on him, had decided to close on Sundays as a display of independence. I knew, after all, that he was a strong-minded man. A year or two before, at a time when France had placed an embargo on spare parts for Israeli jets, Ben had put up a sign in his store that said something like UNTIL GENERAL DEGAULLE CHANGES HIS POLICY TOWARD ISRAEL, BEN SELLS NO MORE FRENCH CHEESE.

"He's trying to drive me from the city," I said to Alice when I arrived home, bearing a half pound of cream cheese that I had finally managed to find after a forty-minute traffic-and-parking struggle in the southern reaches of the Lower East Side—a dry, bland, half pound of cream cheese that tasted as if it might have been made by a Presbyterian missionary rigidly following directions from the Camp Fire Girls recipe book.

"He doesn't even know you," Alice said.

"He didn't know DeGaulle either," I said. But I decided to remain in the city. Out of the city, I wouldn't even be able to get decent cream cheese during the week.

I tried to look on the bright side. I told myself I could always make an extra trip on Friday to Ben's and then return on Sunday for fresh bagels and Nova Scotia; two routinely caught pop-ups may not provide as much beauty as a perfectly executed double play, but they provide precisely as many outs. I reminded myself that the ingredients for the perfect Nova Scotia and cream cheese on bagel were only part of my usual haul on Houston Street. As it happened, Ben's specialty was not even cream cheese but baked farmer cheese—a product I had learned about, years after I started going to Ben's, only because a lady from Scarsdale who shoved in front of me at the counter one morning ordered a baked farmer cheese with caraway seeds and then included an eloquent description of its taste in the speech she delivered to me about being double-parked and in a terrible hurry. (Baked farmer cheese can be eaten cold, which, out of ignorance, is the way I wolfed it down for three or four years, until I heard Ben say that reheating it makes it taste "like a soufflé or a crêpe Suzette or whatever you want"—a description I found to be completely accurate.) How could I begrudge Ben an additional day of rest, I asked myself, when I could come in any weekday and have my choice of baked farmer cheese with scallions or baked farmer cheese with vegetables or even baked farmer cheese with pineapple? Who was I to complain about a little break in my Houston Street routine when there were millions of people all over the world who would never taste Russ & Daughters' chopped herring?

There were, I reminded myself, even non-food reasons to come to Houston Street on Sunday. Whenever I begin to feel oppressed by being shoved ahead of in the various lines I'm forced to stand in around New York, I spend part of a Sunday at Katz's Delicatessen, a block or two east of my combination stores, where the sandwich-makers at the counter always maintain rigid queue discipline while hand-slicing a high-quality pastrami on rye. Fathoming line behavior in various cities requires, I have found, serious research. It was only after I took sample measurings of neighborhood cinema queues in London at a time when the press was printing statistics on the imminent demise of the film industry that I realized why there seem to be so many lines in England: English people apparently queue up as a sort of hobby. A family man might pass a mild autumn evening by taking the wife and kids to stand in the cinema queue for a while and then leading them over for a few minutes in the sweetshop queue and then, as a special treat for the kids, saying, "Perhaps we've time to have a look at the Number Thirty-one bus queue before we turn in." New York line behavior can be explained only by assuming that just about everyone in the line believes himself to be in possession of what the Wall Street people call inside information. Someone has convinced the people in the subway-token line that the next person to the booth is likely to receive not just a subway token but a special golden subway token, the recipient of which will never have to ride the subways again. The people about to board a Madison Avenue bus at five-thirty in the afternoon have somehow permitted themselves to be convinced by a shady-looking little tout that what they are trying to board is not actually a Madison Avenue bus but the last boat from Dunkirk. Some out-of-towner without inside information has no way of knowing that what he is being shoved off of is not merely one of a number of buses going to Sixty-fourth Street but the last chance of escaping the Huns, so he naturally finds the behavior of his fellow citizens excessive.

After a week or two of being badly dealt with by elderly women half my size, I'm always reassured by my first sight of those Katz countermen standing there. They seem to loom over the crowd—casually piling on corned beef, keeping a strict eye on the line in front of them, and passing the time by arguing with each other in Yiddish about what I have always preferred to think was anarcho-syndicalism. I stand there happily while some woman—undoubtedly the wife of the gentleman who elbowed past me in the potato-salad line at the P.S. 3 Fair—tries to sneak in for a quick tongue on rye and receives from the counterman a devastating look and some comment like "And who are you—a movie star maybe?" Katz's is the place in which a counterman who was told by a customer that a particularly lean corned-beef sandwich would earn a commendation to the boss replied, "The boss! May the boss's nose fall off!" I find it a great comfort.

A couple of years after my first daughter was born, I realized that I was going to Houston Street on Sunday partly to have her properly appreciated. At that time, a check of the census statistics for Manhattan had confirmed a suspicion that had been growing in my mind: At least half of the people who saw her on the street were neither Jewish nor Italian, and were therefore culturally handicapped in trying to demonstrate their appreciation of her in a way I considered appropriate. At Russ & Daughters, people pay some attention to a two-year-old. I don't mean quick smiles or routine "Isn't she cute?"s. I mean Notice Is Taken. Lox lies unsliced. Strategic places at the counter are abandoned. Candy fish are pressed into hands. I always thought that Russ & Daughters could get away with charging admission to new parents.

After Ben started closing on Sundays, in fact, I faced the simple truth that I could never give up Sunday mornings at Russ & Daughters completely, even if the entire Nova Scotia supply were lost to the Russian fishing fleet. (I will admit that when I stumble across one of those late-night philosophical discussions about whether war is ever justifiable, the question of how much of the Nova Scotia supply the Soviets can be allowed to swallow up leaps to my mind.) I have always thought that anyone who wants to open up a retail business in New York—a candy store or a Manhattan branch of Harrods—ought to be required to observe Russ & Daughters in action for a week. Russ & Daughters is a splendid refutation of the false teaching that a store selling pickled herring cannot have character and a clean display case at the same time. The daughters of the late founder are particularly warm and cheerful women, and a customer who enters the store having just stormed the counter at Tanenbaum's or subjected himself to the discipline of a Katz counterman could get the impression he has wandered into the Fourth of July outing of a large family. The salesperson—a daughter, a husband of a daughter, lately even a daughter of a daughter—is likely to be friendly enough to disarm even an experienced tormentor of Lower East Side countermen.

"A nice piece of whitefish," a customer says.

"A piece of whitefish," the counterman says cheerfully, moving toward the riches of the smoked-fish section.

"A *nice* piece of whitefish," the customer repeats.

"Right, I'll get you a very nice piece," the counterman says.

The customer waits until the chosen piece is weighed and wrapped —four or five previous pieces having been rejected—and then, looking suddenly indecisive, says, "Is the whitefish *good?*"

"Very good," the counterman says.

"Is it *excellent?*" the customer asks.

"You're going to love it," the counterman says.

The potential licensee can then step forward, sample the whitefish, and learn the most important lesson of his week's observation: He loves it.

Three years after Ben started closing Sundays, I went to the Lower East Side one Sunday morning partly to take a look at the city's experiment of turning Orchard Street into a "mall" on Sunday by forbidding automobile traffic from Delancey to Houston. I found that the absence of cars did make Orchard Street much less crowded and chaotic, which would have been all to the good except that Orchard Street is *supposed* to be crowded and chaotic. Looking down poor, barren Orchard Street, I realized that it is only a matter of time before the city officials of Addis Ababa find themselves approving an avant-garde plan for banning traffic in the city market—a plan proposed by one of those jazzy American urban-design specialists who flourished in Great Society times by knowing how to outfit an office-building complex in a way that qualified it for federal aid under a Department of Housing program to improve drainage facilities in low-rent residential areas. "We'll get a marvelous sweep of space here and a great flow of movement over here," he'll explain, stepping over four or five vegetable peddlers and wedging himself into a three-foot alley. "Naturally, we'll have designated off-street parking for all of these donkeys." I don't mean that I'm opposed to change. Tanenbaum sold his bakery a year or two ago, and I have always spoken approvingly of the transition, once I satisfied myself that the young man who bought it was not going to do anything foolish like closing on Sunday or cutting back on his supply of a favorite pastry of mine called *rugelach*. The mozzarella store on Sullivan Street, Frank's Dairy, changed hands a year or so after Tanenbaum's, and the new proprietor turned out to be a student of the craft—the kind of young man who would answer a customer's question about an interesting-looking kind of cheese not merely by saying that it was used in cooking a special Sicilian dish of liver and onions and cheese but tossing in the information that the one restaurant still serving that dish was a lunch counter on First Avenue. For stores as well as for governments, a stable transition is the test of the system. After rattling around Orchard Street for a few minutes that Sunday, I dropped into Russ & Daughters, and the subject of the stores next door came up.

"Ben's retiring," one of the daughters said.

"Retiring!" I said. I had spent three years making extra trips or making do with inferior cream cheese. Could he now plan, as the final blow, cutting off my supply completely?

"He's training someone to take his place," the daughter said.

Greatly relieved, I went to Ben's the next day to investigate the switchover. The man being trained in the art of farmer cheese, it turned out, was taking over in partnership with the young man who ran what had been Tanenbaum's Bakery. They were even considering the possibility of knocking down the wall in between, creating one store in a space almost as vast as a Checker cab. Despite their youth, the partners are traditionalists in such matters as observing the Sabbath—they are Hassidim from Brooklyn—but they believe in progressive business techniques. I noticed that they had erected a brightly painted double sign between the stores announcing Ben's Cheese Shop and Moishe's Bakery. The bakery had even acquired a motto: "Keep This Place in Mind/A Better One Is Hard to Find." Having a motto is not unknown on Houston Street (the Russ & Daughters' shopping bags say "Queens of Lake Sturgeon"), but it was hardly Tanenbaum's style. Ben's Dairy, where the presence of baked farmer cheese was a secret Ben managed to keep from me for years, now had a sign in the window that not only announced the cheese but listed the varieties on individual slats hanging from the sign, in the way some ice-cream parlors announce their flavors.

"Will the place be run the same way?" I asked Ben and his successor.

"He's going to be closed on Saturdays and Jewish holidays," Ben said firmly.

"Of course. Naturally," I said, trying to control my excitement. "And, uh, the other days?"

"This week," the young man said, "we start opening on Sundays."

Harry Garrison, the eater who had agreed to serve as my consultant in Cincinnati, had been recommended by my friend Marshall J. Dodge III—a fact that gave me pause, particularly after Marshall described him as a calliope-restorer by trade. I don't mean that I harbor any prejudice against calliope-restorers or that I think Marshall would make a frivolous recommendation. Marshall is a practical man. He has a practicality so pure, in fact, that it sometimes makes him appear eccentric. He is an uncompromising bicyclist—partly because bicycling is the most practical way to get around New York—and when he travels to, say, Cincinnati, he merely removes the wheels of one of his bicycles, stuffs the parts into something that resembles a swollen Harvard bookbag, and checks the mysterious bundle along with his luggage. If the ticket agent asks what the bag contains, Marshall looks at him solemnly—Marshall can manage an awesomely solemn look when the occasion calls for one—and says that the bag contains his grandmother's wheelchair. Like New York's most photographed bicyclist, John V. Lindsay—a tall man who was once the mayor—Marshall attended Buckley and St. Paul's and

Yale, and it is implicit in his appearance and manner that he takes the presence of many generations of Dodges at those institutions before him and after him as a matter of course. But if it is practical to take along a knapsack while riding his bicycle, Marshall takes along a knapsack. Then if someone happens to ask him, say, if he knows the address of a good calliope-restorer in Cincinnati, he can reach into the knapsack, pull out a small file of three-by-five cards, and thumb through it until he finds the answer.

What concerned me about depending on Marshall's recommendation for a guide to Cincinnati is that the knapsack is much more likely to produce the address of an expert on antique piano rolls or a supplier of Cajun-dialect phonograph albums than a specialist in French-fried onion rings or barbecue—a natural outgrowth of Marshall's own specialty, which is regional humor. (He has made an album of Down East stories called *Bert and I* and he has presented his monologues before groups in various parts of the country, always arriving by plane and bike.) I hinted about my concern to Marshall but he assured me that Garrison would be the perfect guide to Cincinnati and environs. He was not certain if it had been Garrison who put him on to a small restaurant in Rabbit Hash, Kentucky, that served what Marshall remembered as the best fried chicken in the world, but he was certain that it was Garrison who had introduced him to Professor Harry L. Suter, an elderly musicologist who was able to play the piano and the violin simultaneously by means of an invention the professor called the viola-pan.

Garrison, I found out, not only restores calliopes but also restores and sells player pianos, appears professionally around the state as Uncle Sam the Magician, delivers an occasional lecture on how to detect crooked gambling devices, and in the midst of all those activities manages to spend more than the ordinary amount of time at the table. He was not going to be able to meet me until a few hours after I arrived in Cincinnati, but he had suggested on the phone that for my first taste of authentic Cincinnati chili, at lunch, I might want to try the unadorned product and therefore should start with what is known locally as "a bowl of plain." He had no way of knowing, of course, that I have never eaten the unadorned version of anything in my life and that I once threatened to place a Denver counterman under citizen's arrest for leaving the mayonnaise off my California burger.

"What should I order if I don't want to start with the plain?" I asked.

"Try a four-way," Garrison said.

In Cincinnati, everyone knows that a four-way is chili on spaghetti with cheese and onions added. I never saw any numbers on menus in Cincinnati, but it is accepted that a customer can walk into any chili parlor—an Empress or a Skyliner or any of the independent neighborhood parlors—and say "One three-way" and be assured of getting chili on spaghetti with cheese. Cincinnati eaters take it for granted that the basic way to serve chili is on spaghetti, just as they take it for granted that the other ways to serve it go up to a five-way (chili, spaghetti, onions, cheese, and beans) and that the people who do the serving are Greeks. When the Kiradjieff family, which introduced authentic Cincinnati chili at the Empress in 1922, was sued several years ago by a manager who alleged that he had been fired unfairly, one of his claims amounted to the contention that anyone fired under suspicious circumstances from a chili parlor with Empress's prestige was all through in the Greek community. There are probably people in Cincinnati who reach maturity without realizing that Mexicans eat anything called chili, in the same way that there are probably young men from Nevada who have to be drafted and sent to an out-of-state Army camp before they realize that all laundromats are not equipped with slot machines.

What is called chili in America, of course, has less similarity to the Mexican dish than American football has to the game known as football just about everywhere else in the world. Like American football, though, it long ago became the accepted version within the borders, and anyone in, say, northern New Mexico who wanted to claim that the version served there (green or red chili peppers sliced up and cooked into a kind of stew) is the only one entitled to the name would have no more chance of being listened to than a soccer enthusiast who made a claim to the television networks for equal time with the N.F.L. As American chili goes, what is served in Cincinnati is sweeter than what I used to have at Dixon's and what I still have occasionally at the Alamo—a Tex-Mex chili parlor in Manhattan that offers eight or ten combination plates, all of which taste exactly alike, and is famous for a notation on the menu that says, "All combinations above without beans 25¢ extra." (I know people who have tried to work out the economics of how much the Alamo has to pay a professional bean-extractor to come out ahead on that offer, but a definite figure has eluded them.) The chili in Cincinnati is less ferocious than Texas chili, but I wouldn't want to carry the comparison any further. I decided a long time ago that I like chili, but not enough to argue about it with people from Texas.

To an out-of-towner, the chili in various Cincinnati chili parlors may seem pretty much alike, but there are natives who have stayed up late at night arguing about the relative merits of Empress and Skyline or explaining that the secret of eating at the downtown Empress is to arrive when the chili is at its freshest, which happens to be at about nine in the morning. In Cincinnati, people are constantly dropping into a new neighborhood chili parlor only to find out that it serves the best chili in the world. One chili fanatic I met was a supporter of a place across the river, in Kentucky, that he claimed serves a six-way and a seven-way.

"What could possibly be in a seven-way?" I asked.

"I don't know," he said. "They won't even tell you." I later learned from Bert Workum, a serious eater who works for the Kentucky *Post* in Covington, just across the river from Cincinnati, that the Dixie chili parlor in Kentucky had once served a seven-way by including eggs (fried or scrambled) and cut-up frankfurters but is now serving only a six-way, having abandoned its egg-cooking operation. Workum also told me that the chicken restaurant Marshall J. Dodge III probably had in mind was McKnight's, which is in Cynthiana, Kentucky, rather than in Rabbit Hash. I told him that Dodge was the kind of person who would never say Cynthiana if there was any excuse to say Rabbit Hash.

Garrison had turned out to be a large man who wears three-piece suits and a full beard and has what used to be called an ample stomach. He appreciates good food, but even at a restaurant that he might patronize mainly because it has a pleasant atmosphere or is open late at night or charges reasonable prices he is what one of his friends described as a Clean Plate Ranger. One of his friends, a man who runs a barbecue restaurant called the Barn and Rib Pit in downtown Cincinnati, told me, "I love to see Harry eat ribs. He just inhales those ribs. You look at him and he's just glowin'."

I spent an afternoon with Garrison riding around Cincinnati, and found him to be one of those rare Americans who truly savors his city. I was still a bit concerned that he might be someone who would be more excited about finding an authentic boogie-woogie pianist or maybe a mechanical violin in perfect working order than he would about stumbling onto, say, the classic corn fritter. But he relieved my fears somewhat by describing what we were going to have for dinner at his house as "the best fried chicken in the world." At about that time, by coincidence, we passed a run-down looking restaurant whose sign actually said, WORLD'S BEST FRIED CHICKEN. Garrison glanced at it contemptuously. "I don't see any point in considering his claim at all," he said.

There was a lot of food talk among the dinner guests at Garrison's that evening, and there was also some staggering acorn squash and the best apple pie I have ever tasted. The chicken was delicious, but I still think the best fried chicken I have ever eaten was at a sort of outdoor homecoming that Cherokee County, Georgia, held for Dean Rusk, a native son, shortly after he was named Secretary of State—fried chicken so good that I still nurture a hope, against long odds, that Cherokee County will someday produce another Secretary of State and throw another homecoming.

Garrison finished off the meal by handing around made-in-Cincinnati cigars and treating the entire company to a display of smoke-ring blowing. Garrison's smoke-ring technique includes a remarkable motion by which he more or less nudges the ring along by pushing at the air a few inches behind it—a variation of the assistance that curlers offer a curling stone by sweeping away at the ice in its path. Between rings, Garrison announces his performance with the kind of grandiloquence he must use on the magic stage, and he is as irritable as a matador about the threat of air movement that could mar his artistry. Just when everyone at the table expects a ring to emerge, Garrison is likely to pause, glance around sternly, and say, in a majestic voice, "I detect human breathing in this room." Even after having stopped eating for a while to watch the smoke-ring blowing, none of us felt up to the late-night visit to the Barn and Rib Pit Garrison had contemplated. The fact that I knew the proprietor was white made me less disappointed at missing the Barn and Rib Pit than I might have been. Going to a white-run barbecue is, I think, like going to a gentile internist: It might turn out all right, but you haven't made any attempt to take advantage of the percentages.

Garrison had promised me a special treat for my last night in Ohio—a treat to be found in a restaurant near Oxford—but even as we drove to the restaurant he insisted that precisely what the treat was would have to be a surprise. After the day I had spent, I figured it might require more than a surprise treat to induce me to take any food on my fork. At about eleven, I had stopped at the downtown Empress to see what it looked like, and, deciding that it might be rude to leave without eating (particularly so early in the freshness cycle), had polished off a three-way. For lunch, Garrison had led me to a splendid place called Stenger's Café, which he described as the last of the old-fashioned workingman's bars left in what had been the old German section of Cincinnati known as Over the Rhine. At Stenger's I cleaned a plate on which the counterman had piled

mettwurst, two potato pancakes, a helping of beans, some beets, bread
and butter, and, at the last minute, a piece of beef from a tray I had
spotted being carried across the room. For that, I had parted with one
dollar and twenty-eight cents. My appetite was returning as we drove,
though, and Garrison helped it along by describing what we might have
eaten at a few of the places he had considered taking me to before he
decided on the restaurant in Oxford—including a place in Kentucky that
specialized in farm food like ham with gravy.

"Red-eye gravy?" I asked.

"Red-eye gravy," Garrison said.

We drove along for a few miles while I thought that over.

"Is it too late to turn back toward Kentucky?" I asked.

"You'll love the place we're going," Garrison said. "It's going to have a
fine surprise for you."

The place he had picked out was a restaurant outside Oxford called the
Shady Nook. It turned out to be a normal-looking suburban restaurant
with a sign in four or five colors of neon in the parking lot. Garrison
insisted that we sit at the bar for a while to have shrimp cocktails and
some wine. Behind the bar there was a stage that went completely around
the room, and in front of the stage was a covered square that looked as if
it might be a small orchestra pit. I was beginning to wonder what the
surprise was. I didn't see anything amazing about the shrimp except how
many of them Garrison was eating. Between bites he managed to say
hello to a man he identified as the owner of the Shady Nook and to
explain how Professor Harry L. Suter happened to design the viola-pan as
he whiled away the time on the top floor of his house in Moscow, Ohio,
during the great flood of 1913. Garrison told me that he had hired
Professor Suter to play a Christmas party in 1959, and had the pleasure of
being able to say in the introduction that it was the Professor's first
Cincinnati appearance since the summer of 1917, when he played the
Bell Telephone picnic. I couldn't spot anything extraordinary on the
plates of the people already eating, but somehow I got it in my mind that
the surprise was going to be either The Great Cherry Cobbler or maybe
even The Classic Onion Ring. Suddenly, the recorded music that I had
been listening to without realizing it was turned off. From deep within
what I had thought was an orchestra pit came a rumbling noise. Before
my eyes there arose a gigantic gold, intricately carved, four-keyboard,
three-ton Wurlitzer Theater Organ. The owner of the Shady Nook
climbed up on the stool, high above the bar, and—by playing at least all
four keyboards at once and flicking on and off several dozen switches at

the same time—transformed the Shady Nook into Radio City Music Hall. I was indeed surprised. Harry Garrison looked at the theater organ and looked at me and beamed.

My father owned a restaurant for a few years in Kansas City, although I always suspected he thought of it mainly as an outlet for his poetry. He wrote a two-line poem every day on the lunch menu. At dinner, the restaurant drew mainly a family trade, and the diners had to eat their turkey or breaded veal cutlet or Swiss steak without benefit of rhyme. (I can't remember much about the taste of the food; I suppose that in itself amounts to a description of it.) Although the restaurant was in the residential district, quite a few businessmen came in for lunch—a crowd from an insurance company building not far away, some merchants from a shopping district, salesmen who happened to find themselves in the neighborhood—and they were accustomed to seeing on the menu, in a space between the luncheon specials and the desserts, a poem like "Try Mrs. Trillin's pie, I'm sure one piece'll/Give your motor more power than a diesel." A lot of them came back regularly anyway.

As quick as he was about using the restaurant for his own poetic ends, my father never seemed interested in turning it into a platform for his own ideas on what was good to eat. That would have been a true test of the regulars' loyalty. My father had absolute ideas about food—as well as about a number of other subjects—and once he made up his mind he was about as flexible as Fats Goldberg's eating schedule. More than once he told me, "The best thing in the world to eat is a good ear of corn"—in the matter-of-fact tone of someone announcing the date of the Battle of the Boyne.

"If you were blindfolded, you couldn't tell whether there was cream in your coffee or not," he said to me one night at dinner, after I had declined the cream.

I told him I thought that he was probably not in the best position to speak authoritatively on the subject, since, as it happened, he had never tasted coffee, with or without cream, in his life. (I was never certain why his avoidance of coffee had to be absolute, except that he tended to be an all-or-nothing man. I have since come to believe that people who pride themselves on their will power might sometimes swear things off just to stay in practice—looking at themselves in the mirror on a quiet morning and saying, for no particular reason, "My friend, you have eaten your last scrambled egg.")

He looked at me and shook his head and said, "I don't care what you say, blindfolded you couldn't tell the difference."

When it came to poetry, my father was not an absolutist. Pie was his favorite subject for a couplet, but every three or four weeks he would write about something else—perhaps a couplet like "'Eat your food,' gently said Mom to little son Roddy/'If you don't, I will break every bone in your body.'" The next day he would be back to pies—"Mrs. Trillin's pecan pie, so nutritious and delicious/Will make a wild man mild and a mild man vicious" or "A woman shot her husband in our place last July/He started talking while she was enjoying her pie." He made a strong case in the poems for the pies' being completely free of calories. "Don't blame your weight/On the pie you ate," he would write, or "So you love the sound of the soft-lowing cattle/Then eat lots of pie and be lighter in the saddle." He often returned to the theme of pie being good for one's general health, like mineral water or brisk walks. "A piece of pie baked by Mrs. Trillin," he would write of a pie baked, of course, by a black woman named Thelma, "will do you more good than penicillin." He rhymed pie with "eye" and "good-bye" and "fry" ("'Let's go, warden, I'm ready to fry/My last request was Mrs. Trillin's pie'") and "evening is nigh." His shortest poem, as far as I can tell, was "Don't sigh/Eat pie."

My cousin Nardy owns a restaurant too, and he uses it as an excuse to publish a newsletter about the customers. Nardy, I believe, graduated from the University of Missouri School of Journalism, the same institution that produced Fats Goldberg, the pizza baron, and, I can only assume, dozens of other successful restaurant men, all of whom are more prosperous than the night city editors turned out by other journalism schools. Nardy sees the newsletter as an opportunity for me in the restaurant business. I don't mean I actually want to own a restaurant, any more than Nardy actually wants to cover City Hall for the Wichita *Eagle*. I see myself more as a consultant—an idea man. An amazing number of people do want to own a restaurant. They know a couple of remarkable recipes and they like to meet people and it all seems so easy that the failure rate for new restaurants in New York is sixty-five per cent the first year. On Sunday evenings in Goldberg's Pizzeria, a lot of the people who don't talk to Fats about going on a diet the next morning talk to him about their ideas for starting a restaurant. Once, a woman told him that she wanted to start a restaurant on the strength of a secret recipe for coleslaw. Fats, being a man who started a restaurant on the strength of a pizza recipe and a small joke, did not feel that he was in a position to discourage her. He gave her the same advice he gives all other aspiring restaurant owners—run the place yourself. "People have a funny idea about what owning a restaurant is like," Fats says. "Their idea of running a restaurant is naming it after themselves and then coming in to buy a round of drinks before they go to the theater."

In a way, I already am an idea man for restaurants, although nobody has exactly used my ideas. So far, I have offered Fats Goldberg alone what I figure to be about a hundred thousand dollars' worth of consultation. He appreciates it, and when he comes over to our house he occasionally brings along a medium-sized mushroom-and-pepperoni pizza. When our second daughter was born, he brought her a heart-shaped sausage pizza with her initials written on it in red peppers. I'm not complaining.

Once, Fats called me to ask what I thought of the idea of putting in a sandwich at his pizzerias. Fats figures he loses a lot of groups of people just because of not offering one item for a non-pizza eater to eat. When business is slow at the pizzeria and Fats is in a worrying mood, he finds himself imagining two prosperous young couples who are about to step into a cab and come to Goldberg's. As they enter the cab, one of the wives says, "I hate pizza." Her husband sighs, and the other couple tries to be polite, and they're all lost to some East Side bar with sawdust on the floor and overpriced hamburgers and a spinach-and-bacon salad that has been in the refrigerator so long that the discerning palate cannot tell the spinach from the bacon. Fats and I spend a lot of time on the phone talking about what his non-pizza item should be. When I spoke to him about sandwiches, he had just returned from Kansas City, where he had sampled some of the local sandwiches, as well as just about everything else that was edible and for sale. Fats had gained so much weight in Kansas City that, upon returning, he had even given up his Monday treats. Before he had gone to Kansas City, he spent six months or so watching television advertisements for a new Sara Lee breakfast roll—the kind called a pull-apart—without being able to eat one. When he arrived in Kansas City, one of his first acts was to drive to the A&P and buy a container of pull-aparts. "I ate them all before I got out of the parking lot," he told me. "I think one of them was still frozen."

Fats was complaining about the constant food temptations facing someone walking along the street in New York—the frozen-custard stands, the Greek *souvlaki* joints, the places that sell Sicilian pizza by the slice. "In the suburbs, you have to make a decision to get in the car and go get something to eat," Fats said. "You're not always passing right in front of it."

"Anybody can diet in Mamaroneck, Fats," I said, trying to cheer him up. "This is the Big Apple."

"What do you think about a hamburger called a Goldburger?" Fats asked.

"Not a Goldburger, Fats," I said, "a Pure Goldburger."

Fats drifted toward other possibilities—a way, I suppose, of not having to admit that my Pure Goldburger idea was worth thousands. We discussed Mario's grinder and a sandwich of grilled cheese with *jalepeña* peppers I had eaten in New Mexico and a variety of the New Jersey hoagie and even a Nu-way (a Nu-way, the specialty of a place with the same name that used to exist in Kansas City, is loose ground beef on a bun. My sister and I were the only people I ever knew who would eat them, but Nu-way managed to stay in business for years—on the strength, I have always thought, of an eerie appeal it had for women in hair curlers. There were always so many women in hair curlers at Nu-way that for years I thought it just happened to be near a hairdressers' college). I spent a long time talking about the possibilities of a sandwich that would have, as its main ingredients, Swiss cheese and the kind of prosciuttini I buy at Mario Bosco's.

Suddenly there was a gasp on the other end of the line. "Oh my God!" Fats said. "I just got so hungry I almost fainted."

When my next-door neighbor, the ferociously named Zohar Ben Dov, took over the Riviera Bar, on Sheridan Square, I naturally assumed he would turn to me for advice about French-fried potatoes. People are always coming around to talk French fries with me. I'm constantly under pressure from the McDonald's fancy to acknowledge that frozen French fries can be delicious if fried to the proper crispness. At a party one night, a respectable-looking mother of three told me that Nathan's French fries (at the original Coney Island branch, it goes without saying) are at their finest just after the corn oil is first poured into the Pitman Frialators, before nine-thirty in the morning—at about the time, in other words, allowing for the difference in time zones, that the chili diehards in Cincinnati are drifting into the downtown branch of Empress. I told her that I have never touched a French fry before eleven in the morning and that I never intend to. There is a difference between an authority and a fanatic.

Anticipating Zohar's request for help, I started eating French fries all over town to refresh my palate—having left the field for a few months to look after a well-deserved case of fatness. I made a list of the great French fries I have eaten—the ones that used to be served with fried shrimp on the wharf in Santa Monica, the crude fat ones with parts of the potato skin still visible that I have run across at steak restaurants now and then. I even interviewed Murray Handwerker, the president of Nathan's. Zohar seemed to be taking his time about coming around for a consultation. I realized, of course, that he was busy renovating the building. The Riv, which is just a couple of blocks from where Zohar and I live, is one of those Greenwich Village bars that people who live in the Village count on to remain more or less the same, so Zohar was faced with the problem of making sure the walls would stay up without making the place look as if someone had made sure the walls would stay up. I revised my great French fries list again and polished my notes from the Handwerker interview, but Zohar never did come around.

On quiet afternoons, when my mind wanders, I still see myself as Zohar's French-fry consultant. Zohar and I meet on the street, just after the Riviera deal has been closed. "I know," I say. "You want to tap my know-how on what kind of French fries to serve. You'll want to start by sampling the little wonders at Arthur Bryant's barbecue, just to give you something to shoot at. It's only a two-and-a-half-hour flight to Kansas City."

"I'm kind of busy," Zohar says. "We're renovating."

"I have already stated in public that Arthur Bryant's is to the smooth kind of French fries what Nathan's Coney Island branch is to the fat kind with krinkly edges," I say. I tell Zohar a true story to illustrate the point that the French fries at Nathan's and at Bryant's are interchangeably delicious: An acquaintance of mine who grew up in Kansas City but now lives in New York once stopped in Kansas City on a flight back from California, went to Arthur Bryant's, picked up twenty-eight orders of ribs and some sauce, and got on the next plane to New York. That night he threw a magnificent banquet—a gathering of expatriate Midwesterners coming together in the way British colonial servants might have gathered in the clearing of some steamy African jungle during imperial times for a proper Christmas dinner, complimenting the cook on how close she had come to cooking a true Christmas goose in the makeshift oven and pointing out the significance of the sixpence in the pudding to the few specially favored native civil servants who had been invited. Realizing that even Bryant's fries would not travel, he substituted Nathan's krinkly-cuts—hot from the Eighth Street branch. I completely approved of his decision.

I was sorry he neglected to bring along any burned edges of brisket from Kansas City, but if a man delivers twenty-eight orders of Bryant's ribs to within walking distance of my house in New York, I do not feel in a position to quibble with him.

"Excuse me," Zohar says, turning in the direction of the Riv, "I think I hear a ceiling crumbling."

I go on eating French fries, crossing off the ones that anyone would consider dipping in ketchup. Within a week, I manage to wangle the appointment with Murray Handwerker, and hurry back to the Riviera with an intelligence report. I find Zohar, looking harried, trying to hire some waiters for the Riviera's reopening.

"Nathan's prefers Maine potatoes, Zohar," I say. "I got that from the top man."

"How come everybody in the Village who wants to work as a waiter says he's really an actor?" Zohar says.

"Mr. Handwerker says Idahos are fine for baking—the people in Idaho shouldn't be mad—but too mealy for a firm French fry. Long Island potatoes have too much water in them for French fries. He says Long Islands are good for chowder. I guess they float well."

"What do I want with actors?" Zohar says. "This is not a play about a bar. It's a bar."

I continue testing French fries, although Alice tries to persuade me that enough research has been done. I realize I made a mistake in letting her know that the public-relations man for Nathan's gained thirty-one pounds after joining the firm.

"I must press on," I say to her. "Zohar needs me."

I go right over to the Riv to talk about Suzy-Q's—the skinny but soft kind of French fries that are served all tangled up, usually in a basket. They are as rare in New York as a superior taco. I find Zohar trying to get rid of a sinister-looking man who had offered to put in a coin-operated skittle machine in return for a seventy-five per cent interest in the business—all moneys to be exchanged in cash. "I'm going to Thomforde's in Harlem to check out their Suzy-Q's," I say to Zohar.

"I've got to make a decision among two hundred and thirty-eight brands of draft beer," Zohar says, staring at a table full of beer samples with a look of anticipated nausea.

"Life is not all beer and skittles," I say, getting in a line that can be set up properly only in daydreams on quiet afternoons. "There are French-fried potatoes to be considered."

"Please stop," Zohar says. "Enough. No more with the French fries."

Realizing that Zohar is just feeling guilty about all the help I am giving him, I persevere. I find a struggling young potato farmer near Patchogue who has learned to grow Maine potatoes in Long Island. "He's small potatoes now," I tell Zohar, "but they're not watery." The farmer is willing to grow all of the potatoes needed at the Riv and have them sliced just before delivery by a group of local women who have been poor and idle since a project for making precut old-fashioned quilts was shut down by the Office of Economic Opportunity. I report this triumph to Alice.

"A sort of cottage industry, I suppose," Alice says.

"Strictly French fries," I tell her.

Zohar is grateful. People are coming in all the way from Rego Park just to have a go at the Riv's potatoes. There are rumors in the trade that Nathan's has been sending around scouts.

One of the best ideas I ever gave Fats Goldberg was for a diet restaurant in midtown Manhattan called Slim Pickin's. The name alone, I figure, is worth a couple of hundred thousand. I even told Fats we could call it Fats Goldberg's Slim Pickin's—with the Fats Goldberg written in script, of course—if he wanted to take the idea and run with it, but Fats was not enthusiastic. "People don't like to think about dieting when they go out to eat," I was told by the man who has thought about practically nothing else during every waking moment since May 1, 1959. "Also, you can't have enough variety." That shows how much Fats knows about the dieting habits of Americans who do not happen to use the Fats Goldberg method of eating the same thing every day of their lives except within the city limits of Kansas City, Missouri. What he was thinking of was a restaurant that would serve only those low-caloric specials that are always being offered in midtown coffee shops to guilt-ridden secretaries—broiled lean ground round, cottage cheese, and mauve jello for dessert. I once found the businessman's equivalent in a book that calls itself an executive diet guide and has a list of a lot of expensive restaurants where the dieting executive can spend forty-five dollars to watch his business prospect eat pancakes stuffed with creamed chicken while he chews away at a lean piece of roast beef with no sauce.

What Fats does not seem to understand is that all of the diets these days allow the dieter to eat as much as he wants of one thing or another as long as he stays away from something else, and the forbidden type of food is different in every one of the diets. A restaurant that was set up to accommodate the followers of whichever four or five diets are selling more than a million books that week could therefore serve virtually anything. Drinks are allowed on the drinking man's diet. One diet allows anything that can be passed off as protein. I wouldn't be surprised to hear that someone has come out with an all-potato diet that would permit all of the potatoes the dieter could stuff down—French-fried, cottage-fried, home-fried, mashed, shoestring, *latkes*, dumplings—as long as he puts nothing else to his lips except fourteen quarts of water a day. What could be more appealing to a New York restaurant entrepreneur than a restaurant that serves precisely what all other midtown businessmen's restaurants serve while maintaining a gimmick that leads people to believe that there is some special reason to patronize it? But somehow, Fats Goldberg has resisted the idea of Slim Pickin's. He does occasionally ask me if he should put in a low-calorie salad at the pizzerias, though. Apparently, he sometimes imagines that the one person who keeps the two couples from Goldberg's Pizzeria every night not only hates pizza but is on a diet.

Not long ago, I came up with an idea that I knew Fats would find as irresistible as a double cheeseburger with everything but onions. It is the reverse of Slim Pickin's—a restaurant that would encourage people to be happy in their eating instead of making them feel like a gaggle of Methodist ministers in Las Vegas. We would call it Ah Fat! If Goldberg saw the light and came in as a managing partner, we could even call it Fats Goldberg's Ah Fat! There would be pictures on the wall of famous fatties—Winston Churchill and Babe Ruth and Santa Claus and that crowd. There would also be cheerful sayings on the wall about not watching calories—like YOU CAN ALWAYS START TOMORROW and GO AHEAD—YOU DESERVE IT and TASTES DON'T COUNT. One of the specialties would be a Fats Goldberg Kansas City Special—an exact replica of what Fats asks his mother to cook him for lunch in Kansas City (fried pork tenderloin with gravy, creamed corn, French-fried potatoes, a loaf of Wonder bread). Naturally, we would make use of some of my father's menu poetry—adapting couplets like "Mrs. Trillin bakes like mad, she gets no salaries/Spends most of her time extracting the calories." A notice on the menus would say "All Dishes Cooked in Butter Unless Pure Lard Is Appropriate."

In preparation for presenting the idea to Fats, I even wrote some folk tales that could be handed out with the menus—the way some restaurants patronized by businessmen hand out a synopsis of the twelve o'clock news or the latest market averages. I showed my favorite one to Alice:

Once, in Dayton, Ohio, there lived a shingles salesman named Harry Kahn. He was five feet ten inches tall and weighed two hundred and eighty-five pounds. He enjoyed eating and he despised exercise of any sort—to the point of having an electric eye installed on his refrigerator so that the door opened when he approached. Some of Harry Kahn's friends said that Harry ate constantly because he was unhappy, but Harry was, in fact, very happy, and one of the reasons he was so happy is that he ate constantly and enjoyed it. His wife, who had taken Psychology 110 at Ohio State University, always told Harry he was fat because his mother had used rich foods as a reward when he was a child, although Harry's wife knew very well that Harry had grown up in a Baptist orphanage in Lima, Ohio, where eating between meals was strictly forbidden and the dining hall menu was dominated by Brussels sprouts.

One day, Harry's wife told him that she would divorce him if he didn't go on a diet. She thought that if Harry were thinner he would sell more shingles and they could afford to join the country club. Harry could not bear the thought of losing his wife. She was a loving wife and a loyal companion and she made the best toasted peanut-butter-and-honey sandwiches in the state of Ohio. He went on a strict diet and began to lose weight. In a year, he weighed one hundred and forty-eight pounds. He was very unhappy. He sold the same number of shingles he had sold before.

One day, a foreign-looking man rang Harry Kahn's doorbell and asked him if he was the Harry Kahn who had grown up in an orphanage in Lima, Ohio. Harry said he was. "Praise Allah," the foreign-looking man said, whereupon he fell on his knees and started kissing Harry's high-school graduation ring. He explained that the orphanage had misunderstood Harry's name: It wasn't Harry Kahn but Ari Khan, and he was a member of the Khan Dring Klan, a schismatic Moslem sect. Every forty years, according to age-old custom, the sect selected one of its members, chosen by lot, weighed him, and gave him a ruby for every pound he weighed more than the weight of the average unwed maiden. Harry—or Ari—had been selected.

The foreign-looking man took Harry to Iran, where there was an elaborate ceremony that ended with Harry being weighed. By eating as much as he could on the plane, Harry had managed to get his weight up to one hundred-fifty-one pounds, three pounds heavier than the average maiden of the Khan Dring Klan, which had traditionally equated fat with beauty. The three rubies he received were worth three hundred and eighty-five dollars, not quite enough to cover his fare back to Dayton.

Alice said that it would be thoughtless to show Fats a folk tale that encouraged him to become fat again. "Also," she said, "it's the silliest folk tale I've ever heard."

"It may be sort of silly at that," I said. "Maybe we should start with the one I've written about an Indian brave named Back Behind the Mesa who was shamed by his father into losing weight so he would be able to move through the forest as swiftly as an elk, and was then shot by another brave who mistook him for an elk."

"That one is even sillier," Alice said.

"I have one about two sisters—a fat one and a slim one—who both worked as carhops in Canoga Park, California, waiting to be discovered," I said. "The slim one is discovered and eventually becomes a movie star and then starts drinking and ends up as a dime-a-dance girl in Ocean Park, New Jersey. The fat one is left at the drive-in, and eventually she takes over the business and franchises."

Alice said that the entire idea of Ah Fat! could not possibly be brought up to Fats Goldberg, a man who has a hard enough go as it is trying to keep from weighing three hundred pounds. I finally decided she was right. She is a level-headed person who has, on occasion, moved the basket of Ratner's onion rolls out of my reach when others at the table were too caught up in the excitement of the moment to think about sensible medical precautions. It is a shame, though. After I had already abandoned the project, I thought of one of my best ideas for Ah Fat! Instead of just giving customers their leftover meat in doggie bags the way conventional restaurants do, we would give each customer (at least each customer who had not followed the admonition on our wall plaque— CLEAN YOUR PLATE) not only a doggie bag but a sign that would help him enjoy the contents—a ready-stick sign that would be easily attached to the refrigerator door and would say ANYTHING CONSUMED WHILE YOU'RE STANDING UP HAS FEWER CALORIES IN IT THAN IT WOULD IF IT WERE CONSUMED WHILE YOU WERE SITTING DOWN.

8

Whenever one of the lunchtime regulars at my father's restaurant —somebody like a cheerful young salesman of plastics, say—revealed that he was going to be married, my father said, "Did you check her teeth?" He said it before he offered congratulations. He had a strong feeling that ordinary flaws of personality or looks or background could be corrected or adjusted to, but that bad teeth represented a lifelong financial drain. About the time the dentist who had been treating Alice seemed to start counting on one of her wisdom teeth as a sort of small second income—the way that someone who works in a corporate auditing office might figure on picking up some extra money doing income-tax returns on the side, or the way a mildly corrupt policeman might begin to include some free lunches in his budget—it occurred to me that I had neglected my own father's advice. I also realized, of course, that we were beyond such matters, being together for better or for worse, and all that. It would make no difference to me, I told Alice manfully while I was studying one of the wisdom-tooth bills, if she suddenly confessed a history of root-canal operations. There are more important things in a marriage than teeth, I told her, and, while I was trying to put my finger on precisely what they were, I realized that the question I would ask a young man who told me he had at last found his beloved is "Does she share her food?" The kind of scene I conjure up when I try to envision what could make a man grow to regret his youthful, romantic decision takes place at a twentieth-anniversary dinner in a French restaurant. The husband, a fellow who has a roving eye for the entrees but has managed to settle on the cassoulet, reaches over for a forkful of his wife's trout meunière, which looks delicious, and the wife says, stiffly, "There really

67

isn't much of this, you know." The husband returns the fork to his cassoulet, troutless, and stares out into space, numbed by the vision of sharing his twilight years with a woman who is stingy with her fish.

Fortunately, Alice is so generous in such matters that she would never say to a waiter "I'll take the canneloni, too" if she knew that the person who had just ordered the canneloni also happened to be desperate for a few bites of fettuccini Alfredo. I don't mean we never disagree. We disagreed, for instance, about whether or not she should take advantage of having a number of immigrant Chinese students in an English class she was teaching at City College by trying to worm some restaurant information out of them. I was on the side that said she should.

"Isn't it accepted practice to let students with language problems write about their own experiences so they can gain confidence?" I asked. "It seems perfectly logical to suggest that they use their favorite restaurant as a scene for a reminiscence."

"I'm ashamed of you," she said.

"It would also be helpful if they included translations of a few of the dishes some of those Chinese restaurants always list on the wall," I said. "Remember the old writing-course motto—Individualize by Specific Detail." Some restaurants in Chinatown have, in addition to the menu they hand the simple Westerner, a series of dishes announced on signs tacked to the wall—signs that are almost invariably written in Chinese characters. For complicated reasons, the only Chinese ideogram I can recognize happens to be the one that signifies "revisionist quagmire," so I often have to sit in a Chinese restaurant helplessly while a tableful of Chinese businessmen across the room are stuffing down succulent-looking dishes that were obviously ordered off the wall. Requests to the waiter for a translation always draw unsatisfactory responses—varying, according to the proficiency in English, from "No beer, sorry" to "you no like that" to "I really haven't the time to translate the entire wall so why don't you tell me which one you want translated most?" One would think that if one's wife were in a position to correct a situation that causes one a great deal of frustration and even anger, one's wife would do so. But no marriage is perfect.

"Guess what Tricia Nixon Cox's favorite recipe is," Alice said one morning at breakfast as she came upon the information in the *Times*.

"I'm not sure I'm up to hearing about it," I said. As it happened, I had been daydreaming about grits—the kind of grits that a lot of restaurants in the South just assume you'll want to have nestled next to your eggs at breakfast. When I'm home, I usually have just coffee for breakfast—being full to the gills with guilt over what I consumed the night before—and my thoughts naturally turn to grits, although occasionally I muse about hash browns. My grits daydreams have greatly improved since the days when I thought there was no convenient place to find grits in my neighborhood anyway—a situation that had put me in the position of a gold miner who tries to fantasize about how he's going to spend his winter's horde even though he knows there isn't a town within a thousand miles that has facilities for a proper toot.

The brief fashion for southern black people in the middle-sixties left Manhattan with some soul-food restaurants south of Harlem—it also produced at least one $100-a-plate soul-food benefit at the Waldorf Astoria—but most of them are not the kind of places that open for breakfast. I used to think that the closest place to Greenwich Village a person could eat grits for breakfast was the Criminal Courts building off Foley Square. The coffee shop in the lobby there has served them for years—the number of poor people coming to New York from the South to get in trouble being large enough to make grits a natural part of the menu, the way that American hamburgers must be a natural part of the menu by now in the London Airport. Then I discovered that a small restaurant right around the corner from my house—the Pink Teacup —serves grits all day long. When our younger daughter was born, I went straight from the hospital to the Pink Teacup, thankful that a man no longer had to go all the way to Foley Square to stage a major celebration. William Edgett Smith joined me there for breakfast, and the grits were so good that even Smith realized it—a fact that cheered those of us who were beginning to be concerned that he might be suffering from pathological hypogeusia, a serious impairment of the sense of taste.

"Tricia Nixon Cox's favorite recipe is called Chicken Divan," Alice said.

"Spare me the details, please," I said. "I'm a citizen, after all."

"I will say only that it has two cans of cream of chicken soup poured into it," Alice said. "Also, the White House told the *Times* the President doesn't eat ketchup on his cottage cheese any more."

"It must be one of those pieces about how a man can grow in the presidency," I said. I didn't really mind if the President put ketchup on his cottage cheese—it's a personal matter—but people who pour cans of cream of chicken soup on a defenseless bird that happens to be a chicken already never eat the results quietly at their desks alone. They expect other people to eat it, on wedding-gift china. Anxious to demonstrate their versatility, they prepare some dishes with canned mushroom soup instead of canned cream of chicken soup. I have always thought that the label on canned mushroom soup should be required by statute to say, "For soup purposes only. Using the contents of this can for Beef Stroganoff or turkey casserole is thoughtless and unlawful."

A year or so after Alice interrupted my grits daydream with the news about Chicken Divan, John Hess revealed in the *Times* a Republican cookbook that featured Tricia's mushroom-soup variation (Chicken Imperial) and her mother's recipe for something called Continental Salad, which has as its active ingredients canned beets, canned grapefruit juice, and Jell-O. It occurred to me again that the women who talk most about the importance of preserving the traditional American family never seem to bring any more American enterprise to their traditional role as ma-in-the-kitchen cooks than is required to make the choice between Campbell's and H. J. Heinz. From my palate-numbing experience with William Edgett Smith at the Women's Lib restaurant, I know that there must be some feminists who have gone so far as to include a contempt for cooking along with a contempt for washing the pots. But most of the women I know who would never accept the old idea of a woman's place being in front of the stove—Alice, for instance—would also never be caught using a can of soup for purposes that the Almighty did not intend it to be used. They seem to be good cooks partly out of an inclination to become accomplished at whatever they set out to do—an inclination that leads to a loose set of skills and values that, when the histories of feminist ideology are written, may be set down as The Domestic Deviation.

Alice's ability to cook like a member of the Domestic Deviation is particularly fortunate for me because, unlike a lot of people with enthusiasm for food, I have never had any interest in learning how to cook. I'm a specialist; I just eat. Because of Alice, though, I don't even have to leave home to eat dishes—from a subtle poached salmon to a sausage concoction called Lunenberg Leftovers—that could make the average plastics salesman forget the cost of a between-the-teeth gold inlay. It is good fortune indeed, marred only by my embarrassment when a dinner guest in his middle years reacted to something Alice had done with cheese-in-the-basket, strawberries and Grand Marnier by asking if we would adopt him.

I think that some people in Kansas City at first found Alice's reputation as a cook somewhat intimidating. I have heard her identified as "a gourmet cook" in the same way my cousin Kenny is identified as "a C.P.A." I have explained that she is flexible enough to have become addicted to the pig-in-the-blankets served at the Yankee Doodle in New Haven, but I must admit that I once caught her about to grind fresh Parmesan cheese on my Kraft dinner. It happened in Georgia, while we were borrowing a friend's summer house. During a trip to the local supermarket, I had spotted the kind of macaroni-and-cheese dish that comes in a box and was always called Kraft dinner in our house when I was a child—which was the last time I could remember eating any. It didn't seem to taste right in Georgia. At first, I thought Alice might have already managed to sprinkle some fresh cheese on it before I walked into the kitchen, but the next day I tried some heated up from the refrigerator and realized that what I had been nostalgic for was not Kraft dinner but day-old Kraft dinner.

There was also a tense moment, I remember, the first time our older daughter asked for ketchup. "How did you know about ketchup?" Alice asked, after informing her that we didn't have any.

"Those wild kids down the street probably told her," I said. "Maybe we oughtn't to let her play with them any more."

I have another vision of what brings second thoughts to a man who, as they say, married a pretty face and a record of no cavities. The couple has just arrived in a town they have never visited before. The man is making routine preparations for the evening—scanning the county weekly for notices of any suppers at firehalls or churches, applying his current restaurant-selection system to the Yellow Pages, engaging the desk clerk in a casual conversation that can be led around to asking him where he happened to eat the night he came home from three years in Korea. "Why don't we just eat here at the motel?" the man's wife says. "It seems to be clean."

Alice has sometimes registered a complaint if, at ten-thirty or eleven, I am still circling around the barbecue places of a strange town, sniffing for the smell of hickory smoke and peeking in the windows to check for precut paneling. But she ordinarily joins in restaurant-hunting with some vigor. She is particularly good at searching out Chinese restaurants—a skill that comes partly from confidence, I think, in the way that a professional hunter always seems to come up with the required water buffalo partly because he left the camp assuming he would. Alice has been confident about finding good Chinese restaurants in unlikely places ever since we ate a spectacular Chinese meal at Star Twinkles, one of two restaurants on a remote Central Pacific island called Nauru—an island that is made of phosphate and is gradually disappearing, being more valuable as a mineral than as an island. Her confidence grew in London. Who, after all, would have ever expected to find the Great Dried Beef in the Sky (not to speak of a superb fried-seaweed dish) across from the Golders Green tube stop?

Once, in Kansas City, I was invited to a Chinese banquet in Waldo, which struck me at the time as the equivalent of being invited to sample the finest French *haute cuisine* in Uvalde, Texas. Waldo is a neighborhood that must have started out as a farm town, and what would have constituted a banquet for the Waldo folks I went to school with was an extra helping of chicken-fried steak. (The Waldo classmate I remember best from grade school had more eating experience than most gradeschoolers, having been there so long that he was said to have had a 2S student deferment in sixth grade.) The Chinese banquet in Waldo turned out to be magnificent. When I told Alice, she seemed unsurprised—a reaction that I at first put down to her imperfect acquaintance with Waldo but that I now think was due purely to her confidence in the resourcefulness and cooking skill of the overseas Chinese. Once, in Lisbon, I tried my best to work the phone book in a way that would assuage a longing we both had for certain Chinese dishes—it was the first time my system had been applied to a phone book written in Portuguese—and I think that Alice was actually surprised when we arrived on a quiet residential street and found a darkened building that I now believe must have been the home of a man named José Mandarin.

I have absorbed some of Alice's optimism about Chinese restaurants, and I have suffered for it. In small Midwestern towns, I have sat with quiet confidence as my Chinese dinner was brought to the table by a large Occidental female whose name tag says she is Wilma Sue. Once, in El Paso, I allowed myself to be taken to a Chinese restaurant across the border in Juarez that my host claimed was the best Chinese restaurant on the continent. Would I go to a French restaurant in Juarez? What would I say to someone who offered to buy me a fried-chicken dinner in Juarez? The restaurant, I was able to inform my host at the end of the meal, might rank within the top ten Chinese restaurants in the state of Chihuahua.

When Alice and I—finding ourselves in central Kansas but crazed for mu-hsu pork—unearth a Chinese restaurant that gives every indication of being awful, we are always reluctant to admit that we have been let down again. We retreat gradually. They advertise their steaks and chops, we assure each other, because a strictly Chinese restaurant could not survive in a farm town of three thousand people. Don't worry about the menu, we say when it arrives. Having only chow mein on the menu is merely a way to attract people who wouldn't understand what the chef could do if someone just asked him to go flat out. Toward the end of the meal, there are long silences. Then we decide that something might be salvaged by treating the rice with soy sauce and a bit of gravy that picked up some flavor from the scallions without permission. Occasionally, we mix those last-ditch concoctions separately, and on those occasions Alice always offers me a taste of hers.

The question in my mind when Alice and I arrived at the Breaux Bridge Crawfish Festival was whether to enter the official crawfish-eating contest or content myself with acts of free-lance gluttony. The idea of entering the contest came from Peter Wolf, who had returned to Louisiana from New York to join us at the festival, having concocted some sort of business conference in Houston to serve as an excuse for flying in that direction. Peter was brought up to appreciate what the entire state has to offer. His father was the man who put the state government in perspective for me in 1960, just after I had returned from watching the legislature in Baton Rouge stage some particularly bizarre entertainments in anticipation of the imminent desegregation of the New Orleans public schools. "What you have to remember about Baton Rouge," he said, "is that it's not southern United States, it's northern Costa Rica." Peter's sister, Gail, who still lives in New Orleans, has been able to participate in a lot of serious crawfish eating in the Cajun area of southern Louisiana since she decided that it was the most convenient place to visit with friends who live in Houston—the spot of precise equidistance being, as far as I can interpret Gail's calculations, an area bounded by the Vermilion Restaurant, the L. & L. Seafood Market (suppliers of fresh crawfish), and a racetrack called Evangeline Downs. Gail is so accustomed to crawfish eating that the word "crawfish" is understood rather than expressed in her discussions of restaurants. "They have a great étouffée," she may say of a place, or "They don't serve boiled there." Since she is isolated in New Orleans, miles away from the Atchafalaya Basin—a swampy wilderness that is to crawfish what the Serengeti is to lions—she produces her own crawfish étouffée after each pilgrimage to the L. & L. and stores it in the freezer, like a pioneer woman putting up preserves against the winter.

Peter had simply assumed we would enter the contest. Not entering, he told me while we were safe in New York, would be like going to the festival at Pamplona and not running with the bulls. (I once spent almost the entire week at the festival in Pamplona before I could bring myself to run with the bulls, in fact, the delay having been caused not merely by cowardice but by the fact that the running took place in the morning and I knew that if I participated I did so at the risk of arriving at my favorite café after it had run out of a type of sweet roll I adored.) My hesitation about entering the eating contest at Breaux Bridge was based on equally practical considerations. The contest is conducted with boiled crawfish, and if I had to pick my sport I would say étouffée or bisque rather than boiled. (Crawfish étouffée means smothered crawfish, and is otherwise indescribable; crawfish bisque is indescribable.) Also, I had learned in advance of the festival that, whatever a contestant's capacity, the amount of crawfish he can eat is governed by the amount of crawfish he can peel. (Only the tail of a crawfish is eaten, although people who are not under the pressure of official competition sometimes take the time to mine some fat from the rest of the shell with their index fingers.) Through geographical circumstances over which I have no control, I have little opportunity to keep in practice at peeling crawfish. There are crawfish (or crayfish, or crawdads) all over the country, but outside of Louisiana they are all but ignored—lumps of clay lacking a sculptor. People outside of Louisiana, in fact, often scoff when they hear of people eating crawfish—the way an old farmer in Pennsylvania might scoff at the New York antique dealer who paid fourteen dollars for a quilt that must be at least a hundred years old and doesn't even look very warm. A New York crawfish craver who couldn't make it to the Atchafalaya Basin would have to settle for Paris, where crawfish are called *écrevisses,* except by people from Louisiana, who always call them inferior.

The world record at crawfish eating—the record, at least, according to Breaux Bridge, which is, by resolution of the Louisiana Legislature, the Crawfish Capital of the World—was set by a local man named Andrew Thevenet, who at one Crawfish Festival ate the tails of thirty-three pounds of crawfish in two hours. My doubts about being able to peel that much crawfish in two hours—not to speak of eating it—were increased by some stories I heard about tricks contestants have used in the past. One man was said to have perfected a method of peeling a crawfish with one hand and popping it into his mouth while reaching for the next crawfish with his other hand. Somebody told me that one contestant had spent the evening before the contest "lining his stomach with red beans and rice"—although that sounds to me at least contradictory and maybe suicidal. A pharmacy student who triumphed at the Crawfish Festival two years before I arrived in Breaux Bridge (festivals are held only every other year) drank orange juice with his crawfish instead of the traditional beer, and Gail had heard that the orange juice was laced with exotic chemicals (known only to people like pharmacy students) that somehow provided the same service for crawfish in the stomach that an electric trash-compacter provides for trash. In fairness, I should add that a former contestant told me the student had used no tricks at all.

I was in Breaux Bridge a few days before the festival began, and I found that a lot of people were happy to discuss the question of whether or not Peter and I should enter the crawfish-eating contest. They like to talk about crawfish in general. Once the subject came up, they were likely to spend some time talking about an evening they once spent with some particularly tasty boiled crawfish or a dish they had that was somewhere between an *étouffée* and a stew or a woman in town who used to make crawfish *beignets.* (I don't mean that we talked about nothing other than eating crawfish. I spent a lot of time, for instance, discussing a restaurant in Opelousas named Dee Dee that specializes in oyster gumbo, roast duck, and a marvel called dirty rice.) The Cajun parishes of Louisiana constitute just about the only section of the United States in which good food is taken as the norm in any kitchen, private or public. Before my first trip to Iberia Parish, I asked a serious New Orleans eater where I should eat while I was there. I prepared to take notes on secret routes to secret cafés or the names of local collaborators who might risk divulging to a hungry traveling man where the decent restaurants were. "Eat anywhere," he said.

Taking his advice, Alice and I had lunch one day during that trip in the first tacky-looking bar we came to in a small town not far from New Iberia—one of those places decorated with Jax Beer clocks and fake fishnet and a wire potato-chip dispenser. There were two ketchup bottles on the table. One held ketchup; the other one contained the best remoulade sauce I have ever tasted. I had the blue-plate special, which happened that day to be shrimp *sauce picante.* Alice ordered boiled crawfish, and was brought a tray holding what we estimated to be about a hundred of them. I ordered some Jax, and we stayed the afternoon.

A couple of days before the Crawfish Festival, I asked a local citizen named Woody Marshall—a man who can list among his many accomplishments the invention of crawfish racing as we know it today—whether or not Peter and I could expect to face Andrew Thevenet, the world record-holder, if we entered the eating contest. Marshall said that Thevenet, a man of about seventy, had been so ill that serious eating was over for him. When I expressed my sympathy, Marshall told me about having heard Thevenet, after his retirement, describe a lifetime of eating—the fresh oysters, the venison, the crawfish prepared in ways a crawfish fancier dreams about. "You know what he told me?" Marshall said. "He told me, 'There have been kings who didn't eat as well as I did.'"

Lately, the Cajun parishes have been having what people in Lafayette and Baton Rouge sometimes call a French Renaissance. It is a phenomenon that has engaged the diplomatic interest of, among others, the Republic of France, the Province of Quebec, and the Louisiana State Tourist Commission. What surprises the devout eater about an effort that is devoted to preserving the Cajun atmosphere of southwestern Louisiana is its concentration on the French language as the basis of Cajun culture. Even with the new emphasis on teaching French in primary school and exhorting Cajuns to speak it to their children at home, the language is likely to disappear from Louisiana eventually through lack of use. (The language preservationists have to contend not only with television and Anglo newcomers but with the stigma French has always represented for Cajuns—an echo of all the bad jokes about ignorant swamp-dwellers named Boudreaux who speak with comical accents.) Most of the people in Breaux Bridge who grew up before the war grew up speaking French at home and being punished if caught speaking it at school—including Woody Marshall, despite his Anglo name—but the young people rarely speak it now. When Marshall told me about Andrew Thevenet's royal history of eating, it occurred to me that those in charge of the French

Renaissance might not be concentrating on the strongest element of the culture. Marshall and I were having lunch at the time—a splendid chicken *étouffée* and some French bread for me—at a tiny Breaux Bridge restaurant called Schwets. (The proprietor is not named Mr. Schwet. The restaurant was meant to be called Chouette—a pet name that means "screech owl" in French—but Marshall, who serves as the town sign painter, was, like most Cajuns of his age, raised speaking French rather than spelling it.) It occurred to me that the posters of the kind the state commission for the French Renaissance furnished for the window of Schwets should not say *"Parlez français avec vos enfants à la maison"* or *"Aidez vos enfants à parler le français"* but *"Transmettez vos recettes à vos enfants"*—"Hand down your recipes to your children."

I am a confirmed festival and fair attender. I like world's fairs and state fairs and county fairs and street fairs. My tolerance for fair-organizers' natural inclination to rook us rubes is practically inexhaustible—the only exception I can remember having been the New York World's Fair of 1964, an overblown American industrial show masquerading as a world exhibition, like a nut-and-bolt manufacturer from Illinois wandering around the south of France wearing a beret. If I feel myself becoming irritated at someone who wants to charge me seventy-five cents for an ear of corn (butter and salt included, napkin available at the hotdog stand on the other side of the freak show), I merely recall the words of Nate Eagle, the greatest sideshow barker and carnival promoter of them all, who often said, for publication, "It's not how much it costs them to get in but how much it costs them to get out."

I routinely drive miles out of my way for the most pedestrian county fairs. I even enjoyed the Baltimore City Fair, which is an event so infused with the city-dweller's principal product, contentiousness, that I seemed to spend an entire day wandering by booths at which someone would demand that I support a petition mandating the city of Baltimore to end its discrimination against the use of plastic garbage cans or would thrust into my hands documentation of the devastation that would come from the construction of the Leakin Park Expressway or would explain to me that the Fund for Animals was a kind of Red Cross for animals—a phrase that conjured up for me visions of a kindly lady in a gray uniform offering a wallaby a hot cup of coffee at the scene of his extinction.

Fairs are good places to eat, particularly for stand-up eaters—which is one of the kinds of eaters I am, although when I eat standing up away from home I sometimes miss the familiar cool breeze coming from the open refrigerator. The Baltimore Fair, in fact, had fine Polish sausages in addition to the crab cakes that some of the city's literary figures have attempted to immortalize in sonnet form. (I was not too full to accompany a local couple of my acquaintance to a steamed-crab bout at Obrycki's—where my friends compared the crabs to those served at the crab hall in their neighborhood and at another one downtown and at one next to the market, while I nodded and ate.) The Baltimore Fair also had a Weight Watchers booth—the equivalent, it seemed to me, of a bishop, wearing full vestments and a stern expression, standing quietly at an orgy. When I spotted it, I marched right over and said to the woman who was about to offer me something like an ersatz chocolate milkshake that contained ten calories and tasted as if it had five, "You people ought to be ashamed of yourselves."

If I happened to be in the right part of the state at the appropriate time, I know I would attend, say, the North Louisiana Cotton Festival and Fair at Bastrop, or even the Louisiana Brimstone Fiesta at Sulphur—although, as far as I know, neither of the products celebrated in those places is edible. These days, of course, the festive atmosphere is always dampened a bit by the inevitable discussion about whether the festival I am enjoying is likely to be the last of its kind ever held. The impending demise is always blamed on young people from outside—young people who seem to travel from one event to another, behaving more or less the way a horde of dropped-out fraternity boys might be expected to behave at their first rock festival. The cultural forces that produced this band of celebrants have lately included a merchandising milestone—the development of what are sometimes called "sodapop wines." Although it was not long ago that a lot of citizens in places like Breaux Bridge would have been hard put to find anything good to say about a lot of mindless young people roaming the streets carrying beer cans, they now realize that beer is less inebriating than wine and that a gutter full of beer cans is not as dangerous as a gutter full of broken glass. From what I was told by the organizers of the Crawfish Festival—who had banned drinking from glass containers the year I arrived—I am justified in holding the idea man who developed sodapop wines personally responsible for the fact that the Cochon de Lait Festival in Mansura, Louisiana, ended before I had a chance to sample the *cochon*. May the next belt-tightening in the wine industry (or in the advertising industry, if that is where he's harbored) find him in an expendable position.

In Louisiana, where some mildly legitimate cultural basis can actually be found for some of the festivals (although if I were in charge at

Opelousas, which holds a yam festival every year, I would celebrate Dee Dee's roast duck rather than a bunch of potatoes), there is a kind of pattern that transforms an informal local celebration into one of the stops along the route from Fort Lauderdale. The festival becomes primarily a business proposition, great efforts are made to attract the visitors who are later deplored, the local citizens lose interest or retreat to those events that are unaffected by outsiders (events ordinarily having to do with naming queens, or at least princesses), there is a lot of talk about the outside kids "taking over," and then the discussion turns to whether or not having a festival is worth the trouble after all.

The transformation of the New Orleans Mardi Gras took over a century, but Breaux Bridge managed to telescope the whole process into a dozen years. The Crawfish Festival grew out of the town's centennial, in 1959, and everyone agrees that the first few festivals were joyous occasions—townspeople costumed in old-fashioned Acadian dress, everyone dancing the faisdodo in the streets, jollity at the crawfish races in the afternoon and at the local dance hall at night. The remarkable increase in fame and attendance seemed to be a blessing at first, except to motorists trying to get to Breaux Bridge from Lafayette, the nearest city with a motel. (Even becoming hopelessly stuck on the road could be seen as joyous: Thelma's, a restaurant between Lafayette and Breaux Bridge, is a sort of crawfish festival in itself.) Merchants in Breaux Bridge welcomed the opportunity to remove the glass from their storefronts and peddle as much beer or boiled crawfish as they could stock. The area had begun to develop a sort of crawfish industry that was enhanced by the publicity—peeling plants to service the restaurants, rice farmers "growing" crawfish in ponds to supplement the supply known as "wild" crawfish, even a modern plant whose owners believe that they have a freezing method that will make it possible for people to go into restaurants in St. Louis or Dallas and eat crawfish meat that actually tastes like crawfish meat rather than like balsa wood.

But the popularity of the festival with outsiders made it less popular with a lot of residents of Breaux Bridge, a quiet town on the Bayou Teche that has only five thousand people—a remarkable number of them named Broussard or Guidry or Hebert. The Crawfish Festival association insisted that everyone would be happy with the festival if only it could be controlled and could eventually acquire the reputation of a "family event." It is hardly appropriate, of course, for organizers of a festival to preach sobriety. Woody Marshall, who often uses the same flourishes in speech that are necessary in sign painting, explained it to me as a matter of moderation. "We would appeal to the beautiful youths to practice a degree of restraint so that they are not wantonly drunk, if you know what I mean," he told me, a day or two before the festival. "If the youths persist in conducting themselves in such manner as they have conducted themselves, they will destroy the very festivals they like. But, as we say here, *'Laissez le bon temps rouler'*—'Let the good times roll.'"

The festival I attended was to be an experiment in control—an attempt to hold most of the events in a sort of pasture a mile or so from the business district. I told the festival organizers that I would be happy to attend the festival wherever they held it. I had not been offended by the criticism of outsiders. My wife would be at the festival, so, in a way, we were one of the families attending a family event. Also, in all of the discussions about excesses—about beer cans being thrown and immoral acts being committed in the churchyard and people walking half-naked in the street—nobody had said a word about gluttony.

The day before the festival weekend began, a hard rain turned the pasture into a mudhole. The food booths and the festival events had to be moved back into town. I tried to show some sympathy for the financial burden the sudden move had put on the festival association, but I have to admit to being pleased that the festival would take place where it had always taken place. I'm a traditionalist when it comes to festivals, even when the tradition in question is only ten or twelve years old. Somehow, a festival that is known for inspiring dancing in the streets wouldn't seem quite the same if it inspired dancing in a pasture. The rain seemed to have cut down the crowd, and the festival association—staggered by the move and by the spoilage of thousands of pounds of boiled crawfish it had intended to sell—seemed to forget about the issue of raucous behavior. By the time the festival started, the sun was out.

Woody Marshall, looking spectacular in a bowler and a red vest and sleeve garters, stood next to the crawfish track he had invented, and formally entered the names of the entries in the official logbook he had made a few years before by folding over several old "Allen Ellender for Senator" posters. When he had been charged with the task of building a racetrack for the first festival, Marshall worked for days without finding a solution to the problem of how to compensate for the notorious reluctance of a crawfish to walk in the direction anyone expects it to walk. "Finally," he told me one day, when we were discussing how the track came about, "bull's-eye—I thought of it! A bull's-eye!" The final model is shaped like a target, with the starting gate in the bull's-eye and the finish line anywhere on the outer circle. Marshall keeps the contenders in the starting gate with an out-sized version of the kind of device short-order cooks sometimes use to keep fried eggs in their place on a grill. Having heard previously from Marshall that a racing crawfish could be provided to a visitor in return for a small donation to the festival association kitty, I entered one in the first race. Alice thought about scotch-taping racing colors to his back, but we finally decided that might seem ostentatious. It was pleasure enough to hear our names and hometown announced with a flourish by Marshall as he introduced Number Eight, *Le Gros*.

"I didn't know y'all had any crawfish in New York," said a fraternity boy standing behind me.

"We've just got one that can race worth a damn," I said, nodding toward Number Eight. "I have to bring him down here every two years to get any competition."

The fraternity boy looked impressed, but *Le Gros* ran badly, appearing to be less interested in racing than in, literally, backbiting.

"New York crawfish," the fraternity boy said in a disgusted tone. "Sheeee . . . "

Somehow, the fraternity boy did not impress me as a threat to my enjoyment, maybe because he did not treat ten o'clock in the morning as a time to be drinking sodapop wine but as a time to be drinking a nice old-fashioned can of Schlitz. I was also untroubled by the displays of crawfish T-shirts, crawfish beer mugs, and crawfish aprons. Breaux Bridge could shine through almost any amount of commercialism and Lauderdale-ism as, in fact, the Crawfish Capital of the World. Breaux Bridge people are incapable of turning out the kind of leaden junk food usually peddled to tourists even when they try. Woody Marshall, for instance, invented something called a crawfish dog—he is, as I have said, a man of many accomplishments—and although that may sound pretty awful, it happens to be delicious, except for the hotdog bun. (The recipe in the official program says, "Make roux with shortening and flour, cook until light brown, sauté onions, add crawfish and fat and water and seasoning. Cook 20 minutes and serve on an open-face hotdog bun." If someone could figure out how to make hotdogs taste like crawfish dogs, he could bring back baseball.) The same booth that served beer and ordinary hotdogs sold, for fifty cents, something called a crawfish patty, which is also known as crawfish pie, and which if served in some expense-account French restaurant in New York would keep that restaurant jammed on rainy recession Tuesday evenings. ("Six dollars is, of course, a lot to ask for an appetizer," the review would say, "but the exquisite *Écrevisses à la Teche* at the Cajun d'Or happen to be worth every penny of it.")

A crawfish patty is what I happened to be eating when the time for the crawfish-eating contest approached. I was also drinking a glass (nonbreakable plastic) of non-sodapop wine and reclining under an oak tree and listening to some fine music played by Celbert Cormier and his Musical Kings (a violin, an accordion, two electric guitars, and a drum) and discussing the logistics involved in timing our departure the next day in a way that would put us at a restaurant called The Yellow Bowl in Jeannerette around mealtime.

Peter Wolf, who was doing all of those things himself, was saying that we had waited too late to register and would be unable to participate, since only ten eaters are allowed. (Otherwise, everyone would be up there gobbling up the free crawfish.) I happened to know that only nine people had registered, but I also knew that they included such formidable eaters as the oyster-eating champion of Louisiana, who had downed fifteen and a half dozen oysters in an hour at the Oyster Festival in Galliano—a festival that was somehow kept secret from me for years. I also knew that we had been invited to dinner that evening at the home of Mrs. Harris Champagne, who, according to experts in Breaux Bridge, was the first person to serve crawfish *étouffée* in a restaurant, and I realized that sitting down to a plate of her legendary *étouffée* when already stuffed with boiled would be an act of irresponsibility. It had also occurred to me that if I did become full before approaching Mrs. Champagne's table, I would prefer to become full of patties. Boiled, after all, is not my sport. I told Peter it was a shame we hadn't registered in time.

The oyster-eating champion, a specialist away from his specialty, was the first contestant to drop out. "I'm not full. I could have a hotdog," he said, when I asked him what happened. "But these things don't taste right." The first female contestant in the history of the contest, a trim secretary, dropped out some time later. ("I'm not as hungry as I thought I was," she said.) The winner, Chester McGear, looked like one of the fraternity boys everyone had been so worried about, although he had actually graduated a couple of years before. He wore a sweatshirt emblematic of having consumed ten pitchers of beer in some tavern in Chicago, and he had a small rooting section that chanted "Go, Chester, Go!" or "*Allons, Chester, Allons!*" or "Come on, Chester, Eat That Meat!" He was on his twenty-second pound of crawfish when his final opponent dropped out. I was pleased to see that McGear acted the part of a traditional eating champion. They never admit to being full. My father always used to tell me about a boy who won a pie-eating contest in St. Joe by eating thirty-three pies and then said, "I wooda ate more but my ma was calling me for supper." When the reporters went up on the stand to interview McGear, he remained at his place, and as he answered the questions he absently reached toward the platter in front of him and peeled crawfish and popped them into his mouth, like a man working on the peanut bowl during a cocktail party.

I was relieved not to have had to face him. We all had dinner at Mrs. Champagne's, and Peter, by chance, was seated next to the French consul-general from New Orleans. Peter, exhibiting his interest in Franco-American relations and the southwestern Louisiana French Renaissance and all that, spoke to the consul-general immediately in excellent French, taking the opportunity to ask him why it is that a person cannot get decent shellfish in Paris.

A t the annual meeting of the American Dietetic Association in New Orleans, I lived in constant fear that the dietitians would find out what I had been eating all week. The discovery would be made, I figured, by an undercover operative—some strict diet-balancer who normally worked as the nutritionist in a state home for the aged but was posing as a raving glutton in order to trap me. "How were the oyster loaves at the Acme today?" she would ask casually, chewing on a Baby Ruth bar and fixing me with a look of pure food envy.

"Not bad at all," I would say, thrown off my guard by having met an apparent soulmate in an exhibition hall that included displays for such items as "textured protein granules with beeflike flavor" and some evil-looking powdered substance for which the most appetizing boast was that it was rapidly absorbed in the upper intestine. "I had to have two oyster loaves, in fact, which left room for only an ordinary-sized platter of red beans and rice and homemade sausage at Buster Holmes's place on Burgundy Street. I think if I hadn't had so much beer at the Acme, I might have been able to go a few pieces of Buster's garlic chicken, but—"

"Get him, girls!" the agent would shout, whereupon a gang of dietitians would fall upon me and hold me down while the chairman of the public-policy committee crammed carrot-and-raisin salad down my throat.

"Oysters are extremely high in cholesterol," a lecturer would say while the force-feeding was going on. "If one must eat oysters, oysters on the half shell rather than the fried oysters in the oyster loaf would be a better choice. Buster Holmes's homemade sausage defies scientific analysis."

"There were some good carbohydrates in the beer," I reply weakly between bites. Nobody is listening to me. A line is forming behind the dietitian who is dishing out the carrot-and-raisin salad—a dozen determined-looking ladies holding plates of green vegetables and gray meat. I spot the dietitian from Southwest High School in Kansas City, standing patiently with some broccoli I left on my plate in 1952.

My fears, as it turned out, were without foundation. I should have realized that on the first day of the meeting, when I was having breakfast at the Four Seasons, a pastry shop on Royal Street that has made me happy to be awake on a number of mornings in the past. I had figured that a week during which not only the dietitians but also the franchise operators of Roy Rogers Family Restaurants were meeting would be a good time for someone who is interested in both eating habits and conventions to be in New Orleans, but I had no intention of permitting an inquiry into other people's eating habits to interfere with my own. When I'm in New Orleans, my habit has always been to eat as much as I possibly can—partly, of course, as a precaution against developing some serious nutritional problem like remoulade-sauce deficiency in the event I don't make it back to town for a while. On that first day of the dietitians' meeting, I was demonstrating my usual lack of restraint with Four Seasons *croissants*. After the first few bites, I was in no mood to worry about being observed by some special agent in the pay of the American Dietetic Association. The dietitians, after all, did not have the only game in town for a convention buff. The Independent Oil Compounders were having their annual meeting at the Royal Orleans, right across the street. The National Screw Machine Product Association was meeting at the Royal Sonesta and the Louisiana Nursing Home Association was meeting at the Fontainebleau. The Roosevelt was harboring a slew of narcotics-control agents. I looked around at the other breakfasters defiantly. I was astonished to find myself surrounded by women carrying the program of the annual meeting of the American Dietetic Association. Some of them were even wearing their identification badges. None of them were spying on me, because they were all too busy eating. The woman at the table next to me was attacking not merely a *croissant* but a *croissant* filled with cream and covered with chocolate. Tortes and sweet rolls were disappearing all around me. A lady across the room was wolfing down a huge piece of cheesecake. At nine o'clock in the morning! I should have known then that I had nothing to fear from the dietitians. They are obviously just folks.

If I had any suspicion that the Roy Rogers people might not be just folks, it should have evaporated the moment the first executive I called in their national headquarters picked up the telephone and said, "Howdy, pardner." Unfortunately, my first reaction was that I must have reached the wrong number. According to the information I had been given, Roy Rogers Family Restaurants was owned by the Marriott Corporation, with headquarters in Bethesda, Maryland, just outside Washington. "Howdy, pardner" is not my idea of how a corporation executive in Bethesda, Maryland, is likely to answer his telephone. I have to admit that I had a more serious suspicion that concerned the Marriott people—the suspicion that some of the cardboard food I have been served on airplanes had been delivered by the Marriott catering-service truck I always see pulling away from the plane just before take-off.

Every single day, it turns out, Marriott provides the airlines with one hundred and fifty thousand meals, none of which contains anything a steady patron of Buster's would recognize as food. I have never blamed Marriott for my own absent-mindedness that day between St. Louis and New York when, confusing two of those little plastic cups that are always on meal trays, I poured cream on my salad and French dressing in my coffee, but I do think it's fair to blame them for the fact that I did not become aware of the mistake until it was called to my attention *after I had eaten the entire meal*. The one hundred and fifty thousand airline meals are all prepared in one huge kitchen, the location of which Marriott would do well to keep secret, just in case a traveling salesman who also happens to be a discriminating eater is someday driven to terrorism by the breast of chicken he is served between Miami and Chicago.

Discovering that all Marriott airline meals are prepared in one kitchen intensified a fear I have had for years—that someday, by federal law or some kind of executive order, all meals eaten by everyone in the United States will be prepared in one single gigantic kitchen. Could it have been a mere coincidence that Willard Marriott, who owns what is presumably the kitchen most likely to get the contract, is a personal friend of Richard Nixon, a president who had a history of eating cottage cheese with ketchup (the "old Nixon" we've heard so much about) and has raised a daughter whose favorite recipe is made with canned soup? Is it just happenstance that the Big Boy hamburger defended by William Edgett Smith as the best hamburger in the world—a defense that remains inexplicable by any normal rules of logical argument—is produced by a company that is now a totally owned subsidiary of the Marriott Corporation?

As I see it, the process will start slowly, with agents of various local and state and federal agencies closing restaurants that could serve as rallying points for rebel eaters. Mr. Galatoire shows up one morning at his restaurant on Bourbon Street only to meet two heavies from the New Orleans department of maritime engineering who tell him that his papers are not in order. The country restaurants that serve chicken dinner family-style—those shrines that decorate the table with huge bowls of creamed corn and mashed potatoes and biscuits—are visited by a deputy sheriff who says "Y'all got a license to serve them fresh vegetables?" In Iowa, a neatly-dressed postal inspector informs the Meat Department of the Amana Society that it has been found guilty of using the mails to transport summer sausage. The City Council of San Francisco passes, without debate, an ordinance banning all Chinese restaurants that do not specialize in either chop suey or egg foo yung. Arthur Bryant's Barbecue and Doe's, the legendary tamale restaurant in Greenville, Mississippi, are closed by the Justice Department for premature compliance with the public accommodations section of the Civil Rights Act of 1964. In New York, Gage & Tollner, Sweets, Sloppy Louie's and Lundy's are, within a few weeks, all turned into outlets of Arthur Treacher's Fish 'n Chips. She-crab soup is banned by authorities in Charleston, South Carolina, supposedly as a way of avoiding an anticipated demonstration against it by feminists—although the reaction of the city's feminists to the news is puzzlement and hunger. Then, using as an excuse something like the problems created by farm surpluses or the necessities of civil-defense preparation, the Government announces that all citizens will henceforth be required to eat only food provided by the One Big Kitchen. Those of us who refuse to go along will have to go underground—living in caves in the Arkansas hills with an ace barbecue man who somehow managed to escape the round-up of decent cooks, and maybe sneaking out at night to forage for fresh apples and to buy contraband chopped liver made with real schmaltz.

When I discovered that Marriott owns the Roy Rogers Family Restaurants company and the Bob's Big Boy company as well as the airline-catering operation, I became more convinced than ever that the sudden proliferation of fast-food franchises several years ago was no accident. In the fast-food industry, of course, "family" means people who spend quite a bit of money but don't wreck the furniture. The merchandising method of the industry, as far as I can gather, is based on luring the entire family by appealing to the children—a shrewd device, since even the best-brought-up children seem to like bland food, particularly if it is served by a cowgirl or wrapped in a package that is shaped like a clown. Children can now be lured into the fast-food restaurants and exposed to Styrofoam hamburgers and wood-chip French fries at an impressionable age. Then they enter school, and the dietitians take over with a gray-meat and carrot-and-raisin-salad diet that goes on through college, interrupted only by Marriott airline meals flying to and fro on Christmas vacations. By the time these kids are of voting age, their discrimination in food will amount to a preference for Burger King or McDonald's—a preference based on which one gives away the best decal with its hamburgers—and they will be easy marks for the forces intent on putting over the One Big Kitchen conspiracy.

To test this theory, I asked a friend of mine in New Orleans—Ruth Wolf, Peter's mother—where her New Orleans grandchildren like to eat when she takes them out for lunch. I conducted this bit of research during a dinner a few of us were having at Pascal Manale's, a restaurant that specializes in a dish it calls Manale's Original Barbecue Shrimp—a school of huge shrimp, still in the shell, floating in a sauce made of butter and pepper and a number of other ingredients that, put together in some other proportions, could probably power a small speedboat. I considered the children in question less vulnerable than most to the machinations of the One Big Kitchen conspirators. These children, after all, have a grandmother who appreciates Manale's shrimp and a mother who makes crawfish *étouffée* in her own kitchen while discoursing on the wonders of a Casamento oyster loaf and a father who, at the very moment of our conversation, was devouring one of Manale's crabmeat casseroles while wearing an expression of otherworldly bliss. Their uncle, of course, eats Red Soup on upper Broadway and was nearly a participant in the contest that decided the crawfish-eating championship of the world. "We always have to go to two places for lunch when I take the kids," Ruth Wolf told me. "Stephen insists on going to Roy Rogers for a roast-beef sandwich, and then we have to go to Burger King so Nancy can have one of their hamburgers."

"Very interesting," I said, instantly deciding to change the subject without further comment rather than take a chance of revealing to my friends what I suspected the future held for us. "Do you think the Nobel Committee would look kindly on a suggestion that Mr. Manale be given the Peace Prize this year for these shrimp?"

The salesmen manning the booths at the meeting used the same kind of patter one might expect to hear from salesmen at, say, an oil compounders' convention, but most of what they were selling sounded considerably less appetizing than petroleum. "This is your total diet, not a supplement," a salesman at one booth would say, holding up a tiny cardboard box. "This has your amino acids, your carbohydrates." A few booths away, a young woman would offer passers-by a cracker covered with a gray substance and would say, as cheerfully as she could manage, "Have you tried our meatless chickenlike product?" Recipes were being distributed to show all of the imaginative dishes that could be made from products like "modified chicken breasts" and "dinner balls" and something that comes in what looks like gallon milk cartons and is called Versa 'Taters. ("What it is is a multipurpose potato," the man at the Versa 'Taters booth said. "You just put it in a pan, fill the pan with tap water, let it sit for thirty minutes, and you have cooked potatoes.") Whenever I found a booth that was displaying something I might think about eating—Sara Lee pastries, for instance—the salesman would hand me a chart that gave a complete analysis of what, say, Sara Lee's Double Chocolate Layer Cake consisted of, *including the calories*.

Somehow, the dietitians managed to clean their plates every morning at the Four Seasons anyway—the early risers among them joining those of us who tend to show up a few minutes before nine and loiter on Royal Street until the doors are opened. One day during the meeting, I was walking from the New Orleans convention center, a flashy new building in a cluster of flashy new buildings near the riverfront, when I passed a place called Joe's Jungle Bar. Joe's Jungle, as it is also known, has the look of one of those bars that the patron saint of construction workers always makes sure are left standing in otherwise bulldozed urban-renewal areas so that the people doing the renewing have someplace to drink a beer after work or to watch the baseball game during the lunch break. It had a sign on the window that said, WELCOME, AMERICAN DIETETIC ASSOCIATION. Could it be, I wondered, that a crowd of dietitians had actually been lured into Joe's Jungle? Does justfolksism go that far? I found the prospect disturbing. I was not certain that I wanted to find the person who was in charge of balancing my diet at Southwest High School (a person who must have suffered, poor woman, from desperate efforts to fill her menus with whatever balances hamburgers) perched on a stool in Joe's Jungle Bar drinking Regal beer from a can and cussing the New Orleans Saints' backfield and maybe giving five in the mush to some loudmouth who passes a slighting remark about lima beans. I happened to be in a great hurry at the time. I was on my way to a place that is renowned for a ham-and-roast-beef po' boy sandwich, and I wanted to get there before the line formed so that I would also have time to stop at a store that sold Zatarain's Crab and Shrimp Boil, a few bottles of which I intended to take back to New York with me despite my fear that an airport baggage inspector might find it in my luggage and rule it an explosive. But I immediately went through the bar door. There were, I am relieved to say, no dietitians in Joe's Jungle.

Dietitians did seem more conscientious than most conventioneers about attending the lectures and panels that in most annual meetings I've seen drive the membership toward places like Joe's Jungle. Sensing that something important must have been going on, I resolved one day to attend an entire afternoon of such events myself, even if it meant hearing some balanced-diet talk that I would ordinarily go blocks out of my way to avoid. I have always had trouble following speeches at conventions and sales meetings and annual meetings and conferences—mainly, I think, because so many of the speakers use what my high-school speech teacher called "audiovisual aids." Whether the speaker is a Marriott executive telling Roy Rogers franchisers how they can put over Roy's new Double-R-Bar-Burger or a committee chairman of the American Dietetic Association explaining how dietitians can work for the passage of important federal legislation, he or she always seems to be pointing to a chart or a slide that lists Key Words. I am always left with such a strong impression of the Key Words that I can't remember what they were meant to be the key to—and the words themselves provide no clue, since they seem to be the same words no matter what the subject of the speech is. One of the Key Words is always ACTION. I can never remember if that refers to action in developing an effective advertising campaign or political action or, as might be possible at a dietitians' conference, peristaltic action.

I decided to attend the afternoon meetings anyway, right after I had lunch at Buster's. Although Buster's looks like a corner bar with a lunch counter added, it may be the finest restaurant in the world outside the city limits of Kansas City. A serious meal had been arranged there by Alvin Lambert, a friend of mine who helps run Preservation Hall—a place in which New Orleans jazz is played by some of the black musicians who are talented enough to have helped develop the form and intelligent enough to eat a lot of their meals at Buster's. We started with a huge platter of fried oysters. By the time we were halfway through, Buster's waiter had brought a bowl of spaghetti with a sauce that would probably have brought tears to the eyes of Pascal Manale (as well as to the eyes of anyone who reacts normally to pepper). We ordered a couple of quarts of beer to help with the sauce. Alvin was taking a healthy interest in the oysters and spaghetti, but I didn't feel any pressure to eat with both hands in order to get my share, the way I sometimes feel while eating with Alvin's brother-in-law, Allan Jaffe, with whom I have shared some happy Buster's lunches that lasted until dinnertime. Jaffe—who has managed Preservation Hall since it opened in the early sixties, and has played the tuba in its traveling band for the past few years—was away on a road trip. A few years after the Hall opened, the temptation to insinuate himself and his tuba in the last set of the evening had proven too much for Jaffe, the only person I ever met who attended Valley Forge Military Academy on a tuba scholarship. Eventually, he was playing funerals and church dedications with a street band, and then he was touring the country. Unfortunately, he becomes saddened on the road by hunger for Buster's cooking. Sometimes, he is able to cheer himself up by steering the band's bus toward El Campo, Texas, where he treasures a barbecue place run by a Yugoslav butcher, and when the bus draws within a hundred miles of Kansas City, it detours, by unanimous consent, to Arthur Bryant's. But in some places around the country Jaffe's hunger reaches close to the point of despair. Then he phones Buster and persuades him to pack up some ingredients, climb on a plane (a particularly aromatic plane, once Buster's luggage is aboard), and spend a couple of days with the band. I used to think that Jaffe, by traveling as a member of the Preservation Hall

Jazz Band, was one of the few people I knew who was living out his childhood fantasy—there, after all, is Big Jim Robinson in Carnegie Hall doing his solo, and there, behind him, is the kid from Valley Forge going bom-bom-baba-badee-bom-bom—but then I realized that his true fantasy is not traveling as a member of the Preservation Hall Jazz Band but traveling as a member of the Preservation Hall Jazz Band and having Buster Holmes along as a kind of court chef.

I could see that I might miss the first speech of the afternoon at the dietitians' conference. I knew we would have to spend at least forty minutes eating fried chicken alone. Buster's fried chicken tastes as if it is made from chickens that have spent their entire pampered lives strolling around the barnyard pecking contentedly at huge cloves of garlic. As we were finishing the chicken, the waiter brought out some beans and rice, along with some of Buster's hot sausage.

Empty quart beer bottles were all over the table by the time we finished the beans and rice. The sausage was gone. Somehow, we were still eating an hour later. Finally, knowing I had to get to the conference, I pushed back my chair and resolutely placed my third apple turnover on the table unfinished.

"My compliments to the chef," I gasped, and staggered out into the sunlight.

By the time I reached the convention center, I was puffing ominously, although I had taken a cab the entire way. I walked into the first lecture room I saw—my breath coming in gasps, my pockets rattling with Gelusil tablets. In an attempt to fight off Buster's sausage, I was eating Gelusil, chewing some gum, and sucking on a Life Saver at the same time. The lecture turned out to be on obesity. The lecturer had a slide flashed on the screen and pointed at a word. I assumed the word was ACTION, but I really couldn't see very well. My eyes were watering. The lecturer started talking about the diseases that obesity could be a factor in—gall-bladder trouble, gout. A wave of heartburn passed over me. The lecturer began to discuss diabetes and hypertension. I felt slightly feverish. I broke out in a sweat. Finally, I managed to make my way out of the room and into the fresh air. I knew from previous experience what had happened to me: I had come close to going into garlic shock.

I made my way back to my hotel and resolved to become more sensible about eating. I decided that I would even forego a trip I had planned that evening to Mosca's, a roadhouse whose baked oysters I revere. I had heard that Buster was serving spareribs as his special the following day, and I had no intention of having to miss them.

A HEARTBEAT AWAY

THE INVESTIGATION AND RESIGNATION
OF VICE PRESIDENT SPIRO T. AGNEW

A condensation of the book by

RICHARD M. COHEN and JULES WITCOVER

CHAPTER 1

MY KIND OF MAN

On January 15, 1973, five days before the second inauguration of President Richard M. Nixon and Vice President Spiro T. Agnew, the eyes of the nation's political community were focused on a courtroom in Washington, D.C. There, four men arrested in the break-in of the Democratic National Committee headquarters at the Watergate complex pleaded guilty to conspiracy. Their pleas were to have been the final act in an embarrassment that the Nixon-Agnew administration, in the full flush of 1972's landslide victory, hoped to put behind it. On that same Monday, however, another scene was unfolding in nearby Baltimore that was destined to inject an entirely new element into the equation of Watergate.

The unwitting catalyst in this unforeseen development was an old friend and business associate of Agnew named Lester Matz. During the morning, Matz arrived in the lobby of downtown Baltimore's Mercantile Building for an appointment with a lawyer. Matz was extremely nervous. As the elevator car rose to the law offices of Venable, Baetjer and Howard, its glistening doors reflected the image of an athletic-looking man, tanned the year round by the sun of Saint Croix, where he and his friend Ted Agnew had bought condominiums.

At the law firm's reception desk, he asked for Joseph H. H. Kaplan.

Matz handed Kaplan a subpoena *duces tecum,* issued in the name of a special federal grand jury that had recently been impaneled in Baltimore. It called for the engineering firm of Matz, Childs and Associates, Inc., to produce certain corporate records. Kaplan was not surprised that the firm had received a subpoena. Every lawyer in town had heard that George Beall, the U.S. attorney for Maryland, was investigating kickbacks in Baltimore County, with the objective of indicting Dale Anderson, the county's Democratic executive and political boss.

The records, Matz admitted at once, would indicate that his engineering firm had been generating cash for the purpose of kicking back 5 per cent of its fees for county public-works projects to Baltimore County politicians. It was an old, familiar story, and Kaplan had a ready strategy to deal with it. His advice was orthodox and blunt: tell the government everything.

Matz was hesitant. "Do I have to tell them everything I know?"

Yes, Kaplan said, he did.

In that case, Matz replied uneasily, he could not cooperate.

Why couldn't he? the perplexed Kaplan demanded.

"Because," Matz blurted out, "I have been paying off the Vice President."

For the rest of that morning, as Joe Kaplan sat stunned, Lester Matz related a story that before long would jolt a nation nearly inured to shock after the many months of revelations in the Watergate case. It was a story of old-fashioned graft and greed practiced by the one man regarded more than most as the epitome of righteousness in American politics. Systematically since 1962, the year Agnew became executive of Baltimore County, Matz had been making cash payments to him in return for county public-works contracts. The arrangement had continued after Agnew became governor of Maryland in 1967. In fact, Matz had made payments to Agnew even after his election as Vice President. On one occasion, he had visited Agnew and handed him an envelope containing about $10,000 in cash.

Matz, having concluded his story, asked to use a phone. Kaplan led him to one in the outer office, and from there Matz made two calls to close associates of Agnew. He was in trouble and something had to be done. Agnew must somehow stop this blasted investigation. But the Vice President was very busy. In just five days he would be inaugurated for his second term and would then leave almost immediately for the Far East as a presidential emissary extraordinary.

All over Baltimore, other consulting engineers and architects rushed to the offices of the city's available legal talent, advised by some blunt-talking assistant U.S. attorneys that they should retain counsel "familiar with the federal criminal code." The first subpoenas of nearly one thousand were being served, all bearing the name of assistant U.S. Attorney Russell T. Baker, Jr., and all issued in the name of a special federal grand jury.

George Beall, the thirty-five-year-old U.S. attorney for Maryland, was papering the Baltimore metropolitan area with subpoenas, attempting, or so it was rumored, to prove at the bar of justice what was already no secret in the state of Maryland: Baltimore County public officials were receiving kickbacks.

The special federal grand jury had been impaneled on December 5, 1972, and its task was twofold: to investigate police corruption in Baltimore City and political corruption in Baltimore County. Beall seemed more interested in the latter. On December 11, he, Baker, and Robert Browne, the chief of intelligence for the Internal Revenue Service's Baltimore division, took the Metroliner to Newark to spend a day learning from a master.

The man the Baltimoreans went to see was probably the nation's foremost racket-buster, the U.S. attorney for New Jersey, Herbert Jay Stern. Confident and free with his advice, Stern lectured the inexperienced Beall on how it was done. Move quickly, he advised. Subpoena the county's records and simultaneously subpoena the records of the firms that do the most business with the county. When you have the records, look for the telltale bookkeeping signs that indicate cash is being generated.

On January 4, Baker sent out his first wave of subpoenas—twenty-seven to the firms doing the most business with Baltimore County and the twenty-eighth to the county government itself. No unusual cash flow was found in any of them. It so happened, however, that one of the twenty-seven top firms receiving government business was an architectural company. There in the books of Gaudreau, Inc., a company headed by Paul Gaudreau and his brothers, Robert Browne's IRS agents found the cash they were looking for. The prosecutors had stumbled on another world of corruption—smaller but still numerous contracts for architectural and engineering work that were let not by public, competitive bidding but by private negotiation with public officials.

On January 11, Baker, who handled most of the paper work, authorized a new wave of subpoenas, this one to wash on all those engineers and architects who dealt directly with Baltimore County officeholders. The next day, a Friday, an IRS agent served a subpoena on the consulting engineering firm of Matz, Childs and Associates, demanding that the corporation produce its books.

Nothing in Joe Kaplan's thirty-six years had prepared him for what Matz told him.

The brother of Senator Beall, who had been helped in his campaign by the White House, would hardly prosecute Spiro T. Agnew. It would be an unthinkable crusade for the cavalier Justice Department that John N. Mitchell had handed over to Richard Kleindienst in the pre-Watergate spring of 1972. Moreover, what Matz had to tell was the sort of dynamite information that could buy immunity from prosecution at any stage of investigation. Matz, Kaplan told him, could hold his counsel while the government built a case. Then Matz could strike a deal.

Kaplan's reasoning seemed sound to Matz. Anyway, his friend, Ted Agnew, would see to it that the investigation did not get off the ground. It was, Matz said at the time, the best thing for the country that it did not. He declared, though, that he would rather go to jail than add to the woes of an already troubled nation by implicating the Vice President. And there was friendship, too, and an association that went back more than ten years. Matz had courted Agnew in 1961, and had donated $500 to his 1962 campaign for county executive; both Matz and Childs hoped that with a friend in the county seat of Towson their firm would receive the public-works contracts that up to then had been denied them. They were right; their friend rewarded them with the long-sought contracts. All he asked was 5 per cent of their fees.

Years before, Matz had learned his lesson. As he told the story, his engineering firm and two others had formed a consortium to negotiate a public-works contract in nearby Anne Arundel County. Matz, trained at the Johns Hopkins University and proud of his talents, worked hard for that contract. He was rewarded with a note telling him that the contract had been let to one of the other firms in the consortium. Matz henceforth would often reach for his wallet before bothering to reach for his slide rule.

Now Matz's firm prospered. He rented an apartment in Aspen, Colorado, to indulge his love of skiing and purchased a condominium on Saint Croix in the Virgin Islands, near the one bought by Agnew. He became a man of wealth and substance. In 1970, his charities cost him $90,000. The year before, a different tradition had cost him at least $10,000, for it was in 1969 that he had placed that sum in an envelope and handed it to the Vice President.

At the time Matz told his story to Kaplan, his friend Agnew was nearly at the pinnacle of American political power. In just five days, Richard Milhous Nixon, the son of midwestern Quakers, and Spiro Theodore Agnew, the son of a Greek immigrant, would be sworn in for a second term after one of the largest landslide electoral victories in American history.

Herblock's State of the Union (SIMON & SCHUSTER, 1972)

"AND SOME DAY YOU MIGHT TURN THE BRUSH
OVER TO A NUMBER-2 MAN OF YOUR OWN."

It could be argued that more than most vice-presidential candidates Ted Agnew probably contributed to the dimensions of the 1972 rout of the Democrats. In that first Nixon administration, the former governor of Maryland had emerged as the spokesman of middle-class America. Indeed, he had been selected by the President as the man to rally the "great silent majority."

If it was true, as Nixon suggested, that the country was on the brink of a historic shift of party allegiance among the middle class, the obvious beneficiary of that shift was the voice of Middle America: Spiro T. Agnew. Like Nixon, he was a controversial figure. He had his love cult and his hate cult, but members of each were likely to give him an edge not often or readily allowed Nixon—they saw Agnew as a man of candor. That alone rallied an army of believers to his side.

Back in Baltimore County, however, there was at least one Agnew admirer who sensed a touch of demagoguery in the Vice President's. attacks on the press, student dissidents, and liberals. On February 1, 1970, Lester Matz wrote his friend a nine-page letter in which he reviewed six of Agnew's speeches and suggested changes that he thought would mollify Agnew's critics.

The speeches, Matz wrote, were not well received in the Jewish community, where some people were now suggesting that Agnew was an anti-Semite. Matz also thought that Agnew's attacks on students could prove costly politically.

Agnew never answered that letter, nor did he temper his political rhetoric. Without apology he continued to hammer at the perceived enemies of Middle America, and by January 1973 he was a man near the very top of the political world. Although he clearly relished his associations with the famous, he was not one to forget his old friends. Two nights after his re-election, Agnew had been the guest of honor at a special party commemorating not only the victory at the polls but his fifty-fourth birthday as well. About 300 of the Vice President's best friends were invited for drinks and buffet supper in the Cotillion Room of Washington's Sheraton Park Hotel, where the Agnews lived. The host for the evening was an old Baltimore chum, I. H. Hammerman II, called Bud, a wealthy real-estate developer and mortgage broker.

It was appropriate that Hammerman would be the man who picked up the tab. Bud Hammerman had practically made a career of taking care of Ted Agnew. And before the next year was out it would be known that Bud Hammerman had paid for Agnew's expensive and finely tailored suits, that he had given him cash when he needed it, and, most significantly, that he had been a middleman in a bribery scheme that brought Ted Agnew down.

Other old Agnew friends from Maryland days were still in close contact with the Vice President. One of them was Matz. By the most curious happenstance, on February 1, eleven days after Agnew began his second term, another lawyer who said he had been asked to represent Matz called on George Beall. He was George White, the Vice President's own legal counsel and friend.

White's purpose was simple enough, but it was expressed in the code that lawyers sometimes use when they are trying to get information. In being asked to represent Matz, White told Beall, he was worried about a possible conflict of interest. He was, after all, the Vice President's personal attorney and close adviser. Decoded, his question was clear: was Agnew under investigation?

Beall told White that representing Matz would pose no conflict: Agnew was not under investigation. Beall was after the *current* Baltimore County political leadership, and Agnew had not been a part of that leadership since 1966. Even assuming that Agnew had done something wrong, he was protected by the statute of limitations.

At the time of White's visit, rumors indeed were sweeping Baltimore that Agnew was being implicated in the investigation. The rumors persisted—even though the U.S. attorney was of the Vice President's own party. So Beall moved quickly. On February 6, he went to see the Attorney General of the United States, Richard Kleindienst. Beall told Kleindienst he wanted to alert him that the rumors were false.

Only three days later, on February 9, Kleindienst called back. Agnew, worried, had called him to complain that Beall's investigation into political corruption in Baltimore County had the potential to embarrass him. Moreover, he had reason to believe that one of Beall's assistants, Barnet D. Skolnik, was intent on political mischief. After all, Skolnik had been on Muskie's staff during his 1972 presidential campaign.

Beall repeated the same assurances he had already given Kleindienst. Agnew was protected both by the statute of limitations and by a total lack of evidence that he had ever accepted kickbacks. As for Skolnik, Beall protested, he was his most experienced man, a gifted prosecutor. He agreed, however, to Kleindienst's suggestion that Skolnik assume a "low profile" and refrain from interviewing witnesses who were once close to Agnew.

Beall hung up the phone and later in the day reported Agnew's call to Kleindienst to his three assistants—Baker, Skolnik, and Ronald S. Liebman. The Vice President, Baker suggested, was "acting like a guilty man." This remark drew quizzical looks from his colleagues.

"We're going to get Agnew," Baker said.

The others laughed.

CHAPTER 2

CREATURE OF SUBURBIA

Ten years before the triumphant re-election of President Nixon and Vice President Agnew, a gambling man could have written his own odds on the chances that these two men, or either one of them, would be at the apex of political power in 1972.

Richard Nixon, who had enjoyed the heady trappings of high office as Vice President and had reached for and barely missed the Presidency in 1960, was at rock-bottom on election night 1962. He had run for the governorship of California and lost.

On the night of Nixon's great debacle, Agnew by contrast was at the high point of an undistinguished, small-time career in politics. Having run for public office only once before—a local judgeship—and lost, he was now celebrating his very first election victory, as county executive of Baltimore County. Like most political successes in Agnew's career, this one was a fluke.

As was to happen so often in his career, the opposition played into Agnew's hands. A bitter primary battle between two former political allies split the Democratic ranks and allowed Agnew to sneak through. At forty-three, he most certainly had reached the zenith of his political career, precisely when Richard Nixon, at forty-nine, had reached his nadir.

It was in all ways appropriate that Spiro Agnew should get his start in politics in suburbia. A city boy, he had found Baltimore less than responsive to his talents. To practice law at the culmination of his many job switches, he rented space for a desk in somebody else's downtown Baltimore office. He might have remained mired there indefinitely had not Lester Barrett been named a county judge and moved to Towson, the Baltimore County seat. Agnew, his partner at the time, Sam Kimmel, and a third friend, George White, moved out on Barrett's heels and opened a small office across the street from the county courthouse.

It had been Barrett who had brought Agnew into the Republican Party in the first place. In a county with a four-to-one Democratic registration bulge, Barrett had provided pragmatic advice when Agnew, right after World War II, asked him how a young man got started in county politics. Become a Republican, Barrett had told him: the field of competition is smaller, and although the odds on winning public office are longer, there are other benefits, not the least of which is the law business Republican contacts can bring. Agnew followed that advice. Then and later Agnew led a joiner's life—Kiwanis, P.T.A., Thursday-night bowling, neighborhood socializing, Sunday afternoon at the Baltimore Colts' games. It was a life of mutual dependency or, put less elegantly, of mutual back-scratching.

Baltimore County surrounds but does not include the city of Baltimore. By the mid-1950's, the city had a black population of about one third (now more than half); when the postwar white flight to the suburbs took place in all directions, the result was not the usual redistribution of population by race within a county, but a wholesale abandonment of the city by whites into a separate governmental entity, the city-less suburban county. In the most exact sense, the Baltimore County to which Spiro Agnew moved, was a white noose—96 percent white—around a black inner city. Into this poured not only new residents but also the business interests customarily poised to capitalize on community growth.

In his first post on the county zoning board of appeals, Agnew received an education on the economics and the opportunities of suburban growth. Among those who helped his learning process was the deputy chief engineer and later assistant director of public works for Baltimore County, a man named Jerome B. Wolff. They worked closely together then and later in Agnew's public career in the granting of certain government contracts.

The three-member zoning board—two Democrats and one Republican—was established as a buttress for the public against the avarice of the developers, to whom a favorable rezoning could mean millions of dollars of profit. Spiro Agnew took to the job with zest and optimism. "It was really a quasi-judicial position where we actually made the record in zoning cases and other appeals for the courts," he said later, "and it was good for my law practice to have the prestige connected with this."

According to those who served with him, Agnew performed his duties with fairness, and as the lone Republican became a favorite of the *Baltimore Sun* papers. He forever railed against what he saw as laxness against zoning violators. Contentiousness and righteousness came to be the man's trademarks.

Yet for all Agnew's righteousness, he demonstrated from the start in public life a peculiar sense of propriety. Right after his election as county executive, he telephoned his Republican replacement on the zoning appeals board late one night to discuss an appeal brought by one of his clients who had been a major financial backer in the recent county executive race. The appeal concerned a potentially lucrative rezoning in the town of Pikesville—against the wishes of homeowners in the area.

Agnew later acknowledged the call, but he dismissed it—in a phrase he was to use later concerning other allegations about him as governor of Maryland—as "common practice" among lawyers trying to speed up zoning decisions. The call demonstrated a certain insensitivity that was to surface repeatedly.

Integrity was the characteristic that Agnew sought above all else to convey as a public official. But successful as he was in doing so in his four years as county executive, by 1966 he appeared to be at the end of the road politically. Baltimore County was still overwhelmingly Democratic. So Agnew looked elsewhere for his future. He was, after all, the ranking Republican officeholder in Maryland, and by this time he had some rich and influential friends to share his hours. They were men like Bud Hammerman, Lester Matz, and John Childs; J. Walter Jones, Jr., a wealthy Towson real-estate man; and Tilton Dobbin, president of the Maryland National Bank. These friends had more than a social interest in Agnew; he was a political property of value and it was in their interest as well as his own that the property be preserved. Jones, Matz, and Childs all did considerable business with the county, and it was most helpful to know the man in charge.

Once again, the Democratic Party's talent for political cannibalism worked to Agnew's great advantage. Three Democrats sought their party's gubernatorial nomination in a bitter primary, while Agnew ran uncontested in the Republican primary. The two principal Democratic candidates canceled each other out, and the third man, the ultraconservative, segregationist George P. Mahoney, a perennial loser, sneaked in. A wealthy road contractor, Mahoney had money and the issue of the white backlash in his favor.

Agnew, whose performance on civil-rights issues as county executive had marked him as a mild conservative or moderate, suddenly found himself the darling of Maryland's Democratic liberals. He was the last line of defense against redneckism in Annapolis. Aware of this shift, Agnew campaigned aggressively against Mahoney, whom he characterized as a throwback to the Dark Ages. By 81,775 votes, the electorate chose the bright, pure, courageous flame of Spiro T. Agnew to light the governor's mansion.

Though Mahoney, not Agnew, clearly was the issue in the gubernatorial race, the 1966 campaign contributed some revealing insights into Agnew's mind. Just before his surprise nomination, a story broke charging that Mahoney had been offered a huge bribe by the state's slot-machine interests. Mahoney denied the allegation. But Agnew, seizing a chance to demonstrate his purity, revealed that he had been offered $200,000 in campaign contributions by the same interests. "On three separate occasions I was approached with deals involving the slot machines," he said. "All I had to do was agree not to oppose or veto legislation which might pass the general assembly extending the life of the machines. I told those who approached me on the deals that I didn't even want to talk to the slot people."

The account shook the electorate much more than it seemed to affect Agnew. Three times, attempts had been made to bribe a public official seeking the governorship of the state, and three times he had simply ignored the attempts and kept them to himself. The Baltimore County state's attorney, Frank Newell, said Agnew had a public duty to tell all, but Agnew said he had no intention of revealing the names of those who had approached him.

To admit to having been offered a bribe three times and to having failed to report it was an incredible *gaffe* for a man seeking high public office. It demonstrated the kind of naïveté that one might expect of a political neophyte, and Agnew indeed often seemed an amateur.

The same peculiar sense of what constitutes impropriety also surfaced in the disclosure that in June 1965 Agnew and nine other men had bought for $267,000 a 107-acre tract of land in Anne Arundel County, where a second Chesapeake Bay crossing was planned, parallel to the existing bridge. Several of Agnew's partners were men who did business with Baltimore County, or who were large contributors to the gubernatorial campaign.

Of this, Agnew said: "I see no impropriety of any kind in holding property outside my jurisdiction. . . . I will certainly sell it if I am elected. . . . I don't expect you to believe it but when this transaction was being worked out, not one of us said anything about the parallel bridge. It didn't occur to us."

In Annapolis, many of the same figures who had introduced Ted Agnew to the ways of business-and-politics in suburbia were there beside him as he moved on to a larger and more important playing field. Foremost among them was J. Walter Jones, a man who knew how to live well. He had a comfortable boat tied up in the Annapolis harbor, and the new governor often spent quiet nights aboard, basking in the attention accorded him by all the other Walter Joneses of the business-and-politics fraternity in the state capital. Jones, a connoisseur of wines, had a wine cellar built for the new governor in the basement of the executive mansion, and he and other members of the fraternity stocked it for him.

Unlike previous governors who had risen over the legislative route, Agnew had few cronies in the state legislature. Yet for all his standoffishness with the legislators, Agnew won their respect by running a tidy operation, lobbying a new constitution through a state convention (it was rejected by the voters, to Agnew's dismay), and advancing programs in water pollution, housing, highway construction, mental health, and alcoholism.

Outside Maryland, Agnew remained unknown to the general public. But he soon became recognized among the nation's other governors as a particularly articulate and serious-minded member of that exclusive club. He impressed his fellow governors with his polished appearance and vocabulary, and with his good fellowship on the golf course and the tennis court.

What probably sustained his image as a liberal above all else—while bringing into question his political acumen—was his declared admiration for Governor Rockefeller of New York. Ignoring Rockefeller's public pledge that he would not seek the Presidency in 1968, Governor Agnew announced his intention to dissuade Rockefeller and work for his nomination.

On the afternoon of March 21, 1968, Agnew settled in front of a television set in his office, with reporters around him, to watch what he and just about everybody else expected would be Rockefeller's

Richard M. Nixon with his running mate, Spiro T. Agnew on October 31, 1968

announcement of candidacy. But the New York governor, to Agnew's great embarrassment, instead announced that he would *not* run. It was shortly learned that before going on television Rockefeller had tried to reach Agnew by phone to break the news personally, but had failed. What Agnew construed to be unforgivable thoughtlessness drove him in his humiliation and anger into the political arms of Richard Nixon, and he was on his way. Nixon and Agnew met in New York, were mutually impressed, and Agnew soon was working for Nixon's nomination. In his official duties, too, Agnew began to make moves that would make him attractive to a man like Nixon shopping for a running mate. In the next few weeks, Agnew dealt harshly with three major incidents involving Maryland blacks. The "liberal" governor of Maryland suddenly was perceived as what he always had been—a rigid authoritarian. One of Nixon's chief aides, the conservative Patrick J. Buchanan, gave newspaper clippings to Nixon about Agnew's tough handling of these incidents—and the rest is history.

After a brief flirtation with the prospect of selecting Robert Finch, Nixon settled on Agnew. The grateful unknown told reporters: ". . . I agree with you that the name of Spiro T. Agnew is not a household name. I certainly hope that it will become one within the next couple of months." These were words that would come back to haunt him, but no more so than those Richard Nixon uttered about Agnew at a press party after the convention. "There is a mysticism about men," he said. "There is a quiet confidence. You look a man in the eye and you know he's got it—brains. This guy has got it. If he doesn't, Nixon has made a bum choice."

In nearly five years as Vice President, Agnew became perhaps the most controversial of all the men who have stood a heartbeat away from the Presidency. Through it all, he remained essentially a creature of suburbia—a product of postwar middle-class values, hopes, and dreams.

By November 1972, when the American electorate was called to choose between the team of Richard Nixon and Spiro Agnew and the team of George McGovern and R. Sargent Shriver, it was no contest. Agnew had developed by this time such a strong constituency in Middle America that Nixon could have no thought of replacing him. To a vast segment of the American citizenry, he was "Spiro Our Hero." He was tough and he was outspoken; but more than that, he was, in the eyes of his legions of admirers, the personification of Middle American values—a man of honesty and integrity.

CHAPTER 3

THE BOAT IS LEAVING

E arly in the winter of 1973, there was not a hint on the nightly television news that the world of Spiro T. Agnew was slowly coming apart. By fiat, Agnew was a presidential emissary, off in the Far East conferring with heads of state on the weightiest of matters—"substantive discussions," White House press secretary Ronald L. Ziegler called them.

Returning home, he was greeted with none of the criticism that had marred his earlier foreign assignments. No longer did American newspapers staff an Agnew trip to report on the blunders of the innocent from Towson. The former provincial from Baltimore County had acquitted himself well.

What the world did not know, however, was that he was also a man in trouble. By late February, as he learned of the progress of George Beall's investigation, Agnew asked his aide John Damgard to compile a list of all his contacts with Lester Matz since he became Vice President. Agnew himself took his concerns to the very top of the Justice Department and called Attorney General Richard Kleindienst. The attorney general wasted little time communicating the Vice President's anxieties to Beall in Baltimore. Beall commiserated and understood. However, his assistant, Tim Baker, viewed things differently. Baker maintained that Kleindienst's calls represented the tentative probings of a man with something to hide. Possibly, he conjectured, Agnew had once accepted illegal campaign contributions while he was county executive.

Barney Skolnik, the most experienced and therefore the most influential of the assistant U.S. attorneys assigned to the Baltimore County investigation, scoffed at the notion that Agnew was a petty crook who would be exposed by a quartet of young prosecutors.

Baker, the son of one of Baltimore's leading real-estate men, was the odd man out among the prosecutors. Tall, blond, wealthy, and secure by birth, there was no public school in his past; it was a prep school, then Williams College, and finally Harvard Law. But after Harvard, Tim Baker broke the pattern. Instead of a secure position in a Baltimore or New York law firm, Baker and his wife, Betsy, joined the Peace Corps and spent two years in Liberia. When they returned to Baltimore, Baker had two job offers. The first was from Stephen Sachs, the former U.S. attorney who had since gone into private practice, the second from the new U.S. attorney, George Beall. He asked Sachs for advice and wound up accepting the job with Beall.

From the day Baker signed on in August 1971, he became Skolnik's protégé at corruption trials. They formed an odd pair: Skolnik, irrepressibly sloppy and lackadaisical except when fired up; Baker, a disciplined worker of nearly compulsive work habits.

As Baker learned his new business, his admiration for Skolnik grew. Eventually, he began to talk like his mentor, picking up whole phrases from him.

Ronald Liebman, too, looked up to Skolnik. Like Baker, he was a Baltimorean; unlike his colleague he was the product of the city's public schools, Western Maryland College, and the University of Maryland Law School. Liebman, though, was better than his schooling—a fact apparent to one of Baltimore's leading criminal law firms, Melnicove, Greenberg and Kaufman, which hired him after he had completed a clerkship under Judge R. Dorsey Watkins of the U.S. District Court. Liebman also had applied to Beall for a job and seized the opportunity to join the federal team as an assistant U.S. attorney when a vacancy occurred in August 1972. In Liebman, Skolnik had another disciple in the making.

By the time Agnew's name was first introduced by Matz, the team of Skolnik, Baker, and Liebman was in place, with Skolnik clearly the leader—and expressing nothing but doubt about Baker's Agnew prophecy. In the months to come, Skolnik clung to this position, summoning all the logic at his command to rebut the growing evidence that the trail of corruption that began in Towson was leading straight to Washington. The business at hand was political corruption in Baltimore County.

While Agnew was en route to the Far East in Air Force Two, Robert Browne's IRS agents were poring over the corporate records hauled out of Baltimore County in January. Daily, the agents combed the books of the subpoenaed corporations in a methodical search for the slightest hint that cash was being generated. Finally, in the books of the architectural firm of Gaudreau, Inc., the agents struck gold. Shortly after the firm received an installment payment from the county government for the design of a public building, it would issue a check to a corporate officer, and the amount of the check was almost always 5 per cent of the recent installment from the county. The Gaudreau firm, the agents concluded, was probably kicking back 5 per cent of its fees.

Baker turned his attention to the president of Gaudreau, Inc.; Paul Gaudreau was to mean as much in his own way to the future of Spiro T. Agnew as Richard Nixon had meant to his past.

Paul Gaudreau, it turned out, was in no mood for a fight. At fifty-nine, he was no longer in good health, having recently been hospitalized for the removal of cataracts. For years, Gaudreau was later to admit, he had been kicking back a percentage of his fees on county contracts. Unlike some of his peers, he had no ready excuse for his actions. He was wrong and he knew it. A religious man, who had received his architectural degree from the Catholic University of America, Gaudreau was also a troubled man. When a second subpoena from Baker arrived asking for his personal records, Gaudreau greeted it like a visit from a priest. His mind set, the architect was determined to purge his soul. He called his lawyer, Nevitt Steele, and authorized what turned out to be the first deal the prosecutors struck.

Paul Gaudreau in all respects was a dream witness. Aristocratic in bearing, dignified in manner, not only was he likable, he was also believable. A jury, the prosecutors concluded, would accept both the man and his testimony.

It was January 25 when Gaudreau came to the Baltimore courthouse to admit that he had been kicking back a portion of his fees to William E. Fornoff, the administrative officer of Baltimore County and present county executive Dale Anderson's number-one aide.

Gaudreau, the first major witness in a procession of many that eventually led the prosecutors to Agnew, ironically provided the government with information that, if anything, gave Agnew a reprieve. Although Gaudreau had been receiving large public-works contracts for years, he had not been forced to kick back a portion of his fees until the Anderson administration took over. He gave the administration of County Executive Agnew nothing in exchange for the contracts he won under Agnew's tenure. So for a while what vague scent of corruption the prosecutors may have sniffed whenever Agnew's name surfaced seemed to be contradicted.

Although Gaudreau's cooperation with the government remained a secret, lawyers visiting the U.S. attorney's office could sense a newly acquired cockiness on the part of the prosecutors. And Gaudreau soon had company. Within days, two of the engineers subpoenaed by Baker were talking. Again the revelations were similar. Again it was Fornoff, and again, when the witnesses were asked to provide the names of other engineers who might also be kicking back, the same names surfaced: Matz, Childs and Associates; and Jerome B. Wolff. The name of Wolff would haunt the investigation from the winter day in late January when his name was first mentioned until the muggy summer day in July when his testimony sealed the case against Agnew.

Among his fellow engineers, the brilliant Wolff was hailed as a genius, and it was at least true that he was nationally recognized for his expertise in the new and complex field of environmental planning. He considered himself to be above all a scientist. His hobby, fittingly, was astronomy; his compulsion, ominously for Ted Agnew, was record-keeping.

To others who were not engineers, Wolff was far better known for a different reason—his long and enduring relationship with Ted Agnew. Thumb out, Wolff had hitched a ride with him from Towson to Annapolis and finally to Washington. In Washington, he held the title of vice-presidential adviser for science and technology until 1970, when he returned to private business. In Annapolis, where he was the Agnew-appointed chairman of the State Roads Commission, Wolff performed a pivotal task—he advised the governor on the awarding of state engineering contracts.

In the winter of 1973, though, what the prosecutors were hearing about Wolff had nothing to do with Agnew. Jerry Wolff was just another engineer, president of Greiner Environmental Systems, Inc., a subsidiary of one of Maryland's largest engineering firms, the J. E. Greiner Co. Wolff's firm, the prosecutors were hearing, was kicking back a portion of its fees. Routinely, another subpoena was authorized by Baker. When Wolff received it, he took two actions: he called a lawyer—and he sent a message to Agnew.

For the moment, though, Wolff and his significance were lost in the rush of events. The pieces were beginning to fall into place. Skolnik was exhilarated. Dealing up was his game, and now he was beginning to hold some cards. Gaudreau and the engineers would bring in Fornoff, and he in turn would bring in Anderson. From there, who could tell?

Reviewing the evidence already assembled, Skolnik decided that the next thing to do was to bring to terms Lester Matz, his partner John Childs, and Jerry Wolff, none of whom were turning out to be cooperative. Already, there were hints that the firm of Matz, Childs and Associates was worth investigating. Its rapid success in the highly competitive engineering field was reason enough for suspicion.

Of the approximately two hundred engineering firms in Maryland, Matz, Childs was by far one of the most prosperous. Founded in 1955, the company eighteen years later had more than three hundred and fifty employees and was ranked the ninety-second largest design firm in the nation. In the last decade, more than half of its contracts—231 in all—were awarded by various government agencies, notably those headquartered in Towson.

In addition to all that, the corporation's books, now in the hands of Browne's IRS agents, were turning informer. Once again, the IRS agents were finding indications that cash was being generated. What made them suspicious was the way in which the Matz, Childs firm rewarded some of its key employees with bonuses. Nothing can look so suspicious to an IRS agent as a pattern of bonuses. A cooperating employee, an IRS agent knows, can give the bonus back to the firm in cash almost immediately, retaining just enough to pay his income tax on it. In the case of Matz, Childs and Associates, the cash accumulated in this fashion was kept in a wall safe. And the books tantalized the IRS agents for another reason. The firm frequently used the services of a consultant already under investigation as a suspected bag man and money launderer. The agents suspected that the only service this particular consultant provided the firm was a kickback of his fee (less his percentage).

Taken together, the pattern of bonuses and the steady use of the consultant was a suspicious bundle of information, but it was not hard enough evidence. In order to breathe life into the cold ledgers someone would have to talk. On April 10, Baker subpoenaed six of the highest-ranking employees of the firm and directed them to appear before the grand jury on Thursday, April 12. Then Baker set his trap.

Baker naturally expected that Matz, Childs employees, like the firm's owners, would invoke the Fifth Amendment before the grand jury. Therefore, he decided to take them before a judge and confer "use immunity" on them. A relatively new legal device enacted by the Nixon administration, use immunity enabled a prosecutor to compel a witness to answer any question put to him before the grand jury, in exchange for which the witness was granted immunity so that anything he admitted to under the line of questioning could not be used against him in any prosecution.

Joseph H. H. Kaplan had been expecting the prosecutors to subpoena the Matz, Childs employees, whom he was now also representing. He advised them to invoke the Fifth Amendment, forcing the government to fish elsewhere for its information. So confident was Kaplan of his defensive parry that he planned to be in Delaware later in the day, attending to the problems of a different client. Kaplan had to break that appointment. While he stood helplessly by, the Matz, Childs employees were whisked before a judge, use-immunized, and escorted by Baker into the grand jury room. There, one by one, they confirmed the suspicions of the IRS agents. They had been kicking back their bonuses.

Suddenly, both Lester Matz and John Childs were in very bad

trouble—tax trouble, to be precise. Their firm had been deducting the bonuses as wages—a legitimate business expense—but now there was abundant evidence that the bonuses were not salaries at all. The employees themselves were not sure exactly what one would call them. Bribes? Illegal campaign contributions? Whatever it was, it was not deductible.

Word of what happened in the grand jury room was soon flashed to Washington. Matz, who all along had been receiving pep talks from Agnew via Bud Hammerman, was no longer confident. Wolff, too, was beginning to feel pressed. Abandoning Hammerman as an intermediary, Wolff sat down and wrote directly to the Vice President. Choosing his words meticulously in case the letter was read by a vice-presidential aide, Wolff composed what one of the prosecutors later called a "carefully worded scream for help" that left little doubt that it was in Agnew's best interest that the investigation be halted. Having mailed the letter, Wolff destroyed his only copy.

In Washington, Agnew realized—possibly for the first time—that he was being inexorably drawn into Beall's investigation. He did what so many before him had done—he called a lawyer. His choice was Charles W. Colson, President Nixon's former special counsel, who had left the White House just two months before to establish a private law practice in Washington. Now a partner in the law firm of Colson and Shapiro, he had become friendly with Agnew during his White House years. In a way, the two were alike: both were gut fighters. In a Washington used to "hardball" politics, Chuck Colson stood out because he threw a spitter.

But harried and preoccupied with the preparation of his own Watergate defense, Colson could not take on Agnew's case himself. Instead, he and his partner, David Shapiro, approached a third partner, Judah H. Best. It was, the two senior partners told Best, a simple matter of liaison. Get in touch with George Beall in Baltimore. Tell him that Agnew had heard "cocktail-party rumors" about the investigation and was afraid he might be harmed by prejudicial publicity. Tell him also that the Vice President has no intention of impeding the investigation.

On April 17, five days after the grand jury appearance of the Matz, Childs employees, Judah Best momentarily put aside the legal concerns of his partner Colson, and the preparation of his defense, and called Beall in Baltimore. He arranged an appointment for two days later.

It was not a day, though, for either man to be concerned about the Vice President. The eyes of the nation were on the White House, where the President, after months of ostrich-like behavior on the Watergate scandal, finally had something to say. He announced that after "serious charges" were brought to his attention nearly a month before, he had ordered a new, "intensive" investigation into the Watergate burglary and cover-up. The investigation, the President said, had produced "major developments" and "real progress" in finding the truth about the break-in.

The White House admissions served only to mask other sordid events unfolding behind the scenes. Already, Nixon was demanding the resignation of his counsel, John W. Dean III, and weighing whether he also would have to sacrifice H. R. (Bob) Haldeman and John D. Ehrlichman. At the Justice Department, L. Patrick Gray III, the acting director of the FBI, admitted to Henry E. Petersen, the assistant attorney general in charge of the criminal division, that he had destroyed the files removed from the White House safe of E. Howard Hunt, Jr.

By the end of April, Gray, Dean, Ehrlichman, and Haldeman along with Attorney General Kleindienst would be gone from the government and a new group would take over. Elliot Richardson would move from Defense to Justice and William D. Ruckelshaus from the Environmental Protection Agency to Gray's old FBI office, and eventually to Justice as Richardson's deputy attorney general.

Dean, the once-trusted presidential lawyer, was in seclusion, but his version of Watergate was now leaking all over Washington, casting a pall of suspicion over the entire Nixon administration. In all the stories, in all the accusations and allegations that surfaced as members of the White House team began to cannibalize each other, there was no suggestion that Agnew was in the least way connected with Watergate or any of its ramifications. More and more he was viewed as the possible savior of the GOP, the one man untarnished by the spreading stain of Watergate.

On April 19, the day Dean escalated his struggle for survival by announcing he would not be the White House's Watergate "scapegoat," Jud Best set out for his appointment with Beall in Baltimore. In the office of the U.S. attorney, Best followed his instructions closely, describing Agnew's concern and his willingness to cooperate. Solicitous as usual, Beall assured Best that he would make every effort to see that the Vice President's good name and reputation were not damaged by the investigation. Of course, he had no control over other lawyers or witnesses and could not censor what they might tell the press, but as for the investigation itself, Best could tell his client that he had nothing to worry about. It did not involve Agnew. After fifteen minutes, the two men parted with the understanding that Best would check back from time to time to see if anything had changed.

Upon his return to Washington, Best reported to Agnew on his meeting with Beall. It was the beginning of a long relationship that was to consume Best's spring, summer, and fall. When nine-year-old Stephen Best returned to school four months later, he wrote an essay that told the whole story.

"My father is the lawyer of the Vice President of the United States," Stephen Best wrote. "So we could not go anywhere, but we had a fun time at home. We are planning to go on a trip soon."

CHAPTER 4

SAY YOU GAVE AT THE OFFICE

A year before Ted Agnew's name was injected into the Baltimore County corruption investigation by Lester Matz, Barnet Skolnik quit the office of the U.S. attorney in Baltimore and joined the campaign of Senator Edmund S. Muskie of Maine. He soon realized he had hitched his wagon to a sputtering star. Bogged down writing issue papers, Skolnik left, went to Europe for several months, and in early September 1972 got his old job back with George Beall. On his first day back, Skolnik went to lunch with Tim Baker. Baker asked him how he thought a certain Maryland political figure then under investigation would feel when he learned that Skolnik, his nemesis, was back on the job.

"Terrorized," Skolnik said with a laugh.

Baker understood. It was not that Skolnik enjoyed terrorizing potential witnesses or defendants. It was, rather, that Skolnik appreciated the utility of fear. As stories of Skolnik's methods made the rounds, his reputation grew, until by spring a summons from the prosecutor was greeted in certain quarters of the engineering community like a visit from the Angel of Death. Baker and Liebman, who watched Skolnik in action, took mental notes and attempted to emulate his ways.

It was therefore understandable that many lawyers preferred to deal with Beall. George Beall at the age of thirty-five was a neophyte as a criminal lawyer. Until his appointment as U.S. attorney, he had mostly handled negligence cases.

When Beall took office in August 1970, the reporters covering the federal courthouse settled down for what they thought would be a soporific tenure. In a short time, though, Beall proved them wrong. He pursued drug pushers and the industrial polluters of the state's waters; in cooperation with the IRS, he pioneered a technique of bringing drug suppliers to account through the use of tax laws. Slowly, he made a name for himself.

In appearance, George Beall was a striking man—poised, articulate, and endowed with what many considered to be excellent political instincts. Yet for all that, Beall appeared to lack leadership qualities, and many in Maryland firmly believed that Skolnik was leading him around by the nose. If Skolnik was, in fact, leading him, it was because Beall wanted to travel in that direction.

Like Baker and Liebman, Beall began to pick up Skolnik's phrases. Men under investigation were called "bad men." Jerry Wolff was called "a very bad man" because they thought he was significantly more corrupt than most of the other engineers. In a way, the prosecutors employed terms like these to condition themselves for the job at hand—mean, nasty work that often entailed sending a man to jail. It was one thing to dispose of a mugger in that fashion, but quite another thing when it came to men very much like themselves—college-educated, middle class, articulate.

The power of the Baltimore prosecutors thus was great. Judges generally abided by the recommendation of the U.S. attorney at sentencing time: if he told the court that the convicted defendant had been cooperative and that jail would be unwarranted, the judge was likely to follow that recommendation.

When a prosecutor ran across an uncooperative witness—men like Matz, Childs, or Wolff—he chased him with a special relish. In the unwritten code of prosecutors, no man could be permitted to thumb his nose at the government, and if he did, the prosecutor detoured his investigation to bring the witness to terms. Then, with the government's case developed, he would hammer at the witness unceasingly, threatening imprisonment and the disgrace that went with it. The potential witness, in John Ehrlichman's phrase, would hang twisting in the wind. Trapped, he would finally decide to cooperate. And once that decision was made he became malleable, often zealous, willing to report fact and hearsay.

At that point, the chase ended. Slowly, the prosecutor would rehabilitate the witness he had so recently leveled and prepare him for the moment when he was to appear before a judge and jury and offer his testimony.

By April, this process was just beginning for Matz, Childs, Wolff, and

Fornoff. The four had retained some of the best legal talent in Baltimore and were well prepared for a fight. Fornoff, already doomed by the testimony of Gaudreau and others, had hired Stephen Sachs, who in the two years since he had resigned as U.S. attorney had earned a national reputation as a criminal lawyer.

Matz and Childs, who had already retained Joseph Kaplan, in February had also hired Arnold Weiner, who was Wolff's lawyer as well. At thirty-nine, Weiner was regarded as Sachs's peer. Erudite and worldy, with a love for the cinema and the theater, Arnold Weiner was known as the best deal-maker in Baltimore.

By April, Weiner had emerged as the chief strategist for Matz, Childs, and Wolff. As a lawyer for all three, he had an overview that the prosecution could not hope to obtain for months to come. Unlike his co-counsel Kaplan, Weiner entertained no doubts that Beall would prosecute Agnew. He knew that the information his clients had was far from worthless—as Kaplan for a time believed. So he decided on a waiting game. Let the government build its case. For the kind of information his clients possessed, the boat would always come back.

Matz, too, appreciated the value of his information. But even more than that, he appreciated that scorn and ostracism would rain upon him for being the man who turned informer on the Vice President. What seemed to chill Matz even more than a jail term was the prospect of his picture on the cover of *Time* magazine.

His drift toward making a deal was slowed by his fear of public scorn.

Skolnik, too, was setting his strategy. Matz, Childs, and Wolff intrigued him. Why were the three engineers holding out, refusing to cooperate with the government? Their recalcitrance ran counter to everything Skolnik had learned in his years as an investigating prosecutor. Could it be that they were attempting to shield someone other than Fornoff and Anderson?

While Liebman and Baker continued to press the investigation of Matz, Childs, and Wolff, Barney Skolnik turned his full attention to Fornoff and his lawyer, Sachs. With relish, Skolnik took on his old mentor. When Sachs proposed that Fornoff be given blanket immunity in return for cooperation, Skolnik reminded Sachs of what he himself had once said: You don't give immunity to a major target of an investigation.

This legal tug-of-war was waged between equals. Skolnik by then was ready to indict Fornoff on the basis of evidence supplied by Gaudreau and others, and he wasted little time in hammering that point home.

Sachs knew his client was the linchpin of the cases the government was building against Anderson, and he was determined that the government would pay dearly for the information his client possessed.

Throughout April and into early May, Skolnik and Sachs continued the tug-of-war. Bluff was met with counterbluff, but inevitably Sachs picked up signals that the government indeed had a sound case against his client. After conferring with Fornoff, Sachs called Beall and arranged an appointment for three o'clock on the afternoon of May 4.

At the appointed hour, Beall, Skolnik, and Liebman waited expectantly in Beall's office for Sachs. All of them sensed that the moment of surrender was at hand. Finally the door to Beall's office opened a crack. A hand appeared—waving a white handkerchief. With a burst of laughter, the tension broke and Sachs, a mischievous, little-boy smile on his face, entered to accept the terms of surrender. Fornoff had been "turned." He had agreed to plead guilty to a tax-evasion felony in exchange for a government recommendation that he not be jailed.

How best to use the suddenly available Fornoff was the next question. When he finally appeared for interrogation, the back-slapping official turned out to be less than a stellar witness. Yet his information was golden. He provided a virtual blueprint of the alleged Baltimore County kickback scheme, integral parts of which, Fornoff testified, were the engineering firms of Matz, Childs and Associates and Greiner Environmental Systems, Inc.

Weiner and Kaplan kept a nervous eye on Fornoff, knowing he could harden the case against their clients Matz, Childs, and Wolff. They continued to hold out, waiting until events might force them to the negotiating table. If the government ever tripped over the dark secrets their clients possessed, the lawyers would work a deal, if possible. If the information never came out, they would take their secrets with them to their graves. Their primary obligation was to their clients.

During the spring, Matz and Wolff continued to send messages to Agnew through Bud Hammerman. The responses were always the same: Hold out, don't talk, the Vice President will fix things.

Judah Best was also staying in touch. He called Beall periodically to inquire if any change in the investigation had affected Agnew's status. The answer was always no. But in mid-May, Best decided it was time for another face-to-face meeting with Beall, for he was incensed by rumors his client had heard. Best told Beall that Baker had been overheard at a party saying that the prosecutors were breathing down Agnew's neck. Beall had his standard reply: the Vice President was not under investigation. But Best was unconvinced. When he returned to Washington, he advised Agnew to prepare a log of all visits he had had from Hammerman, Matz, and other engineers. Agnew communicated Best's suggestion to his aide, John Damgard. When the laborious task was completed, the logs filled a bookcase that lined a wall in Damgard's office. It contained, at Agnew's insistence, not only all the visits of the engineers to his office, but also a record of every trip Agnew had made to New York when accompanied by Hammerman.

On the very same day that Best called on Beall, *The Washington Post* contained a front-page story saying that Dale Anderson, "one of Maryland's most powerful Democrats, has been notified by federal officials that he is under investigation," that the investigation also involved several persons who had formerly worked in the administration of County Executive Agnew and others who had been associated with Agnew. "Despite this fact, sources in Baltimore, Washington, and Towson, the seat of Baltimore County, have stated categorically that the Vice President himself is in no way involved in the investigation and that widespread rumors to the contrary are without foundation."

The "widespread rumors" mentioned in the *Post* story were in fact what had prompted the newspaper to look into the Baltimore County situation in the first place. Maryland had been abuzz for some time with reports that Agnew was under investigation and that the probe of Anderson was actually a ruse to throw the press off the track. But the *Post* had more than rumors to go on. Bob Woodward, who along with Carl Bernstein had won a Pulitzer Prize for *The Washington Post* on the Watergate story, had been told by his most trusted source—a government official whom he code-named "Deep Throat"—that FBI files contained unverified allegations that Agnew had accepted a bribe while Vice President.

Woodward's information, as usual, was specific. Agnew had taken the money in cash and placed it in a desk drawer. The amount was $2500. The Baltimore grand jury, the source added, was heading Agnew's way and the Vice President was in fact its target. This seemingly preposterous information was received in April, nearly a month before the prosecutors acknowledged getting the first veiled hint that Agnew had taken kickbacks. At the time, it was not clear if the FBI's files merely documented one of Maryland's recurring rumors—that Agnew had once taken a bribe—or whether the Bureau was simply feeding its ravenous files "cocktail-party chatter."

The evidence from the start was contradictory. Many firmly believed that Agnew was the ultimate target of the investigation. Just as many others, however, argued convincingly that George Beall, a Republican U.S. attorney, had neither the temerity nor the sagacity to investigate his party's second-highest-ranking member.

Adding to the general confusion was the nature of the man Agnew himself. For years, rumors had circulated in Maryland that Agnew accepted bribes, but then, the same sort of rumors circulated about many politicians. Every trail gave out either from lack of evidence or from the strength of the denunciations that came from Agnew. Ted Agnew may not have been a liberal's idea of a hero, but then he was no whore either.

If this view persisted long past the time when some in Maryland knew better, it was due in no small part to the efforts that Beall and his staff made to disguise the turn their investigation was about to take. Until the very day when news that Agnew *was* under investigation surfaced in *The Wall Street Journal* and *The Washington Post*, the prosecutors repeatedly lied to the press.

Arnold Weiner was one who knew better. But Weiner could not have cared less about Agnew. He was being paid by Wolff, Matz, and Childs to keep them out of jail.

Kaplan, meanwhile, was doing some probing of his own. He was in frequent touch with Baker. On Friday, May 18, Kaplan made a routine call to Baker, giving him no hint that he was about to blurt out the secret that had been weighing upon him since January. Baker reminded Kaplan that his clients were certain to be indicted. Kaplan didn't flinch. Both Matz and Childs were aware of that possibility, he replied, and in fact were reconciled to it. They had always been prepared to cooperate with the government, but they had nothing the government would consider of value. Anyway, what they *did* have to say, the government would not be willing to hear.

Baker reacted as if Kaplan had slandered him. What did Kaplan mean by that? Both Matz and Childs had been offered immunity months ago, and it was Kaplan who had rejected the idea. Kaplan cut right in as if Baker had not said a thing. He seemed eager to say his piece. Matz and Childs were in a position to incriminate Fornoff, but that information was probably worthless now. From what he had been hearing, the government already had more than enough evidence to indict Fornoff.

Then, without the slightest fanfare, Kaplan dropped the bombshell. The only person his clients were uniquely in a position to incriminate was—the Vice President of the United States! The government undoubtedly would not be interested in that sort of information.

Baker was outraged at this suggestion that the Justice Department would retreat in the face of an investigation of the Vice President. After all, he had been the one who had insisted for months that Agnew was camouflaging some crime. Now, rather than reacting with shock, he was indignant. The Baltimore U.S. attorney's office, Baker sternly lectured Kaplan, was nonpartisan. Then, as if suspecting that he was being duped, Baker reminded Kaplan that Agnew had not been executive of Baltimore County since December 1966. The statute of limitations would bar prosecution for any crimes during that period.

Kaplan thought maybe Baker had missed the point. Certainly his clients had information about Agnew when he was county executive, he said, but their dealings did not cease when Agnew became governor or, in fact, Vice President.

Baker fought to contain his excitement, but he invoked Skolnik's first rule: Don't alert a lawyer to the fact that his client has information you desperately want. He made the routine assurances that the U.S. attorney's office would make every effort to protect the Matz, Childs firm, but that it could not be held accountable for what appeared in the newspapers. Kaplan said he understood; he would consult with his clients and report back. Baker said that would be fine and then applied one final squeeze: Matz and Childs would soon be indicted, he warned again, and hung up the telephone.

Then Baker erupted. Leaping from his chair, he rushed into Liebman's office. "Get into Skolnik's office," he barked, and then he ducked into Skolnik's office himself. "Have I got news for you!"

In a rush, Baker spilled out the details of Kaplan's jolting call, ending with a hard pitch for an all-out investigation of Agnew. Skolnik, listening and pacing, was not so sure. Instead of the enthusiasm and excitement that Baker had expected of him, Skolnik expressed cynicism and doubt. Maybe Kaplan was talking about campaign violations or some other sort of petty bookkeeping crime. Maybe Kaplan was bluffing. Maybe his clients were lying to him. Still pacing, Skolnik lectured his associates on the harsh realities of investigatory life.

But Baker was having none of it. "What's wrong with you?" he demanded. "You know I'm right! You know I'm right!"

Indeed, Skolnik, the ultimate skeptic, did know. But he was also awed by Baker's report. Dale Anderson was one thing, but this was the Vice President of the United States. Still, if Agnew were a crook, if, indeed, he had broken a federal law at any time in the last five years, then Skolnik and only Skolnik would get the man—Skolnik and not some special

Russell T. Baker, Jr.   *Ronald S. Liebman*

prosecutor zipped in from the Justice Department. This was going to be a Baltimore investigation. There would be no sudden sharp turns to go after Agnew. No need to notify the Justice Department. Just play it by the book. Skolnik issued his orders. Baker would handle Kaplan. He was to keep the pressure on. If Agnew was out there, they would get him by keeping the pressure on Matz, Childs, and Wolff.

With that settled, the three prosecutors marched down the hall to report to Beall. Baker told him of the conversation with Kaplan. The U.S. attorney smiled, recalling Baker's prophecy. Then Skolnik took over: keep up the pressure, George, keep hammering at Matz and soon enough he will serve up Agnew. Beall agreed, and the four prosecutors parted company for the weekend.

Monday finally arrived. With Skolnik at his side, Baker called Kaplan. He had discussed their Friday conversation with Beall, Baker told him, and was authorized to say that the Maryland U.S. attorney's office was prepared to investigate federal crimes committed by anyone. He realized that Matz and Childs had difficult decisions to make, but the government was not prepared to grant them a period of grace. Their indictments were imminent.

Kaplan protested. He had conferred with his clients over the weekend

Barnet D. Skolnik   George Beall

and they were both concerned about the "national implications" of the information they possessed. They were worried lest the downfall of Agnew, added to the national trauma of Watergate, prove to be more than the nation could endure.

Well, Baker replied, both Matz and Childs would have to have faith in the American criminal-justice system. If they refused to cooperate, the government would have only one recourse—to make a case against them, haul them before a judge, immunize them, and compel them to talk about Agnew before a grand jury.

Matz and Childs had cause to worry about the effect their testimony would have on an already troubled nation. But the two engineers had more mundane concerns.

They were afraid they would look like turncoats, men who had squealed on their friends. They requested, and received, assurances that they would be given "use immunity" so it would appear they had been compelled to testify. Another worry was that Wolff might not cooperate, leaving them to face Agnew on their own. That would be an uneven confrontation, a swearing contest between two admittedly corrupt engineers and the Vice President.

Finally, Kaplan played what appeared to be his trump card. His clients, he said, were prepared to be indicted. They had discussed the possibility with their families and were ready, stoically, to go to jail. Baker laughed at the transparent ploy.

There was little cheer, however, in the Matz household. His attorney's word notwithstanding, Lester Matz was far from reconciled to an indictment. He was not, after all, a criminal.

One of those in whom the panicked engineer confided in those gloomy days was his son Harry. His advice to his father was simple: Cooperate. Slowly Matz was coming around to agree with him. No longer was he Agnew's friend. The chummy days in Baltimore County were now just a fond memory.

While Lester Matz and Jerome Wolff wrestled with their options, the prosecutors prepared a surprise they hoped would force both men to terms. Fornoff was about to make his debut as a government witness. On Friday, June 1, Beall's staff alerted news organizations to have reporters on hand the next Monday in the Baltimore courthouse.

It was a carefully planned extravaganza. From the door behind the dais where Judge Alexander Harvey was sitting, William Fornoff strode to the defendant's table. Baker rose and read what the government claimed it would have proved had Fornoff gone to trial. Fornoff, Baker said, "on many occasions" since 1967 "received substantial quantities of money, in cash, from various businesses that had contracts with Baltimore County and wished to acquire such contracts in the future, or both. All such cash received by Mr. Fornoff was delivered by him to another public official in Baltimore County." He was being charged with interfering with IRS agents in the performance of their job. Baker then filed a sealed document with the court that contained the fruits of the months of negotiations between Sachs and Skolnik. The government recommended no jail for Fornoff.

Within moments Baltimore County was feeling the shock tremors. Fornoff had just admitted receiving bribes on behalf of another public official. No one could fail to fill in the missing name: Dale Anderson. Fornoff had also told the prosecutors who had bribed him. Those in the know had little trouble supplying the names: Matz, Childs, and Wolff had to be included in that select set.

The very next day, the first harvest began to come in. To no one's surprise, one of Beall's first calls was from Kaplan. His clients had decided that in "the national interest" they ought to explore the possibility of a deal with the government. He asked for an appointment later that same day, and by three o'clock he and Weiner were in Beall's office. Ten minutes later, Beall asked Skolnik, Baker, Liebman, and deputy U.S. Attorney Paul Kramer to join the meeting.

Kaplan did the talking. His clients, concerned as they were about the national interest, were now prepared to see what the government was willing to offer in exchange for the information they possessed about a "high federal official." What they would like, he said, was a pledge of immunity from prosecution.

No deal, Skolnik snapped. Immunity would not even be discussed until the government had a better reading of what sort of information Matz, Childs, and Wolff possessed. So Kaplan began to drop some enticing hints. The information his clients possessed would provide the government with a hard case against the "high federal official." It would incriminate others who, in turn, would harden the case even further. The crimes committed by the "high federal official" were committed both before and after he joined the federal government.

The prosecutors told Kaplan they would have to consider the question of immunity and would respond by mail within the next several days. Skolnik sternly warned him that if his clients failed to cooperate fully any deal would be called off and they would be prosecuted with a vengeance.

On June 7, in identical letters of negotiation written to Matz, Childs, and Wolff, Beall spelled out the terms under which he would be willing to hear their information. First, he would have to examine the information in detail before any deal could be discussed. Second, he did not want to hear anything on certain corrupt relationships the U.S. attorney's office was already aware of.

The next day, June 8, he stepped up the pressure. "On the basis of [your] extremely limited disclosure," Beall wrote to Kaplan, "you have asked me to indicate if this office would be prepared to grant your clients total immunity in exchange for their cooperation and information. I have concluded that I cannot in the proper exercise of our responsibilities make any representation to you on the basis of limited disclosures." Beall concluded with another warning that Matz and Childs were perilously close to indictment. The letter marked the start of a steady correspondence—as many as two letters a day—between Beall and Kaplan. In the event their talks collapsed, each party wanted to be in a position to document what the ground rules had been for the negotiations.

Finally, on June 13, Weiner told Beall that Wolff was probably ready to cooperate, and asked total immunity for him. Again, as he had done with Matz and Childs, Beall refused to discuss the possibility until he had detailed information in hand.

By this time, however, Matz and Childs had made up their minds to cooperate. The two engineers signed letters of negotiation, spelling out the terms under which the plea bargaining would proceed and their testimony be heard. On June 21, Kaplan and Weiner met with Beall and his staff to turn over the letters.

Arnold Weiner did the talking, in his high, sing-song voice.

Lester Matz and John Childs met during the 1950's when they both worked as municipal engineers for Baltimore. They formed their own firm in 1955, establishing their offices in an old building at 2129 North Charles Street. Matz, a gregarious fellow, went out to seek clients. He found them in Baltimore County, to which thousands of Baltimoreans were then fleeing. All over the county, fortunes were being built as farms made way for housing tracts and sewers and roads were constructed—a heady sight for an engineer. One of the major developers was Bud Hammerman, whose father, Sam, had founded the S. I. Hammerman Organization, a real-estate conglomerate. Another was Wolff, then an engineer in private practice. Before long, the three—Matz, Hammerman, and Wolff—established a business relationship.

The firm of Matz, Childs began to prosper. As a new and politically unconnected firm, however, it received none of the county's public-works contracts. Despite repeated attempts to break into the favored circle of firms that did, Matz, Childs and Associates remained outsiders. Still, Matz was not idle. By 1960, he had befriended the chairman of the county zoning board of appeals—Spiro Agnew. (Within two years, Matz and Agnew became involved in certain transactions with a man who will be referred to in this book as The Close Associate. Matz made the man's identity known to the prosecutors, but it was not publicly disclosed because the man was not cooperating with the investigation.) When Agnew announced that he would run for county executive, Matz and Childs threw in with him, donating $500 to what appeared then to be a doomed cause. The two engineers genuinely admired Agnew, and of course also hoped that his victory would bring them the contracts they believed they deserved.

Over the next four years, Matz, Agnew, and The Close Associate became even friendlier—visiting in each other's homes and celebrating milestone family occasions together. There was also a business relationship. Shortly after Agnew's election, The Close Associate told Matz that the two of them figured to make a lot of money. The comment was not lost on Matz, and a short time later, they met with Agnew. The new county executive told Matz that he had great confidence in The Close Associate. Matz unscrambled this message to mean that he was supposed to work through The Close Associate.

Not long after, The Close Associate asked Matz to prepare a chart listing how much money the engineers receiving county contracts could be expected to kick back. Matz calculated the likely profits on certain jobs, concluded that a 5-per-cent kickback was not unreasonable, gave a copy of the chart to The Close Associate, and took the original to Agnew.

The chart then became a manual by which kickbacks in Baltimore County and to Spiro Agnew were determined. When he turned over the copy of the chart to The Close Associate, Matz was told that he would be expected to pay 5 per cent on engineering contracts and 2½ per cent on surveying contracts. This arrangement, in which both parties would benefit, was soon implemented.

Whenever Matz learned which contracts the county was about to let, he would contact The Close Associate and tell him which ones he wanted. Matz usually delivered the money to The Close Associate in his office, handing him a plain white envelope containing the cash. He paid in installments, generally, making each payment when the county sent him an installment for the work performed. And when the size of the cash payments increased and Matz and Childs found themselves in a cash bind, they began to generate cash by having key employees kick back bonuses.

It was no surprise, then, that in 1966, Matz and Childs were enthusiastic supporters of Agnew's gubernatorial campaign. Their faith in the man's abilities—and his financial value to them—was undiminished. With Jerry Wolff as chairman of the state roads commission and Agnew in the governor's mansion, Matz, Childs and Associates soon began to enjoy a steady flow of state contracts. By then, however, circumstances had made Matz reluctant to continue paying through The Close Associate, for he suspected that the intermediary was skimming money off the top and taking all the credit for the cash he handed over. Matz went to Annapolis for a face-to-face talk with the new governor. In Agnew's ornate office with its majestic fireplace, Matz proceeded to denigrate The Close Associate, warning that he lacked discretion and would sooner or later get them in trouble.

Matz had a proposition. Instead of paying through The Close Associate, why not deliver the cash to Agnew directly? He would put the money in a savings account from which Agnew could draw after he returned to the practice of law. The savings-account money, Matz continued, could perhaps be accounted for later in the form of legal fees. Agnew liked that idea especially.

Subsequently, Matz reconsidered the savings-account scheme and decided that it involved keeping too many records. He did not, however, reconsider his determination to make his payments personally, and from that time forth he dealt directly with Agnew. The contracts kept coming.

All through 1967, Matz, Childs and Associates continued to share in the largess of the Agnew administration. So large were the contracts that Matz and Childs had to defer their payments to Agnew until they received their fees from the state. The fees began to arrive in the summer of 1968, and Matz, now far behind in his obligations to Agnew, was determined quickly to catch up, lest he be suspected of welshing. By July of 1968, his payments totaled about $20,000. With the fees that would soon be in the mail from the state, Matz figured he would owe $30,000 more.

The firm, however, was in a fix. Matz and Childs felt they could not safely generate $30,000 in cash. So Matz turned to a former client who generally dealt in large sums of cash and arranged a "loan." Matz, Childs and Associates loaned this former client $30,000, transferring the funds by corporate check; the client agreed to deliver $30,000 in cash to Matz. On the books of the client's firm the loan was recorded as being repaid in installments of $1700—a sum Matz and Childs thought they could safely manage in cash. When they received a "loan" installment, they simply transferred $1700 in cash to their "debtor."

The friend was able to produce $20,000 of the total almost immediately. Matz showed the cash to Childs, then he stuffed it in a manila envelope and drove to the State House in Annapolis. Taking the elevator to the second floor, he passed through the governor's reception room to the governor's office. There, Matz handed the envelope to Agnew, thanked him for the state contracts, and left. It was the last payment Matz made while Agnew was governor of Maryland.

By 1969, Agnew had been promoted by Richard Nixon and by the American people to the seat of national power. What he gained in stature, however, he lost in the authority to grant contracts. Nevertheless, Matz felt that he owed Agnew money for Maryland contracts received under the old Agnew administration. On a piece of yellow paper, he calculated the sum he thought was due Agnew and called the Vice President's office for an appointment. Matz took the yellow paper and an envelope containing $10,000 in cash and went to see Agnew in his office in the basement of the White House. The engineer showed Agnew his calculations, reviewed them with him, and handed the Vice President the envelope. Agnew took it and put it in a desk drawer. Matz then told Agnew he might "owe" him more money as the contracts negotiated during Agnew's Maryland administration continued to generate fees. Agnew told Matz to call his secretary when the next payment was ready and tell her he had more "information" for the Vice President.

On his return to Towson, Matz told Childs about his transaction with Agnew. This was no longer something he could be casual about, and he admitted to Childs that he was shaken. Matz told one other person about the payoff—Jerry Wolff, then vice presidential assistant for science and technology.

From there on, Matz's common sense conflicted with his sense of obligation. Since Agnew was no longer in a position to award contracts, the pace of the payments diminished, though Matz did make one to him for $2500 in return for a federal contract awarded in 1971 to a subsidiary of Matz, Childs. Then, in the spring of 1972, Matz was contacted by The Close Associate, who pressed hard for a $10,000 contribution. Matz complained to Agnew himself.

"Say you gave at the office," the Vice President told him.

Arnold Weiner took his leave of the U.S. attorney. It was already early evening, and the pleasantly warm early summer day still had some sun left to it. At their home in northwest Baltimore, George and Nancy Beall decided to take advantage of the weather and sit on the porch for a chat. For the first time in a long time, the prosecutor treated himself to a before-dinner drink. As he sipped his Bloody Mary, Beall told his wife about Weiner's disclosures. Nancy Beall reacted with the incredulity of one who knew the public Spiro Agnew.

Lester Matz, she said firmly, was a liar.

CHAPTER 5

ALLY IN WASHINGTON

On May 25, when Elliot L. Richardson took over from Richard Kleindienst as Attorney General of the United States, he had no real idea what his subordinates in Baltimore were up to, and his mind was otherwise occupied. He inherited a deeply demoralized Department of Justice. Kleindienst had stepped down amid the mushrooming Watergate scandal with only the barest hint to Richardson about the Baltimore County investigation. Although Watergate had not implicated Kleindienst directly, it was tainting many of his associates and particularly the man he had succeeded and under whom he had served through the first Nixon administration—John N. Mitchell. And Kleindienst, ever the loyal soldier, had suffered a final indignity on April 30 when President Nixon rewarded his service by including the announcement of his resignation with the forced departures of White House aides H. R. Haldeman, John D. Ehrlichman, and John W. Dean III.

Richardson took over with a dual mission. The first he enunciated publicly—to restore credibility in the administration of justice. The second he did not have to enunciate, because it was obvious for a man of his experience and political ambition—to maintain and if possible enhance his personal integrity and credibility. An extremely proud and conscientious public figure, Richardson had endured since 1969 in one subcabinet and two cabinet posts (under secretary of State, secretary of Health, Education, and Welfare, and secretary of Defense) not only to serve the nation but to preserve his reputation as an independent voice.

Richardson had some definite ideas about the face his new department should show to the American people. "To a large extent," he said, "their respect for government is affected by the fairness and integrity of the law-enforcement process. I think there is an opportunity to restore confidence [by] finding ways in which the law-enforcement process can be made to be, and perceived to be, scrupulous in the ways in which it carries out its job."

In his effort to restore public confidence in the department, Richardson brought with him three young men who had served with him before. They were labeled by one newsman "Richardson's Mafia"—an apt description to the career bureaucrats at Justice. J. T. Smith, executive assistant to Richardson; Jonathan Moore, associate attorney general; and Richard G. Darman, special assistant to the attorney general, constituted Richardson's brainstorming team on all major issues that came before him. In all their deliberations, the three aides were motivated by the same dual objective that Richardson himself sought—to restore the integrity of the department and, bluntly, to protect the new attorney general politically in the process.

Of the three Richardson mafiosi, J. T. Smith, a stocky, stolid, thirty-year-old Washington lawyer given to conservative pin-stripe suits and clipped sentences, was the closest in terms of daily access to the attorney general. He occupied a small office just off Richardson's own and in effect held the key to his boss's door. He maintained Richardson's schedule and controlled his time in and out of the office; if you wanted to see Elliot Richardson, you saw J. T. Smith first. Smith also had other jobs, including editing speeches, but primarily he was the gatekeeper and confidant.

The second man in the triumvirate, Moore, was an intense, dynamic, yet personally gentle man of forty-one, also stocky, with a shock of brown hair that perpetually leaped over his temple and gave him a boyish look. Originally a foreign-policy scholar on the staff of Nelson Rockefeller, Moore played a brief but important role in the 1967–68 presidential aspirations of George Romney. When Romney was stumbling in his inability to cope with the critical issue of Vietnam, Moore helped him arrive at his eventual proposals for winding down the war by turning more responsibility over to the South Vietnamese. Romney and Moore called their plan "de-Americanization," and it got nowhere. A year later, the man who drove Romney out of the New Hampshire primary, Richard M. Nixon, trotted out a very similar approach with a better label on it—"Vietnamization." By that time, though, the name Romney had become a laugh word in the American vocabulary, like Brooklyn and, yes, Spiro T. Agnew. After Romney's collapse, Moore signed on with the equally doomed Rockefeller campaign, then joined Richardson at the State Department at the outset of the Nixon administration. After that, their fortunes were wed. Moore moved with Richardson to HEW, to the Pentagon, and finally to Justice, where he served as personal troubleshooter and political adviser.

The youngest of the trio, thirty-year-old Dick Darman, was doing public-policy analysis for HEW on a consulting basis from the Harvard Center for Educational Policy Research when he was tapped by Richardson to be a deputy assistant secretary, managing Richardson's staff. A *cum laude* graduate of Harvard College who later received a master's degree from the Harvard Business School, Darman became special assistant to Richardson in all three of his cabinet posts. He was responsible for coordination of all top-level policy planning, management, and analysis going to Richardson, and in times of crisis was the third voice and opinion fed into Richardson's decision-making apparatus.

The new team at Justice had barely assembled in the last days of May when Richardson was asked to receive a visitor from nearby Maryland. George Beall was only one of the ninety-four U.S. attorneys in the department, and when he simply showed up at Richardson's office, asking how to get to see the new attorney general, J. T. Smith wasn't sure what to do. "What's the normal procedure?" he asked a secretary. "Does a U.S. attorney just wander in and see the attorney general?" The secretary told Smith that it was just not done. Beall was turned away, but before he left he got an appointment to discuss an important matter that, he said, Kleindienst would have talked to Richardson about.

When Kleindienst was about to step down, Beall had asked him whether he ought to alert his successor to the Maryland kickback investigation. Kleindienst said that he should and also promised that he would mention it to Richardson. The fact was, though, that Kleindienst had only told Richardson there was an investigation going on in Baltimore that he ought to discuss with Beall.

By the time Beall finally did see the attorney general, on June 12, there had been a significant development. William Fornoff's pleading guilty on June 4, which obviously triggered Matz and Jerome Wolff to say they were ready to involve Agnew, gave Beall something to make Richardson take notice. And so Beall decided to tell Richardson that much, at least. He could not go too hard with the story, because Matz and Wolff were still balking at signing the letters of negotiation that would clear the way to getting corroborating testimony against Agnew. And so he told Richardson at first essentially only what he had been telling Kleindienst through the late spring—that the prime target of the kickback investigation was Dale Anderson and that there was yet no hard evidence that Agnew was involved.

Through most of Beall's recitation about his Baltimore County investigation, the attorney general seemed preoccupied but cordial, sitting at his desk with his feet up, chair back, drawing on a pipe, taking notes occasionally. When Beall told him that within recent weeks his team was starting to get second-hand information that indicated the Vice President might be involved, Richardson took more notes.

As Beall talked more about Agnew, Richardson lit up a huge cigar that lasted him the rest of the meeting. Richardson asked to be kept posted, and Beall promised to do so.

According to Richardson's aides, the attorney general didn't say much about what Beall had told him. He asked Kleindienst about Agnew's interest in the Baltimore investigation, and Kleindienst said he just hadn't had a chance to mention it—an indication of how lightly Kleindienst took the possibility of Agnew's involvement, or of how little interest he had in having it pursued.

In Baltimore, however, the prosecutors were now taking the possibility most seriously and were pursuing it with vigor. When Kaplan and Weiner finally came in on June 21 and laid out Matz's whole grisly case against Agnew, the scope and venality of it itself dictated a decision: they must tell Washington what they had.

Attorney General Richardson already was hearing from other sources that Beall and his team were hard at work. One day he received a call from J. Fred Buzhardt, Jr., President Nixon's chief troubleshooting lawyer, relaying a complaint about the tactics being used by members of Beall's staff in connection with allegations involving Agnew. Richardson told Buzhardt that if anyone had any complaints about the conduct of anyone in the Department of Justice, he should make them to Richardson personally; otherwise he would ignore them.

During the week of June 18, Beall phoned Richardson's office with an urgent request for a meeting for himself and his three assistants. After at least two postponements, the team was scheduled for Tuesday, July 3. This was to be the first time that Skolnik, Baker, and Liebman would meet the attorney general. Skolnik, impressed, arrived at Beall's office at about nine o'clock that morning in a new blue suit. He had just bought two suits and was saving one for his wedding on July 14. But no sooner had he entered Beall's office than his boss told him the meeting with Richardson was off. The attorney general's secretary had called to say Richardson was too busy. The three assistants, primed for the big audience with Richardson, were outraged.

"God damn it," Skolnik said to Beall. "Call the secretary up and tell her that we must see the attorney general today. It's a matter of great urgency to the United States."

"Do you really think it's quite that urgent?" Beall asked.

"Yes," Skolnik said emphatically.

So Beall picked up the phone and called back Richardson's secretary.

"I must see the attorney general today," he told her. This time he managed to convey the urgency of the matter, but without mentioning the subject and certainly not the name of Vice President Agnew. Baker, Liebman, and Skolnik stood anxiously as Beall listened for the secretary's response. Finally he hung up and said, "She's going to call me back." In a few minutes Beall's phone rang again.

"Yes, hello. . . . We're on our way." He put down the phone.

The four men rushed downstairs and headed for Washington.

There was more to their urgency than simple eagerness to let their superior know what a big catch they had made. The Baltimoreans feared that he might find out about it from another source.

Richardson was busy. For forty-five tense minutes the Baltimoreans cooled their heels. At around noon they were told the attorney general would see them. They were admitted to the long conference room that adjoins Richardson's office, and they were impressed. To these men who toiled in the colorless federal bureaucracy in Baltimore, where everything was low-cost government-issue, the rich grained furniture and other appointments were another world.

Beall proceeded with rather lengthy introductions of his young aides and the retelling of the general Maryland investigation. Skolnik, Baker, and Liebman grew restless, concerned that they were unduly imposing on the attorney general. But Beall eventually arrived at the part of the story where, as, they all knew, he was going to say the name Agnew. Just then, Richardson's secretary came in and handed him a note. Richardson looked at it, went into his private office, and closed the door.

"Get to it, George," one of the aides said as soon as he was gone. "He's going to throw us out of here."

"I'm right there," Beall said. "I was just about to mention it."

Behind the closed door Richardson was hearing something that by itself was cause enough for apoplexy—and this was even before he heard Beall's revelations. Alexander Haig, the President's new chief of staff, was on the phone telling him that the President was livid over a story that morning in the *Los Angeles Times*. Archibald Cox, the special Watergate prosecutor, had started a preliminary inquiry into the President's real-estate transactions, the story said, centering on the $1.5 million paid for his home in San Clemente.

There was good reason for Nixon to be concerned. The story was published at what was already perhaps the most trying time for him in the Senate Watergate hearings, Haig told the attorney general. Nixon always labored under a persecution complex, and that complex was now working overtime. Tell Richardson to find out exactly what Cox is up to, the President had instructed Haig. Richardson said he would do so, and then he headed back into the conference room.

Richardson was now understandably distracted; when Beall resumed, he doodled on an ever-present pad. Beall at last mentioned the incriminating testimony against Agnew. Richardson, pipe in mouth, a look of deep consternation on his face, stopped doodling and feverishly started taking notes. Baker took over and filled in chapter and verse.

Richardson took it all in, grimly. Compared to this, Nixon's complaint about Cox was a mere temper tantrum. Carefully, he went over all the points that had been raised, asking questions, encouraging his visitors to discuss what collectively should be done next. But whenever they began to get into the matter, there would be another White House phone call.

Richardson, getting up and striding out to mollify the White House, then returning to hear more about a development that might not only rock the administration but throw the Republic into political crisis, was being batted back and forth by events each more bizarre than the one before. What finally tore it for him was yet another call from Haig, during which Nixon himself broke in. He wanted, he told Richardson in no uncertain terms, a flat public denial from Cox that any San Clemente investigation was under way, and he wanted it at once.

When Richardson returned to the conference room, he told the Baltimoreans he owed them some explanation as to why he kept running out on them. "The President's a little upset about Mr. Cox today." To that bit of inside intelligence the prosecutors reacted coolly, as if they heard things like that every day. One of them gave Richardson a kind of knowing smile that said, "Yes, I'm sure the President can be a pain sometimes."

Richardson, for his part, seemed outwardly at least to take the interruptions and the irritations in stride. He grasped at once the dimensions of what the Baltimoreans were telling him, and he never challenged the authenticity of it.

Methodically, Richardson began to raise the big issues. What would the effect of the Agnew case be on the capacity of the administration to govern? Almost from the start, Richardson was appalled at the possibility that, if Agnew were guilty, fate could result in the ascendance of a felon to the Presidency. He wanted immediately to confront the Vice President with the evidence against him. Agnew would have to deny the charges and offer proof of his innocence, or he would have to resign. Richardson authorized Beall to press forward with the investigation in the most thorough manner.

From the very first, the resignation of Vice President Agnew was seen by the attorney general as the most direct, desirable way to serve the public interest. It was a judgment that was to be the cause of considerable debate and some heat.

There was some discussion about whether it would be constitutionally permissible for the Vice President to appear before a grand jury. The group also talked about Matz's pleas for total immunity, and Richardson said only that a grant of total immunity ought to depend on the extent of Matz's cooperation and the strength of his evidence—so a decision should be deferred until a better judgment could be made. He made it

Elliot L. Richardson

clear that he expected such final decisions would be made by Beall, but he told Beall to check with him before making any binding commitments.

It was vital, he stressed, that a case of such magnitude be solid, and that it be proved that Agnew actually had received cash. All those present understood that to confirm this key fact, it would be necessary to conduct a sweeping "net worth" investigation of the Vice President—this meant a check on everything that he and his wife had bought and received during and after the alleged payoff periods. It would have to be what is called a third-party net worth, getting the information from the others in any transaction—shopkeepers, car salesmen, jewelers, even local haberdashers in this case, since Agnew was renowned as a meticulous and impressive dresser—and that, they knew, risked undesirable publicity. But eventually it would have to be done.

Finally, Richardson came to a question that had been on all their minds all along—and his particularly, given Nixon's agitation over the San Clemente story. He turned to one of the prosecutors and, without fanfare, asked simply: "Do you think I ought to tell the President yet?"

That the Attorney General would pose such a question to three young underlings he had never met before both startled and pleased them. Asking the question set a tone of shared concern and responsibility and brought the Baltimoreans quickly into Richardson's camp.

On the question itself, the prosecutors were not anxious to have Nixon told because they were concerned that, in the words of one of Richardson's men, "things told the President might get back to the Vice President. If you have two business partners, you don't tell one that the other is under investigation. And telling the President was telling Haig and Buzhardt. We kept quiet because we were terribly afraid." The prosecutors, also cool to Richardson's notion of confronting Agnew with the evidence, did not want Agnew to start building a defense after the fact, based on any inside knowledge of what the government knew.

Richardson himself weighed the matter heavily, both then and later. The matter was, indisputably, of intense national importance, and it would be most embarrassing if the President were to learn about it from another source, including the press. At the same time, the President had plenty of trouble with Watergate; Agnew might be exonerated after all, and there was no reason to worry Nixon needlessly. So he agreed to sit on the story for the time being.

In making this decision, Richardson got off to a good start with the three assistant U.S. attorneys. They had gone to the meeting with general trepidation, but they were greatly encouraged by his open discussion of a key matter of high administrative policy. Indeed, they were impressed with Richardson in every way, and any thoughts that he was going to snatch up their gem and quickly pawn it to improve his own position—always uncertain—within the uptight administration were dispelled. They had feared they might encounter an obstructionist, and they had found instead an impressive ally.

Richardson, for his part, came out of the meeting shaken. He called in J. T. Smith and told him what he had heard, "by way of reassuring myself that there really wasn't anything I could or should do." That night, when he went to his home overlooking the Potomac in McLean, Virginia, he told his wife, Anne, that "a bad scene was developing, and that it involved the Vice President. I expressed some worries about the fact that I might be perceived to have some personal interest or animus" in seeing Agnew go—since Richardson as well as the Vice President was being mentioned as a possible Republican presidential candidate. "It was a deeply disturbing picture," Richardson said later. "I felt sick, almost. It was as bleak a day as I'd ever had."

CHAPTER 6

THE RING CLOSES

The Baltimoreans, with a mandate to build an airtight case against the Vice President, needed solid documentation. Beyond their wildest expectations, they began to get it at the beginning of July, when Weiner presented the letter of negotiation signed by Jerry Wolff and told the outline of Wolff's story. On July 10, Wolff himself provided the incriminating details:

In April 1966, Wolff was approached by The Close Associate of Baltimore County Executive Agnew. The Close Associate asked Wolff for money in return for county contracts that Agnew had arranged for him to receive. Wolff paid The Close Associate $1250 in cash, another payment of indeterminate amount to another Agnew associate for "legal fees," and one or two other payments.

Later in the same year, when Agnew ran for governor, Wolff gave him a cash contribution of $1000 and also worked in the campaign. If he were elected, Agnew suggested, Wolff might be made chairman-director of the state roads commission. Governor Agnew made good on the promise and Wolff took office on March 1, 1967. One of his chief tasks was to monitor every consulting engineering and construction contract in the state. For all practical purposes he controlled the selection of engineers and architects on every roads commission contract, subject only to Agnew's approval.

Shortly afterward, Agnew's old friend Bud Hammerman approached Wolff. Agnew had instructed him to ask Wolff to join in an arrangement whereby Wolff would notify Hammerman which engineering firms were in line for state contracts, so that Hammerman could contact them for cash payoffs.

For the next eighteen to twenty months, Wolff told Hammerman which engineers were in line for state contracts, and Hammerman kept him informed of which engineers were paying off. In time, the contracting community came to know that Hammerman was the man to see. The engineers were expected to make "political contributions," almost always in cash, and even when there was no campaign to contribute to. Wolff told Hammerman the kickbacks should average 3 to 5 per cent of the contract, but Hammerman took any reasonable amount—sometimes at time of contract award, sometimes as contract payments were made by the state, sometimes in a lump sum, sometimes in installments. When Hammerman got the name of an engineer with a new contract, he would call, "congratulate" him, and arrange for a meeting at which the payoff was made. Hammerman would keep his 25 per cent, give Wolff his 25 per cent, and put Agnew's 50 per cent in a safe-deposit box.

At first Wolff kept his share at home, then he transferred it to two and later to three safe-deposit boxes. He spent most of the money on ordinary personal expenses over the next four years, but he used a small portion of it for kickbacks to other public officials in return for contracts given to two consulting firms in which he retained an interest.

Wolff was a highly qualified engineer, and so it did not seem out of the ordinary that he would make recommendations to the governor on who should do government work, and that Agnew generally would concur in his selections. As a basic premise, Wolff insisted that the firm chosen be competent to do the job, and Agnew and Hammerman on occasion would suggest to Wolff that a particular company ought to receive special consideration. Sometimes Wolff was asked to "recommend" a firm that was not kicking in—in order to create a pattern of general fairness. But Wolff was so clearly the czar in making contract awards that some of the engineers and architects who were not kicking in took to wearing buttons that said, "Who's Afraid of Jerry Wolff?"

Sometime after Agnew's election as Vice President in November 1968, but before his inauguration, Agnew asked Wolff to draw up a list of the contracts awarded during his term as governor to Green Associates, Inc., a Maryland engineering company. Wolff discussed the list with the firm's president, Allen Green, revised it somewhat, and turned it over to Agnew. The clear inference to be drawn from this exercise was that Green had been paying off and Agnew planned to use the list to persuade him to continue.

The details of Wolff's story were damaging enough. But what made his willingness to cooperate with the government even more important was the supporting material he brought with him. He was, in the description of one of the prosecutors, "a pack rat, a guy whose nature is just to keep a lot of documents . . . who had kept an incredible amount of paper contemporaneous with events and had destroyed none of it." He had, the prosecutors found out to their joy, a little book for almost every month of every one of the last ten years, with only a few gaps—none of them in the years 1966–68, when Agnew was governor.

Wolff was able to produce the list he prepared of Green's business with Agnew and other documents that, in one of the prosecutor's words, "screamed authenticity because of the way they were." He also had lists prepared in the summer of 1968, in advance of Agnew's campaign for the Vice Presidency, of all the engineers whom he understood to be paying Agnew, on the assumption Agnew would want to have them to raise campaign funds. He even had a code of pluses and circles by which he marked those who were paying through Hammerman and those who were paying directly to Agnew.

All this incriminating information clearly called for another meeting with Richardson. And so did one other development. On the morning of July 9, Beall had gotten another routine phone call from Judah Best, and he had had to tell him that things were indeed happening. He suggested that Best phone for an appointment when he returned from his trip to Florida.

But Skolnik thought that meeting, or even talking to Agnew's lawyer, was a bad idea. The case against his client had become too strong to maintain any casual relationship with Best. So when Best phoned again, Beall told him that on reflection it seemed to him inappropriate to talk any more. If the need arose for the U.S. attorney's office to get back in touch with Best, Beall said, they certainly would do so. "I understand," Best replied, simply. "Thank you." And he hung up.

From all this, it was clear that the time had come to give the attorney general another full-blown briefing. In the late afternoon of July 11, the team met with Richardson, this time in his small inner office. There sat somebody who Skolnik, Baker, and Liebman had never laid eyes on before. It was a few minutes into the discussion before Richardson in his casual way said: "Oh, by the way, this is J. T. Smith"—his executive assistant and member in good standing of his inner circle.

The attorney general had an agenda this time. The items he wanted to talk about were:

1. When, if ever, and under what conditions should Agnew be confronted with the allegations against him and given an opportunity to answer questions under oath?

2. Should the attorney general advise the President that the investigation was going on?

3. Which potential witnesses in the investigation should be given complete immunity from prosecution?

4. Did the investigation come under the jurisdiction of special prosecutor Archibald Cox?

The first three questions gave the Baltimoreans no pause. At the very thought of Cox being brought in, though, Beall and company saw wings sprouting on their cherished Agnew investigation. But before getting to

Richardson's own agenda, Beall and Baker briefed him on Matz's personal testimony, which they had just taken. Richardson wanted to make certain that the connection could be made between Matz's payments and the contracts he received; the Baltimoreans assured him that Matz had so testified.

Richardson then launched into a long discussion of what could be expected from Agnew in defense. Baker listened for a long time, waiting for a chance to break in, while the attorney general played devil's advocate. Finally, Baker availed himself of a lull and told Richardson about the Agnew-Wolff-Hammerman arrangement and about Wolff's documentation supporting his story. That was all Richardson needed to hear. He realized that they now had evidence on which the Vice President could be indicted.

But once again Richardson raised the idea of going to Agnew and telling him what they had, in the hope that he would resign. To Skolnik, the old pro at thirty-two whose foremost interest was in preserving the case, Richardson's approach was insane.

Yes, Skolnik said, it was certainly true that for several reasons—certainly before any indictments were offered to the grand jury—the Justice Department would want to give the Vice President an opportunity to respond. But in giving him this opportunity you certainly didn't want to give him all your evidence. For one thing, it would give a suspect the opportunity to manufacture and tailor evidence and documents to the evidence you had against him. So with that in mind, you gave him only the general nature of the charges. Second, there was the matter of equal justice, of even-handed treatment for all citizens under investigation by their government. A Vice President ought to be treated exactly the same way as anyone else.

In any event, Skolnik went on, it was premature to confront the Vice President now. Before confronting Agnew, you had to track down all the other individuals whose names had been provided in Wolff's material and build the full, airtight case.

Richardson took over now. He stressed that although an early resignation of Vice President Agnew was in the best interests of the country, he agreed that it still would be necessary to proceed with the investigation and possible prosecution. It was of the utmost importance that the case be handled in such a way that the public was satisfied that whatever the final disposition, justice had been done. As before, the attorney general expressed concern that the President did not know of it.

By this time, none of the four Baltimoreans was opposed any longer to having Richardson tell the President. First of all, they were convinced Nixon already knew about the case. And because they had already developed a strong feeling of support for Richardson, they "didn't want him to get his ass in a sling with the White House," as one of them put it later. At the same time, though, they didn't want the President told in any great detail. They feared that he might say: "That's very interesting. Give me a ninety-page memo on it." Also, they continued to fear that the story would be leaked to Agnew or the press.

It was the impression of the Baltimore team that Richardson started out in this meeting favoring the idea of telling Nixon almost at once, and that he then backed off in the face of these arguments. At any rate, he ended by assuring his visitors that in any report to the President he would exercise discretion. Tentatively at least, he said, he would not advise the President until it was time to inform Agnew.

Richardson also told the Baltimoreans that the fact he was being mentioned publicly as a possible Republican nominee for President in 1976 might create a "problem of appearances"—the whole investigation might be seen as a personal effort by him to knock off the man then regarded as the frontrunner.

One of the Beall team noted that the press had been making pointed inquiries about Agnew in Baltimore. The attorney general made clear that they would have to do whatever was necessary to keep the story out of the press.

Once again the Baltimoreans returned home with the firm support and encouragement of the attorney general, and with instructions to press on to strengthen the case. There were many bases to touch: all those names in the Wolff "library," the engineers like Allen Green he said had participated in the kickback scheme; and, above all, Hammerman.

It so happened that during this intensive period of nailing down the case, Skolnik had on his schedule the only conceivable event that for a criminal prosecutor could take precedence: he was getting married. The wedding was three days after the meeting with Richardson, and Skolnik and his bride would be off on their honeymoon for a week. So Skolnik planned with his colleagues the procedures to be followed in his absence in contacting the key witnesses and potential defendants. The usual approach was to call the individual, ask him if he had a lawyer "knowledgeable about federal criminal practices," and tell him to call the U.S. attorney's office. Then, when the lawyer called, he would be asked to come in, whereupon he would be given "The Speech." Skolnik, who had perfected "The Speech," held a seminar on how to bring it off to best effect. It went something like this: "Your guy is in a lot of trouble. We're investigating the Vice President, and your client's in it. He's going to get indicted unless you cooperate. If you want to cooperate, and you tell us you're interested in pursuing negotiations [on a plea] we'll give you a form letter. We want you to talk to your client and tell him he's got to make a decision, or else he'll go to prison."

Calls started going out on July 12, and two of the earliest were to Allen Green and Bud Hammerman. Green retained one of Washington's most prestigious law firms—Williams, Connolly & Califano; Hammerman turned to Sachs, Greenebaum & Tayler of Washington, seeking the talents of Sidney Sachs. At Williams, Connolly & Califano, Green was assigned to one of the firm's young lawyers, Brendan Sullivan, instead of a principal partner—Edward Bennett Williams, Paul Connolly, or Joseph A. Califano, Jr.—since from what he had said on the phone, there seemed no need for him to have one of the heavies. He had mentioned something about contracts in Maryland—"It wasn't much of a problem," was the impression Califano received at the time. Sullivan, considered one of the firm's brightest prospects, went off to confer with Green.

A night or two afterward, the phone rang at the Califano residence. It was Sullivan, agitated. He had to talk to Califano, but not over the phone. The two arranged a meeting for late the next afternoon on Califano's sailboat.

Sullivan told Califano that Green admitted paying off Agnew. Califano was stunned. Whatever Califano might have thought of Agnew, he was not cheered to learn that the political system had taken another punch to the solar plexus. Califano kept the news to himself.

Within the week, both Sidney Sachs and Brendan Sullivan had paid visits to Baltimore for preliminary talks with the prosecutors. There was a steady traffic to the courthouse as lawyers for panicked contractors hastened to Beall's office.

On the day Skolnik returned from his honeymoon, July 23, Sullivan presented the details of Green's involvement with Agnew—about the $50,000 in cash payoffs while Agnew was governor and Vice President—and Green himself came in shortly afterward. But Hammerman held out. From Green, the prosecutors were able to identify others who had kicked in, and to contact them and deliver "The Speech" to their lawyers. But in addition to corroborating Wolff's account, Green also told an entirely new and incriminating story about his personal dealings with Agnew.

Green first knew Agnew in mid-1963, when Agnew was Baltimore

County executive. When he ran for governor in 1966, Green gave him between $6000 and $10,000 for his campaign, and after his inauguration, Green met him several times in the governor's offices in Baltimore and Annapolis. At one of those meetings, Agnew began to complain about the heavy financial costs of being governor. As leader of the Maryland Republican Party, he said, he needed money for his own political organization as well as funds to help Republican candidates around the state. Not only that, but he had to adopt and maintain a lifestyle far beyond his means. As county executive, he had served at a financial sacrifice, given the low salary of $22,500. The governor's newly raised salary of $25,000 was only the barest improvement. Throughout Agnew's tenure, this theme recurred in his conversations with Green.

As one who had been around the state capitol for some time, Green did not need the message spelled out. He told Agnew his own firm had done well on public contracts and probably would continue to do so; there was no reason why he couldn't help with periodic cash payments. Agnew said he would appreciate such assistance very much.

In the past Green had paid public officials up to an average of 1 percent of the fees he received on public engineering contracts. On this basis, he calculated that he could make six payments a year to Agnew in amounts of $2000, $2500, or $3000 each, depending on how much cash he had at the time—always cash, to prevent anyone tracing the payoffs on the company books. Six times a year he would ask for an appointment with the governor to deliver the money.

The two men usually discussed state business at such meetings, and Green nearly always would take the opportunity to bring up the subject of special interest to him—state road contracts. He would tell Governor Agnew which road and bridge contracts his company was interested in; sometimes Agnew would promise him a contract, sometimes tell him it had been committed.

In each of the two years Agnew was governor, 1967 and 1968, Green paid him $11,000. In the same period, his firm received about ten contracts from the state roads commission with fees of between $3 and $4 million.

Only once during the two years that Agnew was governor did he ever expressly mention any connection between the payments Green made and the state work he received. That occasion came just before Agnew's inauguration as Vice President, when Green made a payoff in Agnew's Baltimore office. Agnew, referring to the list, noted that Green's firm had received a lot of work from the state roads commission: he was glad matters had worked out that way, Agnew said. Then came the poverty plea again. During the two years in the governor's mansion, he still hadn't been able to improve his finances and although his salary as Vice President ($43,000 plus $10,000 for expenses, raised to $62,500 in 1970) would be much higher than his salary as governor, the social and other demands of lofty national office would put even greater pressure on his personal funds. So he hoped Green could continue the help he had been giving him, and he in turn hoped he could help Green get federal contracts. Green told the Vice President-elect he was willing to continue the payments, but he wasn't certain he could produce such large amounts as he had in 1967 and 1968.

Thus it was that Green continued to pay Agnew off personally, delivering $2000 three or four times a year either to the Office of the Vice President in the Old Executive Office Building, or to Agnew's apartment in the Sheraton Park Hotel. As in the past, cash was always in a plain envelope, and Green and Agnew were alone when it was handed over.

The first time he did it, Green felt particularly uncomfortable. Making a payoff in the very office of the second-ranking official in the government of the United States, with the Seal of the Vice President on the wall behind Agnew's desk, was bad enough; but Green was concerned that his conversation with the Vice President might be overheard or even taped. So when he handed over the envelope he told Agnew the money was part of an unfulfilled commitment in "political contributions." As he said it, he raised his eyes to the ceiling, conveying to Agnew the reason he was saying something the Vice President knew was not so.

The last payment Green made was during the Christmas season in 1972, after the U.S. attorney's office in Baltimore had begun looking into corruption in Baltimore County. All told, in addition to the $22,000 Green paid Agnew when he was governor, in 1969 and 1970 he paid the Vice President $8000 a year—four payments of $2000 each; and in 1971 and 1972, $6000 a year—three payments of $2000 each. That brought the total Agnew received from Green over the six years to $50,000.

The Green story was explosive in its detail, and in the portrait it painted of Agnew: a blatantly greedy public official who somehow justified his demands for graft on the social and political obligations placed on him as he climbed the political ladder.

On July 27, the Baltimoreans went for a third time to see Richardson. In a meeting lasting about two and a half hours in the attorney general's office, Skolnik told Richardson that press discovery of the investigation had to be imminent, since the inquiry now involved more and more principals and their lawyers. It was time, he said, to take formal action against Agnew.

Richardson wanted to be absolutely sure there was a federal criminal case to be made against Agnew, in light of the fact that most of the evidence the team had gathered concerned payoffs when he had been governor of Maryland, not Vice President. The Baltimoreans cited applicable federal statutes concerning tax evasion, conspiracy, and extortion. Richardson also asked them if they had researched whether a Vice President could be indicted, and they told him they were satisfied he could.

Richardson told his visitors he had decided it was time to inform the President. He asked, "Do any of you have any moral doubt as to Agnew's guilt?" None of them did.

It was also decided that Beall's team would prepare a formal letter to Agnew advising him in general terms that he was under investigation. Its main purpose was to elicit cooperation without giving too much information away, and specifically to request Agnew's financial records. This step was routine but in this case would be a milestone. Once the Vice President was formally notified he was under criminal investigation, the burden of proof was on the Department of Justice, and the reputation of a national leader was at stake.

Soon thereafter, Richardson went over to the White House to talk about getting an appointment with the President. Richardson told General Haig in sketchy outline the reason for his request, and Haig agreed to arrange an appointment. Agnew had already talked to Haig and the President about his troubles, Richardson learned, and had also asserted his complete innocence. "What I told Haig," Richardson said later, "put a much more serious light on it than anything Haig had learned up to that point."

One might have thought that by now President Nixon would be burning up the wires to reach his attorney general. But there was no word from the White House. Richardson authorized release of the letter to Agnew. As one who had served Nixon for a long time in various positions, he knew that one did not see the President the moment one asked. He knew too that when you told the full story about anything to Bob Haldeman or Al Haig, you were telling it to the President. You had done your duty.

On Tuesday, July 31, the letter of notification to Agnew was ready. Beall phoned Best in Washington and asked him to come to his Baltimore office the next day. Best agreed. Enough was requested in the letter—personal bank records and tax returns—to suck Agnew in; when he complied, the prosecutors hoped, they could hit him with a second request for more incriminating material.

At three o'clock in the afternoon of August 1, five days after the attorney general told Haig about the investigation, Best came to Beall's office. There he found the U.S. attorney and his three assistants.

"Jud," Beall said, "I prepared a letter which I wish to hand you."

"I'd be happy to accept it," said Best, taking the letter in its unsealed envelope. "Do you mind if I read it?"

"No," Beall said. "I think you should."

When Best had read the letter he acknowledged that this was very serious business. Beall apologized for requiring him to come all the way to Baltimore, but he had not wanted to trust such an important matter to the mails. Best assured him he had done the right thing, and thanked him. Best said he would be in touch with his client and would have a reply.

With that, Judah Best drove back to Washington to tell Spiro T. Agnew that he was the first Vice President in American history to be formally placed under criminal investigation.

CHAPTER 7

THE DAM BURSTS

When Spiro Agnew received formal notification that he was under investigation for possible conspiracy, extortion, bribery, and tax evasion, he appeared to be looking even at this very late date to the power and influence of the White House to bail him out.

In April, when Agnew had felt the Maryland kickback scandal moving his way, he had not relied primarily on his own legal and political counselor, George White. Instead, he had sought out the Washington lawyer who had been the most notorious political schemer in the first Nixon administration, Chuck Colson. That Colson, with easy entree to the Oval Office, could be privy to such a morsel of inside political news and not pass it on to the President did not have much credibility among those who knew how Colson operated. Sources in the White House acknowledged later that at least four key presidential aides—General Alexander Haig, the new White House chief of staff; Bryce Harlow, special presidential adviser and old Agnew friend; and the two Watergate troubleshooting lawyers, J. Fred Buzhardt, Jr., and Leonard Garment—knew about Agnew's troubles sometime in July. That they would know and the President would not, strained credibility too.

Although Colson, facing possible indictment in Watergate-related affairs, asked his law partner Judah Best to handle the Agnew case, he was not one to keep his nose out of such a delicious bit of high-powered intrigue. As late as July, he was meeting with Best and Agnew in the Vice President's office.

Anyone who knew how Agnew felt about the President would not have been very surprised that he had looked in that direction for assistance. All Vice Presidents, though constitutionally independent, have in a real sense been subject to the pleasure or displeasure of the Presidents under whom they have served, and Agnew certainly was no exception.

Agnew would not do anything he thought would anger the President or his men. "It bothered him," an associate said, "but he was not as reckless as he appeared. He was not as independent as he appeared. I guess it may have been an authority complex, or maybe it was something else, but his priorities were such that he stood in awe of the White House. I could never understand why he should, on certain essential things. I didn't even think it was politically intelligent to defer to them. I told him, 'What's the worst thing they can do? Take your airplane away? Fly commercially. What do you think's going to happen when Haig and those people over there say, "Well, we don't like the way you're running around the country and making speeches. So we're going to take your airplane away." You say, "Fine, I'll fly Eastern." And then you're going to do that, and you know what the White House—Richard Milhous Nixon—is going to do? They're going to give you two airplanes. Because it will look socially embarrassing.' But there was always a vacillation on his part, not wanting to tear it in terms of his standing in awe of the White House and of the President."

In addition, there was one other reason for Agnew to look to the White House for help. If a Vice President could be indicted, then perhaps, in the climate of Watergate and the suspicions of Nixon's culpability, so could a President. Thus it seemed to be in the interest of the White House to support the defense that neither official could be indicted under the Constitution so long as he remained in office.

There were from this point on really two Agnew defenses, one political, the other legal. The political defense was the responsibility of Best, with Colson and his partner David Shapiro in the wings. For the strictly legal, courtroom defense, Agnew looked elsewhere. On Thursday, August 2—the day after Beall gave his letter to Best—Shapiro, a Democrat and veteran of civil liberties and civil rights cases, phoned Jay H. Topkis, a New York lawyer who had championed these same causes with him.

"Would you be interested in representing somebody in a criminal investigation who is near the top in this administration?"

"All the way to the top?" Topkis inquired.

"No, not all the way to the top."

Topkis began to name names, but not the right one. Each time, Shapiro would say, "Higher, higher." Finally, Shapiro gave the New Yorker some help. "Maryland," he hinted.

"Who's from Maryland?" Topkis replied.

When Topkis finally got the picture, he told Shapiro he was interested but would have to bring the matter up with his firm's new-business committee. What made Shapiro's offer concerning Agnew so remarkable was the identity of that firm: Paul, Weiss, Rifkind, Wharton & Garrison, among the most prestigious Democratic legal powerhouses in the country. Partners in the firm included or had included Arthur Goldberg, Ramsey Clark, Theodore C. Sorensen, and Judge Simon Rifkind (who had handled the projected defense in the abortive impeachment proceedings against Associate Justice William O. Douglas in 1970).

The new-business committee agreed that the firm would take the case. Topkis, a liberal Democrat who had voted for George McGovern in 1972 and had an anti-Nixon poster in his office, chose as his associate Martin London, also a liberal Democrat who had helped to represent Jacqueline Kennedy Onassis in her invasion-of-privacy suit against the photographer Ron Galella.

Topkis asked London, "Marty, is there any reason we can't represent the Vice President of the United States?"

"Are we going to be paid?" London inquired.

"Yes."

"Then there is no reason we can't represent the Vice President."

By now Agnew had conferred several times with General Haig, and at last the matter was deemed of sufficient importance to warrant Nixon's personal involvement. On Friday, August 3, Richardson's appointment with the President finally came through. Haig phoned him to say the President would see him on this unprecedented, shattering dilemma— the next Monday! On Saturday, Haig called again to suggest Richardson meet with Buzhardt and Garment on Sunday so that the two White House lawyers could properly brief Nixon in advance of the meeting.

The Sunday meeting, at Richardson's house, marked the first time that anyone at the White House learned in any detail what the case against the Vice President was. In effect the President's lawyers were confronted, as the President himself was to be the next morning, with a *fait accompli.*

Beall's case was so strong that almost at once the consideration was not how the investigation could be derailed, but how Agnew could be compelled to resign. Once the evidence was known at the White House, one aide said later, "The charter [to Richardson] was, 'You do what you have to do.'"

Buzhardt and Garment did express some concern about the origins and quality of the investigation; about the possibility that these young unknowns—especially Skolnik, who had worked for Muskie—might have run wild in their eagerness to bag such a major prize. Richardson assured them that Skolnik was a professional prosecutor with no partisan motivation. What about self-serving witnesses, trying to save their own skins? Richardson noted that no immunity had yet been granted to anybody. What about impeachment of a Vice President? And in particular, was there any distinction between the President and the Vice President as to whether they could be indicted before impeachment? Richardson said he would have a brief prepared on this question. The President's lawyers pressed these and other questions because they wanted to be sure the President had a factual basis on which to make determinations. But so persuasive was the evidence that Garment and Buzhardt both felt that Agnew ought to resign at once.

Garment, in a briefing paper for the President's meeting with Richardson, quoted Richardson as saying, "If half the evidence stands up, this case will be stronger than any kickback case I have ever seen." But Haig deleted this opinion and sent Nixon just the facts as Buzhardt and Garment had gathered them. The memo was on the President's desk Monday morning.

On Sunday night, Richardson did some preparing, too. He had his aide J. T. Smith track down Robert Dixon, the Justice Department's legal counsel, and asked him to get to the office early the next morning to do a crash research job "on the indictability of a sitting Vice President."

All the men in the Justice Department who were privy to what was going on had expected *The Wall Street Journal* to break the Agnew story on Monday morning, August 6, and when it did not, they knew that Monday would be Richardson's last chance to put the situation to Nixon. Before Richardson went to the White House, Beall and Baker reviewed for him the origins, early goals, and present status of the investigation. They had testimony from a "Mr. X" who had refused to make kickbacks, and they predicted there would be two sets of indictments, probably in mid-September. They would be in a position to indict Agnew for violations of federal acts dealing with bribery, conspiracy, and extortion, but did not think they would be ready to indict for tax evasion. The "net-worth investigation" on Agnew was not yet under way, so it could not be proved that he had undeclared income.

Richardson also was armed by now with Dixon's briefing papers on indictability. Among his conclusions were that as head of the executive branch the President could direct his own prosecution prior to removal from office and exercise his pardon power on himself, whereas the Vice President could do neither and hence could be indicted.

The briefing session lasted until ten minutes before Richardson was to see the President at the White House at 10:30, and he rushed straight from it to 1600 Pennsylvania Avenue. In the Oval Office, Haig and Buzhardt were there waiting with Nixon, a President already groggy from the Watergate developments revealing further excesses of greed for political power in his administration. Now he was to hear details of a much more old-fashioned brand of greed. The attorney general proceeded to provide an outline of the case against the Vice President. Nixon listened attentively, somberly. "The President appeared to be ready to believe it," Richardson said later. "His reaction was remarkably objective and deliberate. . . . He was disturbed and concerned with the correctness of any action or anything he did or did not do. At first he thought he ought to have an independent assessment of the evidence from Henry Petersen and me, on the basis of which he could then decide whether or not the situation called for Agnew's resignation. He later concluded that he ought not to try to be fully informed about the state of the evidence, and that his position ought to be more insulated. I was prepared to give him the assessment. Henry, who had been on a long vacation, had only got back the same day. At that point, the interests of the President, the Vice President and myself seemed to converge on the desirability of Henry's making his own review of the investigation." And so it was ordered that Petersen would assess the case and report to Richardson and Nixon.

In the meantime, though, if Agnew could be persuaded to go quickly and quietly, then so much the better for everybody. When Richardson got back to his office at Justice, Haig called and suggested that he go talk to the Vice President. So Richardson in mid-afternoon went over to the

Old Executive Office Building and called on the Vice President. Agnew's new legal team of Best, Topkis, and London was already there. The story was about to break in *The Wall Street Journal,* and they were considering what kind of statement he ought to put out in response.

Richardson had the assignment to try for a quick knockout blow. He informed Agnew that he was there at the request of the President to provide a summary of the investigation in Baltimore. This he proceeded to do in somewhat more detail than is usual because, he said later, there were considerations "transcending the situation that would apply to a person who was not in immediate line of succession to the Presidency itself."

The Vice President's reaction was aggressively defensive. He was a proud man, with a demonstrated capacity for moral indignation, and he gave it full rein now. As Richardson reeled off the allegations, Agnew interrupted. The whole matter, he insisted irately, was a pack of lies. Matz was crazy. True, he had chosen the architects and engineers for state jobs, but that was normal. Agnew, always a man who deftly and mercilessly sought out others' vulnerabilities and attacked as his best defense, adopted the tactic now—against the prosecutors. They lacked objectivity, he charged. If the investigation were being conducted by a more objective team, it would have turned out differently.

Best complained about the prosecutorial tactics used in Baltimore, and he was particularly incensed about the way the prosecutors kept referring to the Vice President as "Agnew." That was disrespectful. He should have been called "Mister Agnew."

Agnew asked whether all the allegations were restricted to him. Richardson said county officials also were involved. There had been some testimony, he said, that kickbacks by architects and engineers were still being paid.

Once again, Agnew thrashed out at the prosecutors. Not only were they not objective; they were arrogant! Agnew wanted the prosecution in the hands of a more experienced professional. Like Petersen. But Richardson defended Beall on all counts.

Then Agnew, attempting desperately to punch holes in the government's case, started in on Allen Green. Green was constantly seeking his help, and he had a thick file of requests from Green he had turned down. As for Lester Matz, he had seen him only four times in the five years he had been Vice-President.

Now came the old poverty pitch. As for his own finances, he was a man of very modest means, with the bulk of his assets tied up in the house he had just bought. The letter handed to him on August 1 asking for his financial records by August 7 had been delivered without warning, he complained. He was shocked by the prosecutors' tone of contempt toward him, and it left him with no confidence in their investigation.

The lawyers tried to pry more facts loose. London asked for a chance to make a detailed response to the allegations but said he would need a more specific summary, and complained that the attorney general was being particularly stingy with information.

But Richardson was noncommittal. Once Petersen had completed his review of the entire case, he said, the Justice Department would be in touch with Agnew's lawyers as to what the next step should be.

It so happened that at this juncture Henry Petersen knew absolutely nothing about what was going on, not even that there was an Agnew investigation. He had been off on vacation. Now, back at Justice, Richardson called him. "Henry, am I glad to see you! But are you going to be sorry you're here! Sit down, I've got something to tell you." And then the attorney general gave him the whole Agnew story and asked him to conduct a complete review of the investigation, at the request of both the President and the Vice President.

Petersen was not eager to get involved. He asked Richardson to consider two things. Did the attorney general really want him to continue as head of Justice's criminal division, in view of the widespread criticism he had received of his handling of the Watergate investigation? If so, he went on, should a man in his situation, already under fire, get involved in what promised to be an extremely controversial case? Richardson answered "yes."

Richardson also brought one other principal into the matter. He briefed his still-to-be confirmed deputy, William D. Ruckelshaus, and asked him to join the key meetings.

After Richardson left Agnew's office, Agnew and his lawyers continued to work on a statement for the press. At eleven o'clock, Agnew's press secretary, J. Marsh Thomson, finally phoned it to *The Washington Post,* the wire services, the television networks, and—lastly—*The Wall Street Journal.* By then, the *Journal* story was already being reported by the wire services, with the *Post* story not far behind.

The *Journal* story, by Jerry Landauer, began:

Vice President Spiro T. Agnew was formally notified by the Justice Department last week that he is a target of a far-ranging criminal investigation by the U.S. attorney's office in Baltimore.

The allegations against him include bribery, extortion and tax fraud.

The investigation is being carried on in strictest secrecy. On receiving the Justice Department notice, the Vice President sought a White House audience, presumably to inform President Nixon. . . .

Agnew's reply was categorical and remarkably terse:

"I have been informed that I am under investigation for possible violations of the criminal statutes. I will make no further comment until the investigation has been completed, other than to say that I am innocent of any wrongdoing, that I have confidence in the criminal justice system of the United States, and that I am equally confident my innocence will be affirmed."

In Baltimore after midnight, when the prosecutors had all gone to bed, their phones began to ring; reporters from everywhere, scrambling to catch up on the story, pleaded, threatened, and cajoled for more details. But the prosecutors had nothing to say.

By the next morning, Tuesday, August 7, the whole nation and the world knew: Spiro T. Agnew, Vice President of the United States, voice of Middle America, straight-shooting Mr. Candor, Mr. Integrity of the Republican Party and American conservatism, was accused of being a crook and a fraud.

At the Justice Department, Richardson was being pressed by the White House for further assurances that the case was airtight, and, if so, for more of it to be laid out to Agnew in the hope he would resign. At 8:30 that morning, Richardson met with Beall, Petersen, Ruckelshaus, and Smith. He wanted to know, once again, how good the government's case was; bluntly, what were the probabilities of conviction? And second, did it make sense to give Agnew and his lawyers more details than one normally might, in order to speed resolution of a national crisis? He asked Beall to go over the whole case with Petersen and Ruckelshaus so that the two newcomers could render independent judgments on what course to take. Beall agreed, but he argued that it would be highly undesirable to make greater disclosure to Agnew.

Again, the question arose—how much more should the President be told? Nixon might want a full memo on the prosecution of the case, and the group at Justice felt he was entitled to it if he were to exercise his responsibility on the disposition of the matter. But the Baltimoreans, still operating on the premise that Agnew would come to trial and still suspicious that information going to the President might be leaked to Agnew, firmly opposed giving Nixon a full report.

While this inner-circle debate was going on, Agnew's startled friends were beginning to come out of the first shock. They proceeded to examine their man's response and they found it wanting. Vic Gold and Peter Malatesta, who had talked late Monday night by phone, agreed that Agnew had to say more. Gold, who had been Agnew's press secretary and was now a columnist, told Arthur Sohmer, Agnew's gatekeeper, "I think the Vice President is making a very great mistake. His statement is idiotic and I want to see him. I don't care who drew it up, I want to see him." Sohmer checked and told Gold to come over. "I told him," Gold said later, "'You're an innocent man. You can't stand on this. You go right ahead and have a news conference.'" Agnew was noncommittal, and Gold left under the impression there would be no press conference.

At the White House, any thought of Agnew "going public" was distasteful—particularly so because the hunkered-down President was under increasing pressure to speak out on Watergate. If Agnew were to step out on the firing line in his darkest hour of crisis, an invidious comparison would be made. No, Agnew had better keep his mouth shut.

Thus Agnew found himself, as he would more and more in the weeks ahead, caught between pressures from his closest personal advisers to go public and proclaim his innocence, and pressures from the awesome White House to quit or at least play it their cagey way. To Gold and the others who pressed him to speak out, Agnew simply listened and said little. Then, without consulting them again, he asked to see the President late that Tuesday afternoon. He just wanted the President to know that he was innocent, and that he had decided to hold a press conference the next day to say so and to answer questions openly and freely.

The President told Agnew face-to-face that he had complete confidence in him, and the Vice President went back to his own office feeling much better. But within fifteen minutes, General Haig, accompanied by Bryce Harlow, went over to see him with a message. According to a key White House aide speaking later in pure White House gobbledygook, Haig informed Agnew "that if the allegations in respect to him were likely to be sustainable, and if out of those allegations he was likely to be indicted, in his own judgment as a lawyer he ought to consider the timing of his actions to deal with that." Translation: Haig was not there as an executioner; his job was merely to suggest hara-kiri. But Agnew was not buying. He was, he told Haig and Harlow as he had told Nixon, an innocent man beset by enemies.

The next afternoon, August 8, Agnew's press conference was called, with only a few hours' notice, in a studio-auditorium on the fourth floor of the Old Executive Office Building. The television networks decided at once to cover the event live, and by three o'clock more than 200 reporters were there. Agnew came out, tense but in control. In a sense, his whole political career, and his self-image as a righteous man unfairly put upon, had prepared him for this moment.

"Because of defamatory statements that are being leaked to the news media by sources that the news reports refer to as close to the investigation," he began, "I cannot adhere to my original intention to remain silent following my initial statement a few days ago, which asserted my innocence and which indicated I would have nothing further to say until the investigation was completed.

"Under normal circumstances, the traditional safeguard of secrecy under such proceedings would protect the subject. But apparently this protection is not to be extended to the Vice President . . .

"Well, I have no intention to be skewered in this fashion. And since I have no intention to be so skewered, I called this press conference, to label as false and scurrilous and malicious these rumors, these assertions and accusations that are being circulated and to answer your questions regarding them, and any other questions that I might be able to answer concerning the general situation."

One of the first questions asked of him was based on what later proved to be erroneous allegations, that Agnew had received $1000 a week in kickbacks. Did he deny these charges? Agnew knocked it out of the park: "I am denying them outright and I am labeling them, and I think a person in my position at a time like this might be permitted this departure from normal language, as damned lies."

Another question, broader but on the mark: "Mr. Vice President, have you ever received money for your personal use from any person, contractor, doing business with the state of Maryland or the federal government?" Agnew replied: "Absolutely not."

To many television viewers, these categorical answers made the Vice President look like the man who could be counted on to call a spade a spade, and never mince words about it. He added to that impression with other responses: that he had been "thoroughly investigated" before when he had run for governor in 1966 and for Vice President in 1968, and had been exonerated. "I have absolutely nothing to hide in this respect."

In meeting with the President the previous day, Agnew went on, Nixon had expressed his confidence "directly to me." But when he was asked if the possibility that he might resign had come up, Agnew replied: "I'm not going to discuss my conversation with the President. I am sorry."

Herblock's State of the Union (SIMON & SCHUSTER, 1972)

©1973 HERBLOCK

"YOU'RE MY BOY"

Why was all this trouble descending upon him? somebody asked. With the U.S. attorney a Republican, could there be political motivation? Agnew—who of course had been in communication directly or indirectly with Wolff, Matz, and Hammerman—replied unabashedly: "I have no knowledge of who is leaking this information."

One other element in the press conference was worth noting. Although Haig already had suggested that he resign, the Vice President was still pledging undiminished fealty to his leader. Asked why he was having a press conference and Nixon wasn't, Agnew shot back: "The best answer I can give you to that is that President Nixon hasn't received a letter from the United States attorney telling him he's under investigation. . . . And I think the matter of how President Nixon is going to respond to the matters that are being discussed currently regarding him is a matter for his own determination, and I want to repeat I have absolutely total confidence in him . . .

This demonstration of loyalty was not, however, what most intrigued two separate groups of viewers that afternoon. Each was more interested, indeed was almost mesmerized, by the quality and technique of Agnew's press-conference performance.

The Vice President's lawyers, Topkis, London, and Best, gathered at the Washington office of Paul, Weiss, Rifkind, Wharton & Garrison to watch the press conference on television and were delighted at their client's straightforwardness. He would, they all agreed, make one hell of a witness.

Simultaneously, Skolnik, Baker, and Liebman gathered in Liebman's apartment, not far from their Baltimore office. Skolnik, who was looking forward to cross-examining the Vice President of the United States when he was brought to trial sometime in the spring of 1974, studied his quarry like a boxer watching old fight films of an opponent. He and the others were impressed and pleased, because they felt that although Agnew was a worthy adversary, cool and quick, he was giving answers with which they could hang him later.

Though they drew confidence from Agnew's press conference, the prosecutors acknowledged that it was likely to have a great positive effect for Agnew around the country. But, said one of them later, "I don't think we were at all worried about it because we knew what we had. We knew we were going to murder him. . . . I thought he was handling himself very well, that he was an impressive performer, that he would be a tough opponent. But I was also delighted at his willingness to speak out on the merits and answer questions. Because the more questions he answered, the more he would look great in August and terrible in April."

CHAPTER 8

THE CRUELEST MONTH

For Spiro T. Agnew, August was the cruelest month. Helplessly, the nation's second highest constitutional officer stood by as the government and the press sifted through his past, piecing together a picture of a Janus-like figure—one face of honesty toward the public, another of deceit toward those who knew his secret life. Drop by drop, leaked allegations began to erode his public image and standing, until he stood exposed.

The grease under the slipping Agnew was the press. Still high from the heady experience of Watergate, American reporters were zealously determined to report the Agnew story in full and not to be sidetracked by his protestations of innocence. Every day in Washington, Baltimore, and Towson a small army of reporters searched to uncover the secret life of Spiro T. Agnew. It was as if the news media had declared war on his past.

At the same time, Agnew's ultimate security blanket—the White House—began to fray. To a Washington attuned to the near-silence of a high level purge, it was clear that Agnew was fast becoming a nonperson.

Still, in the early part of the month Agnew had some cause for hope. He was not, after all, without weapons. He was, to start, the Vice President of the United States. There were some who believed that the Vice President was immune from criminal investigation. If he could not be indicted, why investigate him?

Agnew could also make common cause with the President, who was himself claiming immunity from the criminal-justice system, while speculation continued about *his* impeachment over the Watergate mess. Surely, a President who stood in danger of impeachment would appreciate the utility of a new-suspect Vice President.

Finally, Agnew had another weapon—his old adversary, the press. He could command from it the headlines and air time he needed to wage the kind of fight Ted Agnew had always fought best—brazening it out. He could rally his constituency, the Middle Americans who believed in him and now distrusted President Nixon, and turn the screws on a Washington already catatonic from scandal.

One aide, in a private memorandum, underlined the view among the staff that Agnew would have to take his case to the people.

"Millions of Americans see you as a symbol of candor and integrity," he concluded. "I am personally convinced that if you continue to hit back at your accusers, while at the same time demonstrating to the satisfaction of the public that you have nothing to hide, we will witness a significant backlash that could leave you stronger than you were when this whole thing first broke."

Armed with this kind of bold advice, Agnew left Washington the day after the press conference for a four-day holiday at the Palm Springs home of Frank Sinatra.

While Agnew played, his lawyers went to work. On the morning of Thursday, August 9, Topkis and London met with Henry Petersen and Philip T. White, his deputy. For this meeting at least, the Baltimore prosecutors—the Justice Department employees with direct responsibility for the investigation—were excluded.

So Agnew's lawyers had the chance to question at the top the manner in which the case had been investigated in the field. If they could convince Petersen of the validity of their client's grievances—that the investigation had been developed in a bungling fashion by prosecutors seeking headlines rather than justice—then they would have performed a valuable service.

This, essentially, was their objective in meeting with Petersen. They attacked the credibility of the prosecutors and of the witnesses against Agnew: the witnesses had contacted the Vice President early in the spring and asked him to have the investigation aborted; when Agnew refused, they had intimated that they would incriminate him. Still, Agnew refused to obstruct justice, and he was always prepared to cooperate with the government. In fact, Agnew would be glad to offer explanations for all the allegations against him—if only he knew what they were. He would be willing to submit to an interview. He might even consider a grand jury appearance. As for the documents Beall had asked for in his August 1 letter, they would be provided in due course—after the lawyers had reviewed them, and after they had made certain that turning them over did not compromise the executive-privilege position the President had asserted on the Watergate tapes, or prejudice a position Agnew might later assert: that he, too, was immune from prosecution. Topkis remarked casually that he would be meeting the next week with Professor Charles Alan Wright of the University of Texas, the President's chief adviser on the question of executive privilege. Regardless, the lawyers added, the Department of Justice could rest assured that the Vice President had no intention of invoking his Fifth Amendment right to withhold the documents.

Petersen sat and listened as White took notes. He was a sagacious and poised prosecutor, and he did not blink. First he defended the Baltimore prosecutors. Both he and the attorney general had every confidence in them. As for the witnesses, Topkis and London had a good point; he, too, was concerned about their credibility, although there was substantial corroborative evidence. He would definitely review the case, and would even consider interviewing the witnesses himself. He would not, however, interview Agnew. If the Vice President had any explanations to offer, he could make them to the prosecutors in Baltimore, although under no circumstances could an interview or even a deposition take the place of a grand jury appearance.

Petersen had one additional caveat. This meeting would be the last without the Baltimore prosecutors. Topkis and London offered no protest. Later, however, they resolved never to conduct their business with Beall and his staff. If Petersen—or even Richardson—would not hear them, then the White House would.

By 6:10 that evening, the busy Petersen was in Richardson's conference room, prepared to report on his meeting with Agnew's lawyers. The four Baltimore prosecutors were there, as well as Richardson, Ruckelshaus, and J. T. Smith. Before Petersen could speak, Richardson asked a series of routine questions and then launched into a sort of professorial soliloquy.

First, the attorney general wanted to know, had there been any new developments? None, Beall reported. Next, what was the status of the net-worth investigation? Progressing, Beall said. Richardson nodded. The net-worth investigation, he told Beall, should not divert the prosecutors from the principal investigation of Agnew, nor alter the timetable that called for a mid-September indictment. If need be, Agnew could be indicted first for bribery, conspiracy, and extortion and sometime later for tax evasion.

Agnew was, of course, a citizen like any other, Richardson said, slipping into his lecture. But he was also the Vice President, and his indictment was likely to precipitate foreign and domestic consequences of considerable importance to the nation. In historic terms, therefore, the group assembled there that day had grave responsibilities. The prosecutors must be sure that the witnesses would testify both before the grand jury and in open court exactly as they had when questioned by the prosecutors.

Richardson paused. By now it was clear that his lecture was directed at the four Baltimore prosecutors. They did not know it, but he was preparing them for Petersen's announcement that he would interview the witnesses and submit them to lie-detector tests—decisions that undercut their authority and had not been foreseen in their dealings with the lawyers for Matz and Wolff.

Richardson continued. Both he as attorney general and Petersen as head of the criminal division had great—and graver—responsibilities than did the prosecutors. He therefore wanted Petersen and himself to be in the best possible position to assess the case before an indictment was sought. Richardson did not spell out what he meant, but it was fairly clear that he was referring to his special responsibility to report to the President.

The President would be returning to Washington from Camp David on August 16, Richardson said, and might want a briefing from him and

Petersen on the investigation and on whether an indictment was likely: the President was entitled to this information to guide his own actions, for under no circumstances did he want to issue an endorsement of Agnew only to be caught later in a "McGovern-Eagleton situation."

Petersen was the man on the spot, Richardson continued, the man the President would turn to for a personal assessment of the case. Nixon believed that Petersen was the only person involved in Watergate who had been thoroughly honest with him; he perceived Petersen as a man of honesty to the point of bluntness.

At that point, Richardson left the room. Baker took the opportunity to admit to Petersen that he and his team had not the slightest idea how to get the White House to supply the logs that would show who had visited Agnew's office in the Old Executive Office Building. Petersen volunteered to handle that chore, and was given the names of Matz, Hammerman, Green, and Jones.

Petersen moved quickly on the Baltimore prosecutors' request. On August 10, he called Leonard Garment at the White House and asked him for the logs. Garment not only promised cooperation but also volunteered to find out whether Agnew's office, like the President's, had been outfitted with recording devices. Garment called back later to tell Petersen it would take twelve men a whole week to review the logs, but the job would be done. The President, it appeared, would be unstinting in his support of the Justice Department. (Garment said later he had no knowledge that the Vice President's office had been bugged.)

That same day, Petersen met with Plato Cacheris, the lawyer for J. Walter Jones, Jr., the real-estate developer from Towson. Cacheris was there to tell Petersen what he had earlier told Beall and Skolnik: Jones was asserting his innocence and would not be a government witness.

The news was a setback. Certainly the government had the evidence to indict Agnew: Jerry Wolff's notes alone were sufficient. An indictment was one thing, though, a conviction was something else again.

Here the government's case might turn out to be less formidable than it looked. Agnew—poised, articulate, and still Vice President—could make a wonderful witness in his own behalf.

What the government needed was a man like Jones: a respected bank president and former fund-raiser for both Agnew and Nixon. He was a nonengineer whose difficulties did not originate with the investigation of corruption in Baltimore County and who could not be accused of serving up Agnew as an offering to the government. But Jones would not or could not cooperate.

The only other alternative was Hammerman. Of all the men who eventually were to cooperate with the government, Bud Hammerman was indisputably the odd man out. Unlike Matz, Green, or Wolff, Hammerman was neither an engineer nor had he been extorted. He was personally close to Agnew. From the suits in Agnew's closet to the new kitchen in Agnew's apartment at the Sheraton Park Hotel, Bud Hammerman was the proud donor. There were other gifts, too—cash when Agnew complained of his financial plight, even a new car and jewelry for Agnew to give to a long-time secretary.

The gifts, Agnew later told others, were pressed on him by Hammerman, who insisted that Agnew had to comport himself in a vice-presidential manner. Hammerman was using his friendship for his own benefit, Agnew was later to complain, dropping the name of the Vice President for business purposes.

Still, Hammerman was hardly a unique Agnew friend. For years, Agnew and his associates had enjoyed symbiotic relationships in which Agnew's name with his title of the moment—county executive, governor, or Vice President—was exchanged for more practical considerations. Jones, who steered Agnew into business deals, had Agnew's name listed on his bank's letterhead. Hammerman, too, benefited from his close association with Agnew. Matz also was an Agnew benefactor; aside from the kickback money, he boasted that he occasionally gave Agnew cash—no strings attached. Harry Dundore, Sr., another Baltimore County chum who appeared smitten with Agnew, also reportedly gave his friend cash gifts. Agnew received some of his household food from Joseph Rash, an executive of Food Fair Stores, Inc. Even in the Sheraton Park Hotel (owned by International Telephone and Telegraph) Agnew as Vice President received a so-called celebrity discount of at least one third of the $1900 monthly rent.

In this respect, Agnew was not much different from many other politicians. Governors at governors' conferences, as Agnew well knew, were routinely showered with gifts from local manufacturers. Congressmen hitched rides on the corporate airplanes of firms doing business with the government, and governmental officials leased cars at a discount from corporations seeking government contracts. Presidents, too, had shown the same weakness. Richard M. Nixon, as it later turned out, had taken advantage of loopholes in the tax code to accumulate a real-estate fortune.

As a Marylander, Agnew at least had a ready explanation for his conduct—the perennial squawk that he was the underpaid, overworked guardian of the political system. To an extent, he had a point. For years, the state's voters had assumed that politics was a calling and had awarded those who entered it with the wages of a monk. Until 1967, the governor's salary was only $15,000 annually (a marked increase from the $4500 a year awarded Theodore Roosevelt McKeldin when he first became governor in 1951 and had to supplement his income through speaking engagements). Even in 1974, the salary was only $25,000, hardly a princely sum for an official who annually prepared a budget of nearly $3 billion and supervised 40,000 employees. The governor, in fact, earned less than any of his cabinet secretaries or even his press secretary. And while the state provided living quarters (the mansion), transportation (the limousines), and an expense account, it provided no funds for the constant political obligations—trips to partisan governor's conferences, a political convention, or meetings held in a Baltimore restaurant where the governor felt obliged to pick up the tab.

As a result, a man either had to be rich or a scoundrel to hold high public office. Those of modest means who zoomed to the top or inched their way to a committee chairmanship soon found that like the rock-and-roll stars of the 1960's, they had their own camp followers, men like Matz or Hammerman, who were willing to pick up a restaurant tab or slip an envelope into the hand of a politician. The envelope somehow enhanced the importance of both parties; it was nice to receive and it was nice to give.

In this environment, Bud Hammerman felt at home. He moved easily among politicians and gave them frequent donations. He shared with others a certain awe of those who wielded power, and he relished his association with the county executive *cum* governor *cum* Vice President *cum*—knock on wood—President. From the available evidence, it seemed also that Hammerman cherished his role as an intermediary in the kickback scheme.

And, ironically, Hammerman could use his cut of the take. The philanthropies established by his father were becoming a burden. In addition, the Hammermans had long been known as political contributors, and while hardly a politician could ignore the Hammerman wealth, neither could the Hammermans ignore the men who made decisions crucial to the success of their business empire.

By August 1973, however, Hammerman's silver spoon had become tarnished. Wolff and his omnipresent notebooks had incriminated him in a dozen shades of ink. The documents, coupled with Wolff's own testimony, had led the prosecutors to still other engineers who had confessed making payments to him. The evidence was damning. Hammerman faced certain indictment—or would have to make a deal. He chose the latter course.

Hammerman, though, would not come cheaply. His value to the government was not lost on his principal attorney, Sidney Sachs, whose Washington firm had represented E. Howard Hunt before both the Senate Watergate Committee and the Watergate grand jury.

It was clear to Sachs that his client's only recourse was to strike a deal. He entered the case in early July, and by the beginning of August, he engaged in negotiations.

On Friday, August 17, Hammerman, Sachs, his associate Hal Witt, and the four prosecutors converged on the Holiday Inn North, in the working-class Baltimore suburb of Glen Burnie. There I. H. Hammerman II turned informer. His face flushed, his hands shaking, Hammerman spelled out ten years of a corrupt relationship with Agnew.

Hammerman had known Agnew for years, but what brought the two men close together was Agnew's election as Baltimore County executive in 1962. The day after the election, Hammerman met with Agnew and congratulated him on his victory. Hammerman, repentant for having supported Agnew's opponent, told the county executive-elect that he knew all campaigns had deficits. He offered Agnew a contribution of $10,000. Agnew rejected the offer but added that he would expect a $30,000 contribution the next time he ran.

From then on, the two were close personal friends. Hammerman brought Agnew into his social set, introducing him to men who would later be substantial financial contributors.

In 1966, when Agnew ran for governor, he gave Hammerman an ultimatum—to choose between himself and his Democratic opponent. Hammerman was clearly in a fix. Whenever an election looked like a toss-up, major Maryland fat cats would generally contribute to both candidates. But Hammerman would not be permitted to lay off his bets on both candidates. He chose Agnew, the underdog, contributing $25,000. Hammerman also stepped out front in Agnew's campaign, becoming a financial chairman. By inauguration day, Marylanders had no doubt that Bud Hammerman was Ted Agnew's boy.

It was not generally known, however, that Hammerman was an intermediary in Agnew's massive kickback scheme, customarily the man who usually retained Agnew's 50 per cent of the graft and squirreled it away in a safe-deposit box. Between the two men, every $1000 was called a "paper." From time to time Agnew called Hammerman and would ask how many "papers" he had and, if Agnew desired, Hammerman would bring them over.

Hammerman's role in the kickback scheme was not strictly limited to engineering firms. At one point, Hammerman discussed with Agnew whether a certain Baltimore bond house should be chosen to float a state bond issue. Agnew was against it unless the officers of the bond house made a cash "contribution." The governor, who apparently did not want the state's largess to be taken for granted, called the bond-house partners—members of Baltimore's aristocracy—"a cheap bunch" who "don't give you any money."

Hammerman talked on and on, corroborating in detail the arrangements about which Wolff had testified earlier.

Spiro T. Agnew, oblivious of what was happening in the motel room in Glen Burnie, was in Centreville on the other side of the Chesapeake Bay that Saturday, addressing a rally for Robert E. Bauman, a Republican state senator seeking the congressional seat left vacant by the suicide of Republican congressman William O. Mills. Looking tanned and relaxed after his Palm Springs holiday, the Vice President worked the sympathetic crowd like an evangelist at a tent meeting. Agnew, after all, was the homestate boy; this was heartland Agnew country—conservative to its core.

"Hang in there!" one man shouted as he shook Agnew's hand.

"I'll be there," Agnew said. "Don't you worry."

"We're going to see you in the White House yet," cheered another.

When *Washington Post* reporter Philip A. McCombs sampled sentiment in the crowd, he reported overwhelming support for Agnew. "I feel that he's innocent," said George Fuller, a retired timekeeper. "When it all comes out, they'll find it's a lot of talk."

Across the bay in Glen Burnie, though, Bud Hammerman was undoing everything Agnew was accomplishing in Centreville.

Sachs, wanting to enhance his client's importance to the government, suggested that Hammerman be "wired" and sent to see Agnew, so the conversation would be recorded. The prosecutors rejected the suggestion. By now they believed they had more than enough evidence to indict Agnew on about fifty counts of bribery, extortion, conspiracy, and tax evasion. There was no need to gamble with the public's abhorrence for electronic eavesdropping.

The next day, Sunday, August 19, George Beall made two calls. The first was placed through the White House switchboard to Elliot

Richardson. Hammerman was in hand, Beall told the attorney general. The second was to Sidney Sachs. The government, Beall said, thought the time had come for Hammerman to sever his relationship with Agnew. What prompted the second call was one placed to Hammerman's home the day before while he was in the Glen Burnie motel. His wife, Lois, had taken the message.

"Where's Bud?" the Vice President asked.

"He's out until six-thirty," Lois Hammerman said.

"I've got to talk to him," Agnew said. "I'm going to launch a new attack. It looks encouraging. I wanted to give him a good weekend. I'll tell him all about it on Monday."

Whether Hammerman ever returned that call or not mattered little. He had done all the talking that counted to the prosecutors, and the long and mutually rewarding friendship of Bud Hammerman and Ted Agnew was at an end.

CHAPTER 9

MY FRIEND THE PRESS

By the middle of August, the revved-up American press, working in the superheated atmosphere generated by two major political scandals, had managed to give the nation a fair idea of the case against the Vice President. Agnew and his lawyers were beginning to do a slow burn. What they believed at first was nothing more than the indiscretions of a few well-placed persons seemed to them to be taking on a sinister cast. The government, they concluded, was purposely leaking the allegations against the Vice President.

The leaks were undoing Agnew, rebutting his public insistence that he was the victim of a horrendous frame-up. Moreover, they were causing internal dissension within his staff, making it difficult for the Vice President to present a unified front to the world. Like the President, Agnew worked in seclusion, relying on his closest aide, Arthur Sohmer, to run the staff. Later, General John (Mike) Dunn also became a trusted assistant.

As for the leaks themselves, canny Washingtonians had plenty of sources for them. It could be, some thought, that Justice Department officials and/or the Baltimore prosecutors were leaking information to the press to prevent any silent abortion of the investigation within the confines of the White House. Others took a different view, laying the blame for the leaks on the White House itself. President Nixon was notoriously unable to demand a resignation. To steadily erode a man's position by leaking the allegations against him was a pure Nixonian tactic.

Speculation about the prosecutors as the source of press stories focused on Skolnik. As a Harvard undergraduate, Skolnik had made no secret that his career choice was politics, and there were some who suspected that he had never abandoned that goal.

On August 15, Agnew mounted a mild public-relations attack. The innocuous personal financial documents that Beall had requested would be turned over to the prosecutors. In keeping with the dignity of his office, though, Agnew refused to have the documents delivered to Baltimore. Beall was forced to send for them, and for the covering letter, which Agnew made public.

"I have done nothing wrong, I have nothing to hide," the Vice President wrote to Beall. "And I have no desire save that justice be done speedily and efficiently." By making the records available, "I do not acknowledge that you or the grand jury have any right to the records of the Vice President. Nor do I acknowledge the propriety of any grand jury investigation of possible wrongdoing on the part of the Vice President so long as he occupies that office. There are constitutional questions which need not at this moment be confronted." In addition, Agnew volunteered to submit to an interview, writing, "I am eager to be of any help I can. Specifically, should you wish, I shall be glad to meet with you and your colleagues for a personal interview so that I may answer any questions you may have."

But whatever triumph Agnew scored with the letter was eradicated the same day. Coupled on the front page of *The Washington Post* with the story of the letter was still another Agnew story—a report that engineers had testified they personally made payments to Agnew. The very next day, *The New York Times*'s Nicholas Gage disclosed Richardson's meeting with Agnew on August 6, providing even more details of the allegations against the Vice President. Agnew took another public-relations pie in the face. The *Times*'s story was particularly galling to Agnew since the meeting with Richardson involved just five persons—the two principals and Agnew's three lawyers. Unlike stories about the investigation itself, this one could not have been leaked by potential witnesses or their lawyers.

The Vice President seethed—and finally exploded—when on Sunday, August 19, *Time* magazine released an advance version of a story, entitled "Heading Toward Indictment?" "'The Department [of Justice] has no choice,'" the magazine quoted a "Justice official in Washington" as saying. "'At least three witnesses have told of delivering cash payments to Agnew. The evidence is so strong that the case must be taken to trial.'" The article gave the reader an outline of the case against Agnew and mentioned that some Justice Department officials were puzzled about "the comparatively paltry amounts of money involved."

"'It's less than you think,'" *Time* quoted one Justice official as saying. "'Agnew wasn't greedy; he was quite cheap.'" Aside from the information and the explosive quotes contained in the article, the *Time* piece was noteworthy in one other respect: it cited Justice Department officials *in Washington* as its source.

Agnew, steaming, called his second news conference of the month on August 21. Reporters alerted just shortly before the event assembled in the auditorium in the Old Executive Office Building, expecting a question-and-answer session. Instead, Agnew read a statement and allowed no questions. Looking fit if a bit thin, he strode onto the stage and—before a national television audience and members of the Washington press corps—proceeded to attack the Justice Department.

As a politician, Agnew said, he had become accustomed to "unsubstantiated charges, rumors, innuendo, and speculation. I have been subjected to these before, and I am accustomed to fighting this kind of battle." What he found intolerable was the effect this kind of publicity might have on the rights of others—particularly private citizens involved in the investigation.

Therefore, Agnew continued, he had written a letter to Attorney General Richardson asking him to conduct an investigation of the source of the leaks. What he wanted was a full-scale inquiry that would use "all available investigatory tools to compel sworn testimony to reveal the identity of unnamed Justice Department officials and 'sources close to the investigation.'"

Agnew made sure the press and the public understood that his anger was directed not at the media but at his enemies in government who were daily sticking barbs into his hide. The press, he said, was not to blame for "publishing information given you by informants within the Department of Justice. The blame must rest with those who give this information to the press and who do so with an obvious motive of interfering with the independent investigative process of the grand jury."

Agnew concluded by once again asserting his innocence and declaring he had nothing to hide. "I have made all requested records available to

"OH, THE THINGS YOU SEE SPREAD AROUND—
INNUENDOS, ACCUSATIONS, ATTACKS!"

the prosecutors and have offered to meet with them and answer any questions they may have."

It was a moment before the press corps reacted. Then there was an explosion of chatter. In a Washington gone stale on innuendo, *double-entendres,* and "on-the-other-hand" statements, Agnew had issued a broadside. Here was a frontal attack on his own administration's Department of Justice, a bald accusation that it was seeking an indictment of him not in the courts, but in the press. Although Agnew had limited his attacks to the department—and had not attacked Richardson by name—he had by implication come perilously close to attacking both the attorney general and the President. Not since the halcyon days of the Truman administration had Washington seen such a division within the ranks.

Beall responded quickly. He would stand by his statement of August 8 denying that the prosecutors were in any way "the source of the information reported by the media concerning this investigation." He, too, was "gravely concerned" about the leaks and would "continue to preserve the secrecy of the proceedings until such time as public disclosure can be properly made."

Richardson also denounced the leaks. "I fully share the Vice President's concern about unfair and inaccurate publicity."

Suddenly, the world had turned upside down. It was not Spiro T. Agnew, arch enemy of the press and the victim of the leaks, calling for "restraint"—self-censorship—on the part of the media, but Elliot Richardson. And the attorney general was bitter. The Justice Department he was striving to rehabilitate was taking a public-relations pounding for allegedly leaking like a sieve. Baker, ever the archivist, had carefully compared all the accurate newspaper stories with the information he thought Justice had given the White House. The conclusion was inescapable: the Executive Mansion was the culprit.

The President was now clearly in a fix. Regardless of his ultimate aim—the removal of Agnew—he could not sit by after his Vice President had publicly complained that he was the victim of what amounted to a conspiracy. Nixon called Agnew and told him he would support his request for an investigation. Nixon's deputy press secretary, Gerald L. Warren announced to the White House press corps, "The President feels that the leaks in a situation such as this are certainly alien to our due process of law and the rights of individuals, and certainly do not assist the proper authorities in investigating certain matters."

The next morning's *Washington Post* lined up squarely in Agnew's corner. The Vice President, a *Post* editorial said, "is well within his rights to be powerfully annoyed if those charged with the responsibility for the investigation are acting in a way careless of the protections that are due him." Similarly, *The New Times* editorialized: "Vice President Agnew had every right to complain that his constitutional rights are being violated by leaks attributed to 'Justice Department sources. . . .'"

The press obviously was in a quandary. One of those who argued that the press was speaking with a forked tongue—editorializing against the leaks while simultaneously pursuing the story—was David S. Broder of *The Washington Post*. Broder wrote: "There hasn't been such a suspiciously conspicuous display of civic virtue since a San Francisco madam led her string of girls to the Red Cross blood bank during World War II." Broder warned the press against relying exclusively on "informed sources."

Broder had a point. But many others in the Washington journalistic community argued that the Nixon administration's sorry record on enforcing justice was reason enough for the press to go all-out to enlighten the public about the case against Agnew. Even Richardson had not yet proved that his Justice Department would be markedly different from that of his Nixon adminstration predecessors. In any case, Agnew was not an ordinary citizen. The public was entitled to learn everything the press could discover about the nature of the case against him.

The pressure was building. Agnew had struck a responsive chord in America and the President was quick to react. In a televised press conference held on the lawn of his San Clemente home the day after Agnew's attack, Nixon announced that he had ordered Richardson to conduct a full investigation into the sources of the leaks. Any Justice Department employee found to be responsible for leaking information to the press would be "summarily dismissed from government service." The President was less emphatic, however, when it came to expressing confidence in the man he had twice chosen as his running mate. Aware that the gist of the case against Agnew involved his two years as governor of Maryland, Nixon carefully limited his endorsement to Agnew's term as Vice President.

The real meaning of Nixon's tepid endorsement was not lost on Agnew's staff. What Nixon said about his Vice President was compared with his earlier affirmation of confidence in Ehrlichman and Haldeman: he had flatly predicted their eventual exoneration. Moreover, the White House chose the next day to reveal in an interview with *The New York Times* that the attempts of Agnew's lawyers to formulate a joint legal strategy with the President had been rebuffed. On the dual issues of executive privilege and indictability, the President's lawyers saw no common interests with the Vice President.

Still, for all of Agnew's growing isolation from the White House and the antipathy with which he was viewed in the inner sanctums of the Justice Department, Richardson had no choice but to launch the investigation ordered by Nixon. In the end, the department reported that 134 employees had signed affidavits denying they were the source of information provided the press.

The issue of the leaks was for a time to overshadow all others. Agnew's lawyers would contend in a motion filed September 28 that the Justice Department had deprived their client of his civil rights by leaking information to the press. The result was that the Justice Department withdrew into a shell, its staff refusing to answer any press questions about Agnew's investigation. It was a perilous tactic, for it left reporters with virtually no way to check the accuracy of information gleaned elsewhere.

By the end of the third week in August, one thing the Vice President and the attorney general had in common was their impatience with the leaks. On Friday, August 24, a visibly upset Richardson assembled nearly everyone who had substantial knowledge of the investigation—about forty persons—and warned them not to talk to the press. He delivered a tirade, attacking the newspapers that editorialized against the leaks but printed accounts of the investigation anyway. In language that few had ever heard the attorney general use, Richardson said that such hypocrisy was "burning my ass. We've got to be goddamn sure that we're not contributing to the leaks."

Soon after, Richardson, Petersen, the Baltimore prosecutors, and Richardson's aides—the Justice Ten—went to the attorney general's private office. The talk turned to framing an answer to a letter Topkis had written to Richardson on August 21, after the attorney general's appearance on ABC's *Issues and Answers:*

Dear Mr. Attorney General,
We write as counsel to the Vice President. We understand that on a television program on Sunday, you said that you personally will make the decision as to what personal information concerning the Vice President will be presented to the Baltimore grand jury. According to the press, you said that the decision would involve two issues: the sufficiency of the evidence and the question of whether the Vice President could be indicted. We would like to be heard by you in connection with the matter. We have no wish to rush you, of course. May we have your early assurance that at a time you deem appropriate and before any final action, we may call upon you for this purpose?

Skolnik reacted to the letter as if it were a personal affront. Topkis's request, he recommended to Richardson, should be denied. The "sufficiency of the evidence" was just another way of saying "allegations against Agnew," Skolnik said; here was the Vice President again asking for evidence against him.

Instead of inviting Agnew's lawyers to a meeting, the reply to Topkis again offered Agnew a chance to provide a statement and appear before the grand jury. In addition, the letter dropped the other shoe. It asked Agnew to supply the documents that the prosecutors wanted in the first place but had not requested in their letter of August—just about every personal financial record a man would be expected to maintain from "1 January 1962 to the present." The records the government asked for included: all cash payments of $100 or more to Agnew by either Hammerman or The Close Associate; political contributions received; gifts of more than $100; savings accounts; savings certificates; securities; bonds; real-estate transactions; loans; mortgages; inheritances; interest; safe-deposit boxes; personal property in excess of $500; gifts of value in excess of $500 made by or in behalf of Agnew to others; insurance policies; and similar information. The government, in effect, was asking Agnew to dig his own grave.

Around the room in Richardson's office, not a man there thought Agnew would comply with this request. There was not a lawyer present who would have allowed a client to incriminate himself in such a fashion. Still, for the Justice Department the idea of his noncompliance was nearly as attractive as compliance. No longer would Agnew be able to strut about declaring that he was doing everything the government was asking of him.

However, Agnew was still the Vice President, next in line of succession. This above all continued to trouble Elliot Richardson and the men around him. Rumors swept the city that the President was behaving irrationally, that White House staff members were calling General Haig "the nurse." While Washington worried, Richardson brooded. This man Agnew should resign. It was, after all, the honorable and decent thing to do.

But Richardson was also the nation's first prosecutor and like his subordinates in the department's office over in Baltimore, he was beginning to enjoy the chase, the thrill of closing in on a man and bringing him to terms. The entire case was now being handled from Washington; Richardson's office was the war room. "You know," the attorney general said to the group at one point, "I can feel the old prosecutorial instincts coming out in myself as we get deeper and deeper into this. My first instincts were to worry about the ability to govern, to function. But now I'm getting the feeling—'Get the bastard!'"

It was an elated group of prosecutors who left the Justice Department that day. It had been a busy week for them. On Thursday, the grand jury had indicted Dale Anderson, Agnew's successor as Baltimore County executive, on thirty-nine counts of bribery, conspiracy, and extortion.

Dale Anderson, who just a few months before had been only a minor political figure from a border state, became a national celebrity of sorts, his indictment front-page news in both The New York Times and The

Washington Post. To the prosecutors, though, the indictment was anticlimactic at best. There were bigger fish to fry.

With the Labor Day weekend approaching, the investigation of Spiro T. Agnew slowed down. Skolnik was off in Pennsylvania, Baker on Martha's Vineyard, Beall at Ocean City, and Richardson on Cape Cod where, the press reported, he was deciding in isolation whether to allow the case against Agnew to proceed to the grand jury. Actually, Richardson had already decided and was waiting only for the signed statements of the witnesses and their agreement to testify for the government.

As for the twenty-three grand jurors, theirs was a frustrating lot. Despite Agnew's frequent references to a "grand jury investigation" directed at himself, it was nothing of the sort. The jurors had yet to hear from a single Agnew witness.

Suddenly, rumors swept Washington that Nixon was cutting short his stay in San Clemente and flying back to Washington for a meeting with Agnew—rumors confirmed first on network radio and then later by White House deputy press secretary Gerald Warren. The meeting was being held at the Vice President's request, Warren said, and had been scheduled since Tuesday.

The report after the meeting was not informative. Nearly two hours had been spent in a "thorough discussion" of the investigation, a White House aide explained, but the President had not requested, nor had the Vice President offered, his resignation.

White House aides went out of their way to discourage speculation that the meeting between Nixon and Agnew was held in a crisis atmosphere. The White House reported that Nixon and Agnew had found time to discuss "domestic priorities and the legislative session coming up. . . ." If so, it was a strange time for the President to choose for such a discussion.

After the meeting, Nixon and Agnew went to their respective helicopters. Both men were at their holiday retreats by the afternoon, almost at the same time that George Beall was trying frantically to find an airplane to take him out to Ocean City. He was fuming. It was hardly fun to have his cherished vacation with his wife and daughter interrupted by a summons from Ruckelshaus to a meeting at Ruckelshaus's home in Rockville, Maryland.

When Beall and his assistants—also summoned from their vacations —arrived, Ruckelshaus was in his flower garden. Soon Petersen pulled up and they all went into the den. Richardson had been grounded in Boston, Ruckelshaus announced regretfully, and could not make the meeting.

But Ruckelshaus had an agenda. Al Haig had called him after Agnew's meeting with the President and had intimated that Nixon would soon want to confer again with Richardson. Their task, Ruckelshaus explained, was to prepare for Richardson's meeting.

Just then Richardson called from Boston and Ruckelshaus left the room to talk to him. He came back to ask how long it would take to finish the investigation—Richardson wanted to know. Sixty days more, was the consensus. The attorney general, Ruckelshaus eventually reported, now authorized the prosecutors to bring the evidence against Agnew before the grand jury as soon as possible. It was the green light the Baltimoreans had awaited for so long.

The discussion then turned to Richardson's expected meeting with the President. Should Richardson simply report that he, Petersen, and the prosecutors were certain of Agnew's guilt, and leave it at that? Should he give the President an oral outline of the case? A detailed memo? Once again the room split into opposing camps, and as Richardson was absent, Petersen stood alone in arguing that the President should be told whatever he asked.

The group struck a compromise: Richardson would offer the President an advance copy of Agnew's indictment.

Petersen then announced himself as certain of Agnew's guilt. The government, Petersen said, had no choice but to prosecute Agnew and prosecute him quickly. If the Justice Department flinched and the detailed allegations of the witnesses became public, it would result in "a scandal of Gargantuan proportions." They had to speed the evidence to the grand jury and seek an indictment.

On September 27, the grand jury summoned its first Agnew witness—a former Agnew fund-raiser turned public-relations man named William J. Muth. He took the Fifth Amendment. Two weeks later, he was brought back, given "use immunity," and compelled to testify.

The grand jury never heard from any of the major witnesses. Instead, the prosecutors began by calling minor figures from Agnew's Baltimore County days. Some of these provided tantalizing allegations. Agnew, one witness charged, had demanded—and received—a nickel-a-pack kickback from cigarette vending machine firms that operated machines in Baltimore County's public buildings. Another said that Agnew had attempted to extort payments from the area's utility companies.

Some of the witnesses, both major and minor, attempted to offer information dealing with Agnew's personal life. The prosecutors, as was their custom, ruled such information out of bounds. Some of these unverified allegations were later pumped into the Washington rumor mill, adding to the story that the Agnew investigation had uncovered what one magazine said would be a "moral bombshell." None of these unsubstantiated allegations made either in the grand jury room or in the interrogation room were included in the forty-page exposition of the evidence against Agnew that the government made public in October.

When the meeting at Ruckelshaus's home concluded, Petersen and the Baltimore prosecutors climbed into their cars and headed off into the muggy Maryland night. The investigation of Spiro T. Agnew was going to a grand jury.

Agnew, however, had other plans.

CHAPTER 10

PLEA BARGAINING

As the Baltimore prosecutors readied their case, Elliot Richardson found himself in an old-fashioned political squeeze play. Word came to him privately that the Vice President, in an effort to avert criminal indictment, was threatening to "go to the House."

That meant, of course, voluntarily setting in motion the impeachment mechanism, making a conscious decision to put his fortunes in the hands not of twelve ordinary citizens of the Republic, but of his political peers. The logic for any politician was obvious: it would be infinitely easier to persuade a majority of 435 men and women, who themselves had lived with the corrosive influence of campaign costs, that the allegations against Agnew amounted to little more than their own accommodations to the financial realities of seeking public office.

The gambit had arithmetic as well as logic in its favor. The House of Representatives impeaches; that is, it acts as the grand jury in the case, considering the allegations and deciding whether the man should be formally charged. If that step is taken, the trial then takes place in the Senate, where a two-thirds majority is required for conviction and removal from office. Another, more pertinent way to put it is this: 34 of the 100 members of the Senate can acquit. In the fall of 1973, there were 43 Republicans in the Senate and, equally significant, many Democrats who for one reason or another might prefer to keep Agnew in office.

The White House was at the outset dead against Agnew's going to the House. "The impeachment track" was fraught with ominous parallel for the President himself. Once committed to the impeachment track, Agnew would be much less likely to agree to the swift solution that the President wanted—his resignation.

Whatever the President might be saying for public consumption, it was now apparent that he wanted his Vice President out. The White House, despairing that Agnew would ever take the hint, resorted to direct action. For the second time since the beginning of the investigation, the President's men on September 10 approached Agnew and in no uncertain terms suggested that he vacate the office.

The next day, Richardson received a call from the White House. Agnew's lawyers wanted to discuss the "procedural options" open to the Vice President. Although no one suggested that this was plea bargaining, the Justice team regarded the overture as a possible signal that, for all his proclamations of innocence, Agnew might be exploring the chances of a deal.

Elliot Richardson gathered his personal aides together, along with George Beall and Henry Petersen, to consider what options they would lay out. Richardson listed four considerations that would have to be satisfied in any negotiated settlement. First, he insisted, there must be prompt resolution of the matter—resignation—in the national interest. Second, justice must be done. Third, any agreed solution had to be publicly understandable and perceived by the public as just. Fourth, full disclosure of the facts had to be made, preferably as part of the court record, so that the public would have a basis on which to conclude that justice had been done and that the solution was equitable. These four points made it clear that Justice would not buy the kind of deal the Baltimore team feared Agnew would seek and the White House would support—resignation in return for no prosecution at all.

On Wednesday morning, September 12, after still another planning session, the attorney general, Petersen, and Beall met with Agnew's three lawyers for an hour in Richardson's office. In this first meeting it turned out that the cautious Justice team had overprepared. Agnew's lawyers were merely trying once again to find out where Justice was going and how fast.

Richardson, after listening for a while, decided it was time to end the fencing. He told the Agnew lawyers that the Justice Department was prepared to press on for indictment. And that concluded the meeting. Later, though, Richardson told his colleagues it would be a "tragedy" if either of the two long roads of indictment or impeachment were to be traveled in this sad affair.

That Richardson preferred to make a deal was sensed at once by Agnew's lawyers. Best went back to Agnew and reported that although the Justice Department was prepared to press for an indictment, the time might have come to negotiate. The Vice President finally agreed to have Best explore the possibility.

Late on the same day, September 12, Richardson agreed to see Best alone, but only for about five minutes. In their short time together, the two men quickly got down to business. Best noticed a framed Latin inscription over the desk of one of Richardson's secretaries that said, "*Orchides Forum Trahite Cordes Et Mentes Veniant.*" "Do you know what that means?" Richardson asked. "Grab them by the balls; the hearts and minds will follow," Best replied. "I see you're a Latinist," Richardson said. Then Best came out with it. They had, he said, a mutual problem that had to be resolved consistent with the best interests of the Republic. He wanted to make a deal.

The plea-bargaining talks began in earnest at 9:30 Thursday morning, September 13, in Richardson's office. Before they started, Richardson —without yet informing Beall of what had happened—phoned him in Baltimore and told him to ask the grand jury to vote to accept evidence in the case; the prosecutors were to start presenting it that same day. Beall did so. The screws were turning on the Vice President even as his lawyer came in to cut a deal.

Despite the prosecutors' fears, it was evident from the start that Agnew was not going to demand that prosecution be dropped altogether in return for his resignation. That the price of any settlement would be Agnew's resignation was assumed by all. Best reported that the Vice President would consider making a plea of *nolo contendere* to a single count, resigning his office in return for a recommendation to the judge from the Department of Justice that no jail sentence be imposed. Staying out of jail was vital to Agnew in any deal. The plea would achieve that prime objective and minimize the stigma, technically at least, of his removal from office. He could then contend outside the courtroom, if he chose, that he still had done nothing wrong. *Nolo contendere* is defined in The American College Dictionary as "a defendant's pleading which does not admit guilt but subjects him to punishment as though he had pleaded guilty, the determination of guilt remaining open in other proceedings."

Richardson was noncommittal, except to say he would discuss the offer with his prosecutorial team.

For two hours in Richardson's office, the Justice Ten reviewed and assessed the morning meeting with Best. Out of the session came no firm consensus, only food for thought. Richardson said two points had to be recognized by all: that the government had a valid case and had behaved properly, and the only reason Agnew was considering resigning was that he realized the government had enough evidence to convict him; at the same time, the government would have to pay a price to get Agnew out quickly, and no one should think otherwise. The overriding requirements, he reiterated, were that there be swift resolution of the matter, that the outcome be just, and that it be so perceived.

There were four basic components in any deal: the "information"—i.e., the charge against Agnew—and his plea to it; what the Justice Department would say—i.e., its full disclosure of the facts; what Agnew would say in response; and the disposition—i.e., the sentencing, and what position Justice would take on it. Of these four, the one that Richardson thought likely to be the most troublesome was the third—what the Vice President would be permitted to say in response to the government's statement. To be acceptable, he said, Agnew's statement would have to acknowledge in some way the force and validity of the government's position. Associate attorney general Jonathan Moore made the point that all the components had to be taken as a package; if one were weakened, another had to be strengthened. The total settlement had to seem fair and just.

A basic difference between the Baltimore prosecutors and the Washingtonians remained. The former seemed to think that resignation was virtually automatic, that Agnew had no other choice. If he elected to go to the House, they indicated, he would be impeached and convicted anyway. But the Washingtonians did not see resignation or impeachment as automatic. Agnew could very well fight both in the courts and on Capitol Hill. "We had done a much better analysis [than the Baltimoreans] of the chances for Spiro getting let off up on the Hill," one of Richardson's lieutenants said later.

Also, the last thing the Washingtonians wanted was to make of Agnew what one of them called "a cornered tiger". That would be pure disaster. Richardson saw insistence on imprisonment as the kind of thing that would back Agnew into a corner.

In a vigorous debate, he and Baker parted company over this question of a jail sentence. Richardson saw it not as a necessary element but as a key bargaining tool with which to force Agnew out of office under conditions of full disclosure. Baker, on the other hand, argued that

Agnew was guilty of venal crimes and the government could prove it. In such cases, he said, public officials usually go to jail.

Richardson listened patiently. When Baker had finished, the attorney general observed: "Yes. Well, every little boy will know that if he gets to be Vice President of the United States and is forced to resign, his name will go down in the history books in disgrace." Baker replied that humiliation and disgrace were not enough; every minor character in the scandal had been disgraced and humiliated. But Richardson was firm, and Baker did not press.

Though the discussion was provocative and at times heated, it was, one aide said, "a very respectful dynamic" that served to get the Baltimoreans and the Washingtonians onto the same general track. Out of the meeting came not only ideas but a sense of working together toward a single purpose, and this carried through and strengthened in the plea bargaining ahead.

On Saturday morning, September 15, at ten, the Justice Ten met again in the conference room off Richardson's office. The meeting, which lasted about seven hours with Richardson attending for the first five, was described by one participant as the single most fascinating session in the whole Agnew case—which was not surprising, for in its course, the government's position on plea bargaining was orchestrated.

Baker opened with his proposition that they first force Agnew's resignation and then prosecute him as a private citizen. Richardson dismissed this out of hand, saying, "That's a total nonstarter." Then he took over, restating the deal Best had offered and inviting comment—not on whether there should be plea bargaining but on what the terms of the plea bargaining would be.

There was some discussion about whether the plea they accepted from Agnew should be *nolo contendere* or guilty, and whether Justice should recommend no jail. But satisfaction was expressed on two counts: that the Vice President actually was offering to quit, and that in so doing a constitutional crisis would be averted. As the discussion went smoothly on, with a consensus apparently building to accept Best's offer, Skolnik sat and seethed. After about an hour and a half nearly everybody else had spoken, and it looked as if the consensus might already have formed. Like an anxious schoolboy, Skolnik raised his hand slightly to catch Richardson's eye, then gave him a please-call-on-me look. Richardson nodded. "I would like to hear from Barney."

Skolnik was in total disagreement with what had been said over the last hour. First of all, he said, the Vice President's resignation was inevitable. When indicted he would have to resign, plea bargain or not.

Skolnik pressed on. The Department of Justice was being blackmailed, he protested, and the public would never consider the deal being offered as a just one if the department accepted it while maintaining the position that Agnew was really guilty of bribery and extortion. He had always believed that it was a mistake to talk as some of the people in that room were talking, to assume that they knew what was in the public interest better than the public did.

The prosecutor spoke with emotion but with his voice under control. He believed very strongly that the department must insist that Agnew admit his crime of bribery; not necessarily formally plead guilty to a bribery count, but at least admit certain facts that would be recognized as bribery and would constitute admission to the crime. What he meant by the department being blackmailed was that despite the fact that it had the evidence and the power to indict Agnew on numerous counts of bribery and extortion, it was being obliged to let him off with nothing more than an admission of a "tax peccadillo." He could not go along. "I dissent," Skolnik said grandly, in the classic legal phrase.

Then Attorney General Richardson spoke. The only thing he really disagreed with, he said, was Skolnik's first premise. He was not at all sure that Agnew's resignation was inevitable. No one could be sure. Yet it was so important that he do so, that even probable inevitability was not enough.

Richardson asked the others in the room for their views.

Most everyone agreed that Agnew must not be let off too leniently. To Skolnik, this meant that his impassioned harangue had saved the day by swinging everyone to his side. But Richardson's young aides did not see it that way at all. Skolnik, in their view, was beating a dead horse. They insisted later that there never had been any intent to permit Agnew to plead to anything short of a tax felony, never to allow him to get away with a "tax peccadillo." The Richardson men saw Skolnik as a lively and impassioned voice, but he seemed to them as much concerned about having a voice in the plea bargaining as in what was decided.

This particular meeting exemplified well the Richardson approach and diplomacy. By the time all had been heard from, only one man at the table still seemed to want to bargain on the terms put forward by the Vice President—Henry Petersen. Petersen, who had been and continued to be tough in his discussions with Agnew's lawyers, in this gathering appeared to place the highest priority on getting Agnew out of office quickly. At one point in the heated discussion, Petersen got up and began pacing behind the long table, as was his custom, his hands thrust through his belt. Suddenly, he wheeled, faced Skolnik, and shouted at him: "The man is the goddamn Vice President of the United States! What are you trying to do? Get him to crawl on his belly?"

Skolnik, the young subordinate, shouted back: "It isn't a question of making him crawl on his belly. It's a question of the public perception of whether or not what we're doing is honorable."

The debate continued, in somewhat less emotional tones. Out of it came a general agreement that at the very least the government should insist on Agnew admitting bribery or facts that amounted to bribery, perhaps in the context of a guilty or *nolo* plea to a count of income-tax evasion.

Once this was agreed to, the team discussed procedure. Moore, wary of Agnew's motives, proposed a devil theory: suppose Agnew was simply trying to trap the Justice Department into a weak deal, with the idea of then "exposing" it—in a televised press conference, say—to undermine the department's whole case? He could say that the Attorney General of the United States was perfectly willing to let him plead *nolo* to one little tax charge and drop all the rest, in spite of all the talk about extortion and bribery. What then? Skolnik suggested that to guard against such a development, Best should be asked to sign a letter indicating that he understood the department would make no deal unless Agnew admitted to bribery or to the facts that evidenced bribery. Richardson balked at this notion: he liked to deal with lawyers in good faith and not oblige them to sign papers. But Skolnik pointed out that it was routine procedure in other Baltimore investigations, not out of lack of good faith, but out of an awareness that plea bargaining could break down.

Richardson finally agreed: a letter setting forth the department's terms for negotiation should be drafted. Petersen still disagreed, but Richardson overruled him. Skolnik said he thought not only Best but also Agnew ought to be asked to sign the letter. Petersen again objected, and this time Richardson sided with him.

By now the meeting had gone on for about five hours. Richardson said he was leaving and asked that the others stay to draft the letter and have it ready for his signature. He thanked them all, in very flowery, patriotic phrases, with his eyes on mainly Skolnik. Then he walked the length of the room to the door. He took the doorknob, turned around, and waved to Skolnik. "Shalom," he said. He turned again and walked out.

For the remaining two hours, the Justice team ate dry ham and cheese sandwiches and drafted the letter to Best. Petersen was in charge (Ruckelshaus also having left). The final version read:

September 15, 1973

Dear Mr. Best:

On Thursday, September 13, 1973, at your request a meeting was held in my office to discuss options presently available to your client, the Vice President, with regard to the investigation of the Vice President and others now under way in the office of the United States Attorney for the District of Maryland. . . . At that time you indicated that one of the options available to the Vice President was resignation of his constitutional office and a plea supporting conviction of a criminal charge arising out of the foregoing investigation, and you suggested that negotiations be instituted on this matter. It is the purpose of this letter to state the terms and conditions under which the Department of Justice will enter into such negotiations with your client. A final agreement between the Department of Justice and your client which does not contain the following terms and conditions will not be acceptable to the Department of Justice:

1. The Vice President will resign from his constitutional office on or before the date upon which one or more judgments of conviction are entered upon him in open court.

2. Your client will enter a plea supporting conviction of a criminal charge arising out of the foregoing investigation.

3. At the time of such a plea, representatives of the Department of Justice will in open court make a full disclosure of the facts ultimately developed by the present investigation.

4. At the time of such plea your client will in open court acknowledge as true the fact that while as Governor of the State of Maryland he did receive and accept cash monies which he knew to be given by engineers knowing as he did so that said monies were given by these engineers with intent on their part to influence the performance of his official duties with regard to the selection of engineers for consulting contract with the State of Maryland. Or as an alternative,

5. At the time of his plea your client will in open court acknowledge as true the fact that he did receive and accept cash monies which he knew to be given by engineers seeking contracts from the State of Maryland, knowing as he did so that said monies were given by said engineers pursuant to an illegal scheme entered into by your client and others in regard to the selection of engineers for such contracts.

During the contemplated negotiations, the Department of Justice intends to continue the present investigation of the Vice President and others to present evidence to the special grand jury now sitting in Baltimore.

The Department of Justice is now willing to participate in the contemplated negotiations only if and when you sign this letter with the full knowledge and authorization of the Vice President. The Department of Justice understands that your signature to this letter does not constitute an admission by your client of any fact at issue, but constitutes only an acknowledgement by your client that you are authorized to proceed to negotiate with the Department of Justice in accordance with the terms and conditions set forth above.

Sincerely,
Elliott L. Richardson
ATTORNEY GENERAL

I acknowledge and agree to the terms and conditions set forth in this letter with the full knowledge and authorization of my client, the Vice President of the United States.

Judah Best
ATTORNEY FOR THE VICE PRESIDENT

On Monday morning, September 17, when the Justice team was to meet with Agnew's lawyers again, word came to Richardson by way of the White House that Agnew was balking at the idea of full disclosure of the evidence the government had accumulated to support its case for his indictment. The attorney general continued to insist that full disclosure was a nonnegotiable item: the fair administration of justice was as much at stake as Agnew's career.

On Tuesday, September 18, they did meet again, and Richardson handed Best the letter. After checking with his client, Best reported that the Vice President did not want him to sign, that acceptance of it should be enough. Richardson didn't press him, and they started talking about a deal—precisely what the Baltimore prosecutors had hoped to avoid, concerned as they were with Moore's devil theory of an irate Agnew later telling the world he was being railroaded on a minor charge. The *nolo* plea did not seem to disturb anyone greatly, and everyone seemed to agree that it could be made to some kind of tax count. But the matter of full disclosure remained a sticking point. After ninety minutes, the meeting broke up and Beall returned to Baltimore.

Later that same afternoon, Petersen called Beall. What Petersen had in mind as "full disclosure," he said, was a summary of the evidence in about two pages. Beall objected even to this. Any real summary would have to be much longer; all that Agnew's lawyers should be given now was a two-page *example* of the sort of information the eventual summary would contain.

On Wednesday, September 19, Richardson, Petersen, and Beall met once again with Best, Topkis, and London.

Again, Best said he would not sign the plea-bargaining letter, and again Richardson did not insist. But he informed Agnew's lawyers that the government therefore intended to go forward with its full-disclosure statement. All that was to be negotiated now was what Agnew would be permitted to say in reply to it in court. As for Agnew's desire to escape imprisonment, Richardson reiterated that he would prefer to make no recommendation, leaving the decision to the judge unless the court insisted he give his view. So this key element remained open. The Vice President was ready, his lawyers said, to admit to one payment received in 1967 on which he had paid no taxes, but that was all.

Thursday, September 20, was a day of frenzied meetings, mounting pressures, and counterpressures that engaged all the principals including the President himself, as Agnew stiffened against the Justice Department's efforts to impose a deal on him and finally went to the Oval Office for relief.

For more than four hours that afternoon, the arguments with Topkis, Best, and London over the fate of the Vice President went on. Topkis emerged as the legal and intellectual heavy of the trio, putting forward the most telling points over what Agnew should or should not say to warrant one plea or another.

Although Richardson had insisted that resignation, a plea to a criminal charge, full disclosure, and some admission of guilt were nonnegotiable terms, Topkis nevertheless came in with a counterproposal—a significantly scaled-down version in which Agnew would admit some facts that would justify a plea of *nolo* to a misdemeanor, skirting any acknowledgment that he knew he was being bribed. Although the specter of jail hung ominously over him, he hung tough. And Richardson, though he kept the door open to further counterproposals, did the same.

Once again Richardson post-mortemed with his lieutenants and Beall's three assistants. Of equal interest, or at least equal amusement, to them all was an opening gambit that Topkis had made and Richardson immediately rejected. It was a statement Topkis had handed him that, he said, the Vice President was willing to make rather than admit a lot of charges.

Of all the chutzpah displayed by Spiro T. Agnew in the course of the investigation against him, this was the prizewinner—a cloying, transparently patronizing paean to his accusers and to the President in the incredible hope that they would not insist that he admit he was a crook:

There have been some suggestions in the media that this investigation was politically inspired; that the prosecutor or even the Attorney General sought to gain political advantage at my expense. I will have no part in any such suggestions. I do not believe them. Having served with Attorney General Richardson for five years in this administration, I know him to be a straight-shooting and devoted public servant. So far as the United States Attorney is concerned, I endorsed his appointment when it was made, and I would do so again today. [He had, in fact, tried to block Beall's appointment.]

Nor do I believe that the President had any role in this matter. I have been honored to serve in this administration. I have always held him in the highest regard as my President and my friend. I hold him in that regard today. Mr. Richardson and Mr. Beall are of course responsible for this prosecution of me, but I believe that they are only doing their jobs. I have no reason to believe that they act out of any political or personal motivation. When a prosecutor learns of evidence, it is his job to investigate, and if the evidence seems to support a charge, it is his duty to prosecute. That is what they have done here, no more and no less. I have no reason to complain of anything they have done.

This remarkable document, in addition to providing some comic relief, offered the tense prosecutorial team a new measure of the man they were jousting with: a desperate man, a cold, pragmatic, unprincipled man who, for all his pride, was willing to abandon it publicly to stay out of jail.

While his lawyers were busy trying to float this and other proposals past the Justice Department, Agnew himself was going to the top. Secretly, he asked for and received a one-on-one appointment with the President. The meeting ran on so long that Agnew had to cancel a tennis date; meanwhile the White House put a firm clamp-down on any acknowledgment of the meeting. It was very rapidly clear from developments, however, that Agnew was there to complain to the President that Richardson and the Justice Department were making it too tough for him to strike a deal, asking too much, especially in wanting him to plead to a felony and admit he had accepted payoffs made for the purpose of influencing him.

At the close of this whirlwind day, Richardson was summoned to the White House to discuss the whole matter with Haig and Buzhardt. The two White House men made clear in no uncertain terms that Agnew had to go, and go quickly, and Richardson must not be allowed to stand in the way with his overly tough terms. But Richardson held firm to his nonnegotiable conditions.

The next morning Richardson called in his lieutenants to discuss it once again. He told them Agnew had been in to see the President and had said he wasn't going to quit under the terms offered. Obviously, they would never accept language in an Agnew statement that simply said the government was presenting a case but he wasn't guilty. But was there some give in the Justice position, Richardson asked each of them? Moore said they should hold fast. There was a point at which the Justice Department had to be willing to rely on the traditional steps to solve a case, and to say so. Petersen agreed, and so did the others.

When Richardson called Buzhardt to tell him he was standing pat, he was braced for resistance. Instead, Haig called back and told him the President thought he was doing the right thing, and then Haig and Buzhardt said they now thought so too. Apparently Nixon had reconsidered, and decided that rather than precipitate a blowup, he'd better go along. After all, it was no time to lose an attorney general. Nixon's lawyers were in stiff and unyielding negotiations with Watergate prosecutor Cox over release of the White House tapes in *that* stormy, unpredictable case.

Richardson later would not acknowledge that there had been strong White House pressure on the Justice Department to soften its position, but the prosecutors knew, and were greatly disturbed by it—none more than Petersen, who for all his dutiful bureaucratic background and style was a staunch defender of the integrity of the Justice Department.

There followed through the course of Friday a series of phone calls—between Richardson and Buzhardt, between Richardson and Best (who was in Buzhardt's office much of the day), and between Beall and his associates back in Baltimore. The interplay was predictable—the White House and Best leaning on Richardson to soften, the Baltimoreans imploring Beall to lean on him to hold fast.

Buzhardt, a relentless broker, pressured for some significant concession. The Agnew side continued to be particularly hung up on the word "knowing" in the plea-bargaining letter's fourth paragraph, and finally Richardson agreed that it could be dropped if a few minor adjustments were made elsewhere in the statement. Petersen came up with a section that then became the focal point of all further debate. Known to all the participants as H.E.P. No. 3, it said:

Mr. Agnew's decision to resign and enter a plea of *nolo contendere* rests on the belief that the public interest requires a swift resolution of the problems generated by the investigation of his actions. Mr. Agnew acknowledges that, pursuant to a longstanding practice in the State of Maryland, he, directly and through agents, upon assuming the office of Governor, made arrangements for the payment of money to himself and his representatives by contractors who sought consulting contracts with the State of Maryland.

Mr. Agnew further acknowledges that contracts were awarded to those who paid such monies and that he was aware that contracts were awarded by state agencies to those companies. Government witnesses will testify that preferential treatment was accorded the paying companies, pursuant to an understanding with the Governor. Mr. Agnew stresses, however, that no contract was awarded to contractors who were not competent to perform the work, and he further states that there were, of course, many instances where State contracts were awarded without any arrangement for the payment of money by the contractor. He is confident that testimony presented on his own behalf would make this inescapably clear.

In all the circumstances, Mr. Agnew has concluded that a protracted investigation and trial, with the controversy surrounding them, would seriously prejudice the national interest. These, briefly stated, are the reasons why he is entering a plea of *nolo contendere* to the charge that he did receive payments which he failed to report for purposes of income taxation, and that such failure constitutes a wilful evasion of Federal tax liability.

This Petersen draft was very close to what Agnew eventually did agree to. But in Baltimore, the reaction to the offer was as might have been expected—anguish. To Petersen, it may have been a mild softening, giving away nothing vital, but to the Baltimoreans it was a clear retreat. It was one thing for Agnew's lawyers to propose a compromise that weakened what the government had said were its nonnegotiable terms. It was quite another for the government itself to come back with a weaker position. Beall, in Washington, got a telephone earful from his colleagues, but the prosecutors offered a few suggestions after they had simmered down. Best finally came over to the Justice Department at 8:45 that night and Richardson handed him H.E.P. No. 3. He took it, read it, and said he would be back in touch. The Vice President would want to consider it over the weekend.

The Baltimoreans waited, and hoped that what they considered a major mistake would not be seized by Agnew, and that in further talks the damage wrought to the government position could be repaired. Late that night, however, something happened that provided at least a rationale for Agnew to break off negotiations. The *Washington Post* appeared with a story by Richard M. Cohen and Lou Cannon that blew the cover on the plea bargaining:

Vice President Agnew's lawyers and Justice Department officials have been engaged in what was described yesterday as delicate negotiations concerning a possible Agnew resignation to be coupled with a guilty plea to a relatively minor offense, according to informed sources.

The negotiations, according to two sources, could be described as plea bargaining. One informed source refused to say whether the negotiations were close to a conclusion or to reveal the details of what has been discussed at the Justice Department. A Capitol Hill source said: "We've got it on good authority that Agnew is engaged in plea bargaining—that Agnew's resignation is part of it."

This news brought to public attention for the first time the reality that Agnew might indeed step down. None were more jolted by the story than Agnew's faithful staff and old friends. The solidarity that had existed within the Agnew inner circle began to show some cracks, though it yet held together.

The weekend was one of soul-searching and waiting all around. Richardson's team, in its fashion of preparing for all eventualities, began to draft a position for Justice in the event the negotiations broke down. They knew that if that happened, there would be a wild scramble to place blame. Richardson himself felt that if Agnew balked, it would be because he could not bring himself to go along with their insistence that he make admission beyond mere tax avoidance. He talked again with Haig and Buzhardt; Agnew deliberated. It was possible that a move to Judge Hoffman to obtain his approval of the deal might be at hand, and Richardson did not want the settlement to get away. The prospect of Agnew's taking his case to the public in a dirty, brawling spectacle dismayed him, but no more so than the idea of destiny suddenly elevating the man to the national leadership.

Up in Baltimore, the young prosecutors were running other pictures through their minds, such as one of the biggest fishes in American prosecutorial history getting off the hook with little more than a rip in his gill. On Monday, Skolnik, Baker, and Liebman in their despair prepared a memo to Beall saying they did not want to have anything to do with the plea bargaining any more. The three men most directly responsible for bringing Agnew to book suggested that in the event agreement were reached on the basis of H.E.P. No. 3, they might be obliged to do whatever in conscience they thought necessary—a hint they might publicly disavow the settlement. In the meantime, they would proceed as authorized to start presenting evidence to the grand jury, and they asked that their decision be communicated to the attorney general. This dramatic memo of dissent, had it become public, would have jabbed a gaping hole in Richardson's boat. The downcast trio eventually realized that and never gave the memo to Beall.

In Washington, on Monday, September 24, Richardson and his chief aides waited all day to hear from Best, who was across town at the Old Executive Office Building with his client. Agnew was livid. As far as he was concerned, the *Post* story about the negotiations had been leaked by the Justice Department for the dual purpose of embarrassing him and eroding his bargaining position. The Vice President, in the words of one associate, said he was "being screwed to the wall." He was innocent, he said, "and the public must believe I'm innocent. This makes it impossible to have a fair trial." Elliot Richardson and his young punks with Harvard degrees could wait until hell froze over before the Vice President of the United States would authorize his representatives to return to the bargaining table.

As in wartime when there is a deadlock in truce talks, Agnew decided to return to the battlefield to improve his bargaining position. But the group at the Justice Department did not know that. All day they waited and heard nothing from Agnew.

What they heard instead was the heartbeat of Richard Milhous Nixon. This alone, they knew, kept Spiro T. Agnew, a man they were convinced to a moral certainty stood on the brink of indictment as a felon, from the Presidency of the United States.

CHAPTER 11

GOING ON THE OFFENSIVE

On the morning of Tuesday, September 25, convinced that the plea bargaining had failed, Attorney General Elliot Richardson, accompanied by Henry Petersen, went to see President Nixon. Richardson told Nixon the Justice Department had all the evidence it needed to indict Agnew and the time had come to turn it over to the Baltimore grand jury and seek an indictment against him.

This judgment did not set well at the White House, where the President's lawyers in the Watergate case were busy building the legal position that a President could not be indicted. They wanted Justice to proceed before the grand jury without addressing the issue of whether a Vice President could be indicted or tried.

Richardson argued to the President that the Justice Department could not present the government's case against Agnew in court without taking a clear stand that the Vice President could be indicted and tried *before* first having been impeached and convicted in Congress. But, he said, it was Justice's plan, after any indictment, to offer to defer to the House of Representatives, so that it could launch impeachment proceedings if it chose before a criminal trial was begun. In fact, some consideration was given to seeking only a presentment from the grand jury—a report of findings, without an indictment—and then turning over the whole package to the House. The Justice Department would contend that if the House acted, then Justice had no authority to go to trial until after the impeachment proceedings had been carried out.

The idea of giving way to the House was more to the White House's liking—short of a swift and clean resignation, which now seemed out of the question. The reason for such interest was, obviously, the same as in their concern about Richardson going too far and too fast on the indictment track: Nixon's own legal dilemma on Watergate. If the House started an impeachment inquiry, the action could obviate a court struggle on the question of the indictability of a Vice President—or President —while he was still in office.

Richardson and Petersen had not been gone long from the Oval Office when Agnew arrived to see Nixon. The tortured Vice President told the President—did not ask him, the White House emphasized later—that he had decided to go to the House of Representatives for a hearing and, he hoped, a "vindication." The news was not, of course, a surprise to Nixon. Agnew and his lawyers had passed the word as early as the Labor Day weekend that they were contemplating this course. Just as the President's own lawyers did in the Watergate affair, Agnew clung to the contention that he could not be tried in a criminal proceeding so long as he was in office; that the only recourse to those who wanted to remove him was impeachment.

The fact that the tactic put Agnew publicly in direct conflict with the official prosecutorial arm of the administration in which he served did not seem to disturb Nixon. In effect, he stood back and gave his blessing to the collision course on which each side was now embarked. This seeming neutrality was a bizarre demonstration of presidential decisiveness and leadership in crisis, and it showed well that the surmise had been correct that he feared alienating Agnew's Middle American constituency.

Over at Justice, Richardson was in the midst of preparing a statement that the evidence against Agnew would begin to go to the grand jury, when a presidential aide phoned to ask that no news be released until 4 P.M. By the time the Justice Department's press release came out, Agnew had been to Capitol Hill and had called on the Speaker of the House of Representatives, Carl Albert—the man who would be next in line to succeed to the President if the Vice President were removed from office or resigned. He presented Albert with a letter that cast in its most positive terms the end run his lawyers had worked out. He was requesting "a full inquiry" (he did not ask to be impeached but that's what it amounted to) "in the dual interests of preserving the Constitutional stature of my office and accomplishing my personal vindication." His lawyers had advised him, he wrote, "that the Constitution bars a criminal proceeding of any kind—federal or state, county or town—against a President or Vice President while he holds office," and therefore he could neither "acquiesce" in any such criminal proceeding nor look to it for vindication.

Agnew cited as a precedent for a House investigation the similar request made by Vice President John C. Calhoun in 1826, when faced with charges that he had profited from an Army contract while he was secretary of war. Like Calhoun, Agnew said, he would cooperate fully and, like Calhoun, "I am confident that . . . I shall be vindicated by the House."

Albert decided the next day, September 26, to let Agnew stew in his own juice. Of the three options open to Agnew—resignation, possible indictment, or impeachment—the third was swiftly cut off, at least until after indictment. Albert said it would not be proper for the House to act on a matter before the courts. The abrupt termination of the plea bargaining had seemingly ruled out the possibility of resignation, and so there was only the court test. Agnew told his key aides he was determined to fight it.

Agnew's lawyers asked the court to "enter a protective order prohibiting the grand jury from conducting any investigation looking to possible indictment of applicant [Agnew] and from issuing any indictment, presentment or other charge or statement pertaining to applicant." It asked the court to prohibit the Justice Department from presenting any evidence at all to the grand jury.

These requests were based on two grounds. The first became known as the "constitutional issue," and it was straightforward: "The Constitution forbids that the Vice President be indicted or convicted in any criminal court." The second, however, was more subtle, possibly unprecedented. Agnew's lawyers maintained that the news leaks had deprived Agnew of "all hope of a fair hearing on the merits." But, not stopping there, they laid the blame for the leaks squarely on the government itself and contended that the prosecution had poisoned its own case. In case anyone missed the point, Topkis, London, and Best attached a ten-page affidavit in which they accused the Justice Department of mounting a "deliberate campaign" to leak information.

Attached to the affidavit were copies of stories that had appeared in *The New York Times, The Washington Post, The Baltimore Sun, Time,* and *Newsweek.* Three in particular seemed to rankle the lawyers: the *New York Times* story that reported on Agnew's meeting with Richardson; a CBS report in which Petersen was quoted as saying, "We've got the evidence; we've got it cold"; and the *Washington Post* story about the plea bargaining.

Agnew's motion had the prosecutors and Richardson livid. They had no quarrel with the constitutional brief. But asking the court to abort the investigation because of the leaks was a different matter. To a man, the prosecutorial side felt that Agnew had moved prematurely; that he had no call to raise the specter of pretrial publicity even before he was indicted.

Moreover, the strident tone in Topkis's affidavit, the prosecutors felt, was an unwarranted attack on the Justice Department. Topkis had not offered any evidence that the information had come from the government other than to cite stories that quoted "Justice Department sources." That was hardly proof positive.

Topkis, for one, agreed. He had no intention of laying out his proof in an affidavit. His strategy called for Agnew's side to subpoena the reporters who had written the stories (and some Justice Department officials) and ask the newsmen two questions: did they actually write the story, and, if so, were they being truthful when they cited "Justice Department sources"? There, Topkis would stop. If the reporters answered "yes" to both questions, the lawyer envisioned telling the judge a *prima facie* case existed to indicate that the government was the culprit.

But Topkis miscalculated. The news organizations whose reporters were subpoenaed—*The New York Times, The Washington Star-News, The Washington Post, Time, Newsweek,* the New York *Daily News,* CBS, and NBC—were some of the wealthiest in the land and prepared to bear the expense of protracted litigation. None of them was ready to answer any of Topkis's questions, regardless of how innocuous they might be. At that point, a judge might hold the newsmen in contempt of court and order them jailed. It would all depend on the judge, and the man chosen to preside over the Agnew case turned out to be a most unpredictable wild card.

Walter Edward Hoffman had been selected by Chief Judge Clement F. Haynsworth, Jr., of the U.S. Court of Appeals for the Fourth District, which included Maryland and Virginia. Hoffman, who normally presided in Norfolk, Virginia, was selected on August 12 after all nine of the federal judges in Baltimore had disqualified themselves, citing some past association with Agnew. In Baltimore, Hoffman was an unknown commodity. He was a judge who instinctively questioned positions of the government. Indeed, he appeared almost to have an antigovernment streak in him. And, most notably, he had a pronounced hostility to the press, which he treated as an unnecessary nuisance.

Richardson assigned his solicitor general, Robert H. Bork, to prepare Justice's position combating the Agnew brief. It was a position in which the White House, not surprisingly, shared a great deal of interest. Eventually, Bork's brief made a strong and clear distinction: the President could not be indicted while still in office; the Vice President could. Suddenly, Agnew had one less argument to use with the White House. His and the President's legal fortunes were no longer intertwined.

In addition to the legal track open to Agnew, he had another that he had used often in his career as Vice President and as ambassador to Middle America—taking his case to the people. The objective of his legal moves was obvious and direct; what was sought in his "going public" was less so.

Agnew's first volley in the attempt to mobilize public opinion was fired on Thursday, September 27, when he held a thinly veiled background interview with James B. Reston, the *New York Times*'s prestigious columnist. The lead on the story, which ran the next day, did not quote Agnew directly as the source but left no doubt that he was: "Vice President Agnew has made up his mind about the next phase of what he calls his 'nightmare.' He does not intend to resign, even if he is indicted by the Baltimore grand jury, but to fight for exoneration through the courts, and keep appealing to the House of Representatives for a full and open hearing, no matter how long it takes."

Reston's article also fingered Petersen as Agnew's primary target. "Mr. Agnew is obviously angry about Mr. Petersen and the criminal division of the Justice Department," Reston wrote. "He feels that they are on the defensive because, as he suspects, they did not turn up much evidence in the Watergate case that came out later in the Senate hearings, that they mishandled an important case about organized crime, that they resented the appointment of Archibald Cox as special prosecutor . . . and were now trying to make up for their losses at his expense." The Vice President was not criticizing the President's handling of the case "but is less sure about members of the President's staff." The President "has never pressed him to resign or even to take a single step he did not want to take."

Reston's article concluded: "[Agnew] guesses that despite many doubts, he really would have tried for the Presidency in 1976 but this is obviously 'all over' now. But the fight is not all over, he insists, but just beginning, for he has to clear himself, and this is what he says he is determined to do."

The interview with Reston was, in effect, Agnew's declaration of war. The next thing was to select a proper battleground for his first personal assault. He was to go to California that weekend to address the National Federation of Republican Women; David Keene, his political adviser, was asked to review a routine speech. Keene sent it to Agnew with a memo saying if Agnew did indeed intend to speak out, this was the ideal occasion.

En route to Los Angeles, Agnew, his military aide General Mike Dunn, and Peter Malatesta stopped off in Palm Springs on Friday as the guests of Frank Sinatra. Agnew and Sinatra played golf in the afternoon, and later they gathered with the others, including Mrs. Agnew and their daughter Susan, in the living room of Sinatra's place. "We sat around that afternoon and he was in a terribly pensive mood, he was low," one of those present said later. Before dinner, three or four of the insiders—including Sinatra—discussed Topic A over drinks, unanimous that Agnew had to go to the people with his side of the story.

The next morning, after breakfast at Sinatra's, the party boarded the Vice President's Jetstar for Los Angeles. En route, Agnew took a piece of white paper and felt-tip pen from his pocket and began quietly to jot down notes for an addendum to the speech. In Los Angeles, the party went by car to the Republican women's convention, where about 2000 loyalists—and alerted network television cameras—were waiting to hear the embattled Vice President. Signs proclaimed the overwhelmingly prevalent sentiment: "Spiro My Hero" and "Agnew for President."

Agnew strode calmly to the speaker's platform amid a tumultuous greeting that told him emphatically: We don't believe it. He read through his formal text—in which his only reference to his troubles was a broad discussion of the need for grand jury secrecy to avoid his own "cruel form of kangaroo trial in the media"—then, taking the folded white sheet from his pocket but looking directly into the television cameras, he began what doubtless was one of the most scathing attacks ever made against members of a national administration by a ranking figure in that same administration. Henry Petersen again was the prime target.

"In the past several months I have been living in purgatory," Agnew began extemporaneously. "I have found myself the recipient of undefined, unclear, and unattributed accusations that have surfaced in the largest and most widely circulated organs of our communications media. I want to say at this point—clearly and unequivocally—I am innocent of the charges against me."

The declaration ignited the attentive women to wild cheering and applause. Even as Agnew resumed it continued, but he pressed on above the din: "I have not used my office, nor abused my public trust as county executive, as governor, or as Vice President to enrich myself at the expense of my fellow Americans."

Then the onslaught really started. "I say this to you," he declared firmly, "that conduct of high individuals in the Department of Justice, particularly the conduct of the chief of the criminal investigation division of that department [Petersen], is unprofessional and malicious and outrageous, if I am to believe what has been printed in the news magazines and said on the television networks of this country, and I have had no denial that this is the case."

Referring to his motion before Judge Hoffman about the leaks, Agnew said that if he could examine the officials and were to find that they "have abused their sacred trust and forsaken their professional standards, then I will ask the President of the United States to summarily discharge those individuals."

Agnew reiterated his basic argument that he was the scapegoat for others under criminal investigation who were trying to save their own necks by buying immunity. That was why he felt he had to turn to the House, he said—because "the well has been most successfully poisoned" in the courts by the Justice Department.

And then, finally, was the categorical no-surrender declaration: "I want to make another thing so clear that it cannot be mistaken in the future. Because of these tactics which have been employed against me, because small and fearful men have been frightened into furnishing evidence against me—they have perjured themselves in many cases, it's my understanding—I will not resign if indicted. I will not resign if indicted.

"Our Constitution says that every man is entitled to a fair trial and a presumption of innocence. I intend to rely on the spirit as well as the letter of those guarantees. I would forsake the principles of the Founding Fathers if I abandoned this fight. And I do not intend to abandon it. . . ."

It was clear enough. The consensus at Sinatra's place in Palm Springs the night before had been converted unequivocally into the firm public posture of Spiro Agnew: he would fight to the end.

Back at the Justice Department in Washington there was little relaxation or elation. There was only chagrin and bewilderment at the

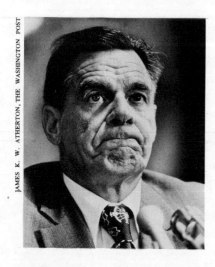

Henry E. Petersen

tactic. Petersen had been working at the department and was driving home in his car when Agnew's speech came over the radio. He heard most of the formal, impersonal part of it before arriving at his house. He was eating his lunch in another room, with the television set on in the living room, when Agnew concluded his text and launched into his attack of the Justice Department and its anti-crime chief.

"I ran into the living room to watch him attack me," Petersen recalled. "And I commented to my wife, I said, 'Jean, he just made a terrible mistake.' That's so commonplace in this business—for the prosecutor to be attacked when he's got a very, very strong case." At the same time, though, Petersen was aware that this was no commonplace investigation and that he could not counterattack. "I told her also, 'I'm not going to be able to say anything. This is going to be a tough week, and we're just going to have to grin and bear it, and it will all resolve itself when the evidence comes out.'

"But it's one thing to say that to your wife. It really is difficult to walk around and take it."

In Baltimore, the prosecutors were shocked at Agnew's Los Angeles harangue. They had been bracing themselves for an attack from Agnew, but they had thought the target would be Skolnik, whom Agnew had repeatedly denigrated in private. Baker, who caught only the last part of the speech, was flabbergasted. Agnew had committed an enormous tactical error, he thought. It was one thing to attack someone like Skolnik—a virtual nobody—but Petersen? The prosecutors couldn't understand the strategy.

The theory ran somewhat differently among Richardson's men. "We had been led to believe that Agnew had a phased escalation strategy," one of them said later. "First, he was going to attack Henry Petersen. Then, he was going to attack Beall and the Baltimoreans—*ad hominem* arguments. Next Richardson. Next the President. A four-stage shot." This incredible bit of cold-blooded intelligence actually came from the White House, the Justice aide said.

On the day before Agnew's speech, Richardson had gotten a message directly from the President himself that was most revealing. When the attorney general had been at the White House to tell Nixon that he had determined the Vice President was indictable under the Constitution, and that he was going forward with presentation of a brief to that effect, the President had made no response to that. But, according to the notes of one of those de-briefed by Richardson immediately thereafter, he told Richardson that he was "looking forward to getting the Agnew thing over with, at which point he would fire Cox" or get rid of him some other way. Richardson apparently did not take this remark seriously, this insider said later, adding with a grin, "Not as seriously as he should have." Ten days after Agnew's resignation, Cox was indeed fired, at the cost of Richardson's own resignation in protest.

This presidential comment dovetailed with what the attorney general and his close aides were in fact actively discussing as "the hat-trick hypothesis." A hat trick in hockey—which is king in Richardson's Boston—is three goals scored by a single player in one game. "We thought possibly the President wanted to get rid of Richardson, Agnew, and Cox," one Richardson associate said, "but that he would get rid of them in some combination deal that would begin with Agnew." Such was the climate of deep distrust of the White House and the President within the inner sanctum of his own attorney general's office.

The idea that Agnew might have a strategy of "phased escalation," aimed first at Petersen and eventually targeting the President himself as the cause of Agnew's woes, would have been incredible to the men around the Vice President. Repeatedly and to a man, those who would allow themselves any criticism of him at all would focus on only one shortcoming—that he held the President, and the power of the Presidency, and the influence of the men around it, in too much awe.

The Los Angeles speech, however, while not attacking the President or even Richardson, left no doubt in any quarter that there would be no resignation by Spiro Agnew, no matter what signals might be flashed from the White House. The explicitness, even viciousness of his speech, seemed to seal that conclusion. The Justice Department accordingly pressed on with its case against him, the White House braced itself for the worst, and the Agnew loyalists looked forward with the faith of true believers to their boss's two-fisted counterattack.

CHAPTER 12

A CANDLE IS ONLY SO LONG

In the golden days of Spiro Agnew's divisive oratory, in his days of alliterative anarchy when such perversions of the English language as "nattering nabobs of negativism" and "hopeless, hysterical, hypochondriacs of history" tripped tastelessly from his tongue, he had been widely applauded for talking straight. And so it had been with his Los Angeles tirade against the Justice Department.

Among those who got the message most clearly was the President of the United States, and he was outraged. When Agnew's rhetoric attacked the President's own official family, in inference it attacked him. Richard Nixon already was under criticism for seeming to stand blithely aside as his attorney general pressed for an indictment against his Vice President while the latter ran off to the Hill for relief. And now, remaining silent in the face of Agnew's public slap at his Justice Department and at his favorite, Petersen, Nixon looked like a marshmallow, and he knew it. Going after Petersen as Agnew did was Agnew's fatal mistake—as Petersen himself judged—and he was about to find that out in unmistakable terms.

The President's first step was to determine whether Agnew knew what he was talking about when he accused Petersen. Richardson was asked for, and swiftly provided, assurances that Petersen had not leaked to the press. Next, the President phoned Elliot Richardson at home. While Nixon believed he must maintain a posture of neutrality, in order not to alienate the Agnew constituency, he "wanted me to know that he was supporting me. . . ."

Agnew's blunder on Petersen was compounded in the eyes of the White House on Tuesday, October 2, when Marsh Thomson predicted to reporters that more of the same bombast dished out in Los Angeles was in the offing for the Vice President's next speech.

At the White House, Thomson's remarks, printed on page one of *The Washington Post* the next morning, were a red flag of defiance.

PAY LESS ATTENTION TO KOOKS AND DEMAGOGUES!

TV

PRESS

ADMINISTRATION

©1970 HERBLOCK

"GOSH, WHAT IF THEY SHOULD
TAKE US UP ON THAT?"

Alexander Haig called Art Sohmer, Agnew's right-hand man, and told him point blank: the President wanted no more public attacks on Petersen, the Justice Department, or the Nixon administration, or there would never be a deal. And without a deal, Agnew should know where the trail would certainly end—behind bars. For openers, this fellow Thomson had to be throttled, as evidence to the White House that Agnew got the message.

That same day, October 3, President Nixon delivered another message to Agnew—more publicly. He called a rare informal press conference in his office, and, while telling the reporters that he regarded Agnew's decision not to resign even if indicted "an altogether proper one," Nixon characterized the charges against Agnew as "serious and not frivolous." Also, most significantly, he defended Henry Petersen. Richardson had assured him, Nixon reported, that there was no such evidence to support Agnew's charges, especially on the matter of leaks.

That issue—the leaks and their potential or real damage to the Vice President's chances for a fair hearing and trial in the courts or Congress—now emerged as a basic defense in Agnew's desperate legal fight to avert disaster. Jay Topkis, having filed the brief seeking to halt the grand jury investigation, had begun to try to build his case with personal testimony from reporters. He phoned Richard Cohen of *The Washington Post* and asked him to identify his sources on the Agnew story. Cohen, on the instruction of his superiors, told Topkis to contact Joseph Califano, who was the *Post's* lawyer. Others who received similar calls were Fred Graham of CBS News, and Ben A. Franklin of *The New York Times*. They also declined to identify their sources.

On October 3, the same day as Nixon's press conference, Judge Hoffman in Baltimore took steps that threatened to move the focus of the case off Agnew's guilt or innocence and turn it into a freedom-of-the-press debate. He assembled members of the grand jury in open court for a lecture about their responsibility to ignore news reports and decide their course solely on the evidence presented to them in secrecy. Before doing so, he summoned Agnew's three lawyers and three of the prosecutors —Beall, Skolnik, and Liebman—to Room 630 in the courthouse. The judge distributed to each of them a copy of the supplemental charge he was about to make to the grand jury and asked them if they had any comments. "Unfortunately, in the present-day grab for priority in getting news items, the news media frequently overlook the rights of others, especially where criminal matters are involved," the charge warned. "We are rapidly approaching the day when the perpetual conflict between the news media, operating as they do under freedom of speech and freedom of the press, and the judicial system, charged with protecting the rights of persons under investigation for criminal acts, must be resolved." In other words, Hoffman would not mind making this a landmark case on the press.

Beall could hardly believe what was happening. Raising this basic press question in an already historic case was dismaying enough; but cutting the defendant's lawyers in on the decision on how to instruct the grand jury was just too much.

After a long and bruising legal exchange, Martin London got to the crux of the matter. His client would like to begin taking depositions on the leaks issue as soon as possible.

This time Beall and Skolnik rose in unison. If the judge allowed

Agnew's lawyers to begin taking depositions, he was presupposing the merits of their claim—namely that the leaks had come from the government. Moreover, Beall argued, taking the depositions seemed to be a transparent attempt to tie up the prosecutors in the civil action at the expense of the criminal case they were building. Beall wanted a crack at the other side—including Agnew.

Judge Hoffman, however, was not yet willing to have the government have its way. He would have to think about whether the government had the right to call Agnew's lawyers and Agnew himself as witnesses in the civil case. As for London's request to start taking depositions, Hoffman signed it on the spot. Hoffman added that he wanted to be present when the witnesses were deposed, since he wanted to be able to judge their demeanor when answering questions, even ask some questions himself, possibly. Now Topkis had gotten more than he bargained for. What Hoffman was saying, the lawyer knew well, was that he wanted to be able to hold in contempt immediately any reporter who would not answer a question. The last thing Agnew or his lawyers wanted at that point was to see reporters from some of the most powerful news-gathering organizations in the country thrown into the ancient Baltimore City jail on contempt-of-court charges.

Topkis, however, raised no objections to Hoffman's request. He told the judge he wanted to depose Richardson, Petersen, and Beall and would submit more names later that morning. When the list arrived in Hoffman's temporary chambers it read: "Witnesses: Elliot L. Richardson, Henry E. Petersen, George Beall, Glen E. Pommerening, Jonathan Moore, *Time* magazine authors of 8/27 and 9/3 stories, Fred Graham, Nicholas Gage, Robert Walters and Ronald Sarro, *Newsweek* author of 8/20 article, [and] Richard Cohen."

The whole episode had been so casual that it was possible to lose sight of what had just happened. The Attorney General of the United States, for one, would be commanded to appear in court to deny that he was a common gossipmonger. Next would come the other Justice Department officials, one-by-one, all the way down to Skolnik (later added to the list). Topkis and Skolnik had taken an immediate dislike to each other: it would be a wonderful confrontation.

Beall and Skolnik, dismayed by the carte blanche Hoffman had given Agnew's lawyers, returned angrily to their offices, where Beall fired off a memo suggesting that Justice bring in a lawyer to defend Justice officials and the prosecutors in the motion. Within a day, the department named the U.S. attorney for Chicago, James Thompson, to handle the case.

By Friday, Thompson was in Baltimore interviewing his new clients—Beall and Skolnik. For the two, it was a most uncomfortable—and unique—experience. Skolnik, who had been served with his subpoena that morning, spent until noon briefing Thompson on whatever information he had on the source of the leaks.

For Agnew, the civil suit about the news leaks was not so pressing as the President's clear message conveyed in his press conference and in the instructions to deflate Marsh Thomson: lay off, or else. When Agnew left for a Chicago speech on Thursday, October 4, he seemed particularly preoccupied.

It was in an atmosphere of general pessimism and desperation that Agnew's plane arrived in Chicago for what Thomson had billed in advance as another Agnew bombshell. The Agnew party arrived in early afternoon, and for an hour in his suite at the Drake the Vice President conferred with W. Clement Stone. Stone, who had acknowledged contributions of $2.1 million to the Nixon-Agnew ticket in 1972 and who was not a bashful man about hard-money figures, would only say afterward that he was getting "a response in volume" for the Agnew legal-defense fund from all parts of the country. Actually, Justice Department sources learned later that a phone bank to receive pledges had generated only $310 in a week!

Presumably this gloomy result was conveyed to Agnew, who by now doubtless was toting up the pluses and minuses of his fight to stay in office and finding himself in the red in nearly every column: the government had the goods on him; the impeachment route appeared to be shut off; the public plea bargaining in Los Angeles had created neither a groundswell of support nor a whipped attorney general coming to him with a softer deal; and money to fight in the courts wasn't coming in, either. Internal Revenue agents were tracking down his spending habits practically to the last nickel. His attempts in court to fight indictability were about to be undercut. And there was the national interest to be considered, and the peace of mind of his family. Agnew made these points himself in conversation with his lawyers. And, finally, there was the threatening pressure from the President: that he must lay off scapegoating and demagoguing administration officials or take the consequences.

Agnew spoke that night in the Imperial Ballroom of the Conrad Hilton to a full house of party faithful, who were expecting a ringing defense of himself and a renewed attack on his adversaries. Usually all business on the speaking platform, uttering some of the most incendiary rhetoric in the annals of political oratory, Agnew this time seemed to some of the reporters to be downright gloomy, worn-out, and distracted.

At the outset, the Vice President turned his gaze to the national reporters. "Tonight is not going to be an X-rated political show," he told them. "It's just going to be PG. So if you have to go someplace, go.

"A candle is only so long before it burns out."

That one cryptic remark was pregnant with suggestion. The reporters who heard it, and who considered it in the context of the rest of the speech and Agnew's gloomy demeanor, thought they were onto something. Malatesta didn't put much significance in it. "I don't believe that when he went to Chicago he knew he was going to resign," he said later. "I didn't lose any sleep over it that night."

On Friday afternoon, October 5, Agnew returned to Washington. By that time, the subpoenas sought by Agnew's lawyers had been served on nine reporters, and the Justice Department had filed its brief (written by

Mr. and Mrs. Agnew the day after the resignation

Bork) denying Agnew's contention that the Constitution protected him from being indicted in office. The serving of the subpoenas once again cast Agnew in his old role as tormentor of the press. To a reporter, there is no greater sin than turning on the law to force him to testify about his sources. So this new development was not likely to help Agnew in the long run. Within three days, Justice had submitted a persuasive brief opposing the subpoenaing of newsmen and denying Agnew's charge of a "conspiracy" to release information about his case.

Bork's brief on the constitutional question, taking the Vice President out of the boat in which the President hoped to sail past possible indictment himself in the Watergate affair, also left Agnew more exposed than he had been only a few days before. It is conceivable that this fact was particularly persuasive to Agnew and his lawyers in determining whether to continue the fight. In any event, a series of developments now began that finally culminated in the first resignation in disgrace of a Vice President of the United States.

Judah Best had another conference with his client on Friday. It must have been obvious to both of them that there simply was not much left for Agnew to go on. If it had not been clear before, it was clear now that the power of the White House, for which Spiro Agnew had such awe, was solidly arrayed against him. He told Best to contact Fred Buzhardt and get the plea bargaining going again.

Buzhardt, who was in Key Biscayne, didn't want to return to Washington, for fear the press would see him and realize what was happening, so he asked Agnew's lawyer to meet him at the Miami International Airport that night. Best went home, changed into sports clothes, donned sun glasses, and boarded an Eastern Airlines night flight. Buzhardt met him at the gate at about 1:30 A.M., and they drove to the nearby Marriott Motor Hotel. The visitor registered as "Jud Best" and gave the New York address of his firm. Best told Buzhardt that Agnew was ready to make a deal on the same basis as offered when the talks had broken down two weeks earlier. The only difference, he said, was that Agnew wanted to make a statement in court denying the allegations—exactly what Richardson and Company were determined not to permit him to do.

Buzhardt was conciliatory. He said the Vice President should feel he was under no pressure to do anything, that if he wanted to fight, if he wanted to keep trying the impeachment route, he was free to do so. Best said he had already made another stab on Capitol Hill, and that his instructions from Agnew were to see what could be done concerning a deal. He then produced a draft of the statement Agnew wanted to make. Buzhardt studied it; he thought something could be worked out, he said.

About five hours later, the phone rang in Elliot Richardson's home in McLean. It was Buzhardt. They spoke for a few minutes, and then Richardson called Richard Darman, his special assistant, and asked him to come over right away. "When I got there," Darman said later, "I discovered we were back in the plea-bargaining business."

What had brought Agnew back to the bargaining table, Richardson was told by the White House, was the exhaustive net-worth investigation that the small army of IRS agents had undertaken.

With the wraps off the Agnew investigation, the IRS had opened a full-court press on the Vice President's spending habits. It was an intimidating example of governmental power—as intimidating, possibly, as the phone call from Haig. Had it continued, it might have resulted in an airtight tax case against Agnew that would have made his plea bargaining all the more difficult. Moreover, the spicy insights into Agnew's personal life that the prosecutors had already ruled out of bounds might well have surfaced here. If Agnew had spent money in ways that could prove personally embarrassing, only a gentlemen's agreement between the two sides could keep the information from the public eye at a trial. But by now, as Agnew knew well, he had drawn too much blood at the Justice Department to rely on its good graces.

About 10:30 on Saturday morning, October 6, Buzhardt phoned Best at the Miami motel and suggested that they talk again in a little while—Best might as well go back to Washington and call him when he arrived there. Best did so, and Buzhardt then told him he could inform his client that it looked as if there were a deal. Best called Richardson and they discussed where the talks stood. When the negotiations had broken off fifteen days earlier, the parties had been debating the relatively minor matter of what Agnew would be permitted to say in a formal statement to reply to the charges. Best told Richardson Agnew required a further softening, and he dictated to the attorney general's secretary the same statement he had handed to Buzhardt in the Miami motel the night before.

"The issue was would we allow some dilution of the statement we got hung up on last time," Richardson recalled later. The attorney general held firm that there would have to be some admission, and that the accused could not be free to engage in Agnewisms against the prosecutors. As a last sop, Richardson agreed to the inclusion of a statement by Agnew that said Agnew was not guilty of anything he hadn't admitted to.

To counter this concession, Richardson insisted on two things: Justice would say the offense took place not only in 1967, as Agnew wanted, but in other years as well, and the Agnew camp would have nothing to say about what went into Justice's full disclosure statement of evidence against him.

The time for niggling over the fine print was approaching an end. All that was left was to work out the details and the scenario of the actual resignation and settlement, and then to obtain Judge Hoffman's approval.

In Key Biscayne, Fred Buzhardt by now had passed the word on developments to Haig and President Nixon. Among the handful of presidential aides in Florida that weekend was Pat Buchanan, the media monitor and occasional speechwriter, who shortly before had made a brilliant appearance before the Senate Watergate Committee. The President had asked him to work on a speech about Watergate.

On Saturday Haig called Buchanan in. About the Watergate speech he was drafting—the President wanted a new tentative ending for it, in which the President would announce that the Vice President was resigning. Buchanan, who had been kept out of all the Agnew talks because of his loyalties to both men, was again stunned. Not only was he to write that Agnew was resigning but Haig told him that the new ending should indicate a possible recommendation for the new Vice President, and he gave Buchanan a name—not Gerald R. Ford, the man ultimately selected, not John B. Connally or Nelson A. Rockefeller or Ronald Reagan. (Buchanan later declined to say whose name it was, and would only suggest that it would have been a surprise.) Later, Ray Price, the White House aide in charge of all speechwriting, told Buchanan to write draft endings for several others, including Connally, Rockefeller, and Reagan. On Sunday, Haig told Buchanan that Agnew's resignation might come the next day.

On the government side, Richardson had one critical task to handle—bringing aboard the hard-nosed young Baltimoreans, still intent on indictment. First he called his own circle to join him in McLean, and for five hours they engaged in their customary preparations. Petersen and Beall were notified by phone.

Beall called his men and told them to get to the Justice Department by Sunday afternoon too. Psychologically, the Baltimore prosecutors had been conditioned by now to the idea that plea bargaining was over and they were moving on toward indictment. Richardson was going to have to bring them around once more.

The Sunday meeting was held in the conference room off Richardson's office, with all the Justice Ten present. The attorney general reviewed the events of the weekend, reiterated his reasons for pressing for a speedy settlement, and tried hard to reassure the Baltimoreans. As to their concern that Agnew might privately agree to an apparent deal and then blow the whistle publicly, both Richardson and Petersen said it was implausible. But if that happened, Richardson said, the department was reserving the right to answer publicly that Agnew had been plea bargaining again. As for feelings that Agnew ought to be made to admit to more, the attorney general suggested it was always possible that Judge Hoffman himself might extract more admission from him at the arraignment. But the important thing was the department's own full-disclosure statement. That would make or break the issue of the justice of the government's actions.

Skolnik, who had been brooding throughout about the resumption of plea bargaining and about the fact that a no-trial, no-jail deal was apparently emerging as a *fait accompli*, launched into a forceful and at times heated demurrer. He warned that there was a possibility that he would find himself unable to participate in the arraignment.

Baker took a shot at the Petersen draft of H.E.P. No. 3, and argued that the government should go back to the original wording on what Agnew would and would not admit. Of Agnew's three cards to play—resignation, going to the House, and a civil suit—he had played the last two ineffectively, Baker said, so the government was in a stronger position now than before and should be tougher. Petersen interrupted: weren't Baker and Skolnik "frightened," he asked, at the prospect of Agnew remaining Vice President, considering all they knew about him? Skolnik admitted he was, but Agnew would have to resign anyway, he said.

Agnew himself, Richardson said, was distraught and in no psychological condition to start a crusade to vindicate himself. He was a beaten man, but he also was "a wounded animal" who wanted the best deal he could get so he could later earn a living and rationalize his conduct to his own family. Richardson added he didn't think Agnew would make any further admissions, and he didn't think he could force him to do so. What was going on, he said, was a game of chicken between the government and Agnew over Agnew's statement in court. For him to be allowed to make some self-serving remarks was not a sufficient reason to refuse to make a deal with him.

There was, however, one last hurdle: Agnew's lawyers, as a last-minute concession, wanted to see in advance the full disclosure that the government would make. The strongest objections to this came from Petersen. He feared that once they saw the full facts they would back out of the bargain and then use the information to construct a better defense. Richardson didn't want to let them see it either, but, more important, he didn't want any snags to develop. He suggested that rather than full disclosure (which eventually took forty pages) a summary could be prepared to satisfy Agnew's lawyers yet essentially not tell them anything they didn't already know.

Before the Sunday meeting adjourned, Richardson made one final effort to persuade the Baltimore team of the justice and wisdom of his position. He told them he did not believe they really had taken the full measure of what would be done to the country if the Agnew litigation was allowed to run its course. It would be a divisive, prolonged contest that would impair the administration's capacity to govern. Also, while he thought the President would comply with the Supreme Court's order to turn over the White House tapes on Watergate, there was always the possibility that he might not. Richardson didn't want a situation in which the President was defying the Supreme Court, while the man next in line of succession was under indictment.

There was also the question of Nixon's health. While Richardson was on vacation in August, Nixon had been rushed to the hospital with viral pneumonia. When he first heard about it, Richardson said, he hadn't believed it; Nixon he thought, must have had a stroke, and he was frightened, knowing what he did about Agnew. Remembering that, Richardson told the others, he wanted the man out.

On the question of disposition of the case—the sentencing—Richardson said he would make no recommendation unless it was clear Judge Hoffman required it. He wanted none of his Justice Department subordinates to take a public position on jail or no jail. But if any of the Baltimoreans disagreed with the eventual disposition, he would not hold it against him if he felt it necessary to publicly dissociate himself from the disposition or the court arraignment—as Skolnik had indicated he might feel compelled to do. He only hoped that no one would act in a way that questioned Richardson's "honesty of purpose."

This invitation to act in conscience, and his remark about their assessment of his motives, touched the prosecutorial team. "I really didn't know why he said that," one of them observed later. "My God, he probably never met four people who were more impressed with his honesty of purpose than the four of us."

The attorney general was not without a keen awareness, however, that the dissociation of one or all of the Baltimore prosecutors from the terms of the final settlement would be an embarrassment. And he knew, too, that Skolnik was the key man—an experienced and forceful prosecutor, clearly the one the others looked to for direction. But his vulnerability, the Richardson team thought, was his personal desire to be part of the action and, in this case, part of history. Always the diplomat and handler of men, Richardson waited for the right moment and then dealt swiftly, deftly, and effectively with "the Skolnik problem." In the discussion about the final plea-bargaining talks before Judge Hoffman, Richardson suddenly turned to Skolnik and said, "It wouldn't be right to have all the Baltimore team there, Barney, but would you be willing to join the negotiating team?"

In the words of one of Richardson's admittedly partisan lieutenants later, "It was a stroke of genius on Elliot's part. From that moment on, Barney Skolnik was more Catholic than the Pope. Nothing changed substantially. The final settlement was little more than what was being considered when Barney said he couldn't participate any more, but Barney bought it." When Baker and Liebman heard Skolnik had been asked to go, they tried to talk him out of it, but he clearly wanted to be in on the climax. The crafty, independent Barney Skolnik was enlisted by Richardson, whether he realized it or not.

CHAPTER 13

SEALING THE DEAL

The opening scene for the final act in the plea bargaining that cost Spiro Agnew the Vice Presidency took place in Room 208 of the Olde Colony Motor Lodge in Alexandria, Virginia, just across the Potomac River from the capital. There, Judge Walter Hoffman had agreed to meet representatives of the Justice Department and the Vice President on Monday, October 8. The line-up for Agnew was Jay Topkis, Martin London, and Judah Best; for the government Henry Petersen, George Beall, and Barney Skolnik. The Justice team met with Elliot Richardson before going over to Alexandria and received its instructions: to present the agreed-on package to Judge Hoffman—the *nolo contendere* plea to one count of tax evasion, coupled with the government's full-disclosure statement and Agnew's statement, which would be a slightly revised version of H.E.P. No. 3. Plus, importantly, they were to advise the judge that Justice had no recommendation on Agnew's request for a sentence of no jail. It was their job to find out whether Hoffman would go along with this arrangement and whether he would agree to no jail, preferably without a recommendation from Justice, or whether he would insist on such a recommendation.

Judge Hoffman took a commanding position at the head of a coffee table. Agnew's lawyers sat on individual chairs on one side of the table, the government lawyers faced them on a sofa.

Topkis outlined what Agnew was willing to do: waive indictment and plea *nolo contendere* to one count of tax evasion for 1967, a felony, with the government submitting a statement of all the facts in the case, broader than just the facts to support the tax charge. The Vice President would respond with his "right of allocution"—the right to give his side before sentencing. Judge Hoffman broke in. He hoped that by allocution Topkis was not suggesting that Agnew in spite of his *nolo* plea was thinking of coming in and saying he had no intent to do what he did. If so, there could be no deal. Topkis said that would be no problem, but he reminded Hoffman that this was a *nolo* plea, not a guilty plea.

The remark was pivotal. It showed the Justice team at the outset that Topkis was doing all he could to take the curse off the *nolo* plea. But, more important, it elicited a response from Judge Hoffman that reassured them that the judge would be no pushover. Wait a minute, Hoffman said. The only difference between a guilty plea and a *nolo* plea was that in a *nolo* plea the government didn't have to show it could prove the case. It didn't give the defendant the right to assert he was innocent.

Topkis in response read the agreed-to Agnew statement—with one important exception. He left out the phrase that said Agnew knew that the payments he received were required to be reported for income-tax purposes

Well, Judge Hoffman said, much of what Topkis had just read was obviously for public consumption. But even though the plea was *nolo*, he had to advise the defendant through his lawyers that *nolo contendere* was the same as a guilty plea and the statement, while admitting Agnew received payments that were taxable, failed to say he knew he was required to report them on his tax return. If Agnew were to read that statement in court, Hoffman said, he would have to ask him if he had intentionally omitted this income for the purpose of defrauding the government.

Best spoke up. Did the judge mean that he would actually ask Agnew in court whether he had an intent to defraud? That's what he meant, Judge

Hoffman said. Topkis said he wasn't sure Agnew would agree to make such an admission. Petersen, who didn't want to see the whole thing go up in smoke at the eleventh hour, came up with an idea. How about if the Vice President simply said he knew that the payments he received were required to be reported? Hoffman said that would be fine.

At this point, Topkis made his big move. Without fanfare, he proceeded to tell the judge what had been alleged concerning the sentence: it was their "common belief," he said, that no commitment to jail was needed. Judge Hoffman asked for the government's view about sentencing. Following Richardson's orders exactly, Petersen told Hoffman that the government preferred to leave the matter of sentencing to the court.

Topkis interjected. He was not authorized by his client to go into court with a deal unless the court indicated in advance its agreement—presumably including no jail. Judge Hoffman told him that he couldn't be a party to a plea-bargaining agreement in the absence of the defendant in court, and so could not give him a definite answer then. Well, Topkis said to the astonishment of the Justice team, it was his understanding that it was the agreement of both parties that Agnew would not go to jail, and it was a "startlement" to him that the government now was saying it took no position on sentencing.

Judge Hoffman seemed to be indicating strongly he would not send Agnew to jail. But he told Topkis specifically that under the circumstances he could only say now that he could not commit himself—the same would be true even if the government recommended no jail. By saying he would hold court at any time, even in the wee hours of the morning, Hoffman was indicating he would do all he could to avoid press coverage, but Agnew would have to present the plea in public, and, considering who he was, it was not likely that they could escape press coverage at whatever hour.

Peterson then took the floor. While the government was not prepared to recommend anything concerning the sentence, there were several things the court should know, he said. Some co-conspirators in the case had agreed to plead guilty and would be coming before it for sentencing, and there were other investigations that would involve other public officials. Also, there were large public concerns involved—the integrity of the investigation and of the judicial process, the stability of the government, and the public interest in succession if a tragedy were to strike the President. All of these things were proper concerns for the court.

Then, aware of Judge Hoffman's near-paranoia about the press and about leaking court business to reporters, Petersen said everyone of importance in the Justice Department was ready to swear under oath that they had never done so. The department's interest in plea bargaining, he wanted to assure the judge, was not because it wanted to avoid submitting depositions on the leaks matter. But Petersen had hit a raw nerve, and Hoffman interjected quickly. Perhaps Petersen was right, but somebody sure had leaked—the newsmen outside the motel were clear evidence of that. He didn't know where the leak had come from, but if a press story appeared next morning stating what the purpose of the meeting had been, it would be obvious that the government was the culprit, since the story would certainly not be in Agnew's interest.

Once again Judge Hoffman returned to the final disposition. He inquired whether Petersen agreed there would be no other federal criminal proceeding against Agnew. Petersen said that was so—assuming Agnew resigned from the Vice Presidency first. Hoffman said he had no power over that; that is, this was an element to be worked out between the two parties and consummated before Agnew entered the court. It was what everybody wanted—Agnew appearing before Hoffman as a private citizen, not as Vice President of the United States copping a plea while still in office.

Topkis promised to let everyone know by 11 o'clock next morning whether they would meet in Ruckelshaus's conference room. The parties left Hoffman's room separately—it was about 7:15—and had their pictures taken by a waiting cameraman. A television reporter asked Skolnik: "Will you tell us whether or not there was plea bargaining going on in there?" Skolnik replied: "No comment." Petersen, Beall, and Skolnik drove back to the department, where they went immediately to Richardson's office.

They told the attorney general that Judge Hoffman had been extremely ambiguous on how a no-jail recommendation would affect his decision, but that he seemed very close to agreeing to let them know in advance in chambers what his decision was. Petersen asked Skolnik to read his notes on the sentencing portion of the meeting, so that Richardson would have as accurate a picture of the judge's position as possible. Richardson listened. Then he said what he had never said right out before in the presence of the Baltimore prosecutors—that he *was* ready to recommend no jail, but only if without it the deal would fall through. It was clear that he was struggling with himself over taking that final, critical step. An Attorney General of the United States who actively participated in a decision that set a felonious Vice President free would not contribute to the restoration of public confidence in the equal application of the law. He just had to know beyond any doubt that the step was necessary.

Elliot L. Richardson then proceeded to do something no small-town lawyer would even consider—he announced he was going to phone the judge and just ask him. Skolnik spoke up: the attorney general could not do that! It would be an *ex parte* communication with the court! He could make a conference call with one of Agnew's lawyers on an extension, but he couldn't call the judge himself. Skolnik's remonstrance came out in a tone of mild disbelief that Richardson would seriously consider the idea—and Petersen shared it. But Richardson had made up his mind. He wasn't trying to influence the judge about anything—he just needed clarification. So he picked up the phone, while Skolnik, Petersen, and Beall stood by looking shocked, and J. T. Smith, who knew Richardson better than any of them and knew he could not be stopped, gazed into the middle distance, looking bemused. They all listened, waiting to hear the case blow up in their faces as a result of one elementary legal *faux pas*. Instead, what they heard, to their great relief, was the attorney general, even before he could say what he was going to say and should not have said, being bawled out by Hoffman like a schoolboy—not for making an *ex parte* call, but for leaking the motel meeting!

Richardson hung up, never having asked Hoffman the question that might have gotten him deeper into the soup. Richardson was angry, and he paced, clutching himself around the waist as if he had a stomach-ache, griping about Hoffman's accusations. Well, he finally said, calming down, there wasn't anything else anybody could do now, and he sent them all home. Before the final good nights, the attorney general asked Beall and Skolnik what the other Baltimoreans' reaction to the deal was likely to be. Skolnik quickly replied that he would talk to Baker and Liebman and see that they went along.

In all, it was a momentous and dramatic evening for the lawyers on both sides. For others, including Spiro T. Agnew, it seemed to be a night like many others. Earlier that day, the Vice President and a small personal party had flown to New York, where he was to make a speech before a builders' group at a lunch in the Waldorf-Astoria Tuesday. Agnew spent an hour or so with an old friend and political true believer, William Rusher, publisher of *The National Review,* during which he again declared his innocence and hinted that White House pressures were forcing his hand and making a scapegoat of him.

The next morning in Washington, Richardson discussed several points again with Petersen, Beall, and Skolnik while they waited to hear whether there would be another meeting with the judge. Agnew's lawyers called Richardson to say that they wanted no mention in the summary statement of The Close Associate by name. Skolnik thought that would be no problem. But more important, was it in the Justice Department's interests to join with Agnew's lawyers in asking Judge Hoffman to indicate in advance whether he would go for no jail? Richardson saw no reason why not, but Skolnik said it was important that Hoffman see the seven-page summary before he decided. There was always the danger that if Hoffman agreed to no jail first and *then* saw how much evidence of offenses other than tax evasion there was, he would scrub the arrangement as being too soft. Richardson agreed.

Soon Topkis, London, and Best joined the group to discuss outstanding questions before meeting with Judge Hoffman. The major item was again the no-jail recommendation. Before he would even consider it, Richardson said, he again had to have the Agnew side's agreement to a full disclosure of the facts as drawn up by the Justice Department. Topkis said that he and his colleagues wanted to see it before they went into court; Richardson said they would be shown it when a bargain was struck, but it was to be absolutely nonnegotiable.

Skolnik didn't want the full case shown to the Agnew lawyers until they got to court, but Best assured him they just wanted to "check it for typos." What would happen when the Agnew lawyers saw the finished product was a source of some uneasiness. The Baltimore prosecutors feared that it might cause Agnew to say no deal. But Richardson gave the Agnew men his word that the longer statement would merely expand on the seven-page summary.

As for a no-jail recommendation, Richardson said he had informed the Agnew lawyers at the time the first round of plea bargaining broke off that if a government recommendation were crucial, he would make it, but he had to be satisfied that the judge really required it. Hoffman had been ambiguous, so this time he would attend the meeting with Hoffman himself that afternoon. Although there was disagreement within the department about such a recommendation, Richardson said, he would make it if the judge demanded it, on the grounds that the public interest was best served by avoiding a constitutional crisis through a drawn-out trial or impeachment proceedings. This statement was met by a large sigh of relief from the Agnew lawyers.

It turned out that Agnew wanted to avoid not only jail itself, but also a suspended sentence or a humiliating probation. Richardson said that would be up to the court to decide.

London next urged Richardson to lend his weight to persuading Hoffman to indicate in advance what his decision on no jail was. Richardson said he was willing to do that.

Topkis also urged Richardson to appear personally in court at the arraignment, obviously to add weight to the no-jail recommendation. His appearance, Topkis said, would lend dignity, help the court, and help demonstrate the settlement was fair. Richardson took the idea under consideration.

Finally, there were a number of other concessions the Agnew lawyers wanted. They wanted dropped from the full disclosure any reference to Matz's payment of $2500 in cash to Agnew when he was Vice President in return for the award of a General Services Administration contract to the small engineering firm in which Matz had an interest. Topkis argued that it was not in the national interest to trot out accusations of improper behavior in the Vice Presidency. Richardson refused to delete this reference; he did not want the government later charged with suppressing evidence in order to justify a lenient outcome. There were bound to be people who still would not believe Agnew was guilty, and a charge of suppressing evidence or covering it up could lead to a congressional inquiry, and nobody wanted that.

Topkis also asked that specific amounts of income Agnew received in the various payoffs not be mentioned because there would be trouble with the Internal Revenue Service on collection of back taxes. Petersen said the tax division would insist on it. But Richardson did agree to cut out some less important charges in the short summary (including the one about Agnew receiving vending-machine payola).

That was the deal. Topkis asked for a complete scenario of what would occur at the arraignment; also, he wanted the requirement of mug shots and fingerprints of the defendant waived. The arraignment was set for two o'clock the next afternoon.

At lunch, Beall and Skolnik phoned Baker and Liebman in Baltimore and told them about the last-minute adjustments. For Skolnik particularly, this was a sticky task. As expected, Baker and Liebman balked, but two facts were persuasive with them—Richardson's assurances that they would be free to express disagreement if they felt it necessary, and Richardson's decision to *personally* recommend no jail—either in person or by letter to the court. Baker also objected to showing the full-disclosure statement to Agnew's lawyers. At two o'clock, the same group that had met with Judge Hoffman in the motel the previous evening, plus Richardson, now gathered with him in Ruckelshaus's conference room. Hoffman sat at the head of the conference table. Again Agnew's lawyers and the Justice team lined up facing each other. The attorney general waited until everyone was settled and then began.

He told Hoffman that he had met with Agnew's lawyers again and had reached more complete agreement on points previously unresolved. He asked Agnew's lawyers if they agreed that he give Judge Hoffman the seven-page summary of evidence, and they said yes. Hoffman said he knew nothing about the evidence except that he had read in the newspapers that it concerned kickbacks. He said he also didn't know whether the government would be making a specific recommendation on sentencing, but in any case it was his responsibility. He had written articles urging harsh treatment of public officials guilty of tax evasion as an example and a deterrent, and he knew they could be thrown back at him if he broke with past practice. But he also was aware that a more important question of the national interest was involved.

Richardson, as Topkis had suggested he do, then asked the judge whether he might infer that a recommendation from the government would be not only appropriate but would be given substantial weight. A true plea bargain, Hoffman replied, should include an agreement on sentencing. Richardson took up the invitation. The issue of disposition, he said, was peculiarly difficult for the government. There were co-defendants who had cooperated, and the government's evidence against Agnew was very compelling. Also, the government lawyers were split on whether Agnew should be sent to jail or not. In these circumstances, he said, the department felt that if not called upon to help the judge decide, it would not do so. But he inferred a recommendation would be helpful to the court and so he was prepared to make one.

Judge Hoffman said it would be helpful. If Agnew were just another Norfolk lawyer, he would probably give him a split sentence—some time in jail and some time on probation, because he had a strong feeling that lawyers and other professional people convicted should serve some time as a deterrent to others.

This was his attitude, Judge Hoffman said, without having looked at the summary of evidence, which he imagined would not be too complimentary to Agnew. It might show some nontax evidence, he guessed, but he could not take that into account because this was solely a tax case. By the same token, he had read Agnew's statement, and the defendant could say whatever he liked, but his denial of the other charges carried no more weight in the tax case than did the government's nontax charges; it was all for public consumption. Clearly, Hoffman said, a long-term sentence would be inappropriate. He was trying to look at the case as if the defendant were an ordinary citizen—but Agnew was also a governor at the time in question and a qualified lawyer. As a judge, Hoffman had written an important article for the instruction of new judges on the subject of equal treatment, and it was going to be very difficult for him to depart from his prior stated principles. If the parties were going into a public courtroom, he said, he would certainly ask if the government had a position on sentencing.

Richardson was satisfied. In light of that, he said, and the overriding national interest involved, he would make a recommendation. His own reasons for his position would become clearer after the judge had seen the government's evidence.

After he had read the summary Judge Hoffman resumed the meeting. He said the summary obliged him to reiterate that he was trying an income-tax evasion case only. In his sentence, he would have to prepare some statement explaining why he was literally disregarding the factual government summary and Agnew's response, and acting solely on the one tax count. What he seemed to be saying here was that the overwhelming government case of bribery, extortion, and conspiracy as presented in the summary supporting the single tax-evasion charge was going to make it difficult for him to let Agnew off without a jail term. He could take mitigating factors into consideration, Judge Hoffman said, such as Agnew's character. Richardson said he would agree to that; the purpose of the full disclosure was not to influence the judge in sentencing but to satisfy public opinion and scrutiny about the performance of the Department of Justice in a case of such importance.

Judge Hoffman was being moved close to a decision on no jail, and Richardson deftly eased him closer. It had been suggested by Agnew's lawyers that the judge might be willing to indicate in advance, in camera, what his decision would be, and the government agreed this was important to do. If the course negotiated by the parties were to be pursued into open court, he said, they should know in advance that the course could be run to completion.

Well, Judge Hoffman replied, he had indicated what he would do without a recommendation. He was doing a little pushing himself, evidently, and Richardson was willing to waltz. He himself, said Richardson, as a former U.S. attorney and state attorney general, would normally recommend a jail sentence. But he felt it necessary to keep in view that the Vice President stood in immediate succession to the President and could be called on to assume the Presidency at any moment.

Hoffman interrupted. He understood that Agnew was going to resign. Yes, Richardson said, but only as part of the deal now under discussion. It was in the public interest that Agnew resign and be replaced quickly in the succession to the Presidency. That was the first factor in his recommendation. The second was his awareness of the effect of resignation plus subsequent conviction on a felony charge on a man who had been Vice President of the United States. The imposition of this penalty could not be measured against the normal penalties that could be imposed. Finally, he said, there did seem to be room for appropriate recommendation of Agnew's service to the nation in foreign policy, in federal-state relations, and as president of the Senate. And so he was recommending that no jail sentence be given.

Hoffman said the attorney general's recommendation would be given great weight. All parties to the deal would be taken to task by the public, he warned them, but so long as the whole matter was on the record, that did not matter. Then, without further fanfare, he asked: did they want to have the arraignment the next day?

The faster the better, Topkis put in quickly. His side was fearful of leaks. And it was not only the Justice Department that was considering the national interest, he said. So was his client. Judge Hoffman said he had no doubt of that.

The meeting then got down to mechanics. Judge Hoffman had no authority to impose resignation from office as a condition of any sentence, he reminded the lawyers, and some procedure should be established to have a copy of Agnew's letter of resignation to the secretary of state—the proper officer of the government to receive it—handed to the court. Some plans already had been worked out, Topkis reported. George Kaufmann, representing the Vice President, would be standing by in Secretary of State Henry Kissinger's office with instructions to turn over the letter at the appropriate time. A phone line would be held open from the courtroom in Baltimore to Kissinger's office and the instant it was clear that there were no last-minute snags in the deal, Kaufmann would submit the letter. Thus, Agnew would stand before the arraignment as a private citizen; history would not have to record that a sitting Vice President had pleaded to a felony.

There was then some discussion about sparing Agnew undue

humiliation. Hoffman said there were certain questions that the law required be asked of a person making a *nolo* plea. Those would be asked. But he was not going to insult Agnew by asking him whether he was or had recently been under the influence of drugs or alcohol, as was also usually required.

Judge Hoffman said he didn't mind taking the brunt of criticism for the plea bargain, and would prepare a statement approving the joint recommendation of no jail. It would note that he had disregarded the government summary and Agnew's denials; it might add that he would ordinarily impose a jail sentence and probation but that this was an unusual situation.

Topkis continued to press for having the case disposed of expeditiously and with no humiliation to the Vice President and the nation. He again asked that the court not direct Agnew to be fingerprinted or photographed, and Petersen said the department had no objection. Hoffman agreed to that. Topkis also implored the court not to give a suspended jail sentence. It was functionless. Hoffman said he didn't care, though he generally did put a convicted man on probation, and asked the government side if it had any objection. Richardson said the government had no strong feelings about it.

The group then discussed the arraignment. There was to be a hearing at ten o'clock the next morning on the leaks issue, and the judge said he assumed the deal would moot the need for presenting depositions in that regard. Topkis interjected that he would love to get the answers on who had leaked the Agnew investigation stories but, smiling, said he would make the sacrifice.

Hoffman, predictably, was worried about how to handle the ever-present press. He was going to Baltimore that night and would prepare his statement there. The press would be told only that depositions on the leaks would be deferred pending a proceeding at two o'clock. Then, if the deal went through, the depositions would be canceled. The assumption would be, they guessed correctly, that the press would conclude that the two-o'clock session would be on the leaks issue, nothing more. It was agreed to permit the Secret Service to exercise its usual precautions around the courtroom for Agnew's appearance. It was also agreed that Beall would introduce Richardson to state the government's position—this would be for an Attorney General of the United States a precedent-setting appearance for a *nolo* plea in a federal district court proceeding. Topkis then would state that Agnew had resigned, and Agnew would give his statement prior to sentencing.

At this juncture, there was a final ripple. Richardson, concerned to eliminate any eleventh-hour snags over the full-disclosure statement, advised Judge Hoffman that what he would file would be a lot longer than the summary he had already submitted. The estimate was that it would be sixty pages. Hoffman didn't like this. He would go along with seven or ten pages, but he didn't care for the idea of a full amplification, especially one that Agnew's lawyers hadn't seen. Topkis, who earlier had said he would go along, admitted he didn't care for it either.

For a moment, the whole deal looked as if it might be scuttled. Judge Hoffman finally said, well, don't change the spirit of the seven pages. Agnew's statement had been drafted in light of them, and he didn't want any new information inserted to complicate things. Topkis put in that Richardson had told him the longer statement would just be an amplification, and Richardson agreed. Hoffman seemed satisfied. He simply warned the Justice team to beware of prejudicing future cases with what was used in the longer statement. Richardson, along with Skolnik, who would be writing the longer version with Baker and Liebman, indicated they were aware of that problem.

Topkis was not finished. Maybe the government could hold off and file the full disclosure a week later? But now Judge Hoffman was getting impatient with the hassling over this point. The seven pages had certainly been enough to convince him, Hoffman said, that a stiffer sentence ordinarily would be warranted. They painted Agnew as scoundrel enough to vindicate the Justice Department's actions, so why were sixty pages needed?

Richardson paused and measured his words very carefully. A bitter attack had been launched on the government for its conduct of this case, he said, without mentioning Agnew. He was referring not merely to criticism about the news leaks but to charges that the government had sought to take advantage of perjured testimony. These charges would subject the department to endless digging and worrying by investigative reporters if the full facts it had gathered were not disclosed now. Well, Hoffman said, he was not going to proceed with the two-o'clock arraignment until Agnew's lawyers saw what the long statement included, because he was not going to permit the government at the last minute to slip in a "mickey."

Richardson was a picture of controlled exasperation. The Vice President's attorneys had understood from the outset of plea bargaining that a more complete summary of evidence would be filed, Richardson said. They had agreed to that, subject only to viewing it first to see that it was consistent with the seven-page summary. Well, Hoffman interjected — by now also angrily — the Vice President would just say he denied it all.

But Richardson pressed on. A historic, unprecedented action was being brought before the court, he said, and it would have a historic, unprecedented result. The government had a responsibility to satisfy the country that the result was based on all relevant factors, including the government's evidence.

Judge Hoffman still wasn't buying. Wouldn't it come out in future trials? Richardson said that was unlikely, because many of the co-defendants would plead guilty and waive trial. Would it be agreeable if he had the more extensive statement in the hands of Agnew's lawyers by first thing in the morning? Hoffman said yes, but he wanted to hold a hearing after that and before the arraignment. Again Richardson stressed that Agnew's lawyers had already agreed that they would see it only to satisfy themselves that it was consistent with the seven-page summary.

Topkis said he trusted Richardson but was concerned because the statement would be drafted by individuals who were not present. And perhaps the statement wouldn't be ready until half an hour before they were all to go to court. Petersen volunteered that Beall and Skolnik would review the material.

Without consulting with Beall and Skolnik (who with Baker and Liebman had to do the work), the attorney general promised he would have the document ready by eight o'clock the next morning.

After the meeting, Richardson, Beall, and Skolnik adjourned to the attorney general's private office. It was agreed that Beall and Skolnik would return to Baltimore, help Baker and Liebman finish taking statements from Matz, Wolff, Green, and Hammerman, and write the summary of evidence. Richardson and Petersen said they would drive to Baltimore to read the final draft when it was ready, before dispatching it to Best's office. Skolnik dictated a draft of a letter for Topkis to sign, acknowledging the draft was being shown to him merely to verify it was only an amplification of the seven-page summary.

While the Justice team was making its final preparations, Topkis, London, and Best returned to Agnew's office in the Old Executive Office Building to convey the news to the Vice President that the deal had been struck. From about six o'clock until about 7:30 that night, Agnew composed his resignation and a letter to the President; only the lawyers, Art Sohmer, and Mike Dunn were present with him. The Vice President's secretary typed both letters, and arrangements were made for

Kaufmann to deliver the resignation to Secretary of State Kissinger. Through all this, Agnew remained cool, dignified, restrained. These last, tragic documents having been written, the Vice President of the United States left his office, walked out of the building and across the way to the White House. Spiro T. Agnew, proud, erect, trim, was admitted to the Oval Office, where he personally informed the already beleaguered President of the United States that he would have one less burden to bear.

CHAPTER 14

THE INSTRUMENT OF RESIGNATION

The Baltimore-Washington Parkway, thirty-nine miles long, is a pleasant precursor of the antiseptic and boring federal expressways of the 1960's and 1970's. In the previous five years, Spiro T. Agnew had traveled this road, both literally and figuratively, out of his modest Baltimore beginnings to the very doorstep of the White House. When he took the oath of the Vice Presidency for the second time on January 20, 1973, he signaled to all who knew him that it was his intention to seek occupancy of that historic national house in 1976. There was no sense in being Vice President for a second term, he often told aides and even acknowledged publicly, unless he was going to go after the Presidency.

Now, in the late evening of October 9, 1973, and the early hours of October 10, the Baltimore-Washington Parkway was for Spiro T. Agnew a dismal road back from grandeur and power. While unsuspecting motorists cruised the parkway, the principal players in the deposing of a Vice President busily shuttled between the two cities.

George Beall and Barney Skolnik were the first. Their work in Washington done, they arrived back in Baltimore at around six o'clock, while Agnew, in Washington, was still preparing his letters of resignation.

Agnew's lawyers, after helping the Vice President with his letters, returned to Judah Best's office. Best, who shared Richardson's appreciation for the judgment of history, was troubled by what would turn out to be a footnote. The Vice President, he told his colleagues, should resign before pleading *nolo contendere,* so that history would be unable to record that a sitting Vice President was simultaneously a felon. Jay Topkis and Martin London, who thought this was one hell of a time to start nitpicking, offered the facetious suggestion that the clock in

Henry Kissinger's office be stopped at two o'clock, so that the Vice President's resignation could be recorded as having been accepted by the secretary of state before the plea was announced in the courtroom. Finally, the lawyers worked out their strategy and Best went home. From his house in Arlington, he called George Kaufmann and went over the arrangements one more time.

In Baltimore, Tim Baker and Ron Liebman were hard at work writing the all-important full-disclosure statement. Central to the preparation of that document were signed statements from the four principal witnesses—Matz, Wolff, Green, and Hammerman.

One by one, the lawyers for the four had been phoned and told they and their clients must come in that evening to write and sign the statements. With each one, the prosecutors hinted that the hurry-up routine had something to do with the issue of leaks and the court hearing scheduled for the next day. Allen Green's lawyer, Brendan Sullivan, was a bit mystified by this strange summons to Baltimore and he went to see his associate, Joe Califano, about it. Califano, however, had problems of his own. As chief counsel for the Washington Post Company, he was busy preparing his motion to quash the subpoenas served on *Newsweek,* its writer Stephan Lesher, and Richard Cohen of the *Post.* Along with two associates, Richard M. Cooper and Gregory B. Craig, Califano worked through most of the night.

As a matter of fact, Califano had been working on a crash basis ever since the subpoenas were served the Friday before, with two goals in mind: to quash the subpoenas served on Cohen and *Newsweek,* and to keep Cohen out of jail. Califano's strategy had been dictated by Benjamin C. Bradlee, the *Post's* executive editor. "It goes without saying that *The Washington Post* will not reveal its sources. We will go to jail first," he said.

First, Cohen of course would answer no questions relating to the sources for any Agnew article. Second, Califano, in behalf of Katharine Graham, publisher of the *Post,* asserted in an affidavit that she had "ultimate responsibility for the custody" of Cohen's notes. If Judge Walter Hoffman granted Califano's motion and recognized Mrs. Graham's ownership of Cohen's notes, the judge might then have to demand that she surrender the notes or face jail herself. Mrs. Graham was prepared for that eventuality.

Califano did not stop there. He planned to confront the judge with fourteen affidavits—nine from *Post* reporters, editors, and executives; four from newsmen from other organizations; and one from Richard

Neustadt, a professor of political science at Harvard—each stressing the importance of confidential sources to the gathering of news. Neustadt maintained that news stories based on information gathered from confidential sources were invaluable to the government itself since they facilitated internal communication within the vast bureaucracy.

While the affidavits and the motion to quash were being prepared, Califano planned for the worst. In concert with the lawyers for all but one of the other news organizations, he retained a Richmond, Virginia, law firm in the event Judge Hoffman rejected the motion to quash and immediately ordered a reporter to jail for contempt of court. By Tuesday, the Virginia firm had scouted the locations of the appeals judges, ready to contact them if necessary. A private plane was readied for Mrs. Graham in case she had to hurry to Baltimore from a speaking engagement in Hartford, Connecticut. In the end, this wasted effort would cost The Washington Post Company about $25,000 in legal fees and another $5000 in expenses. Little wonder, then, that Califano paid scant attention to Brendan Sullivan's bewilderment that Tuesday evening.

Sullivan and his client, Allen Green, were the first to arrive at the Baltimore courthouse that night. Lester Matz and Jerome Wolff came in with their lawyers, Joe Kaplan and Arnold Weiner, at about 8:30, and Bud Hammerman with Sidney Sachs about an hour later. None was told of the momentous development that required this crash effort, nor were the men aware that the whole assemblage of heavy-hitters against Agnew was in the building.

An assembly line procedure was established to write, edit, review, and type the statements and, from them, the summary of evidence. The pressure of time precluded a complete rewriting of the statements into the court summary, and so the prosecutors functioned like three editors on a newspaper desk—Xeroxing the statements, cutting paragraphs out with scissors, and pasting or stapling them back in more readable order. Four secretaries worked through the night typing each new draft, which then would run the gamut of Skolnik, Baker, and Liebman.

There was not much time for literary flourish, but the sheer narrative force of the straightforward confessions was compelling, and the Baker-Skolnik team combined to provide a kicker that was worthy of the best short-story writer. The final paragraph, as written by Baker and edited by Skolnik, discussed Matz's refusal to give The Close Associate $10,000 for the 1972 Nixon-Agnew campaign, and ended: " . . . Matz complained about these solicitations to Mr. Agnew, who told Matz to say that he gave at the office."

At about midnight or so, the team had nearly completed the first draft. Beall phoned Richardson, at home in McLean, to report on the progress. The attorney general said he would contact Henry Petersen and the two of them would head for Baltimore in half an hour.

Skolnik, Baker, and Liebman were still at work then they arrived at about 2 A.M. About twenty-five of the forty pages were ready, and Richardson and Petersen began to read through them, eating doughnuts and drinking coffee brought in by the marshals. Richardson had a great deal riding on the summary of evidence; if it failed to make a persuasive yet fair case against Agnew, he would be accused of railroading the Vice President out of office; if it were too strong, he would be accused of making too lenient a deal. In the end, the latter allegation was heard from many quarters anyway, but Richardson had made clear to the prosecutors that he wanted the disclosure to be as strong as they could legitimately make it, without distortion of evidence or testimony.

When the last statement was ready, the three prosecutors repaired to Beall's office, there to find Richardson and Petersen at Beall's desk marking up the draft with pens. When he heard them walk in, Richardson turned, administered his broadest smile, and commended the authors profusely. "It's a good job," he said to them once, then again, and again. He and Petersen made only a very few minor corrections, and again the draft went to the four weary secretaries.

Beall had reserved rooms for Richardson and Petersen at the Baltimore Hilton, but they decided instead to go back to Washington. Richardson wanted to be in his office in the morning to handle any last-minute details that might crop up, including possible complications raised by Agnew or his lawyers, or calls from the White House. He and Petersen went home for a couple of hours' sleep, a shower and shave, and then headed for the Justice Department.

Between four and seven o'clock in Baltimore, the prosecutors addressed themselves to a final technical chore, the proofreading of the forty-page statement.

At about a quarter past seven, Beall called for the two U.S. marshals who had been on duty through the night—Al Smith and Gerald Testerman—and handed them two envelopes, one containing the statement, and the other containing the letter to Topkis from Richardson stating that the summary was being shown to the Agnew lawyers strictly for verification purposes. The documents were supposed to be in the hands of the lawyers by eight o'clock that morning.

Jud Best had already been up for a long time. At three o'clock that morning, he had given up on getting any sleep and had spent the rest of the night in his wood-paneled study, there alternating between pacing the floor and sitting on the couch, reading a history of the Greek wars. Over and over again he planned the approaching day. Then, just after dawn, he heard the thump of *The Washington Post* hitting the front door. Best scanned the paper quickly, hoping he would not find a story about plea bargaining that would upset the deal at the last minute. Best was relieved. The *Post*, obviously, was oblivious to what was happening. Forsaking his Fiat sports car for the day, he borrowed his wife's Mercedes-Benz and drove to his office across the Potomac where he met London, Topkis, and Max Gittler, a lawyer who had helped Topkis in writing the briefs.

After receiving the documents from the marshals, the lawyers walked over to the Old Executive Office Building. Agnew was not there. Best picked up the letter of resignation and dispatched a copy of it to the White House, along with the letter to the President. Then he telephoned the White House to arrange for the admittance of Kaufmann later in the day. He wrote down the phone number in Kissinger's White House office, where Kaufmann would be waiting. The lawyers returned to the offices of Colson and Shapiro, handed Kaufmann the letter addressed to Kissinger, and then got into the Mercedes for the drive to Baltimore.

Now began a period of nail-biting, general anticipation, and apprehension. The deal was cut, in the prosecutors' parlance, but it could still become unstuck. In Baltimore, in the final stages of proofreading the statement, the other prosecutors had noticed that their colleague, Liebman, was becoming extremely irritable. He was not one to function well without sleep, and none of them had slept at all that night. They agreed, as soon as the marshals had left, to go home for an hour or two, just long enough to get cleaned up, and to return to the office for the historic events of the unfolding day.

Beall went home, took a shower, shaved, dressed, and came downstairs for a big breakfast. On the table, waiting for him, was a heart-shaped note of congratulations from his wife, Nancy. Skolnik saw his wife just before she went to work and told her to be sure to be in the courtroom at two o'clock that afternoon. He was beginning to relax when the phone rang.

It was Liebman. "Talk to me," he said to Skolnik, in a frightened voice. "I just want you to talk to me."

"Ron, what the hell's the matter?" Skolnik asked.

"I thought I was falling," Liebman said, "I thought I was falling."

"What are you talking about?" asked Skolnik, bewildered.

"I fell asleep," Liebman told him. "I knew I wasn't supposed to do it, but I lay down and I fell asleep and I was so scared because I was dreaming and I thought I was falling. And I woke up and I didn't know where I was. I knew I had to talk to somebody, so I just dialed. Just talk to me for a minute and I'll be all right."

"For Christ's sake," Skolnik said. "Now look, take it easy. It's Barney, and you're all right. You're very tired and you shouldn't have fallen asleep. When you haven't slept the worst thing you can do is sleep for five minutes." Skolnik continued on like that, and talked about being on the brink of a major event in American history. "Go slosh some water on your face and take a shower," he told Liebman. "Then calm down and you'll be all right."

All during the morning, Skolnik busied himself with mechanical matters, such as arranging the seating in the courtroom for Richardson, Petersen, and the prosecutors, and discussing security precautions with courtroom officials. Through all this, nothing was said about what would in fact happen at two o'clock.

As a courtesy to Matz, Wolff, Green, and Hammerman, it was decided to advise them through their lawyers—without disclosing the purpose of the two-o'clock hearing—that something was about to happen that would reveal their involvement in the Agnew case. At about noon, the three assistant U.S. attorneys placed calls to Kaplan, Weiner, Sullivan, and Sachs. Most took the warning with some gratitude, but Sullivan became irate and screamed at Baker for nearly twenty minutes, charging that he had been lied to, that he had been told his client would not yet surface publicly. He issued what the prosecutors took to be a veiled threat to file a suit to enjoin them from taking whatever action it was they were warning him about. To deter him, Skolnik called back and engaged him in a long, mollifying conversation the purpose of which was to make it impossible for Sullivan to get to the court in time to disrupt the proceedings.

Shortly after noon, a somber Elliot Richardson, accompanied by Henry Petersen, J. T. Smith, and Richard Darman, climbed into his limousine and headed up the parkway once again. William Ruckelshaus and Jonathan Moore stayed behind to provide communications and to prepare statements for the press. They kept in touch with Richardson over his car telephone, watching the wire-service tickers to be sure there was no leak, and giving him information as he read over his prepared statement en route.

At the courthouse, Richardson and his party went to Beall's office. By now the courtroom had been opened to the press and to lawyers, and everyone flocked in—the reporters under the impression they would be covering a hearing on the leaks, the lawyers prepared to defend their newsmen clients.

Califano was one of the first. He and his associates had left Washington at 6:30 that morning by chauffeured limousine, arriving at the courthouse much too early to file their papers. After driving around for a while, Califano had gotten out in front of the courthouse and been mobbed by reporters.

Now Califano was moving into the courtroom, wondering what the two-o'clock hearing would be about. By then, he had been notified that it wasn't about leaks but that Judge Hoffman might turn to them as soon as it was over.

A few minutes before two o'clock, Richardson, Petersen, and the four Baltimore prosecutors set out together with security men around them, down the hall to the courtroom. A sense of the drama now began to crowd in. Skolnik confessed later to having been momentarily mesmerized. He caught sight of the jammed courtroom ahead, with the doors open and a sea of faces expectantly looking toward the bench, and he glided along as if on air. "I don't remember to whom I was talking because my ears were full of 'Hail to the Chief,'" he said later. "I was just aware of history; we were striding down to history." Earlier, Richardson had shown Skolnik a draft of his statement and had asked for his opinion. Skolnik had made a suggestion and Richardson had incorporated it. Now, as they walked toward the courtroom, Richardson turned and asked him over his shoulder, "How is the statement now? Is it okay?" Skolnik replied, "Yes, great." Richardson smiled. "Good," he said. The capture of Barney Skolnik was complete.

The arrangement of chairs before the bench was such that the full prosecutorial team was obliged to file past the defense counsel's table, where Topkis, London, and Best already sat. They had arrived in Baltimore around noon, had eaten lunch, and then had gone directly to the courtroom, a marshal leading them through the crush of reporters, who immediately recognized them and peppered them with questions. As Richardson, Petersen, and the rest went by, they shook hands and exchanged pleasantries as if it were a class reunion—all, that is, except Skolnik, who stiffly shook hands but remained sober-faced.

Richardson, Petersen, and Beall sat at the prosecution table, with Skolnik, Baker, and Liebman in chairs just behind them. As Richardson got settled, Best walked over to him and asked, "Are you prepared to honor the agreement?"

"Oh, yes, certainly," Richardson replied, and he showed Best the statement he was about to read in court.

Just then, a Secret Service agent approached Best and told him his client had arrived in the building. He had come up from Washington with only Art Sohmer and the driver. At precisely three minutes after two o'clock, Spiro T. Agnew, Vice President of the United States, strode briskly into the courtroom. He was dressed impeccably, as always, in a perfectly pressed blue suit and blue-and-tan striped tie, his graying hair slicked neatly back off his tanned but now thin and tight-lipped face. There were murmurs as he made his unannounced entrance.

The Vice President shook hands with his three lawyers and then sat down with them. Best leaned over and whispered, "The attorney general has assured me he will honor the agreement. Do you authorize me to cause your resignation to be handed into the secretary of state?"

"Certainly," Agnew answered.

Best walked to the judge's chambers and got Kaufmann on the line being held open outside Kissinger's office in the White House. Then, using the precise language he had decided on in the sleepless early hours of the day—direct from the federal code—he said, "You are authorized to deliver into the secretary of state the instrument of resignation."

Best held the phone and waited as Kaufmann went into Kissinger's office and handed him the official resignation. It said:

"Dear Mr. Secretary: I hereby resign the Office of Vice President of the United States, effective immediately. Sincerely, Spiro T. Agnew."

Then Kaufmann returned to the phone and told Best:

"The instrument of resignation was delivered into the secretary of state at fourteen-oh-five."

"What?" Best asked.

"Two-oh-five," Kaufmann said.

Best walked back into the courtroom and went over to Agnew. "Sir," he said, "your resignation, sir, has been delivered." Agnew made no reply. Best then handed Topkis a note conveying the information for inclusion in Topkis's remarks to the court.

Now Judge Hoffman walked in. All rose, then sat again as the clerk announced his arrival and concluded with the traditional "God save the United States and this honorable court." Judge Hoffman first addressed the spectators and press, who thought they were attending a hearing on the question of newspaper leaks. "You will not be permitted to leave at any time during the course of the proceeding," he told them firmly, "and there will be no disturbances or outcries of any kind from anyone. If so, the marshals have received instructions to take you into custody." Then he had the courtroom locked.

"I am advised that Spiro T. Agnew desires at this time to execute a waiver of indictment in open court," Hoffman said, addressing Topkis. The lawyer said the judge was correct. "Mr. Agnew," Judge Hoffman now remarked, looking at the defendant, "before executing the waiver of indictment, I am required to advise you that you have a right, under the Constitution of the United States, to require that an indictment be returned against you, charging you with the commission of any crime. Therefore, you should not execute the waiver form unless you do so freely, voluntarily, and with full knowledge of your rights in the matter. Do you fully understand your rights?"

"I do, your honor," Agnew said, standing at the defendant's table, tense and grim, but in a firm voice.

Each time the judge addressed him in the next few minutes, Agnew would stand, reply, and sit down again. It was a humiliation, a visible ebbing of power. "Down and up, down and up," one of the Richardson lieutenants recalled later. "He was obeying in the simple, polite way of a trained schoolboy."

Hoffman ascertained from Topkis that Agnew had seen the criminal information against him and was waiving formal arraignment. Then he asked, "Mr. Topkis, what plea are you advised does the defendant wish to enter in connection with the charge as stated in the criminal information?"

"On behalf of the defendant, your honor," Topkis replied, "we lodge a plea of *nolo contendere.*"

Hoffman turned again to the ex-Vice President. "Mr. Agnew, is that correct and is that your plea?"

"That is my plea, your honor," Agnew said in a firm voice.

"I am required to advise you, Mr. Agnew," Judge Hoffman said, "that a plea of *nolo contendere* is, insofar as this criminal proceeding is concerned today, the full equivalent to a plea of guilty and that, while a plea of *nolo contendere* may protect you in certain collateral proceedings, it has no bearing upon the disposition of the present case. Do you thoroughly understand the consequences of a plea of *nolo contendere?*"

"I do, your honor," Agnew replied.

The judge then asked Agnew a series of questions required under court procedure. Each time, the answer came in a clear voice.

"Do you fully understand the nature and the seriousness of the charge as stated in the criminal information?"

"I do."

"Have you had all the time necessary to confer with your counsel as to any possible defenses to the charge as set forth in the criminal information?"

"I have, your honor."

"Has anyone connected with the federal government persuaded or induced you to enter this plea of *nolo contendere?*"

"No one has."

"Totally aside from any plea agreement, has anyone held out to you any offer of leniency in connection with this matter?"

"No, sir."

"Congress has provided by law that a person convicted of federal income-tax evasion can be punished by a maximum fine of ten thousand dollars, a maximum term of imprisonment of five years, either or both. Have you been fully advised of the maximum sentence provided by law?"

"I have been so advised."

"Do you realize that, by pleading *nolo contendere,* you are not entitled to a trial by jury; whereas, if you entered a plea of not guilty, you would be entitled to a trial by jury?"

"I do."

"Do you realize that, by entering a plea of *nolo contendere,* the Department of Justice is not required to prove its case beyond a reasonable doubt; that is to say that your plea of *nolo contendere* is an admission by you that the Department of Justice is possessed of sufficient evidence to prove its case beyond a reasonable doubt?"

"I do."

"Do you realize that, by entering a plea of *nolo contendere,* you waive your rights under the Fifth Amendment with respect to testifying against yourself as the same pertains to the charge as stated in the criminal information?"

"I do so realize it."

Judge Hoffman then recited the terms of the plea agreement—resignation, no further federal prosecution, and a recommendation by the attorney general for an unsupervised probation and fine.

"Mr. Agnew," he asked, "do you thoroughly understand the plea agreement and do you now ratify and approve the same?"

"I do so," Agnew said, "and I understand it."

"Thank you, Mr. Agnew," the judge said, "and now you may take your seat. Subject to further proceedings, I will accept your plea of *nolo contendere.*"

Agnew sat down and Topkis got up. "At two-oh-five P.M.," he told the court, "there was delivered into the office of the secretary of state a letter, subscribed by the Vice President, in which he resigns his office." Topkis said he and the attorney general had agreed to waive the requirement of pre-sentence investigation so that the judge could proceed at once to impose sentence.

Next it was Richardson's turn. He rose and read the statement he had written, a statement he hoped would make clear that the scope of the government's allegations against Agnew went far beyond simple tax evasion; that the national interest as well as justice was being served in the compromise struck.

"May it please the court," he said, "I am, like every other participant in these proceedings, deeply conscious of the critical national interests which surround them. The agreement between the parties now before the court is one which must be just and honorable, and which must be perceived to be just and honorable, not simply to the parties but above all to the American people.

"From the outset of the negotiations which have culminated in these proceedings," the attorney general continued, "the Department of Justice has regarded as an integral requirement of any agreement a full disclosure of the surrounding circumstances, for only with knowledge of these circumstances can the American people fairly judge the justice of the outcome. One critical component of these circumstances is the government's evidence. In accordance, therefore, with the agreement of counsel, I offer for the permanent record of these proceedings an exposition of the evidence accumulated by the investigation against the defendant conducted by the office of the United States Attorney for the District of Maryland as of October 10, 1973. Because this exposition is complete and detailed, it is sufficient for present purposes simply to state that this evidence establishes a pattern of substantial cash payments to the defendant during the period when he served as governor of Maryland in return for engineering contracts with the state of Maryland.

"Payments by the principal in one large engineering firm began while the defendant was county executive of Baltimore County in the early 1960's and continued into 1971. The evidence also discloses payments of another engineer up to and including December 1972. None of the government's major witnesses has been promised immunity from prosecution, and each of the witnesses who would testify to having made direct payments to the Vice President has signed a sworn statement subject to the penalties of perjury."

Richardson now got to the core of his position. "In the light of the serious wrongdoing shown by its evidence," he went on, "the government might have insisted, if permitted by the court to do so, on pressing forward with the return of an indictment charging bribery and extortion. To have done this, however, would have been likely to inflict upon the nation serious and permanent scars. It would have been the defendant's right to put the prosecution to its proof. The Department of Justice had conceded the power of Congress, once an indictment had been returned, to proceed by impeachment. The Congress could well have elected to exercise this constitutional power. If the Congress chose not to act, the defendant could, while retaining office, either have insisted upon his right to a trial by jury or have continued to contest the right of the government to try an incumbent Vice President. Whichever of these courses were followed would have consumed not simply months but years—with potentially disastrous consequences to vital interests of the United States. Confidence in the adequacy of our fundamental institutions would itself have been put to severe trial. It is unthinkable that this nation should have been required to endure the anguish and uncertainty of a prolonged period in which the man next in line of succession to the Presidency was fighting the charges brought against him by his own government.

"On the basis of these considerations, I am satisfied that the public interest is better served by this court's acceptance of the defendant's plea of nolo contendere to a single count information charging income tax evasion."

Richardson then addressed himself to the one issue he had hoped to avoid, the one issue that he knew would put the fair administration of justice to its most severe and probably most lasting public test—letting Agnew off without imprisonment.

"There remains the question of the government's position toward the sentence to be imposed," he said. "One possible course would have been to avoid this difficult and painful issue by declining to make an affirmative recommendation [which, of course, he had much preferred to do]. It became apparent, however, in the course of the negotiations that without such a recommendation no agreement could be achieved. No agreement could have been achieved, moreover, if that recommendation did not include an appeal for leniency.

"I am firmly convinced that in all the circumstances leniency is justified. I am keenly aware, first, of the historic magnitude of the penalties inherent in the Vice President's resignation from his high office and his acceptance of a judgment of conviction for a felony. To propose that a man who has suffered these penalties should, in addition, be incarcerated in a penal institution, however briefly, is more than I, as head of the government's prosecuting arm, can recommend or wish." They were words of compassion, and Elliot Richardson made them sound as if they came from his heart.

"Also deserving of consideration is the public service rendered by the defendant during more than four and one-half years as the nation's second highest elected official," he added in deference to a suggestion by Agnew's lawyers. "He has been an effective spokesman for the executive branch in the councils of state and local government. He has knowledgeably and articulately represented the United States in meetings with the heads of other governments. He has participated actively and constructively in the deliberations of the government in a diverse range of fields.

"Out of compassion for the man, out of respect for the office he has held, and out of appreciation for the fact that by his resignation he has spared the nation the prolonged agony that would have attended upon his trial," Richardson concluded, "I urge that the sentence imposed on the defendant by this court not include confinement." Then Elliot L. Richardson, Attorney General of the United States, took his seat.

Now it was Agnew's turn. A private citizen for minutes only, he rose again at the defendant's table, holding a single sheet of paper in both hands—the statement that had been written in conjunction with the prosecutors and approved by them word by word in what had been the prime issue for much of the plea bargaining. But before he started reading, Agnew turned toward Richardson and his colleagues—of whom he had been so very critical only days before. "May I say at the outset," he observed, "I want to express my appreciation for the courtesy and cooperation extended me through my counsel in their deliberations with the prosecutors and throughout the consultations on this matter." The Justice team was surprised, and moved. Then Agnew began, reading in an even voice:

"My decision to resign and enter a plea of *nolo contendere* rests on my firm belief that the public interest requires swift disposition of the problems which are facing me. I am advised that a full legal defense of the probable charges against me could consume several years. I am concerned that intense media interest in the case would distract public attention from important national problems—to the country's detriment.

"I am aware that witnesses are prepared to testify that I and my agents received payments from consulting engineers doing business with the state of Maryland during the period I was governor. With the exception of the admission that follows, I deny these assertions of illegal acts on my part made by the government witnesses. I admit that I did receive payments during the year 1967 which were not expended for political purposes and that, therefore, these payments were income taxable to me in that year and that I so knew." That was the meat of it: the single actionable admission on which the charge of income-tax evasion was based. [In the formal plea, Agnew acknowledged that he had evaded payment of $13,551.47 in federal income taxes for 1967.]

Next was the admission that those who had paid off benefited from the state—an admission couched in veiled phrases designed to take some of the curse off, in public-relations terms. "I further acknowledge that contracts were awarded by state agencies in 1967 and other years to those who made such payments, and that I was aware of such awards. I am aware that government witnesses are prepared to testify that preferential treatment was accorded to the paying companies pursuant to an understanding with me when I was the governor. I stress, however, that no contracts were awarded to contractors who were not competent to perform the work and in most instances state contracts were awarded without any arrangement for the payment of money by the contractor. I deny that the payments in any way influenced my official actions. I am confident, moreover, that testimony presented in my behalf would make it clear that I at no time conducted my official duties as county executive or governor of Maryland in a manner harmful to the interests of the county or state, or my duties as Vice President of the United States in a manner harmful to the nation, and, further assert that my acceptance of contributions was part of a long-established pattern of political fund-raising in the state. At no time have I enriched myself at the expense of the public trust." He did not deny being paid off, in other words, only that the payoffs had influenced him. And he was only doing what others before him had done.

"In all the circumstances," Agnew said, finally, "I have concluded that protracted proceedings before the grand jury, the Congress, and the courts, with the speculation and controversy surrounding them, would seriously prejudice the national interest. These, briefly stated, are the reasons I am entering a plea of *nolo contendere* to the charge that I did receive payments in 1967 which I failed to report for the purposes of income taxation." With that, Spiro T. Agnew, private citizen, sat down.

Now Judge Hoffman spoke, outlining his position on the arrangement made between Agnew and the Justice Department. "For the past two days," he said, "counsel for the defendant and the representatives of the Department of Justice have engaged in what is known as 'plea bargaining,' a practice which has received the judicial approval of the Supreme Court of the United States. As the judge of the court, I have refrained from making any recommendation to the parties involved as I was unaware of the facts involving the alleged charges. The agreement finally reached between the parties, and which has been fully set forth by Mr. Topkis, one of the attorneys for the defendant, and Mr. Richardson, the distinguished Attorney General of the United States, was the result of some relinquishment of rights on both sides. We are all aware of the fact that some persons will criticize the result and the sentence to be imposed but, in a case such as this, it would be impossible to satisfy everyone.

"Once the agreement was reached between the parties, it had to be submitted to the judge for his approval or disapproval. It was late yesterday afternoon when I learned the final details of the negotiations. I insisted that all details would have to be submitted in open court and in the presence of the defendant before any formal approval or disapproval could be given. Such has now been accomplished and it becomes my duty to proceed.

"The judge must accept the final responsibility as to any sentence, but this does not mean that he should disregard the negotiations and advices of the parties who are far more familiar with the facts, the national interest, and the consequences flowing from any sentence to be imposed." Here Hoffman made clear that he would sentence Agnew only on the one specific charge to which he was pleading; the rest, he implied correctly, was part of a public-relations battle between the Justice team and Agnew for public acceptance or rejection of Agnew's greater guilt.

"As far as the court is involved," Hoffman said, "the defendant is on trial for willful evasion of income taxes for the calendar year 1967, which charge is a felony in the eyes of the law. He has entered a plea of *nolo contendere* which, so far as this criminal prosecution is concerned, is the full equivalent of a plea of guilty. Such a plea frequently is accepted in income-tax-evasion cases as there are generally civil consequences flowing therefrom and the criminal court is not interested in the precise amount of taxes which may be due. The plea of *nolo contendere* merely permits the parties to further litigate the amount due without regard to the conviction following such a plea.

"A detailed statement has been filed by the Department of Justice and refuted by the defendant, all of which are wholly unrelated to the charge of income-tax evasion. These statements are a part of the understanding between the parties and are submitted merely because of the charges and countercharges which have received so much advance publicity. Of course, the agreement further provides that the federal government will take no further action against the defendant as to any federal criminal charge which had its inception prior to today, reserving the right to proceed against him in any appropriate civil action for monies allegedly due. Furthermore, neither this court nor the Department of Justice can limit the right of any state or organization to take action against the defendant. Since the Department of Justice, pursuant to its agreement, will be barred from prosecuting the defendant as to any criminal charge heretofore existing, the truth of these charges and countercharges can never be established by any judicial decision or action. It would have been my preference to omit these statements and end the verbal warfare as to this tragic event in history, but I am not inclined to reject the agreement for this reason alone.

"There is a fundamental rule of law that every person accused of a crime is presumed to be innocent until such time as the guilt is established beyond a reasonable doubt. It is for this reason that I must disregard, for the purpose of imposing sentence, the charges, counter-charges, and denials which do not pertain to the single count of income-tax evasion. I have so advised counsel for the parties and they are in agreement that this is my duty.

"We come then to the charge of income-tax evasion which, as I stated, is a felony and a most serious charge in itself. In approving the plea agreement between the parties, I have not overlooked my prior writings and sentences in other income-tax cases. Generally speaking, where the defendant is a lawyer, a tax accountant, or a business executive, I resort to the practice of imposing a fine and a term of imprisonment, but provide that the actual period of confinement be limited to a period of from two to five months, with the defendant being placed on probation for the balance of the term. The reason for taking such action is that our method of filing income-tax returns is fundamentally based upon the honor of the individual reporting his income, and a sentence of actual confinement serves as a deterrent to others who are required to file their returns.

"But for the strong recommendation of the attorney general in this case, I would be inclined to follow the same procedure. However, I am persuaded that the national interests in the present case are so great and so compelling—all as described by the chief law-enforcement officer of the United States—that the ends of justice would be better served by making an exception to the general rule. I therefore approve the plea agreement between the parties."

Judge Hoffman then asked Agnew to stand, and offered him a chance to speak again.

"I have no further comment, your honor," he said.

"It is the judgment of this court," Hoffman told him, "that imposition of any sentence be suspended for a period of three years, conditioned that you, Spiro T. Agnew, at all times will be of uniform good behavior, that you will not violate the laws of the United States or any state; that, as a further condition of this probation you are to pay a fine in the sum of ten thousand dollars within thirty days from this date or otherwise stand committed for nonpayment of said fine; and that you shall not be required to be under the supervision of the probation officer of this court unless otherwise ordered by the court."

Agnew turned, tight-lipped and somber, and strode quickly from the court—so quickly that Richardson and Petersen, each independently moving to express their condolences to him, could not catch up with him. Jud Best, encountering Art Sohmer at the curbside outside the courthouse, said, "Art, it isn't going to be easy from here on in."

"I know," said Sohmer. "But I've been with him all through his career and I'm not going to leave him now." He moved swiftly toward Agnew's gold-and-black Cadillac limousine and hopped in. Agnew, Sohmer, and the standard retinue of Secret Service agents headed out toward suburban Randallstown and the Byers Funeral Home, where the body of Agnew's half brother W. Roy Pollard, who had died a few days before, was awaiting burial. Photographers leaned forward to snap the final pictures of Agnew on his last day as Vice President of the United States.

Agnew left behind a stunned group of bystanders. Joe Califano, mobbed going into the courthouse that morning, departed unnoticed. In the courthouse itself, reporters huddled on the stairs, thumbing through the forty-page exposition of evidence. Ripples of surprise came with every turn of the page. "This is incredible stuff!" exclaimed the courthouse reporter for a Baltimore newspaper, over and over again. Even the press corps was unprepared for the extraordinary document that just moments before had sunk Agnew. Almost at once, though, Agnew's home town seemed to accept the news. In a restaurant that night, the wife of a Baltimore state senator denounced not Agnew but rather the men who had been witnesses against him. An aide to Governor Marvin Mandel echoed the same theme.

At the Baltimore Hilton, a public-relations aide for the J. E. Greiner Company made the rounds of the rooms occupied by reporters, handing out a press release. Jerome B. Wolff was henceforth no longer an employee of the engineering firm.

The news of Agnew's resignation went out to Washington and the world like an electric shock. Agnew's staff, which had been kept in the dark for so long and had persevered in loyalty and trust through it all, had had only a few minutes' warning. As Agnew was going into the courtroom, General Mike Dunn had summoned the full staff to a meeting—even secretaries were told to come and leave the phones unattended. Dunn announced without fanfare—and without adequate explanation, in the view of some of the aides—that the man for whom they had gone out on a limb was quitting. "Our leader is today resigning his high office," Dunn said, and the Vice President had asked him to convey his thanks to all of them for their service. A fist came pounding down on the conference table, shattering the silence—otherwise marred only by some women weeping.

"Don't you think the Vice President owes it to us to thank us himself?" a voice asked. The question went unanswered, and the meeting broke up.

A few minutes later, at about 2:20, the phone rang at the desk of Lisa Brown, Marsh Thomson's secretary. It was Richard Pyle of the Associated Press Washington bureau. An aide in the AP's Baltimore bureau, Roxanne Snead, had seen Agnew going into the courthouse a short time earlier and had phoned her office, which in turn notified Washington. Reporters on the scene were now in the courtroom and unable to get out. AP put out a bulletin saying only that Agnew was in the courthouse, purpose unknown. What, Pyle now asked Lisa Brown, was going on?

"I can't tell you very much about it," the secretary said, obviously upset. "The Vice President has just resigned."

"What?" Pyle asked, incredulously.

"We have just come from a meeting at which we were told the Vice President resigned as of two-oh-five this afternoon."

Pyle turned to the AP's assistant bureau chief and one-time top political reporter, Walter R. Mears. "Wally, Agnew's just resigned," he said.

Mears, without changing his stoical expression and barely raising his voice, swung around, and called across the room: "Clear the A wire" (the main AP national wire). Then he told Pyle to start writing. But the reporter's hands were shaking so much that he could not hit the keys.

©1973 HERBLOCK

THE SIDE-SHOW CLOSES

Mears, dead-pan, sat at the typewriter and told Pyle to dictate the story to him. In seconds, another bulletin went out that said: "Vice President Spiro T. Agnew resigned today, his secretary said."

It was a clean beat for the AP. Another nine minutes passed before the opposition, United Press International, reported the same startling news. Within seconds the word was flashed to the nation's newspapers and television networks, and millions watching the fifth game of the National League playoffs between Cincinnati and New York suddenly saw a legend spelled out across the bottom of their screens reporting the political end of Spiro T. Agnew.

At the White House, the customary exchange of letters between a resigning official and a grateful President was disclosed. Agnew had written:

Dear Mr. President:

As you are aware, the accusations against me cannot be resolved without a long, divisive and debilitating struggle in the Congress and in the Courts. I have concluded that, painful as it is to me and to my family, it is in the best interests of the Nation that I relinquish the Vice Presidency.

Accordingly, I have today resigned the Office of Vice President of the United States. A copy of the instrument of resignation is enclosed.

It has been a privilege to serve with you. May I express to the American people, through you, my deep gratitude for their confidence in twice electing me to be Vice President.

Sincerely,
Spiro T. Agnew

Nixon, who had wanted Agnew out and the quicker the better, replied:

Dear Ted:

The most difficult of decisions are often those that are the most personal, and I know your decision to resign as Vice President has been as difficult as any facing a man in public life could be. Your departure from the Administration leaves me with a great sense of personal loss. You have been a valued associate throughout these nearly five years that we have served together. However, I respect your decision, and I also respect the concern for the national interest that led you to conclude that a resolution of the matter in this way, rather than through an extended battle in the Courts and the Congress, was advisable in order to prevent a protracted period of national division and uncertainty.

As Vice President, you have addressed the great issues of our times with courage and candor. Your strong patriotism, and your profound dedication to the welfare of the Nation, have been an inspiration to all who have served with you as well as to millions of others throughout the country.

I have been deeply saddened by this whole course of events, and I hope that you and your family will be sustained in the days ahead by a well-justified pride in all that you have contributed to the Nation by your years of service as Vice President.

Sincerely,
Richard Nixon

It was all so courteous, so friendly, so tidy—and so final.

STRESS

WHAT IT IS
WHAT IT CAN DO TO YOUR HEALTH
HOW TO FIGHT BACK

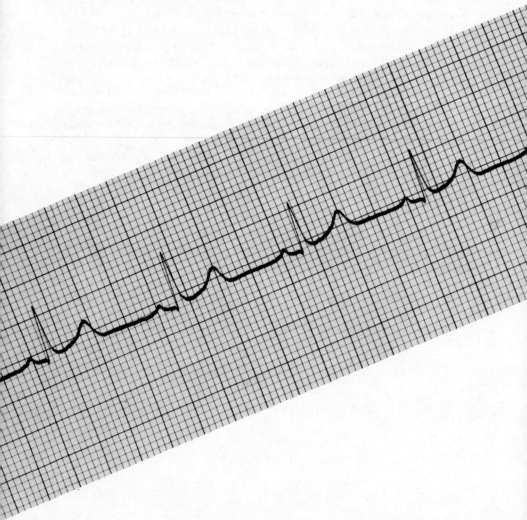

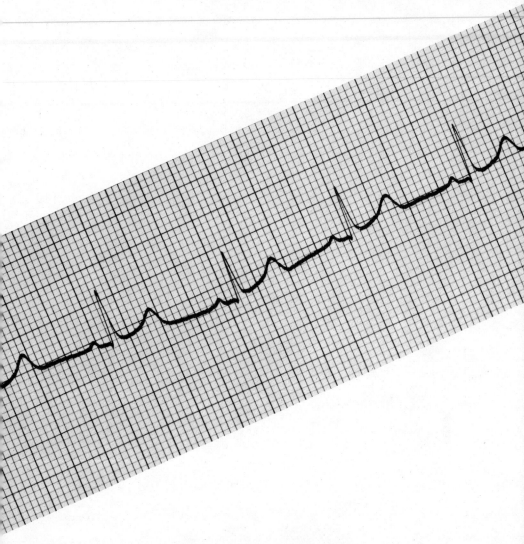

A condensation of the book by

WALTER McQUADE and ANN AIKMAN

PART I
STRESS IN THE TAKE SOCIETY

The past hundred years have witnessed a drastic change in the nature of sickness—and of medical practice. A century ago the average physician was a generalist with little doubt in his mind that the patient, in all his complex humanity, was the problem to solve. Sir William Osler, a famous Canadian clinician, said, "It is much more important to know what sort of patient has a disease than what sort of disease a patient has." Claude Bernard, the most renowned of nineteenth-century French physiologists, maintained that disease is resisted by a central equilibrium within the patient. Illnesses hover constantly about us, he said, their seeds blown by the wind, but they do not take root in the *terrain* unless it is ready to receive them. By *terrain* Bernard meant the human body, a collection of cells and systems that is constantly shifting, altering, adjusting to pressures from within and without.

But even in Bernard's time, medicine was beginning to forsake these notions in its excitement over the work of the great microbiologists; the focus passed from the *terrain* to the specifics of what lurked in the wind, as laboratory men like Koch and Pasteur began identifying and then conquering infectious microbes, one after the other. Because of their work, the great infectious scourges of eighteenth- and nineteenth-century America—diphtheria, typhus and the like—have all disappeared from the twentieth-century list of the ten leading causes of serious illness and death. Nevertheless, the hospitals are fuller than ever, and so today the old question is being asked again: What does make people sick?

It is the thesis of a growing number of medical scientists—and of this exploratory book—that the basic cause of much twentieth-century disease is a shadow which has slowly darkened our lives, like the smog that has darkened our cities. This shadow is stress.

A man walks down a city street late at night. He becomes aware he is being followed by three tall teenagers. To elude them he enters a subway station and pays his fare. But the footfalls continue to echo behind him. The subway platform is otherwise deserted. His body tightens. He walks faster, still followed, afraid to turn around. This is stress.

A young mother in a big-city ghetto supports her three small children by working as a domestic. One day she receives notification that her local day-care center is closing down for lack of funds. She can't afford a private nursery. But if she quits her job to take care of the children she'll have to go on welfare. This too is stress.

A businessman drives to work and parks his car in the slot with his name lettered on it, one small evidence of his success within a firm that for twenty years has sustained the good life for himself and his family. Entering his office, he finds on his desk a memo from the executive vice president: "The chairman wants a study of the savings possible in merging your division with warehousing and relocating in Mississippi." He reacts with a surge of interior chemistry. Flash go the hormones into his blood; up goes his pulse beat; but he can neither confront the threat physically nor flee. Under his forced calm builds repressed rage without any adequate target—except himself.

To add specifics, if this man is one of those hard-driving, competitive perfectionists whom many corporations prize, and if this kind of stress is chronic in his life, the experts will tell you he is a prime candidate for an early coronary attack (an even likelier candidate than American men in general, whose chances of having a heart attack before age sixty have risen to one in five). If not a coronary, it might be hypertension, ulcers, asthma, emphysema, arthritis, ulcerative colitis, migraine, backache, or perhaps a collision on the road: stressed people are more accident prone.

Prehistoric man survived in a dangerous world because, along with an elaborate brain, he possessed the mechanisms for instant physical response when threatened. Picture such a man, many thousands of years ago, resting in the sun in front of his cave after the hunt. Suddenly he feels the shadow of a predatory animal, stalking. Without thinking he reacts with a mighty rush of automatic resources. His heartbeat quickens. His blood pressure rises. Into his blood pour hormones that send sugar to his muscles and brain, mobilizing full energy. His digestive processes turn off at once so that this energy, undiverted, can be directed toward meeting the threat. Red cells flood into the arteries to help the body take in oxygen and cast off carbon dioxide. He clubs the intruder—or flees.

Animals respond this way still. A snake coils and strikes. A lion springs.

A deer speeds into the bush. But when modern men and women feel threatened, various constraints of twentieth-century civilization compel them to clamp a lid on their instinctive impulses. Over the course of time, medical science now tells us, the accumulated effects of these frustrated physical reactions damage the circulatory system, the digestive tract, the lungs, the muscles, and the joints, and hasten the general process of aging. We don't catch migraine, or coronary disease, or perhaps even cancer, despite the virus theory. These sicknesses happen to us because we are rendered vulnerable by the way we choose to live—or, more often, the life that has chosen us.

Stress disease is relatively absent in some parts of the world. In Gabon, Africa, the infant mortality rate is 229 per thousand compared with 19.8 here, but coronary thrombosis at age forty is almost unheard of. And in a few sections of the globe, such as Georgia in the Caucasus, people live unusually long lives, sometimes well past a hundred years. What usually characterizes these communities is not the perfect diet, or clement weather, or the absence of harmful habits like smoking and drinking. Rather it is a kind of social serenity, together with simple physical work in which the young and the very old both have a contribution to make, a place in the social organization that is securely their own.

Neither does stress strike all individuals equally. Some people seem to thrive on it; it is their meat—Churchill comes to mind. A rather different example is the Russian writer Alexander Solzhenitsyn. If you spend your life doing something that really matters to you, and doing it well, you can withstand a great deal.

Most of us do not fare so well. For airport flight dispatchers stress is endemic. Assembly-line mechanics, waitresses, taxi drivers, college students competing to get into medical school—all are anything but immune. People living in a rapidly deteriorating neighborhood know stress well. Even youthful residents of a rural commune, as winter progresses, the larder shrinks, and communal tempers become edgy, may find themselves susceptible. All social shifts generate stress, and there are signs that women's vulnerability is increasing as fast as their independence. A century ago peptic ulcers were a woman's ailment, by a ratio of seven to three. Then, as frontier rigors were replaced by industrial ones, life got easier for women and harder for men, and from 1920 to 1940 nine out of ten victims were male. But since mid-century the incidence of ulcers in women is again on the rise.

Stress, of course, is nothing new to humanity. From time immemorial all people—and to a degree all animals—have shared three fundamental stresses, passed down over the centuries as part of the primordial heritage.

The first of the primal stresses is the threat of mortal combat. It is a threat that Americans seldom have to deal with physically, but television and the newspapers are full of it, and it is an important influence in most people's lives.

When combat threatens, the caveman reaction occurs. The heart starts beating faster; blood pressure rises; the digestive system slows down; and numerous other changes take place, all automatic and all aimed against the enemy. These changes occur not only to an infantryman in combat, but to a child frightened by strange noises in the night, to boys fighting on the playground, and to men and women caught up in the rarefied game of office politics. The changes are useful to the infantryman and to the boys; but they only make the frightened child more fearful, and in the long run they can have a deadly effect on the ambitious person trying to outmaneuver competitors.

The second primal threat to survival is the basic problem of getting enough to eat—or, early in life, of being given enough to eat. When food is given, recognition is given, love is given; and when food is withheld these other things are withheld too, so that a child's feeding experience soon becomes mixed with all kinds of feelings about himself and his value in relation to other people, and also about the giving and receiving of anything between two individuals. People with dependency problems, people who feel they don't receive what they deserve in life, are likely to develop stomach problems. Wanting makes them hunger, literally.

The third primal threat to survival differs from the others in that it is a problem with no solution. You can attack or flee an enemy, you can yell for food (or love, or money) and at least have hope of results, but what can you do about the certainty that one day you will die?

To begin, you can try to make your life worth living, for as long as it lasts. You can also develop religions and philosophies to reassure yourself. Even the steeliest of atheists believes in some depth of himself not that God exists, perhaps, but that he himself will survive. Conversely, the most serene believer knows in his soul what lies ahead of him, and goes in fear not only of death itself, but of those occasions when death's prospect will rise to confront him. It confronts him in particular when he gets sick.

The phenomenon of religious belief is a large subject, but viewing it just from the point of view of a book about physical illness, it must be said that religion in a devout believer has little equal as an allayer of stress. This is true of all religions, but particularly true of some. The Judaic-Christian tradition, for instance, takes on all the primal stresses, and if it does not dispose of them completely it makes them surprisingly bearable. Whatever role the believer plays in his world, however humble, it argues, is an important role, created by God for a reason. It tells him he can't win them all, and that the people who seem to win them all don't really win. And it tells him that God loves him and will go on taking care of him no matter what he does.

The waning power of religion is one reason why life has become so stressful in the Western world, and also why many people today are turning once again to religious faith, the more evangelical, it seems, the more popular.

But modern societies have also lost other supports that in the past helped people endure toil, hardship and suffering: a stabilizing stoicism that most of us can no longer really comprehend; a feeling of worth derived from the exercise of individual craftsmanship—things made by hand and mind, not stamped out by a machine; a feeling of permanent place in the social order. In the twentieth century the great increase in physical abundance has been accompanied by a deep erosion of these intangible sources of strength and comfort.

Particularly potent have been the side effects of one of the industrial world's most precious products: social mobility. A Negro recently became an admiral in the U.S. Navy; women are working as telephone linesmen (and men as operators); homosexuality is coming into the open. All these developments, almost unthinkable only a generation ago, proclaim our growing freedom. We value this freedom, and rightly so, but perhaps we should be more realistic about the price we pay for it. Assuming we are free to succeed, we are thereby equally free to fail. Thus each individual is thrust into an endless race in which losing or lagging becomes proof of profound personal inadequacy. And in the course of this race we are constantly measuring ourselves against our competitors. When they gain, we lose.

Ours is a "take" society, so much so that while everyone knows immediately what the word "take" means—to grasp, to go out and seize possession of—defining the word "give" requires thought. Giving has to do with a pouring forth. It may take the form of love, or of philanthropy, or of teaching, or of art, or simply of a relaxed and easy adjustment to circumstance.

If the mark of success in life has very little to do with what you give and almost everything to do with what you take, you get a society like ours, with its emphasis on ambition and status, on cars and weedless lawns, on culture as acquisition rather than as enjoyment. A take society has a lean and hungry spirit of meanness and jealousy. Enough is never enough.

Industrialism itself works hard to project a philanthropic image, the image of the all-bountiful giver working round the clock to satisfy people's needs through a procession of increasingly ingenious products. Perhaps this conception is historically valid, but industry by now is not so much responding to the age-old needs of people as working to arouse new ones, whipping up longings for products that we never missed when they did not exist. The products aren't gifts anyway, obviously; we "take" them by working hard to amass the money or the credit necessary for their purchase. And we do not really need to receive more anyway. What we need ·to learn now is to give. But when the culture cannot teach us how, when the only way to regain the balance is through the individual, this imposes great stress on the individual.

The machine age is very hard, too, on the human body. The body was designed for physical use, marvelously designed—in fact it is probably the only piece of equipment in your life that improves with work. Every time you exercise your typewriter or your washing machine they lose a little. Every time you exercise your body, it gains.

Our bodies know this, but they don't know anything about the machine age. We keep telling them to be quiet, we don't need them any more, except maybe to push a button or shift a gear, but they won't listen; they keep clamoring to be used.

Perhaps more than anything else tne twentieth century believes in change—and change itself can stress people, as is shown in a recently published study by Thomas J. Holmes of the University of Washington. Holmes and his helpers have spent the past twenty years following hundreds of individuals as they wander through the land mines of modern life: their wives or husbands suddenly die or file for divorce; they are fired from jobs; a family fight breaks out; they are forced to pull up stakes and move from one part of the country to another; their sexual lives fall out of adjustment. Or perhaps there is a sudden change for the better: a longed-for pregnancy; a promotion at the office.

Holmes rates the impact of these life changes on a scale starting with 100 for the most serious, death of a spouse, down through such events as divorce (rate 73); being sent to jail, 63; being fired, 47; and thirty-nine other occurrences, right down to going on vacation, 13; and getting a parking ticket, 11. He calls the numbers Life Change Units.

Over the years Holmes has weighed these Life Change Units against the health of his subjects. High scores, he has established, precipitate the common stress diseases; and he warns that an accumulation of more than two hundred units in a single year is more than the average American can take without getting sick.

But sameness, too little change, also produces stress. If a person is brought to a standstill, balanced motionless against threatening forces—especially forces he cannot deal with in physical ways—he will often give way and develop an organic illness as a literal expression of his frustration. Mistaken marriages often do this to people, aging them fast, settling them into the routine of least resistance. Prisons do it too.

If man loses hope of changing his situation, anticipating just more of the miserable sameness day after day, year after year, disspirit can breed specific disease, with symptoms which conventional doctors can chart and follow, but not always understand—and very seldom cure. Man is a dynamic creature, meant to move ahead. It is by adjusting to change that the species has evolved, and that its individual members grow and develop. This is true even of the elderly: a recent study at a hospital in Tuscaloosa, Alabama, indicates that one cause of senescence is the loss of challenge in the lives of aged patients.

Modern men and women, then, prey on their own physical health, and that of their family and friends; frustration and unhappiness grate together to make them sick in body as in spirit. Is there anything they can do about it?

This book offers some answers to this question. Some are quite old, derived for Western use from placid Eastern spiritual traditions. Others are as subtly European as psychotherapy, or as ebulliently technological as biological feedback. All involve management of emotions, and of challenges. Some are easy to undertake; others require a complex voyage into self. Central to them all is a return to a consideration of the wholeness we need as humans to survive medically, and the necessity to take action ourselves, not merely sit in doctors' waiting rooms.

The first wave of systematic stress research, dominating the field in the '30s, '40s and early '50s, was the psychosomatic movement, which labored to define those personality types most likely to contract ulcers, heart trouble, migraine, arthritis, and other specific ills. That work continues to stand up, yet it has not turned out to be as useful as was first hoped. The emphasis today has passed to the physical and chemical pathways that stress takes within the body.

In our present decade the man who has stepped forward to occupy the stage most prominently is Hans Selye, a slightly-built, Austrian-born endocrinologist with a brilliant and assertive mind.

An intimation of Selye's life work came to him in his early manhood. He recalls, "I was a second-year medical student in Prague when my professor brought in five patients for the students to diagnose—one with cancer, one with gastric ulcer, et cetera. It struck me that the professor never spoke about what was common to them all, only about the differences. All these patients had lost weight, lost energy, and lost their appetites. Had I already been a physician at that time, I wouldn't have thought about it, but as it was I asked my professor if I could work on it in my free time, but he thought it was silly.

"That was in 1926. Ten years later, as assistant professor at McGill in Montreal, I was trying to isolate a hormone in the laboratory. I was working with extracts of cow ovaries and injecting them into rats. All of the rats, when later subjected to stress, had the same reaction—adrenal overreaction, duodenal and gastric ulcers, and shrinking thymus, spleen and lymph nodes. The worse the stress the stronger the reaction. Then I tried injecting other materials, even simple dirt. I even tried electric shock, and got the same results."

He also tried inducing fear and rage in the laboratory animals. Again he got the same physical results. From this puzzling beginning, in which he discovered the existence of a generalized reaction to almost any kind of stress, he gradually groped toward the conviction that the endocrine glands, particularly the adrenals, were the body's prime reactors to stress. He says, "They are the only organs that do not shrink under stress; they thrive and enlarge. If you remove them, and subject an animal to stress, it can't live. But if you remove them and then inject extract of cattle adrenals, stress resistance will vary in direct proportion to the amount of the injection, and can even be put back to normal."

Selye defines stress as the nonspecific response of the body to any demand made on it. He explains that when the brain signals the attack of a stressor—which could equally be a predatory beast, or a threatening office memorandum—the pituitary and adrenal glands produce such hormones as ACTH, cortisone and cortisol, which stimulate protective bodily reactions. If the stress is a fresh wound, the blood rushes inflammatory substances in to seal it off; if the stress is a broken bone, swelling occurs around the break. The pro-inflammatory hormones are balanced by anti-inflammatory hormones, which prevent the body from reacting so strongly that the reaction causes more harm than the injury.

Stress is not only a killer, Selye emphasizes, but also a drastic wearing force. Different men have different hereditary capacities to withstand stress, he holds, but once each man's "adaptation energy" has been expended, there is no known way to replenish it. Selye believes that some time in the future it may be possible to produce from the tissues of young animals a substance that could restore human adaptation energy.

Selye likens each person's supply of adaptation energy to a nation's deposits of oil; once the man or woman has summoned it up and burned it, it is gone—and so, soon, is he. If a person blunders into a distressing marriage, or embarks on a consuming, competitive career, he or she spends that portion of adaptation energy fast and ages fast.

Long acknowledged as a top endocrinologist and biochemist, Dr. Selye also ventures out of his specialized territory into the larger subject of how people should live their lives. This diversion bothers some medical men, but it makes Selye himself a particularly interesting scientist. His recommendation, put simply, is to work very hard in life at something that interests you and that you are good at. The aim of life, he says, is self-expression—an aim usually difficult to fulfill in our industrial society.

It is because of Selye's insights and long devotion to the chemistry of stress that many of the narrowest of physicians have come to agree that stress is indeed a genuine disease of our time. Even Louis Pasteur himself finally reached that conclusion more than half a century ago. Lying on his death bed in 1895, he reflected once again on his long scientific disagreement with Claude Bernard. Pasteur's dying words were: "Bernard was right. The microbe is nothing, the *terrain* is everything."

PART II

WHAT STRESS CAN DO TO YOU

CHAPTER 1

THE CARDIOVASCULAR SYSTEM
Heart attack, hypertension, angina,
arrhythmia, migraine

When you feel threatened, even by such a minor sensation as stage fright, it is your cardiovascular stystem which most clearly responds, changing the entire tempo of your body. The pulses pound.

Blood pressure rises. The hands turn cold as blood is diverted from the skin to the vital organs.

If this temporary adjustment becomes habitual, a number of conditions may develop, ranging from simple arrhythmia—a chronically eccentric heartbeat—through hypertension, to the dreaded coronary attack, which kills far more Americans today than any other ailment, particularly Americans in prime middle age.

The heart attack is a very modern affliction. Most of mankind's major illnesses have been described in medical literature as far back as Hippocrates' day, but coronaries are not among them. The late Dr. Paul Dudley White recalled that in the first two years after he set up practice in 1921 he saw only three or four coronary cases. The growth in coronary heart disease seems to follow in an almost eerie way the rise in gross national product: it is as if the advanced industrial nations had some kind of patent on this ejection device of the jet age.

Over the past twenty years Ancel Keyes of Minnesota and other nutrition experts have virtually convinced this nation that a diet high in cholesterol is responsible for the epidemic of heart trouble. Their evidence includes a particularly plausible study of the incidence of heart trouble among those Japanese who remain in Japan, eating a very low fat diet, compared with those who have emigrated to Hawaii, who eat a diet somewhat higher in saturated fat, and those who have moved on to the U.S. mainland, who generally share the American diet, high in hard fats. In this study there was virtually no heart trouble among the Japanese subjects in Japan. In Hawaii, there was some. In the U.S. the emigrants' heart trouble was on the usual elevated American scale.

Some subsequent research has cast doubt, however, or at least confusion, on the Keyes study. The Harvard School of Nutrition did an exhaustive investigation into the health of 579 men who migrated from Ireland to Boston, men with brothers who remained in Ireland, where the consumption of saturated fat, especially butter, is among the highest in the world. Although the emigrants to America actually ate less saturated fat and thus were presumably safer, they had more heart trouble than their kin in Ireland. Finnish farmers eat a high hard fat diet and have a lot of heart attacks. Masai tribesmen in Africa take in an even higher fat diet, and have none.

The mystery remains: Is it really the consumption of hard fat by mouth that raises the level of cholesterol and other dangerous artery-clogging substances in the blood? Not exclusively, it would seem, for even in the U.S. many people who consume such diets have low cholesterol ratings.

Dr. Ray Rosenman, a San Francisco cardiologist, and a member of one of the leading heart research teams in this country, says, "Diet, exercise, family history, and blood cholesterol are important, but the thing that has increased over the years when heart disease has grown so alarmingly is pace. Man is the only animal that perceives time, and our civilization is marked by a continually faster and faster speed."

In the past thirty-five years there has been sufficient research into the correlation between physical and personality types to produce a compelling picture of the kinds of people prone to heart disease. The research is not so much consecutive as cumulative. Examining it is like peeling an onion. The outer layers are new and pungent, but as one peels back into the work of the 1930's, the evidence is in many ways even stronger. This earlier work concerns not only coronaries, but a spectrum of other cardiovascular ailments, and it tries to discover not only what kind of person is likely to get sick, but what makes him that way.

Dr. Rosenman and his partner, Dr. Meyer Friedman, are today's most interesting heart investigators, because the most recent peels are theirs.

Twenty years ago these two cardiologists were deep in the study of the standard heart risk factors: cigarette smoking, blood pressure, diet, obesity, and in particular serum cholesterol. Like most cardiologists then—and now—their principal emphasis was on the build-up of fatty acids in the blood, which can eventually harden in the artery walls, narrowing the channel and keeping blood from the heart itself. Friedman says now, "I was cholesterol-oriented because I am a laboratory man and cholesterol does produce disease in animals. It was also something we could work on. So we thought, 'Let's get cholesterol down.'"

Nevertheless, puzzling factors kept cropping up—among them the low incidence of heart disease in American women. Friedman points out, "Although American women seem to be protected from heart trouble, Mexican women have as much heart disease as their men. It is also one to one in Southern Italy, but it is four to one in Northern Italy. An American Negress in Chicago or North Carolina has more heart disease than her husband. Therefore it can't be sexual hormones. As a good scientist—my definition of a good scientist is one who looks at the exception—I should have connected. But I didn't think it through."

One day in the early 1950's an upholsterer came in to redo the Friedman-Rosenman waiting room, and was puzzled by the condition of the chairs. The only place the chairs were worn, he said, was at the front edge of the seats. This Dr. Friedman interprets today as an indication that "Our individual patients were signaling us. Over 90 percent were showing signs of struggle in their lives."

From these simple beginnings came a program that was to involve thousands of staff hours and hundreds of thousands of research dollars during the succeeding two decades. The result is an impressive case for the idea that stress and behavior are principal culprits in the high incidence of heart attacks among middle-age Americans; that personality patterns are of vital importance; and—perhaps—that these personality patterns can be changed before it is too late.

Friedman and Rosenman sent questionnaires to a group of advertising men and engineers in San Francisco, asking them what factors seemed to have preceded heart attacks among friends and colleagues, and giving ten choices of answer, including all the standard risks such as diet and cigarette consumption, plus anxiety, work, excessive competition, and stress of making deadlines. Fewer than 3 percent mentioned the normal risk items, and fewer than 4 percent selected anxiety or work. More than seventy picked excessive competition and stress of making deadlines.

Then came a study with accountants which involved more than opinion, and which began to attract considerable attention. Accountants were chosen for the study because their work rises and falls in intensity, alternating spells of easy routine with periods such as tax time when everyone knocks himself out to meet a deadline. All were asked to keep detailed diaries of what they ate, and Friedman and Rosenman arranged to examine each twice a month, measuring cholesterol levels during both slack periods and times of heavy pressure.

Two significant cholesterol peaks occurred: first, when the accountants were closing out the yearly books of their clients in January, and again in March to mid-April when they were heavily involved in preparing income tax returns. Not everyone reacted to the stress in the same degree, but there was an overall jump of fatty acids in the blood during these periods, with a falling off in months of more placid work. The correlation between work loads and cholesterol readings was direct, and was independent of individual variations in diet, weight, or amount of exercise.

At the same time they were studying the accountants, Friedman and Rosenman also began considering the matter of individual differences in temperament that might influence people's reactions to stress. No two individuals handle stress identically, but which one ends up with heart disease and which one doesn't?

"Thus emerged our Type A and Type B," says Rosenman.

Type A, either male or female, is characterized by intense drive, aggressiveness, ambition, competitiveness, pressure for getting things done, and the habit of pitting himself against the clock. He may give an impression of iron control, or wear a mask of easy geniality, but the strain glints through.

By contrast, Type B's manner is more genuinely easy. He is open. He is not always glancing at his watch. He is not so preoccupied with achievement, is less competitive, and even speaks in a more modulated style.

Most people are mixtures of Type A and Type B, of course, and Rosenman and Friedman have sharpened their interviewing techniques to the point where they recognize four distinct subdivisions of each group, ranging from A-1, the most virulent, down to B-4, the mildest.

The general picture that emerges of the two types is familiar, recognizable—and a bit broad. The extreme Type A is the man who, while waiting to see the dentist, is on the telephone making business calls. He speaks in staccato, and has a tendency to end his sentences in a rush. He frequently sighs faintly between words (Dr. Friedman identifies this as "deadly—a sign of emotional exhaustion"). Type A is seldom out of his office or shop sick. He rarely goes to a doctor, and almost never to a psychiatrist—he does not feel he needs either. Indeed many Type A's die of otherwise recoverable coronaries simply because they wait too long to call for help.

Type A is often a little hard to get along with. His chuckle is rather grim. He does not drive people who work under him as hard as he drives himself, but he has little time to waste with them. He wants respect, not affection. Yet in some ways he can be said to be more sensitive than the milder Type B. He hates to fire anyone and will go to great lengths to avoid it. Sometimes the only way he can resolve such a situation is by mounting a general office crisis. If he himself has ever been fired it is not for underachievement but probably because of a personality clash with a colleague or superior.

Type A, surprisingly, goes to bed earlier than Type B. He doesn't get much out of home life anyway, and might as well prepare for the day ahead with a good night's rest, whereas Type B will get interested in something and sit up late, or simply socialize. Type A smokes cigarettes, never a pipe. Headwaiters learn not to keep him waiting for a reservation; if they do, they lose him. They like him because he doesn't linger over his meals, and doesn't complain about the cooking. He salts the meal before he tastes it, and has never sent a bottle of wine back to the cellar.

Type A's have little time for exercise. When they do play golf it is fast through, and in tennis they can be difficult partners. On vacation they like to go to lively, competitive places and if possible to combine the vacation with business. They never return to work a day or two late; they are more likely to be back early. Most days they stay on at the office well into the evening, and when they do leave, their desk tops are clear.

But in the competition for the top jobs in their companies, says Dr. Friedman, A's often lose out to B's. They lose because they are too competitive. They make decisions too fast—in minutes, instead of days—and so may make serious business mistakes. They are intoxicated by numerical competition: how many units sold in Phoenix, how many miles traveled in February. Life to an A-1 is a race against a clock and an adding machine. He lives by numbers in a constant effort to build up higher totals.

And even in business, higher totals aren't always what wins. In Friedman's words, "A's are dead creatively. They will add A and B and get C, where a creative B person would come up with a brilliant R." He adds, "A's have no respect for B's, but the smart B uses an A. The great salesmen are A's. The corporation presidents are usually B's."

Women span the types too, Rosenman says. In one study specifically of women, suburban matrons turned out to be mostly B's, but top-level executive secretaries tended to be A's, with higher cholesterol ratings even though their diets were lower in fat. In another study, Friedman and Rosenman tested two orders of nuns. One was a teaching order, whose members were required to have Ph.D.'s. They were highly competitive, mostly Type A. The other order was more contemplative and, true to type, were mostly B's.

What is most tragic of all in this picture of hopeful, driving energy is that the Type A's are two or three times more likely than the Type B's to get coronary heart disease in middle age.

What Type A's need but cannot easily achieve is restraint, says Dr. Friedman, and he speaks out of personal experience. He is himself a high Type A, and suffered a heart attack in 1967. Dr. Rosenman, both experts agree, is a natural B.

Friedman, since his heart attack, has been carefully impersonating a Type B, even to dressing in a deliberately casual way—relaxed tweed sports jacket complete with a pipe in the pocket. "My cholesterol was 292 at the time of the attack," he says. "Afterward, in the hospital, I reread Marcel Proust's *Remembrance of Things Past,* and it fell to 210. Then I went home, still scrupulously on the same diet, and it started back up again."

His own prescription for moderating his Type A propensities: "I have changed my life style. I live in Sausalito now. We no longer go to cocktail parties, and I'm off all my committees except one. I daydream. I go into St. Mary's Cathedral at lunch time and look at the stained glass windows." In 1972 he went to Texas for the heart-bypass operation, and gave up even his pipe.

Of the typical coronary patient he says, "He has become no longer human. You must give him back his personality. You have to pull his attention to the joys of *being*, as compared with those of *having* things which signal his success, get him away from that awful obsession with numbers.

"You can't change personality, but you can engineer a new regimen. Have him walk in parks and notice the sequence of what blossoms when. Any noncompetitive, nonmechanized kind of exercise." Friedman abhors jogging, which he calls the best way to achieve sudden death at thirty-five. "You should only start jogging if you have had a cardiogram while on a treadmill with a fibrillator right there. An A who is jogging tends to say, 'I did two miles in twenty minutes yesterday. I'll try for nineteen minutes today.'"

Almost forty years ago, at a time when Friedman was still in medical school, Dr. Flanders Dunbar and several of her colleagues at New York's Columbia Presbyterian Medical Center began mulling over the common emotional characteristics of patients with certain diseases, including hypertension, heart trouble of all kinds, rheumatic fever and diabetes. Over the course of five years, they studied some 1,600 of these patients—not a specially selected group, just the normal hospital population. The results, when finally correlated, were startling. Four out of five patients were discovered to have character traits and emotional problems peculiar to their disease group.

Dr. Dunbar's research into heart attacks does not dispute any of Friedman and Rosenman's later findings, but she did dig deeper into the personality they have since labeled Type A, and she also investigated the traits of the victims of other common cardiovascular ailments: hypertension, angina and cardiac arrhythmia.

In Dr. Dunbar's heart attack patients, men outnumbered women six to one, and she, like most other physicians, labeled their affliction "a middle-age male disease." She observed that the coronary-prone have great difficulty sharing responsibility and find it hard to get along with their superiors. Many of them are self-made men or highly trained professionals. Their overriding personality trait she describes as "compulsive striving. They would rather die than fail. The more difficult things become and the more unhappy they become, the harder they work. . . ." Physically they take poor care of themselves—they eat the wrong kind of food, and try to replenish their energy with coffee and cigarettes. Socially they are "successful" but without much enjoyment of it all. Their style of conversation is highly rational and often a little argumentative, and they cannot express their inner feelings easily.

When this kind of person is struck down by a heart attack his first response, Dr. Dunbar observed, is usually a basic despair which sometimes turns into extreme depression. More often than not, however, he pulls himself together again, says that nothing is seriously wrong, and against his doctor's orders resumes his driven existence as soon as he can possibly manage it. Whereupon he very often dies of a second attack.

Why is the coronary patient this way? Dr. Dunbar's study reveals a number of common patterns in the background. One of these patterns is heart disease in other people the patient has known, especially in his mother—although the fact that the person involved was often not a blood relative suggests that nongenetic factors may be important. Another background item: as children and young adults, both men and women of the coronary group tended to identify with their fathers, although at the same time they also felt a good deal of hostility toward them. They were fond of their mothers, whom they found easy to dominate; but their fathers they were determined to outdo by rising to a high position in life. Many of them succeeded in this, and then, as adults, showed a marked tendency to cut both parents out of their lives.

The father became translated in adult life into the boss, whom they surpassed if they could, or tried to get the best of if they couldn't. They were easily hurt by their superiors. When this happened they did not walk off the job, but curried favor and bided their time, in anticipation of another contest of wills.

Dr. Dunbar identified the biggest off-job problem in these patients as family and sex. Most of the women in the group were frigid and most of the men had frigid wives. She attributes this situation to the intense drive of these patients, to their difficulty in accepting partners of any kind, and also to the grind of the long hours they kept, the lack of vacations, and so forth. But the coronary patient was found to be repressed in many other ways too. Conflict, even with his superiors at work, is pushed out of his conscious mind, to seethe and roil just below the surface. And he succeeds in keeping it there by means of his great defense: work.

Dr. Dunbar was working in the 1930's, a decade so strenuous that the mortality from coronaries increased more than 100 percent in the United States during just four years. Self-destruction was in the air, and the self-destructive heart attack became almost a way out for those who were overwhelmed by this particular brand of stress. Mere advice did not help her patients. She decided to try psychiatry.

"The coronary patient is a particularly satisfying person with whom to work therapeutically," she wrote. "His lifelong habit of working things out for himself makes it easy to enlist his interest and co-operation . . . in none of the cases . . . were the results anything but favorable." She warned other practitioners, however, about the same enduring independence in the coronary-prone, about the "frequent cheerfulness of these patients, their tendency to joke and take it like a good fellow. This is not an indication of a good adjustment to the illness, as is so often assumed, but simply one more expression of the patient's characteristic, and in terms of emotional economy, damaging behavior pattern. In our series the patients who were the 'best sports' about their illness were the ones who died."

HYPERTENSION

In hypertension, the heart pumps blood to the body under abnormally high pressure. The causes, it is agreed widely, include emotional stress. More women than men suffer from hypertension.

The prevalence of hypertension rises and falls from one country to another, reflecting various cultural tensions. It is a frequent cause of death in Japan, for example, though almost unknown in other areas of the Pacific. In the United States it is a common disease of blacks in the large Northern cities; it seldom occurs among the black population of Africa.

Blood pressure fluctuates in healthy people as well as in sick people, sometimes rising because of the actions of the heart muscle, sometimes because the arteries resist the normal flow of blood. Dr. Harold Wolff of New York Hospital found that these two different mechanisms for elevating the blood pressure have their psychological parallels. He called the first type the "exercise pattern." It can be produced by physical exertion, such as running, or by emotional disturbance. The heartbeat goes up in an effort to push more blood through the body, without necessarily encountering more resistance. Dr. Wolff found that when he interviewed people of this type they seemed to be quite willing to express their feelings and conflicts.

The disease known as essential hypertension, however, is caused by arterial constriction, which actually reduces the flow of blood through the body. This is what occurs normally when a healthy human suffers a cut or hemorrhage: the arteries contract and the blood thickens in an automatic effort to minimize loss of the essential fluid. The person suffering from essential hypertension maintains an exterior calm during interviews, but a professional can discern evidence of strong underlying feelings. In a sense she, or he, is unable to bleed emotionally. Hypertension is of course dangerous, and can lead to heart attacks, strokes, and kidney damage.

Flanders Dunbar's study found both similarities and some definite differences between heart attack patients and patients with high blood pressure. The typical hypertensive is just as ambitious in his way as the coronary type, she reported, but a great deal less self-confident. Like him, he spends his life in unspoken conflict with authority. But unlike him, he has little expectation of winning that conflict, with the result that he may imprison himself early in a job that is beneath his capacity, with little responsibility and little future.

In childhood he most often got on poorly with his father and was not allowed to talk back, so that a mixture of anger and guilt has been building up inside him for many years, to be directed in adulthood against his employer, or in the case of some husbands and wives, against each other. Hypertensives' relations with their mothers were close, and remain so—they never really succeed in breaking away as the coronary type does, and throughout their lives swing back and forth between a longing to be taken care of and a resentment against overprotection. Hypertensives are easily upset—by criticism, by disorder, by imperfection of any kind—but do not know how to handle upsetting situations. They are by turns anxious to please and longing to rebel. They will explode in irritability one day, then the next subside into a kind of limp willingness to put up with anything for the sake of peace—and neither approach solves their problems. Nor do their customary forms of solace: liquor, sex, food and cigarettes. In fact these often help to bring on the illness, which usually follows some precipitating event—perhaps separation from a loved one, or money difficulties—by a period of several months, during which the person eats, drinks, and smokes too much and gets involved in love affairs, breaking through his—or her—normal reserve into what Dr. Dunbar describes as "volcanic eruptions of irritability, humor or sentiment."

Hypertensives turn out to be quite responsive to psychiatric counseling. Their many conflicting needs—for dependence versus independence, for failure versus success, for self-indulgence versus self-punishment—constitute a good handle for a competent therapist.

ANGINA AND ARRHYTHMIA

One way of reacting to stress is ordinary neurotic behavior, and there is reason to believe that people who have developed this pattern are better off in terms of physical health than people who haven't. Two forms of heart disease—angina, and cardiac arrhythmia—are cases in point.

Angina is the illness in which not enough oxygen reaches the heart: the symptoms are stabbing chest pains and a feeling of suffocation. The disease is less serious than a heart attack, and the kind of person who gets it is often a paler version of the coronary-prone. Success is important to him, and so is money, but he does not feel the desperate drive to outdo everyone in sight, the insatiable craving to beat the boss, that runs the coronary personality ragged. But above all, though both are inwardly neurotic the angina patient shows it more. He is aware of his underlying fears and anxieties, and he expresses them in his behavior, in the form of nervous tension, moments of impulsiveness, and sometimes various phobias. He dreams more, and is apt to have an active fantasy life.

Despite these distinctions, however, patients with different forms of heart disease tend to resemble one another in basic personality and behavior. Their traits overlap, just as their diseases do, and of course patients who have had heart attacks often go on to develop angina or arrhythmia.

MIGRAINE

Headaches of all types cause more than half the visits to doctors' offices in this country, as well as a sizable proportion of TV commercials for over-the-counter medications. Of the disabling and periodic types, migraine strikes one in eight Americans at some point in their lives, and is caused by dilation of the blood vessels in the scalp. It thus qualifies as a cardiovascular ailment. A distinctly different kind of headache, the kind due to muscular tension, is discussed in Part Two, Chapter Four, but migraine's pain is so devastating that it can bring on tension headaches too, pain attracting more pain.

Characteristically migraine attacks one side of the head at a time, and it is often very regular in its visits—perhaps hitting on the same day, same hour, every week. More women than men get migraines, but the very worst pattern of migraines—clusters, which occur in close series—claim more men than women. Before the migraine settles in, its victims frequently experience what is called aura: the arteries in the scalp first constrict, causing strange visual effects, or the feeling of nausea. Then the arteries react by dilating, and the painful interior pounding begins.

Several decades ago Harold G. Wolff made a pioneering study of the relations between migraine and personality, and today his work is still considered definitive by the experts. In connecting stress directly with migraine, he pointed out a paradoxical twist. It is not during the periods when stress is bearing down hardest that migraine patients usually get their headaches. Instead, it is when the pressure lifts and they are, so to speak, off duty. It often comes on leisurely weekends. Sunday is a notorious migraine day.

Perhaps the truth is that the average migraine patient doesn't know what to do with leisure; for him, as for the coronary type, the meaning of life is work. But the coronary type works hard in order to dominate his world, while the migraine patient has rather different motives.

At bottom he is insecure, according to the Wolff study. What he really wants is to be loved, but he will settle for being admired, or simply approved of: anything to still his gnawing sense of worthlessness. It is for this reason that he drives himself so hard, selflessly taking on thankless chores, burdening himself with ever-increasing responsibilities, conscientious, rigid, somewhat fanatical. And where does it get him? No one really appreciates all he does—not even himself, because no matter how hard he works he can't quite live up to his expectations. Neither can he cope with the feelings of resentment and disappointment building up inside him. He can only try to drown them out through harder labor.

It isn't surprising, then, that when leisure finally does catch up with him he cracks. It is then that his migraine strikes—and with it, often, many long-buried feelings. In fact the patient's whole behavior may change, if only for the duration of his attack. In the words of Dr. Arnold P. Friedman, who has treated thousands of migraine patients, "Transitory depression, overdrawn social behavior, irritability, poor judgment with open expression of impulsivity, hostility, and destructiveness may occur with the attack, in contrast to the typical behavior of the patient . . . who is considerate of others, controlled, and outwardly calm."

Treatment of migraine in this country has been mainly by drugs: aspirin, of course, to raise the pain threshold, and ergotomine tartrate (frequently mixed with caffeine) which constricts the painfully dilated arteries. Before the modern era of medicine magic was commonly used, often effectively, and even today placebo pills help a surprising number of patients. One migraine sufferer, a butcher by trade, has discovered he can cure his attacks simply by spending ten or fifteen minutes inside his walk-in freezer.

But the best results occur when the physician helps the patient understand not only the physical workings of his arteries, but the ways in which his emotions may be affecting them. In Part Four, Chapter Two is described a very new and promising treatment for migraine that involves the will and the mind, with no drugs at all.

CHAPTER 2

THE DIGESTIVE SYSTEM AND RELATED ORGANS
Ulcers, colitis, constipation, diarrhea, diabetes

The fact that eating forms so much of our social apparatus, that the act of savoring, for example, is such an integral part of partying, that courting means having dinner together, that breakfast and supper remain the central rituals of family life—to say nothing of the infamous business lunch—closely connects the taking in of nourishment to all the subtle complications of our private lives. It isn't surprising, then, that when you are under pressure, the body's clearest signal of that fact may come when you swallow. The effects turn up in the esophagus, the stomach, the duodenum, the small intestines, the colon, including the sigmoid and rectum, and all the links and locks in between. Other organs involved in the processing of food, such as the kidneys and pancreas, are also frequent victims of stress.

The digestive system begins at the mouth, where food is chewed and salivated and then sent down through the esophagus to the stomach. The stomach takes the food and continues the breaking-down process—kneading it with vigorous muscular contractions and attacking it with hydrochloric acid and enzymes, aided by the hordes of bacteria which abound in the lower intestinal system. The small intestine and, to some degree, the stomach select the substances that the body can use and pass them into the blood stream. What remains is then sent on to the colon, a flexible tube about three inches in diameter and over four feet long. The colon does absorb further water and salts, and some vitamins are manufactured in it by bacterial action, but its main function might be called transportation. Its contractions propel waste into the rectum for final disposal through the anus. By the time feces are ejected, a relatively small percentage is actual food residue, except for cellulose. Most of it is material shed by the walls of the digestive system, bacteria, gas and water.

Before going further into the gastro-intestinal diseases and their personality prototypes, it is worth pointing out what a tremendously hardy apparatus the human digestive system is when nothing is worrying it. It has been demonstrated that any irritant tolerated by the skin of the forearm can also be tolerated within the healthy stomach. In fact the lining of the stomach is tougher than the exterior skin: stomach acid, when mixed with pepsin (one of the stomach's two protein-digesting enzymes) can actually burn a hole in the skin of the arm.

ULCERS

If an infant does not get enough affection and reassurance while being fed, it may demoralize him, or at least his digestive functions, permanently. Unconsciously, in later life he connects feeding and love and longs deeply for both. He may develop a weight problem, from constantly nibbling on snacks whether hungry or not. He may even become a compulsive eater, prey to secret, panicky binges in which he gobbles up everything in sight till he vomits. Or he may turn into one of the estimated eight million Americans, male and female, who suffer from ulcers.

People with stomach ulcers have gastric systems that are in constant motion, or, it could be said, in constant emotion. They are always hungry. Their digestive juices run full time whether their bodies actually need nourishment or not. Even the most conservative of internists will admit that there is an "ulcer type" whose tendencies are inflamed by conventional life stresses, a highly competitive man or woman, a go-getter—often a business executive, of either sex—who drives for independence from the rest of the world and for conventional success in life, while holding down the even stronger unconscious urge to be nurtured and taken care of. These people are usually found to be full of hostility, but they are blocked off from expressing it—they want too much to be loved. The right kind of marriage is particularly important to them. If one finds a mate of considerable tenderness, able to comfort and sustain, the ulcer type can still compete in business hours and not sustain stomach pains. But many, of course, do not find the right mate. Doctors Edward Weiss and O. Spurgeon English write in their standard work *Psychosomatic Medicine* (W. B. Saunders Co., Philadelphia, 1943): "Bed and board in adult life are as indissolubly connected as sustenance and sensibility in infant life. . . . Men with functional disturbances of the stomach have a very high incidence of marital difficulties." This was written twenty years ago; today it is more true of the distaff side of marriages as well.

In treating ulcers, medical men commonly resort to surgery or drugs, plus, of course, the standard ulcer diet, a frequent ingestion of bland foods to give the aroused gastric juices something to work on and keep them from gnawing at the stomach lining. In the operation called gastrectomy, portions of the stomach wall are cut away, not only to remove the ulcerated sections but to decrease the stomach surface and thus eliminate some of its acid-secreting capacity. A more significant surgical solution, endorsing the fact that ulcers can be caused by emotions, is the procedure of severing the vagus nerve, the transmitting line by which the brain sends its messages to the stomach. Vagotomy does usually lower the output of acid, although there are occasional side effects, ranging from diarrhea and nausea to loss of weight.

But the purely surgical approach is often unsatisfactory in the end. Gastrectomy patients very commonly develop ulcers again after a year or two. Even cutting the vagus nerve, though it may do away with the ulcer, doesn't always solve the real problem. A patient who has come to depend on gastric symptoms to achieve a precarious emotional balance may react to the operation by looking for other psychosomatic ailments, or by lapsing into a mental depression.

The opposite of ulcers, a slowdown of stomach function, can be caused by general discouragement or depression. Too little acid and pepsin are produced. In this way people exposed to sudden danger lose all appetite, and sometimes become nauseous, or vomit. An infectious disease can do the same thing, especially when accompanied by fever. In cancer of the stomach, interestingly, even when the cancer starts as an ulcer lesion, the affliction seems usually to slow down the secretion of stomach acid, and there is surprisingly little pain. The predominant emotion is dejection rather than the inner rage of ulcers.

THE BOWELS

Some people are wryly proud of their ulcers as battle citations in the war of life. But there are equally disturbing ailments lower in the alimentary canal which make for little social discussion past the cruder years of childhood. These are the troubles of the irritable colon, prone to constipation, diarrhea, or, as is not uncommon, an alternation of both annoyances, and are commonly traced back to unreasonable toilet training in infancy. The extreme of this problem is ulcerative colitis, when the wall of the colon becomes so damaged that bowel movements are bloody and uncontrollable. This is a stress-related ailment which not infrequently results in early death.

The connection between bowel disorders and toilet training has been established through countless psychiatric case studies. Franz Alexander offers as an example the child who is rewarded for a bowel movement by being given a piece of candy. "In some such manner," he writes, "the excrement becomes associated with the concept of possession. This explains its close relationship to money, which is one of the best-established facts uncovered by psychoanalysis. Every excremental act is evaluated by the child as a kind of donation to the adults, an attitude often reinforced by the mother's great interest in the child's excrement."

Sweeping—even bizarre—as this judgment may seem, most of us can provide corroboration for it from life. The emotional overtones of the two most common afflictions of the bowels are rather undeniable. Constipation goes with depression and dullness, diarrhea with panic. Both are centered in the colon, which, like the stomach, is designed to work intermittently, not continuously. When it overworks the result is diarrhea; when it underworks, constipation; and stress is often the culprit in both.

Constipated people are often going through a period of dejection. They are discouraged, bored, and rather grim—determined to keep on going, but with little ambition to do much more than that. Those suffering from chronic diarrhea own more flaming feelings: anger, resentment, hostility, sometimes vague guilt, a terrible touchiness toward being slighted by people or events. On the surface, however, they customarily wear a manner of polite passivity.

Hundreds of pills and potions are available from the pharmacy for both conditions, of course, and some of them work, at least temporarily. But when the patient comes under great stress—either on life's surface or in his subconscious—the medicines are of brief effectiveness. Real relief from constipation is best bought by a turning upward of the current of life itself, some good breaks. The cloud of depression drifts off, or is somehow driven off. Relief from chronic diarrhea can result from a lessening of the tensions of life that panic the colon; for example, when you begin getting along better with the in-laws with whom you share a house, or when you move away from them. When someone gets rid of an onerous financial obligation and starts living within his means, he may get rid of diarrhea too.

ULCERATIVE COLITIS

In ulcerative colitis, the membrane of the colon so deteriorates that it bleeds a great deal, and many eventually perforate. Many factors may be involved in this malady, including the immunological system (see following chapter). But whatever may be the exact coincidence of events, the personality profile of the usual victim bears a recurrent set of characteristics, say leading specialists, and the patients' sufferings are made even more miserable by the intensification of stress in their lives, whether it is easily identified pressure from job or family, or long repressed neurosis planted in childhood.

A deep feeling of utter helplessness is common among ulcerative colitis patients. This is easily understandable, once the demeaning affliction has begun with a person's bowels. Specialists in the field believe, however, that feelings of helplessness frequently precede the onslaught of the illness, and that the patient's prior emotional state helps render his colon vulnerable.

These patients are usually very tidy, restrained people, frequently a little prim, notably mild and mannerly, conscientious, punctual, and inhibited in the normal patterns of their lives. They are also usually thin-skinned, alert to real or imagined insults from the world. They fear rejection and so make but few advances toward other people. Ingratiating and seemingly submissive, they have few firm friends.

What they do have is very strong, special attachments, usually toward older people, whom they often end up marrying. Male patients in particular tend to marry wives who are really mother substitutes. Such marriages are frequently unhappy, partly because of sexual inhibition. Few men or women with ulcerative colitis have ever enjoyed active, satisfying sex lives.

So close is the attachment toward one or two people that the ulcerative colitis type sometimes feels within himself that he is a proxy, or even an appendage, of the other person's personality. Often this dominant figure is a woman, and, of course, the emotional path leads back to the patient's mother, who, as described by the patients themselves, is frequently cold, or masochistic. She enjoys being a martyr, particularly to a sick child.

The bondage with such mothers is never broken. When the inevitable pressures of the world descend on the ulcerative colitis type, when he or she feels abandoned, left on his own, unprepared to deliver some deed the world is demanding, he expresses his despair through his gastro-intestinal equipment.

In their book *The Human Colon,* Doctors William J. Grace, Stewart Wolf and Harold G. Wolff analyzed nineteen random patients, fifteen women and four men who had been plagued with ulcerative colitis for periods of six months to twenty-four years. Psychiatric interviews and counseling over the course of many months exposed many characteristics:

> . . . The women were fastidious housekeepers. One woman had a weekly housework schedule which she followed almost to the hour. Another insisted that each piece of daily used chinaware be in its own fixed place, with the handles of the cups all pointing in one direction. If this order were disturbed she became uneasy and as soon as possible restored the objects to their "proper" place. Daily scrubbing of the bathroom and kitchen floor and all the woodwork was part of another patient's routine. One patient found so much housework to do in a three-room apartment that it occupied her whole day. One patient washed and sterilized each object or toy her two-year-old child threw out of its playpen before giving it back to the child.
>
> Overdependence was usually observed in attitudes toward mother, parent-substitute, or spouse. Exacerbations of colitis usually occurred when their dependent position was threatened by unsympathetic behavior or by separation from or illness in a loved one. . . . One patient accompanied her husband, a salesman, on every trip he made, even if it were only for a day. Another woman felt happy and secure and relatively free of symptoms only on weekends when her husband came home. A male patient had an exacerbation of his illness during his wife's menopause when she was irritable and unable to provide him with the show of affection to which he had become accustomed. One woman lived for twenty years of her married life in her mother's home because she felt she could not get along without her emotional support.
>
> This overdependent attitude was reflected by most of the patients in their need to please other people and to be on good terms even with casual acquaintances such as shoe clerks and delivery men. One woman said, "I can't stand anybody being mad at me." In all of the twelve married patients sexual adjustment was poor.

The principal treatment of the nineteen patients was counseling, in addition to conventional medical care. Each was seen every few days or weeks, depending on need, the total time per patient ranging from twelve hours to twenty-five or more. Success was reported with eleven patients, slight improvement with two. No success at all was reported in those patients who would not, or could not, accept the physician as a friend, eager to help with solving the pressures of daily life.

DIABETES

Diabetes mellitus is another widespread disorder in the nutritive chain.

The body cannot function without sugar, its chief source of energy. This sugar comes of course from the food you eat—chiefly from carbohydrates. It is processed by the digestive system and sent to the liver, where it is stored and released in the form of glucose into the blood stream, as needed. Glucose can only be converted into actual energy, however, after it enters the individual cells of the body, and in order to penetrate the cells it usually needs insulin, a hormone secreted by the pancreas. Only the brain can metabolize glucose without the aid of insulin.

It is because of an insulin deficiency that diabetics' cells are unable to absorb enough glucose, which simply accumulates in the blood. Eventually the body must get rid of it, and does so through urination, which necessarily draws large amounts of water, plus salt and potassium, from the patient's tissues, upsetting his interior chemistry. Meantime, unable to utilize glucose the body cells start burning fat instead. Fat is a relatively inefficient fuel. When it is burned, acetone and other organic acids are released into the blood stream, further upsetting chemical balance. If the condition goes unchecked the brain is affected and a diabetic coma occurs.

There is plenty of evidence connecting diabetes with stress. In stressful situations, whether jungle warfare, marital battling, or office confrontations, it has been shown repeatedly that the sugar content of the participants' blood increases sharply. It has also been demonstrated that a patient's diabetes worsens under stress. A diabetic teenager, arguing with her mother, deteriorates even under insulin medication. To maintain balance she will need a higher dosage.

But does stress actually cause diabetes?

Some researchers are convinced that it does, at least in part. They believe that chronically high levels of sugar in the blood, brought about by persistent emotional problems, can place such a burden on the pancreas that it finally collapses. The result is a permanent insulin deficiency.

Certainly many diabetics do have problems—not only with their disease, but with their lives. In Dr. Dunbar's group of diabetics, at Columbia Presbyterian, many of the men were homosexuals, and most of the women had marital problems. A disproportionate number of both sexes had trouble in competing, and felt defeated and depressed about life in general. These feelings they concealed, both from others and from themselves—they had very few emotional outlets, either in action, speech or fantasy.

Franz Alexander also studied diabetics and was struck, as was Dr. Dunbar, by their excessive dependency on their mothers, a dependency that usually centered on food and often resulted in peculiar eating habits—spells when they ate very little followed by periods of insatiable appetite. This kind of behavior creates special problems for the diabetic, of course, because his very life depends on keeping a strict balance between his diet and his insulin medication. If the balance tips one way he may suffer insulin shock; if the other, a diabetic coma. Diabetics are notorious for the chances they take.

In fact, by the time their disease first strikes them, most diabetics have been overeating for years, and Alexander likened their condition to emotional starvation, in which the longing to be loved becomes replaced by a craving for food.

Other investigators, however, feel differently. Maybe diabetics have such big appetites because they really are starved—not emotionally, but physically, since so much of the sugar they eat never reaches their cells. There is also a strong hereditary factor in diabetes, possibly a congenital deficiency in the pancreas.

The real truth probably lies somewhere in between. Like many of the chronic diseases of our time, diabetes in all likelihood is multifactorial—the combined product of heredity, functional imbalances within the body, and stress. Emotional problems make it worse—certainly they make it harder to treat—but whether they can bring diabetes about in the first place remains to be shown.

CHAPTER 3

STRESS AND THE IMMUNITY SCREEN
Infections, allergies, auto-immunity, cancer

Elise and David Fischer are to have a dinner party tonight—the Harrises (old friends), plus the new couple across the hall, the Spragues. Elise feels festive. The boeuf à la mode is marinating. She is busy rolling out a pie crust when the phone rings.

"Elise? Helen Harris. Dear, I hate to do this to you, but we're going to have to beg off. Frank's mother's in the hospital. She's being operated on tomorrow morning, and we're taking the five o'clock plane."

"I'm so sorry, Helen."

Elise hangs up, feeling disturbed. Then she remembers the dinner. Hell! She can't have the Spragues by themselves, she hardly knows them yet. Maybe the Steinhardts can fill in. She picks up the phone again.

No luck. Leon's arthritis is acting up. He's been lying in bed swallowing aspirins all day.

Elise reaches for her phone book wondering who to call now. Then suddenly the doorbell rings, and her problem is solved. It is Anne Sprague, clutching a box of Kleenex. "I'm so sorry," she croaks. "I thought I was better yesterday, but now I'm running a fever again. It must be the flu."

"You poor thing! Now you go right back to bed! And don't worry about tonight, hear?"

Slightly dazed, Elise shuts her door again, passes through the kitchen (avoiding the unfinished pie) and steps out onto her balcony. It is a fine spring afternoon. The grass glistens in the sunlight. The maple trees are flowering. But Elise feels discouraged. Poor old Mrs. Harris! And it's going to take a week to eat up all that food.

Suddenly Elise sneezes. The roof of her mouth begins to itch, and her eyes to water. Her head starts filling up. It's her hay fever! Swiftly she steps inside again, slamming the door shut behind her, and hastens to the medicine cabinet, thinking angrily, "What's happening to us all!"

Two common threads run through the disparate afflictions that canceled the Fischers' dinner party. One of these threads is the immunological system. This is the system designed to protect the body against infection. But it doesn't always work fast enough—hence, Mrs. Sprague's flu. And sometimes it makes mistakes. One of its commonest mistakes goes by the name of allergy—Elise Fischer's problem. And most medical authorities now suspect that a faulty immune response is also what causes cancer, and that it may help to cause arthritis.

The second thread is stress. Run-down people get infections easily, and stress runs people down. It isn't only a matter of insufficient sleep, or too many cigarettes. It is now known that stress actually disturbs the immunological system itself. In the words of Hans Selye, "If a microbe is in or around us all the time and yet causes no disease until we are exposed to stress, what is the 'cause' of our illness, the microbe or the stress?"

The science of immunology has a curious history. For centuries, infectious disease was mankind's biggest single health problem. One reason our ancestors had fewer heart attacks, of course, is that many of them didn't live long enough—diphtheria, smallpox and cholera carried them off first. But with the discoveries of Pasteur and Koch, all that began to change.

Then in the 1940's, penicillin appeared, presently followed by the antibiotics and all at once immunology began to look like a dying enterprise. Why spend years developing a vaccine against a disease when you can snuff it out in a day or two with pills?

Paradoxically, it was only at this time that the study of immunology began to come into its own. Because its practical applications seemed to be fading, the work in the field began to broaden and deepen, and the result has been a surge of new research, some of it conflicting, much of it as yet inconclusive, but fascinatingly full of implications about some of the most esoteric aspects of human physiology. Meanwhile, of course, antibiotics have not turned out to be all that was hoped. They're useful, but no substitute for immunity, and so the search for new vaccines flourishes once more.

INFECTIONS

When a person is in good health it sometimes seems that the human body is a fortress against infection, with a capable crew of tireless guards—known in immunology as antibodies—on patrol night and day, keeping the interior clear of the enemy. But it is not that way at all. Actually, we are tenanted with microbial agents just as thickly, and as essentially, as feudal lords were surrounded by serfs—with many of the vassals living in the castle twenty-four hours a day, covertly eyeing the silver goblets, tapestries and swords. When the lord's control begins to slip, the vassals may suddenly turn on him and take over.

Nevertheless, the lord could not get along without his serfs; nor can we do without the microbial life that teems within us. It assists in the digestion of food, for example. And we can tolerate even its injurious members, so long as we keep strong. Some of them we control by limiting their numbers. Others remain harmless because they are restricted to certain parts of the castle. Germs that can cause encephalitis when they enter the brain are commonly present in the healthy throat. The skin is not bothered by staphylococcus albus, but let it enter the abdominal cavity, as sometimes happens in surgery, and you may be in trouble. In fact the more sealed-off the organ, the more susceptible it is to infectious agents. The unbroken skin can withstand almost any insult. The central nervous system, the heart valves and the joints are all highly vulnerable.

The best points of entry for a microbe are the orifices of the body, especially the mouth and nose, because these are gateways for the intake of air and food, and inevitably a swarm of microbes comes along too. But usually the body knows how to protect itself. The lungs, when they exhale, expel foreign bodies that entered on the inhale—explosively at times, with coughs and sneezes. Saliva in the mouth contains chemicals deadly to many microbes, and those that survive pass down to the stomach where hydrochloric acid continues the slaughter. The wax in your ears is another protective device, as are the tears that form in your eyes.

Even when the skin is broken the body is still well designed for defense. It seals off the enemy near the point of entry, by the process known as inflammation. The skirmishing exacts a price. An inflamed area of flesh hurts, and there is some destruction of tissue; if the inflammation is severe it may impede normal functions for a while. But when it works—as it usually does—it is worth it. The invaders are cut off and surrounded, and then white blood cells come in to destroy them. In a few hours or days the job is done, and healing repairs the damage.

Some attacking microbes are tougher than others—so tough that inflammation alone cannot handle them. When this happens the body falls back on its last, and strongest, line of defense: the complicated mechanism known as specific immunity.

Specific immunity is the ability of the body to distinguish between self and not-self, and having made the distinction, to destroy the not-self elements. What is startling about this ability is that it resides not in some advanced organ like the brain, but in a part of the body one is hardly aware of—the lymphatic system. The lymphatic system contains cells known as lymphocytes, and each of these lymphocytes carries on its surface a certain kind of molecule called an immunoglobulin molecule, which recognizes foreign microbes.

Just how they do so was a subject of controversy for many years, but today the so-called clonal theory is generally accepted. According to this theory, each of the immunoglobulin molecules in the body has its own special shape and electrical charge, designed to fit the shape and electrical charge of a specific foreign protein molecule in the world outside, much as a key fits a lock. The first time one of these foreign molecules penetrates the defenses of the body, it sooner or later meets up with its matching immunoglobulin molecule, which then proceeds to attach itself to the invader. The invader is called an antigen. And the immunoglobulin molecule which attacks it is known as an antibody.

When antibody attacks antigen, a number of events occur. First, antigens reside on the surface of the invading microbe, and are used by it to gather food, so when they become smothered by antibodies the microbe begins to starve. This smothering also prevents the microbe from releasing chemical substances that can damage tissues and destroy white blood cells.

But something more drastic also happens. The lymphocyte that houses the antibody, known as a T-lymphocyte, begins to reproduce, creating more and more T-lymphocytes, each containing the same antibody specific to this particular antigen; and a second type of lymphocyte, the so-called B-lymphocyte, is in some way stimulated to change into a plasma cell.

A plasma cell is basically a manufacturing plant. What it produces is the same antibody that the T-lymphocytes produce, only in far greater numbers. And these antibodies produced by the plasma cell do not remain with the parent cell as the antibodies of T-lymphocytes do. They are released into the blood and circulate to almost every tissue of the body.

If this is the person's first encounter with the microbe in question, a week or two—sometimes longer—will pass before these so-called humoral antibodies—the ones manufactured by the plasma cells—become numerous enough to handle a major invasion. During this period, the patient is sick. Inflammation makes him hurt in assorted places. He feels tired and weak because so much of his energy goes into building up his defenses. He may even run a fever. But fever helps too, because it speeds antibody production, and in some cases it may affect the invader more directly. A microbe that flourishes in a 98.6-degree environment may start to wilt at 103 degrees.

Even after the patient recovers, his plasma cells continue for months to manufacture antibodies against the now defeated antigen, so that should it return it can be dealt with promptly. If no second invasion occurs, however, antibody production gradually drops, until by the end of a couple of years a test of the patient's blood will show that he is approximately back where he started.

And yet he is *not* back where he started—that is the marvel of specific immunity. If the same microbe finally launches another attack, the defending lymphocytes will recognize the old enemy and go to work a great deal faster—so fast that in most cases the person won't have time to get sick. Inflammation and fever aren't necessary. The instant proliferation of antibodies overwhelms the invasion before it can get under way.

Which is why measles and mumps are one-time diseases.

Then what about flu and strep infections, not to mention colds—the nuisance diseases, that recur over and over in the lives of perfectly healthy people?

The answer is that none of these is a single disease. There are some fifty known varieties of strep bacteria in Group A alone. The common cold is nothing but a set of symptoms which can be set off by any of approximately a hundred microbes. And over the years these microbial agents have a way of mutating—that is, of altering the genetic structure passed on from parent microbe to child microbe, which alters the antigens, which in turn means you lose your hard-won immunity. In other words, although theoretically you could acquire immunity to all hundred forms of the common cold, through several years of constant coughing and nose-running, by the end of that time the first forms on your list would have mutated and you would have to start over again.

The body's defenses against invasion do not operate full force at all times. In the first months of life the immunity screen is still under construction, and in old age it begins to deteriorate: both babies and the elderly are very susceptible to infection.

And so are people under stress. It is now known that stress weakens the immune response by very specific physical pathways. What happens is that emotional problems rouse the hypothalamus in the brain. The hypothalamus then rouses the pituitary gland. The pituitary rouses the adrenal glands. And the adrenals start sending out increased amounts of a kind of hormone called a glucocorticoid.

It is these excess glucocorticoids that do the damage. Under their influence a person produces fewer antibodies, and his inflammatory response dwindles. Experiments have shown that when polio virus is injected into the brains of hamsters, 27 percent will die of the disease, but if accompanied by a strong shot of cortisone the death rate rises to 100 percent. In real life the results may be less dramatic. Nevertheless, when problems are piled on problems and the last thing you want is to get sick, it is precisely then—and precisely because of the problems—that you may suddenly come down with a fever.

ALLERGIES

People get sick not only when their resistance lowers, but also when it rises too high. These are the people with the inflammatory diseases like an allergy or arthritis—diseases in which the body is injured not by some malevolent microbe, but by its own protective devices, senselessly firing away at a harmless challenge, sometimes at no challenge at all.

This is indisputably true of allergy, still it remains in many ways a mystifying affliction. One of the curious facts about the allergic reaction is that stress hormones in the form of drugs (cortisone, for example), usually bring relief, yet stress itself, as experienced in daily life, tends to make it worse. And allergics don't respond to all invaders in the same fashion. The asthmatic reacts normally to chicken pox and measles. It is only house dust, or pollen, or animal dander that sets him gasping for breath.

Plasma cells produce several different types of antibodies, and it is now known that one of them, Immunoglobulin E (IgE), is especially active in allergy. IgE not only attacks the invading antigen, it also stimulates the body to release certain chemicals—histamine is one—which cause tissues to swell, mucus secretions to rise, and air passages in the lungs to contract. Perhaps further research into IgE will clear up the mystery of allergy.

For years, of course, some psychologists have been claiming that allergy is at heart an emotional disease. In many patients no physical antigen is discoverable, a situation that may be true of 50 percent of asthmatics. Allergists themselves say that in all probability an antigen does exist, and will be located eventually, when techniques of detection improve; but their case remains to be demonstrated. Meanwhile, psychologists have unearthed some interesting evidence to support their view.

A group headed by Dr. J. J. Groen, at a hospital in Amsterdam, for some years ran experiments on asthma. In one of these, a woman who was allergic to horses began to wheeze when merely shown a photograph of a horse. A second woman, hypersensitive to goldfish, reacted not only to a toy fish, but to an empty fish bowl. Still other patients were conditioned to respond allergically to ordinary uncontaminated air. For instance, a woman allergic to pollen inhaled alternating doses of pollen-laden air, room air and pure oxygen. After a number of such sessions she reached the point where the room air and even the oxygen brought on her asthma just as forcefully as the pollen did—in fact, just placing the mouthpiece of the inhalator between her lips could induce an attack.

An attack of asthma can be brought on not only by an idea, but also by emotions that the patient has learned to connect with wheezing, coughing, or other allergic symptoms. Very often these emotions involve his or her mother. The mother of an allergic child tends to behave in a rather special way. She cannot greet an asthma attack in her child as calmly as she would a cold, or even a bout of pneumonia. It is more frightening—and it is also more avoidable. So she becomes bossy and overprotective. No, he can't play baseball in the vacant lot with the other kids—doesn't he know there's ragweed down there? And he's got to go to bed earlier than his friends, because it's when he gets tired that his attacks are worst. Catching cold brings them on too, so he'd better wear his rubbers today—there's a 40 percent chance of rain.

The psychogenic view of allergy holds that the mother's attitude is not so much a reaction to her child's allergy as it is a part of her basic personality; she is thus overprotective to start with, and this is one reason why he has become allergic. Whatever the etiology the child reacts by becoming excessively dependent on his mother, but at the same time he feels rebellious against her. These are the feelings that become connected with his allergic attacks—so much so that when other circumstances rouse these feelings an allergic attack may take place even if the physical antigen is absent.

The best cure for some severely asthmatic children is to send them away from home. In Holland before World War II, they were often sent to Switzerland, where their improvement was ascribed to the change of altitude. But when the war came and foreign travel was no longer possible, doctors found they could get just as good results by sending these children to homes in a neighboring Dutch town. In these cases no steps were taken to desensitize the environment. The children simply got better—and it was noted that a letter from home might bring on the first real attack in months.

Many asthma patients find it hard to express their feelings. Their longing to be taken care of prevents them from acting rebellious, and their rebelliousness prevents them from acting dependent, so they can become almost immobilized emotionally. As a medical group they are notorious for their inability to weep. Some psychologists say an asthma attack is nothing but a suppressed cry for Mother, and it can often be broken up if the patient bursts into tears. Others feel it is more a protest against maternal domination—the patient's way of saying he feels smothered. Franz Alexander links asthma to the breath-holding habit common in some children—a device something like a hunger strike, to protest against the quality of maternal love.

RHEUMATOID ARTHRITIS

In rheumatoid arthritis, seemingly, the villain is inflammation pure and simple—no microbial agent or other invader has ever been identified with it, although many doctors believe such an invader does exist and will some day be found. Again like allergy, rheumatoid arthritis is made worse by stress of all kinds, and yet it is relieved by taking cortisone or ACTH, the hormones the body puts forth in situations of acute stress. For these and other reasons, some doctors believe arthritis is allergic.

But there are important differences between the two states. Most allergies attack organs that are relatively exposed: the digestive tract, the nose and lungs, the skin. Yet the joints are one of the best protected areas.

Rheumatoid arthritis will be discussed further in the following chapter, "The Skeletal-Muscular System." It comes up here because so many investigators are coming to believe that the real villain is a specific derangement in some people's bodily defenses called auto-immunity. Auto-immunity has been implicated in a number of other serious ailments, ranging from ulcerative colitis to schizophrenia—and, to complete the circle, possibly even allergy itself.

Auto-immunity is a condition in which the immune system fails in its most important single task—the distinction between self and not-self— and starts manufacturing antibodies against the patient's own tissue. Just why and how this happens has not yet been discovered. Some think mutation is involved—noncancerous changes in certain body cells, with a consequent change in their antigens.

Auto-immunity may also occur when an invading microbe happens to possess antigens that are almost identical to the antigens of the patient's own body tissue. In rheumatic fever, for instance, the streptococcus antigen may so closely resemble certain protein molecules within the heart valves that antibodies manufactured against the first will also attack the second.

A third possibility has to do with the antigen-antibody complexes often found in the blood of patients with auto-immune diseases. Here is a situation where antibody attacks antigen but fails to destroy it—probably because antibody production is somewhat deficient. It is possible that these clumps of antigen-antibody become, in effect, new antigens, and the body fights back the only way it knows how. In the blood of three out of four rheumatoid arthritis patients a substance is found known as the rheumatoid factor. It appears to consist of two antibodies—one presumably against some unidentified invader, the second against the anti-invader antibody. These persist indefinitely. Presumably the invader itself is harmless, and the pain and crippling are wholly caused by the immune reaction.

Interestingly, among patients with ulcerative colitis, another disease that may involve auto-immune mechanisms, 15 percent also suffer from a mild form of arthritis, which usually disappears if the colitis clears up.

CANCER

In cancer the body also fails in its task of surveillance—the task of recognizing an enemy within its gates—but with reverse results. Here foe is mistaken for friend, and a deadly enemy is allowed to live and multiply inside the body without interference.

Cancerous mutations, it is now believed, are a regular occurrence in the lives of perfectly healthy people, who never know it because their immune systems destroy the mutant cell before it can multiply. But every now and then, in a certain individual, at a certain point in time, this reaction fails to take place. The mutant cell, despite its new antigens, survives, and gradually multiplies, and becomes a tumor, and the person goes to his doctor, who discovers he has cancer.

How does a cell become cancerous in the first place? What exactly is a mutation?

A mutation is a change in the hereditary material within an originally normal cell. The individual cells of the body have a set of genetic characteristics which they pass on, through the DNA of the cell nucleus, to succeeding cells. Thus muscle cells reproduce muscle cells, just as ten-fingered parents reproduce ten-fingered children. Once in a great while, however, a nine-fingered baby is born, and this is because of a mutation in the cells of the very early embryo.

Many physical agents cause mutations. Chemicals can cause them; so can injuries and burns; so can X-ray, ultraviolet light, and ultrasonic agitation. And so can viruses.

A virus is the smallest and simplest organism known to man—in fact it only barely qualifies as an organism at all. You can take a little glass bottle, fill it with a few million viruses, put a stopper on it and store it on a shelf for fifty years, and you might as well be storing a handful of sand: inside that bottle absolutely nothing will happen, no intake of food or air, no output of waste, no reproduction, no death. If at the end of fifty years you pull out the stopper and release the viruses into the presence of living cells, then, and only then will they come to life of a sort. A virus is a kind of parasite, but like no other parasite. Its only known function is reproduction, and it can only reproduce inside a living cell. It does this by taking over the DNA of the cell nucleus and forcing it to serve the needs of the virus rather than of the cell—and the sole need of the virus is the reproduction of other viruses. Finally the cell bursts, releasing all these new viruses into the body, where they proceed to attack yet other cells and repeat the whole cycle.

Viruses are to blame for such assorted diseases as measles, polio, hepatitis and most colds, and they can also cause cancer—definitely, in animals, and most probably in humans as well. This is hardly surprising. If a virus attacks the living cell by attacking its DNA, and if DNA is the material that passes hereditary traits from parent cell to child cell, then it is only logical to expect mutations to result. And cellular mutation is the basic single fact about cancer.

Mutations induced by viruses are more dramatic than those caused by other forces, such as chemicals or radiation. A viral cancer is highly antigenic, and normally provokes a strong counterattack from the lymphocytes. If this counterattack is weakened, however, by stress or some other factor, viral cancers survive and begin to grow. They grow faster than chemical cancers.

What makes a tumor grow? Or why do some tumors fail to grow? Some individual cancer cells, even if they survive the attack of antibodies, remain dormant for long spells—some for a lifetime, others for a period of years before they suddenly begin to multiply. No one is sure why this dormant stage is so common, but it is probably because of the immune system. Although unable to destroy the cells outright, it is still capable of controlling their numbers.

And probably a sudden lowering of these immune defenses is what makes a long dormant cancer begin to grow.

In his book, *Cancer, the Wayward Cell,* Dr. Victor Richards points out that cancer cells do not actually reproduce all that fast. The real problem is that their reproduction rate is greater than their death rate. In normal cells these two rates are balanced—probably through a device known as contact inhibition. A normal cell does not reproduce when it is snugly surrounded by fellow cells; reproduction happens only if one or more of the other cells dies and disappears. Electrical impulses may be involved—and it is known that cancer cells are highly resistant to electrical charges.

Another difference between cancer cells and normal cells is that normal cells are differentiated—that is, each type of cell has a certain function to perform, and a certain structure suited to that function. Thus a bone cell is very different from a muscle cell, so much so that under a microscope the bone cell of a human looks more like the bone cell of a mouse than like some other kind of cell from the human body.

One of the peculiarities of cancer cells is that they are not differentiated in this fashion. They are what scientists call de-differentiated. In fact, in many ways they behave like the original group of cells in the first few hours of an embryo's life, just after conception and before different types of tissue begin to form. The sole purpose of such embryonic cells is, of course, rapid growth. They neither contract muscles, nor secrete hormones, nor manufacture blood, nor perform any other specialized task. What they do is multiply. In an embryo such cells begin to mature and acquire their own identity within a few days. But in cancer this doesn't happen. A tumor not only fails to develop special functions to serve the body, the way normal cells do, but as it gets larger it begins to compete with normal cells for space and fuel, until eventually it takes over and destroys vital organs, and the body dies, tumor and all.

Stress helps to cause cancer because it depresses the immune response, the body's only real means of defending itself against malignant cells. It does this through the action of the adrenal cortex hormones, which particularly affect the T-lymphocytes. Searching out foreign antigens in the body is one of the tasks of these T-lymphocytes, and significantly they measure at low levels in the tissues of most cancer patients.

But body reactions quite unconnected with immunity may go on to promote metastasis: the spreading of cancer from its original site to other organs. Metastasis takes place when cancer cells break away from a tumor, enter the blood stream, travel to a new area and become implanted there. Surgery sometimes can actually initiate this process, by causing a tumor to shed cells, and the same thing may happen because of muscular responses to stress, such as chronic spasms in the colon or lungs. Dr. George F. Solomon of Stanford University also believes that the increased coagulability of the blood, a normal reaction to stress, causes deposits of fibrin to form on the walls of blood vessels which may snag passing cancer cells. The cells then take up residence and begin growing into surrounding tissues.

Is it stress in general that makes people cancer prone, or is it a particular kind of stress? No one is really sure, but during the past hundred and fifty years numerous physicians have called attention to a distinctive state of mind in their cancer patients. Some have called it melancholy; others, hopelessness, or despair, or deep-seated disappointment. Often it is associated with the recent loss of a relative or close friend.

In the early 1950's a clinical psychologist, Dr. Lawrence LeShan, of the Institute of Applied Biology, decided to investigate this state of mind. Over a period of twelve years he tested four hundred and fifty adult cancer patients, forty-five of whom received intensive individual psychotherapy. What he came up with is a portrait of a personality as individual, certainly as haunting, as any in medical literature.

This is how Dr. LeShan describes his typical cancer patient:

Early in life, apparently during the first seven years, damage was done to the child's developing ability to relate. Often this was accentuated by a physical event, such as the loss of a parent, the death of a sibling, or something of this sort. From his experience at this time, the child learned to feel that emotional relationships brought pain and desertion. Loneliness was his doom. In the usual manner of children, this was attributed to some fault of his own rather than to the result of accidental forces. Guilt and self-condemnation were the inevitable response.

The traumatic situation or crisis had not the kind of timing and intensity which would be likely to produce obvious neurotic symptoms or to prepare the individual for psychosis in the event of later stress. From a surface viewpoint, he managed to adjust adequately to his environment. However, the orientation that social relationships were dangerous and that there was something very much wrong with him, persisted and colored his life. Little real energy was invested in relationships. His cathexes to other people were essentially superficial and no matter what he achieved, his basic feelings of failure predominated. To use Kierkegaard's phrase, he was "in despair of being himself. . . ."

Sometime in his development, usually in our cases in late adolescence or early adulthood, a situation arose that offered an opportunity for relating to others; a perceived chance to end the deep loneliness he felt. This possibility seemed somehow "safe." Over a period of time, a period of slow and cautious experimentation, he began to pour his energies into this channel. The feelings of isolation and "lostness," the deep loneliness were greatly, but never completely, eased by this relationship. A tremendous amount of psychic and usually physical energy was poured into it. The cathexis gave a meaning to life. For a period ranging from one year to over forty, they had a meaningful existence and a channel into which to pour their energy.

Sometimes it was a job with a role for which they seemed particularly well adapted and which they enjoyed. Sometimes as a spouse, a parent or both, they found a way of life that brought them closer to satisfaction and relatedness than they had ever dreamed was possible. They still found it difficult to express or defend their own wishes, but in the interest of their group or of the relationship, they could act very strongly.

For a shorter or longer period, life continued on this plane. Then the blow fell. Circumstances brought an end to the relationship; their role was lost. Job retirement was forced on them, a spouse died, children grew up, became independent and no longer needed them. The immediate reaction varies. Some made desperate efforts to find substitute relationships. They tried to obtain new jobs, to make new friends, to find a new group, only to fail. Others were crushed by the blow. From a superficial view, all continued to "adjust." They continued to

286

function and went about their daily business, but there was no more meaning and hope to their lives. Nothing gave them real satisfaction. It seemed to them as though the thing they had expected and feared all their lives—utter isolation and rejection—was now their eternal doom. . . .

The early fantasy of something being basically wrong with them, something that made them unacceptable to others, returned in full force. Their energy level declined . . . The color and zest went out of life. At some time from six months to eight years after the crucial cathexis was lost, the first symptoms of cancer appeared in the cases we observed.

Dr. LeShan also found a high statistical correlation between malignancy and specific life events in these patients—for instance, the birth of a younger brother or sister before the patient had reached his second birthday, or an unhappy marriage, particularly in women who developed cancer of the cervix. But what impressed him most strongly was this more generalized life pattern of disappointment, loneliness and loss of hope.

One of his patients said to him: "You know how it is with a house with no insulation and with cracks in the walls? The more heat you put in, the more leaks out. You can never get it warm. I always knew that was how it was with me in life. I had to keep putting and putting out and there was never any reflection back toward me. If I was going to get warm inside, I'd have to do it alone, and no matter how much you do, you can't do that."

Another said: "Last time I hoped, and look what happened. As soon as my defenses were down, of course it happened and I was left alone again. I'll never hope again. It's too much."

And a third used to say: "If the rock drops on the egg—poor egg. If the egg drops on the rock—poor egg."

CHAPTER 4

THE SKELETAL-MUSCULAR SYSTEM
Backache, tension headache, arthritis, the accident-prone

Watching passersby on a busy street from a bus window, you can learn quite a bit about them, even if you can't see their eyes or hear what they are saying. You learn it from the way they move.

A nine-year-old breaks into an exuberant run. He's just been released from school.

A woman in her twenties passes confidently along, shoulders easy, handbag swinging, the trace of a smile on her lips—a person who knows where she is going.

Half a block behind, but gaining, comes a man with big shoulders and a heavy stride. His arms don't move as he walks, elbows back, hands clenched, staring into the faces of the people who pass him. They do not return his glance. He is an aggressive man, an angry man, and they don't want to get involved with him.

These people are all using their bones and muscles to accomplish something, even if it is only a walk in the afternoon sunshine. At the same time they are using this equipment to express something about themselves. Sometimes they are saying what they feel; sometimes what they would like to feel. Most of the time they are saying a little of both.

A smile is a muscular act. So is a frown. Everyone expresses feelings muscularly. But some people do it more than others: babies and young children, and also certain adults. Often, though not always, these are people who find it a little hard to express themselves in words. Included are many athletes, carpenters, actors and dancers, both professional and amateur, as well as quite a few people with chronic medical problems. This is not surprising. Obviously a quarterback exposes himself to certain risks that a file clerk does not.

But it isn't quite that simple. Actually, of the many people who suffer from ailments involving the skeletal-muscular system, only some are strong physical-action types. Others appear to be almost the opposite, at first glance. It is a first glance that is deceptive, however. The truth is that muscles and bones are used not only to express feelings, but to repress them. The skeletal-muscular type of person can go either way.

BACKACHE AND TENSION HEADACHE

"Sitting tight" describes the state of the typical patient with chronic functional backache. His problem is not that he lifts too many heavy loads or overdoes at the gym. On the contrary.

A muscle is like many other parts of the body—it isn't normally injured by use, even by a great deal of use. Exercise strengthens muscles, partly because it makes them more flexible. This flexibility is important. Muscles contract when they are performing a job. But when the job is finished they should know how to relax. The difference in the length of a muscle between a state of rest and a state of exertion is one measure of its efficiency.

When a person feels like acting but does not allow himself to act, his muscles remain tensed in readiness, sometimes for months or years at a time, immobilized into a state of semi-contraction even during sleep. If this condition goes on long enough, the muscle gradually loses its elasticity, and with it much of its effectiveness. Such a muscle is overused. It never gets a chance to rest. And in order to perform even a minor action it must contract extra hard to make up for its permanently shortened condition.

This is chronic muscle spasm, by far the commonest cause of trouble for people who suffer the miseries of recurrent backache. What are these people like?

At heart most of them are *action* types. Action is their natural way of achieving things, of solving problems and of expressing anger, and many come from a childhood studded by temper tantrums and fighting. But in adult life this approach does not seem to have paid off, and they have ceased to trust it. They are competitive people who feel they are not getting "their own," resentful of those they feel are to blame—often a boss, or a husband or wife—and deeply unsure of what to do about it all. Angry and apprehensive, they cannot take action, yet they are constantly on guard and ready to act. Their muscles are often tense all over the body. But it is the muscles of the back that usually feel the strain because they are the most vulnerable. Evolutionally speaking, man is a descendant of four-legged animals; his erect posture is a relatively recent development, and his back muscles are still in the process of catching up. They are supposed to get help from the stomach muscles and hip flexors, but these are so weakened by today's sedentary living that they often have little to contribute.

Chronic muscle tension can hurt in other areas besides the back. Some people get toothaches from habitually clenching their jaws—a muscular exertion which, if it persists long enough, can also affect the bones in the gum and lead to early tooth loss. A more common affliction is the tension headache. Here it is the muscles of the neck and scalp that cause the trouble. Most people come down with this kind of headache at some point in their lives, but some have it regularly and a few get headaches that persist for a year or longer. Usually, like backache patients, they are restless, unsure people constantly poised for action but unable to trust their own impulses.

One of the problems in both backache and tension headache is the cyclical nature of the pain. Muscle tension makes you hurt; then hurting makes you tense your muscles further, which makes you hurt still more.

It isn't easy to relax when you hurt. This is why some doctors give tranquilizers, along with aspirin, to a headache patient. Heat and massage help a sore back because they help the muscles let go.

ARTHRITIS

Muscles and bones are the sturdy workhorses of the human body, tough, energetic, and quick to mend if injured. But crucial to their operations is a more delicate piece of machinery: the joint. A professional football player knows this well. A broken finger or a pulled calf muscle is nothing in his life. It is his knees that he worries about.

When a joint becomes inflamed, the condition is called arthritis. Injury can cause arthritis; so can infection; so can ordinary wear and tear over years of living. Most elderly people are at least mildly arthritic, especially if they are overweight. Their condition is called osteoarthritis.

The real crippler, however, is rheumatoid arthritis, a disease that attacks people in the prime of life. Sometimes it stays a year or two and then mysteriously vanishes. Usually it settles in for good, slowly spreading pain and stiffness from one joint to another. In severe cases scar tissue forms at the adjoining bone ends and eventually turns into bone itself, freezing the joint into permanent immobility. Rheumatoid arthritis can be treated, but no one knows how to cure it. No one even knows its cause.

Like many chronic diseases, it may have a number of causes all working together—one of which may well be a faulty immune response in the body, another of which is probably stress. As we know, stress does affect the immunologic system. In addition, there is some evidence that stress affects arthritis more directly.

For years, physicians have been struck both by the fact that emotional problems seem to make arthritis worse, and by certain similarities in the way many arthritis patients behave. Often they are rather rigid, domineering people, somewhat shy socially, who early in life learned to take out their feelings in aggressive physical action. They play tennis. They swim. They garden. They go for long, vigorous walks—and it is hard for an ordinary person to keep up. Like the backache victim, they associate physical activity with the expression of aggression and hostility. Unlike him, they have found it a satisfying and on the whole trustworthy outlet for these emotions.

Nevertheless, hostility is a problem for them, and often it hinges on sexual roles. In rheumatoid arthritis, three out of four patients are women, and most of them resent the fact. Though they usually marry and raise families, they tend to select rather passive husbands whom they can keep under control, and they are the same with their children. This does not mean they mistreat their families. Often they are unusually solicitous—fine cooks and tireless household managers, magnanimous and even in their way loving, so long as they remain in control. In fact, they are somewhat masochistic about it all. By knocking themselves out caring for husband and children, they relieve not only their inner hostility, but also the feeling of guilt that this hostility produces. Theirs is a pattern of life aimed at balancing these two emotions, and sometimes it goes on working indefinitely.

But sometimes it doesn't. The husband, feeling vaguely threatened, begins to assert himself. The children grow older and rebel against all that care. Sexual relations, always difficult, come to seem an outright humiliation. With the passage of years, too, the person's physical energy begins to dwindle, and with it her accepted emotional outlets. She's no longer up to three sets of tennis, and repainting the downstairs ceilings leaves her worn out and depressed. In other words, one reason she gets sick is not that she expresses her feelings through physical labor and exercise, but because physical labor and exercise no longer work for her.

Rheumatoid factor is an element found in the blood of most patients with rheumatoid arthritis. Interestingly, it is sometimes found in the blood of healthy people as well—including, at times, athletes after a hard game. In 1965 Drs. George F. Solomon and R. H. Moos published a study comparing a group of rheumatoid arthritis patients with various healthy relatives. Some of these healthy relatives possessed the rheumatoid factor, and some did not. Those without the factor remained healthy despite the usual assortment of psychological problems common to the general population. But the striking thing about those who did possess the rheumatoid factor was their sound emotional balance. Often they resembled their arthritic relatives in taking a physically active approach to life—and often from similar motives. But in their case the approach was working well for them. Solomon and Moos concluded by suggesting that stress alone doesn't produce arthritis, and neither does the rheumatoid factor, but perhaps the two together do.

A number of physicians suspect that muscle tension of the sort involved in back trouble and tension headaches also contributes to arthritis. Franz Alexander noted that the onset of the disease was often preceded by attacks of muscular pain. And it has been shown that arthritics under emotional pressure do respond with abnormal muscle tension, particularly in the muscles closest to the afflicted joints. It is possible that this tension injures the joints in small ways, making them more susceptible to disease, or even altering their chemical make-up and thereby arousing an immune reaction within the body.

This possibility has been discussed in the preceding chapter. At any rate it seems clear that there is more to the disease than simple mechanical strain. Rheumatoid arthritis affects the whole body, not just the joints. Among its symptoms are fever, anemia, and reduced blood flow to the extremities. Perhaps more important, in rheumatoid arthritis the body loses collagen, a basic element in all connective tissue, resulting in weight loss, brittle bones, loose ligaments, and a withering of the skin. Normally collagen makes up a third of the body's total weight. No one knows how it is formed, but pituitary and sex hormones both appear to influence its manufacture.

ACCIDENTS

In medical research, when you decide to investigate a disease the customary procedure is to get together a group of people who are afflicted, plus a group of people who are not, and then to compare the two groups, the aim being to weed out irrelevant factors.

Back in the 1930's when Flanders Dunbar undertook her massive study of psychogenic factors in the patient population at Columbia Presbyterian, she chose accident patients, primarily fracture cases, as her control group. Her logic seemed sound. An accident by definition is a coincidence, the result not of causative forces, mental or physical, at work in the body, but of random chance. Before long, however, Dr. Dunbar began to wonder; and by the time her study was complete, she was ready with another definition. In the typical fracture patient, she asserted, the statistics run much too high to be explained by chance; accidents are not accidental; psychogenic forces *are* at work. And the concept of the accident-prone received major new support.

Perhaps the only safe thing to say is that there are accidents and accidents. I know of a ten-year-old boy who is forever getting injured, one of those scrappy, enthusiastic children who never seem to learn. It's all quite hard on his mother. Last summer he went away to camp for the first time, and two days after his departure she received a phone call from the nurse—Jeff had had "a little tumble" out of a tree, and broken his arm. It had been set by a doctor, though, and he was fine: a brave little fellow. Ten days later the second call came—he had stepped on a rusty nail in the stables: was he up to date on his booster shots? Then on the following night came the third call, this one from Jeff himself.

"Mom, I'm in the hospital."

"Oh Jeff! What have you done now!"

With a certain pride he answered: "I got struck by lightning."

During a thunderstorm, he had picked up the camp phone to call home when lightning hit the lines and passed through him, knocking him cold: the next thing he knew he was in the emergency room having his pants cut off him—lightning had welded the zipper together.

In short, even in the accident-prone, accidents can be accidental. Jeff recovered swiftly and went on to sprain a finger and cut a leg (three stitches), before returning home at the end of August, two inches taller. It had been a great summer, he said.

The statistics may be arguable but the fact remains: people like Jeff exist. How do they get that way?

It sometimes seems that the accident-prone constitute not one but two groups of people, with certain overlapping traits but also a number of distinctions. Both groups are doers—busy, on the go, interested in challenging and mastering their physical environment. Exposure is an important element in accidents. Jeff will do anything on a dare, and is proud of it.

He is proud, too, of his courage in the face of injury. He hasn't really cried from pain since he was seven, that time the doctor probed for gravel in his wounded palm. He doesn't enjoy pain, but he enjoys rising above it, rather in the same way he enjoys recovering from his various injuries. He has a sense of mastering adversity, even perhaps of some power over fate itself. Look at all the things that have happened to him. Yet he still goes on, every year taller and tougher and more capable. He must be made of very strong stuff.

A psychologist might suggest that underneath Jeff's feelings lies a deep and unspoken fear—of helplessness, of mutilation, of death—and perhaps also certain inner doubts about his manliness; and that Jeff fights down these fears and doubts by acting aggressive and daring. This is true of some people, obviously, although hard to believe in the case of this young boy.

Jeff is one kind of accident-repeater. There is a second kind, driven by somewhat darker motives. Both kinds are impulsive people, willing to take chances, with an aggressive approach to life. Perhaps the difference lies in the quality of their aggression. Jeff is scrappy and hyperactive. But the other kind of accident-repeater is angry. Sometimes his anger is quite evident. You can spot him on the expressway through your rear-view mirror, and you quickly ease over into the right lane, grateful to let him zoom past and out of your life.

But sometimes the anger is very deeply hidden, both from the world and from the person himself. This seemed to be the case with most of Dr. Dunbar's fracture patients—a group that at first glance seemed characterized by easy sociability and a happy-go-lucky air. Paradoxically, these patients in many ways took unusually good care of themselves—the kind of people who go in for sports, diets, and body-building—and in fact their general health was excellent. Almost all were enthusiastic athletes, but their injuries rarely occurred on a playing field. Instead it was a momentary and inexplicable clumsiness—at the head of a flight of stairs, or stepping off a curb—that brought them to the hospital. The question was: Why did it keep happening?

The statistics led Dr. Dunbar to investigate further, and eventually to uncover a mass of evidence. Beneath the amiable exterior, most of these people were actually deeply hostile—and early in life they had shown it. Seventy percent had been difficult children, with such problems as stealing and truancy. This was true despite their harsh upbringing—or perhaps because of it. Actually, they were punished frequently and sometimes savagely, but with little effect.

Defiance of authority was the name of the game—overt and outspoken in childhood, later buried beneath that complex cover of easy cheerfulness, but still operative. These people could not stand having anyone over them for long. Many had quit school before they graduated, and even during the depression they were forever quitting jobs. They also quit marriages with unusual ease. Yet they did not seem to want to assume power themselves. They were reluctant to have children, and showed little ambition to climb the organizational ladder at work, or even to aim for a general goal in life. Authority was not something to acquire, but something to get away from.

But they could never get away from it altogether, and it was when this basic problem in their lives came to a head in feelings of hostility and resentment that the accidents usually occurred. Guilt, too, was involved. Possibly through their punishment-studded childhoods they acquired a permanent need for the whippings of an angry father. One woman said of her accidental fall, "Well, God brought me to my knees just as my parents used to do."

Accident patients do punish themselves. Often they also punish other people—the spouse who will have to care for them during convalescence, the boss who keeps the salary going without any return in labor (or who may well get slapped with a lawsuit if the accident occurred at work). Almost a third of Dr. Dunbar's patients were legal compensation cases.

Many accidents, of course, punish perfectly innocent bystanders, along with the perpetrator, and some accidents kill, especially when an automobile is involved. Between the impulse toward self-punishment and the impulse toward suicide, the line is very hazy. The same is true for suicide and murder. According to Karl Menninger's famous dictum, a suicidal person wants three things: to kill; to be killed; and to die. Hostility, intense and unrelieved, underlies all of these three aims, and when this hostility goes unacknowledged, a car can be a more appropriate weapon than a gun.

PART III

HOW IT HAPPENS: THE PATHWAYS OF STRESS

CHAPTER 1

HOW THE MIND HANDLES STRESS

I t is in the mind that we confront a problem, not in the stomach or the joints—though the mind may call on the stomach for a solution, or may pass the problem on to the joints if the solution fails.

A problem presents itself to the mind in three stages. We perceive it (we need to cross the street, say), analyze it (we study the flow of traffic), and reach our decision. Finally we take action, we cross. Does all this sound too simple, too logical? Yes it does, for this is not the way people behave when they are under pressure. Logic may constitute the first line of attack, but behind logic lies a whole battery of emotional artillery. These emotions are supposed to provide supportive fire, and they do, but to carry the military analogy further, they are also capable of hitting their own front line troops in the process. And if the battle goes badly and defeat threatens, the emotions may take over altogether, sometimes with disastrous results.

A wife, angry at her husband, knows this; she *can't* leave him, she tells herself; so instead she encourages the interest of the bachelor living in the next apartment.

An accountant is refused a raise in salary, and his first furious impulse is to hit his employer. But what does he really do?

What do *you* do in this kind of situation?

First of all, yes, you perceive. You watch the boss smile in that cool way of his, and your ears take in his words: "Fogarty, you're in accounting, you know the situation as well as I do: a raise is out of the question this year, sad to say." You perceive all right—and the emotions start to churn. The faint sweat of fear that accompanied you into his office is adumbrated by anger. And in fear and anger you pass on to the stage of analysis: "What a skinflint the bastard is! I *know* he raised Thompson! He never has recognized all I do for this lousy outfit!" The problem thus analyzed, you then start looking for solutions. "I'll go down to Harris and Harris first thing tomorrow morning. They can use me! Only what if they can't? And all that money I put into the retirement fund." And so forth and so on, all your thoughts permeated by fear, anger, anxiety, and guilt.

What is unfortunate, however, is that these emotions may do nothing to support your only real means for solution: clear, realistic reasoning. On the contrary, you're too disturbed to think straight. You haven't even allowed yourself to consider the possibility that bothers you most: What if you don't deserve a raise? What if you're not worth it?

Fogarty's emotions are not only telling him what to do, they also are taking steps to enable him to do it with maximum effect, chiefly by informing the endocrine system that a battle is at hand. Adrenaline from the adrenal medulla and glucagon and insulin from the pancreas flood him with a surge of surplus energy. Assorted other hormones constrict his arteries, raise his heartbeat, and drain the blood out of his skin.

With these and other processes all going on inside his body, is it surprising that Fogarty finds it hard to be rational? Indeed, he's up against not one problem but two: the problem of the problem, so to speak, and the problem of his response to the problem—and the second of these is the more immediate. In fact Fogarty's best hope of success may be to go home first and split logs for an hour or two with a good, heavy sledge; and then, and only then, sit down and start figuring out how to approach Harris and Harris.

Physiologically, the brain is tne organ of the mind. But in order to describe the mind's operations we have evolved the science of psychology. When we talk psychology, we talk not of the cerebrum and brain stem, but of the conscious and the unconscious, the id, the ego, and the superego. These are the classical Freudian concepts, although today they are the subject of dispute or modification by some schools of psychology (see Part Four).

If the mind rules the body, it is the ego that rules the mind, according to Freud, and to the extent that it rules firmly and realistically, the individual person possesses that ill-defined but undoubted blessing known as mental health. This kind of rule is not easy to maintain, for the ego must contend with the area of instinct and passion, which Freud christened the id, and also with the area of conscience, which he named the superego. To put it very roughly, instinct says "I must!"; conscience says "I mustn't!" The ego says, "Let's get together and work something out." The ego not only handles the conflicts between the id and the superego, but between the inner self and the outside worlds of society and of nature. The ego, in short, is the commanding general of the human organism. In this connection it is also the part of the mind that learns from experience. It remembers. It anticipates. It plans.

What are these inner demands that the ego must deal with and balance? People in their daily lives all need such things as food, drink, shelter, rest; success and power; communion with other people; sex; intellectual and physical growth; a sense of good and evil; a sense of beauty; a little fun; and a sense of self, a sense of the meaning of one's life. A person will lead a satisfying life if he can more or less fill all these needs. And in order to do so, he resorts to two basic forms of human behavior. One is aggression. The other is dependency.

Psychologically speaking, an act of aggression is not necessarily an act of war—aggression is not limited to hostility. Perhaps it is best defined as independent self-assertion, which can be either constructive or destructive. Spanking your children is aggressive. So is building a house. So is holding up a gas station. So is working your way through college. It is the do-it-yourself approach to problems.

Dependency, of course, is the get-someone-else-to-do-it approach, but it almost always involves some admixture of aggression. An infant doesn't have to go out and find its own food, it is fed by its mother, but it does have to cry first, and crying is an aggressive act.

Aggression and dependency, then, are the ways to get what we feel we need in life, and as a result they are so important to us that in a sense they become needs themselves. Individual people, through experience, sometimes learn that one form of behavior works better for them than the other, and so we end up with some people who are mainly aggressive and some who are mainly dependent. We acquire these traits during childhood, sometimes only to discover that they don't work so well in adult life, and by that time it is hard to change. This is the case with many backache patients, who as children learned to get what they wanted by being scrappy and aggressive, but now can find no outlet for their ingrained impulses except through painful muscular tension.

In fact all of us, every day of our lives, use both aggressive behavior and dependent behavior to satisfy our needs, and we often employ them simultaneously. Fogarty, of the accounting department of Prentice and Sons, is no exception. His problem is that he needs more money. If he were exceedingly aggressive, there are several directions in which he might go. He might rob a bank. Or he might decide to become self-sufficient—invest his meager savings in a farm, start raising vegetables and livestock, and give his wife Alice a spinning wheel and loom for Christmas. If he were exceedingly dependent, on the other hand, he could abandon Alice and the children and move back in with his well-heeled mother. But Fogarty, like most people, compromises. Perhaps he shows dependency in trying to make Prentice satisfy his needs. But it is aggressive of him to demand a raise (as he knows—it took several days to work up his courage), and of course he has to be somewhat aggressive to work at the job in return for the salary.

So he uses a combination of aggression and dependency—and he fails. He has, of course, other options, Harris and Harris, for one. But say he fails there too, say he can't get a higher salary anywhere. What then?

Then the only thing he can do is try to reduce his needs—move into a smaller house, and inform his children that if they want to go to college they will have to work their way through. He will also have to alter his definition of himself—to get used to the melancholy idea that he is worth fifteen thousand dollars a year, but no more.

These changes are hard on Fogarty, and it is not surprising that they are accompanied by changes in his aggression-dependency balance. Because a major problem in life continues unsolved, he will begin to resemble what Dr. George Engel calls the helpless-hopeless type, and what Harold Wolff defined as the angry nonparticipant. Like a general who has led his men to defeat and now has trouble getting them to obey orders, his ego falters in its control. And his aggression, since it has failed as a constructive tool, becomes destructive and turns into hostility.

Dependency and constructive aggression know how to work together; dependency and hostility only get in each other's way. For instance, Fogarty is dependent on Prentice for that fifteen thousand dollars a year. But he wishes Prentice dead because it isn't eighteen thousand. But were his wish to come true, he wouldn't even get the fifteen thousand.

When hostility and dependency churn together, anxiety results. And the anxiety then proceeds to increase the hostility: for Fogarty blames Prentice for his anxious state. At the same time, his hostility makes him feel guilty—so much so that to make up for it he may indeed start playing a servile role. Or he may turn the hostility inward against himself and become depressed. This way he can expend the hostility, and at the same time assuage the guilt by punishing himself. Depression, in short, has a way of bringing the emotional economy together, which may account for its popularity. But it's not much of a life, and in the long run, Fogarty will be better off venting his hostility not on himself but on the government, for failing to curb inflation, or on the younger generation, for fifteen thousand dollars a year would do very nicely if it weren't for his children.

Simplest of all, of course, Fogarty can bury the whole mess—hostility, anxiety, guilt and all—and go on as if nothing were wrong. The trouble is, this doesn't solve the salary problem, and it doesn't solve the emotional problem either. The emotions may be buried, but they're buried alive. They may be out of sight, but in consequence they're out of control, shut off from the rational and integrating dominion of the ego.

CHAPTER 2

HOW THE BODY HANDLES STRESS

Lying cheerily in a hospital bed after a hip operation a few months ago, Hans Selye observed: "You know, we are still evolving from the Neanderthal mold; the trouble is, our problems evolve quickly but our bodies evolve slowly, very slowly. People like to assume that the body always works intelligently. But this is not so. The body is like the mind. It, too, gets confused and makes mistakes."

Where stress is concerned, what usually happens is that mind and body make the same mistake together, through physiological actions and reactions that unbalance the delicate relationships among molecules, cells, tissues, organs, and systems of the body—one adjustment demanding another, and the other yet another, and so on. The neuro-endocrine system plays a leading role in this process, and when the stress is emotional in nature, it is the brain that sets the process off.

Comparing the mind with the brain is a little like comparing a poem to a mountain, though less so than it used to be; and perhaps one day we will be able to close the gap—to describe, for instance, exactly what physical events occur in the central nervous system when guilt is felt. When this happens, if it ever does, the two fields of psychology and neurology will become one.

But even today we know enough to make some correlations. Rational processes such as memory, planning, perception and intellectual rumination—in short, many of the everyday functions of the ego—take place, we know, in the cerebral cortex of the brain. And many of the instinctive drives—hunger, sex, sleep, pleasure, to name a few—seem to be activated in the hypothalamic area; at any rate they can be stimulated or inhibited by electrical manipulation of that area.

The whole arrangement is deeply complicated, but the basic principles that underlie it can be stated fairly simply.

One of these is the principle of balance. Any animal must react to threats if he is to survive, but at the same time he must not overreact. It makes sense for an antelope to run from a lion, but not if he runs so fast and so far that his heart bursts. To prevent this kind of thing the living organism contains many safeguards, some of them physical, some emotional. For example, there are few threats that evoke either pure fear or pure anger, perhaps there are none; the two emotions mix together and balance each other, rendering people's behavior more realistic. Without the cautionary influence of fear, anger becomes explosive and self-damaging. Pure fear, unalloyed by the assertive quality of anger, degenerates into helpless surrender.

Like the emotions, the neuro-endocrine system, too, is full of checks and balances. The cerebral cortex and the hypothalamus operate in this fashion. And so do the endocrine hormones.

One part of the adrenal gland, for instance, the adrenal cortex, secretes a group of hormones known as corticoids. Some of these are what Dr. Selye calls pro-inflammatory, and some are anti-inflammatory. In situations of mild stress it is the pro-inflammatory corticoids that dominate, and it is easy to see why. As we learned earlier, inflammation is a very effective way to handle a particular kind of stress situation—the entrance of a foreign object, such as a splinter or microbe, into the body. When this happens, inflammation walls the invader off in one area and destroys it there, leaving the rest of the body free to operate normally.

Nevertheless, there are many situations where inflammation is damaging. In a vital organ like the liver or the heart, it can cause serious trouble. And if it fails, as it sometimes does, to confine the threat—if a microbe escapes and attacks the rest of the body—then inflammation ceases to be useful. It is for these reasons that the adrenal glands secrete the anti-inflammatory corticoids as well as the pro-inflammatory ones; and when stress is severe, prolonged, and general throughout the body, then the AC's predominate over the PC's. Cortisone is one of the anti-inflammatory corticoids.

Beyond these general principles, just how does the neuro-endocrine system, our physical machinery for handling stress, operate? We will start with the *hypothalamus,* a part of the brain which, as we have seen, has a shifting and somewhat troubled relationship with that higher portion of the brain called the *cerebral cortex:* the cerebral cortex does its best to keep the hypothalamus under control, with but mixed results. The hypothalamus controls the *autonomic nervous system,* which in turn helps control the internal organs of the body. And the hypothalamus also controls the so-called master gland of the endocrine system, the *pituitary.*

This pituitary master gland consists of two lobes. One, the *posterior lobe,* is made mainly of nervous tissue which, when stimulated, releases into the blood a hormone known as *vasopressin.* Vasopressin contracts the muscles in the walls of the arteries, raising the blood pressure.

The *anterior lobe* of the pituitary, by contrast, contains mostly glandular, rather.than nerve, tissue, and of its six major hormones only two are activated by stress. The first is *ACTH* (AdrenoCorticoTrophic Hormone). The second is the *thyrotrophic* hormone, or TTH. Both of these have powerful effects on the body, but only indirectly: what they do is to stimulate two other glands—TTH, the thyroid gland; and ACTH, the adrenal cortex. The adrenal cortex in turn helps to stimulate the pancreas, so that in the end the pituitary affects almost all the endocrine glands.

It is important to note that the pituitary doesn't just pour forth a little of everything when stimulated; it is selective in its secretions. This is because the message-carrying substances from the hypothalamus are themselves selective. Even ACTH and TTH, though both are stimulated by stress, don't as a rule increase together. The first cold day of autumn causes a rise in TTH because thyroxine, the thyroid hormone, makes people warmer by raising their metabolic rate—which is why you feel peppy in winter and lazy in summer. But temperature has little effect on ACTH.

In fact, the relative behavior of the thyroid and the adrenal cortex shows some of that balancing tendency so common in the neuro-endocrine system. People with busy thyroids are likely to have a quiet adrenal cortex, and vice versa.

The *thyroid* gland is located in the throat, adjacent to the larynx or voice box, and a few inches below the pituitary. Its secretions set the body's basal metabolism—which is the rate at which the individual cells burn oxygen—and help determine how much energy a person has. If the metabolism is very slow, the person tires easily, feels cold, and is probably overweight; much of the food he eats is not burned off so it has to go into storage. Conversely, if the metabolic rate is too high, the person may be excessively thin, sweat readily, and feel nervous and shaky. His heart beats too fast, and his breathing is unusually deep and rapid. Like the person with the underactive thyroid, however, he too feels tired much of the time, for even when he sleeps his body is overworking. Both types may go on to develop a goiter—a swelling in the throat caused by enlargement of the thyroid gland.

Thyroxine, the chief thyroid hormone, not only affects the speed at which the body consumes fuel, it is also important in the maturing process—including physical growth, but particularly sexual and mental development. Unless they are treated, young children whose thyroids are severely underactive become cretins: dwarfs in size, who never experience puberty and are mentally retarded. Interestingly, Franz Alexander writes that many people with overactive thyroids share a common emotional problem, but have developed a specialized physiological way of handling it. The problem is dependency—the feeling that they can't cope with life without a mother's help. Because this help is unavailable, they swing to the opposite extreme—feigning a maturity they do not really possess, and driving themselves to take on more and more responsibility, particularly if it involves the care of dependent people such as children or invalids. For unknown reasons the majority of hyperthyroid patients are women.

Probably the most complicated of the endocrine glands are the *adrenals,* which lie on top of the two kidneys. Like the pituitary, the adrenal glands have two sections, and again, like the pituitary, one of the sections consists mainly of nervous tissue and the other mainly of glandular tissue. The neural section is called the *adrenal medulla,* and it is stimulated not by a hormone but by a nerve, known as the splanchnic nerve. The hormones that the adrenal medulla secretes are *adrenalin* and *nor-adrenalin.*

Everyone knows what adrenalin feels like—it is the sensation you get after a bus almost runs you down, or a bolt of lightning strikes the tree outside your window: a sudden burst of rather marvelous bodily exhilaration that would probably be thoroughly pleasant if it were not so closely associated with fear. In fact, some endocrinologists suspect that adrenalin is a fear hormone, and that nor-adrenalin is an anger hormone. But as fear usually contains some anger, and anger some fear, so adrenalin and nor-adrenalin are commonly released together into the blood in varying proportions. Adrenalin runs higher in rabbits and older children, nor-adrenalin higher in lions and babies (presumably because babies are as yet too ignorant to feel much fear).

What do adrenalin and nor-adrenalin do for a person, besides making him feel that rather eerie exuberance?

They equip him for emergency action—first through their effects on the cardiovascular system. They constrict his arteries and make his heart beat faster, in order to rush more blood to his muscles and brain. They draw the blood back from the skin and also quicken its clotting time, so he will bleed less if injured. And to fight possible infection, they raise his white blood count.

Second, they take action to speed up his metabolism. They increase his red blood count, delivering more oxygen to the cells so he burns his fuel faster; and they increase the supply of fuel itself, by stimulating the liver and the muscles to release sugar into the blood. When this happens the pancreas measures the rise in blood sugar, and begins pouring insulin into the blood, enabling the excess sugar to enter the cells.

Adrenalin performs one other important function in relation to stress: it cooperates with thyroxine, the hormone of the thyroid. When thyroxine measures high in the blood, all the body tissues seem to become more sensitive to adrenalin.

Surrounding the adrenal medulla, where adrenalin and nor-adrenalin are manufactured, is the exterior covering of glandular tissue known as the *adrenal cortex*. This is the area of the adrenals that is activated by ACTH, the hormone from the pituitary, and it is here that the so-called pro-inflammatory and anti-inflammatory corticoids are produced. There are over thirty of these adrenal corticoids, and they break down into two groups, generally called the mineralo-corticoids and the gluco-corticoids. The mineralo-corticoids are the ones that promote inflammation, and they do this by their influence on the kidneys that lie just beneath.

Primarily, however, ACTH ups the level of the gluco-corticoids, and these are anti-inflammatory in action. Like adrenalin and thyroxine, the gluco-corticoids also give you more energy. Thyroxine does this by increasing the rate at which the cells burn oxygen. Adrenalin does it by suddenly increasing the supply of sugar in the blood. The gluco-corticoids also increase blood sugar, but in a slower and more persistent fashion. They do this by stimulating the pancreatic glands to produce not *insulin,* the more familiar pancreatic hormone, but its antagonist *glucagon.* Where glucagon raises the blood sugar level of the body by stimulating the liver to release sugar, insulin lowers it, by moving the sugar out of the blood and into the cells.

The body's endocrine glands, then, play complex and important roles in our reactions to stress. What about the sexual glands?

The sexual glands—the testes in males, and the ovaries and placenta in females—would seem irrelevant: in fact a rise in stress hormones actually causes a fall in sex hormones. But even here the situation is not so simple. Without going into the complicated structure and functions of these glands, it is important to realize that the hormones they secrete, particularly the male androgens, have a substantial influence on aggressive feelings. Aggressiveness is one of the emotions people use in dealing with stressful situations. But if it is excessive, aggression can also cause stress, disturbing a person's emotional economy, as well as his relations with the rest of the world.

What makes a neuro-endocrine system go wrong? Sometimes it is a matter of what you're born with. Sometimes life itself is the problem —some people are beset from early childhood by one insoluble problem after another, until their stress equipment gradually wears down from overwork.

Still other people come up against a normal quota of problems, but react to them in an unbalanced fashion, perhaps overutilizing the thyroid, for example.

This kind of highly localized response to stress at first glance looks sensible—in fact it closely resembles the mechanism of inflammation which we talked about a few pages back. Behind both lies the principle of specialization: spare the whole by delegating to the part. But it only works when it works, so to speak—when it actually solves the specific stress problem. If the response is wrong, then the problem persists; and then the response persists too, if it's the only one you have learned how to make.

CHAPTER 3

HOW THE MIND BETRAYS THE BODY

The whole lesson of Fogarty's childhood was that if he worked hard and was a good boy, he might go anywhere. Now he knows otherwise. But what is he to do? It is too late for him to abandon his family or to start on a life of crime, or even to relieve his bitterness by taking it out on innocent people. He cannot change his way of life: he's still a good boy who works hard, but a defeated and angry one now.

Nevertheless, emotion does out, one way or another. We have got to say what we feel and mean; when we can't say it in words or actions, we say it physiologically.

In the twentieth century we spend a good deal of time denying the truth about our feelings, perhaps because our means for expressing these feelings have become quite meager. We seldom allow ourselves to take physical action—both *fight* and *flight*, the standard animal responses, are frowned upon. And we have lost most of the so-called projective techniques that primitive societies developed to explain and to solve human difficulties.

We blame our problems on ourselves, and seek to solve them through inner change, a very difficult procedure. When this is not effective, we dispose of the problem by burying it—or think that we do.

People like Fogarty don't choose the psychosomatic response. It chooses them, because they are not in a position to make any other choice and their feelings must find release somewhere.

Then why does stress disease happen the *way* it happens? Why does one patient come down with ulcers, another with a heart attack, and a third with a skin allergy?

First, the psychosomatic response varies from individual to individual because everyone's physical equipment varies: the defective part of the engine fails first. Sometimes problems are inherited, but sometimes they are acquired, through misuse of originally healthy bodily equipment over a period of many years. A baby may be born with normal lungs, but all kinds of things go wrong after birth. Perhaps in the first few years of life the child comes for one reason or another to fear aggression, in himself and others; he learns to avoid sports and physical exertion of all kinds; he is soft spoken, does not scream and shout like his brothers and sisters, seldom even cries. His grandparents may approve these qualities in him, but his lungs will suffer, simply because he does not use them enough. He may also form an unconscious habit when under strain of suspending his breath slightly. Most children do this when they are attempting a difficult manual task, such as building a house of cards, or learning to write in script. It is a natural expression of the need for care, for restrained control. But some children feel this need in any situation of pressure. Under stress they can never really let themselves go. They take a deep breath—but they let out only a shallow one.

Such a child is using a harmful pattern of breathing in order to repress his feelings, and when he gets older he is very likely to carry the process further by becoming a smoker. Still later in life he may develop chronic bronchitis or emphysema.

Once rooted, the psychosomatic response gradually becomes a habit—and a very hard one to break. A person who lives with an illness long enough gradually discovers that it does things for him.

He learns that sickness is a very good way to get taken care of—and the sicker he is, the truer this is. The patient with mild arthritis still must earn a living and fulfill his general obligations. But let his condition become severe and all that changes. He is hospitalized, perhaps operated on. No one expects him to take care of his family, or even himself—others must take over the load as best they can. Even the increased pain he suffers has a tricky way of serving him, because it eases his conscience.

This simple longing to be taken care of is only one of the feelings people express by getting sick. Another is guilt, which calls out for painful, self-punishing afflictions like arthritis and migraine. A third— and the most important of all, probably—is the feeling of anger.

In the previous chapter we learned how anger can start up the whole neuro-endocrine machine for aggressive physical action and keep it running, eventually wearing out vulnerable body parts if action never occurs. This is one of the paths anger follows in stress disease. Another is simple muscular tension. Muscular tension can take benign forms, such as nail biting, or general restlessness. It can also cause backache and headaches. But in a severely repressed person, even these expressions are inhibited. Such a person forces himself to keep calm on the outside, but may be in all kinds of trouble within, for his tension then passes to the autonomic nervous system, where it can cause spasms in the digestive tract or lungs, or in the muscles of the artery walls.

Still, is it necessarily always bad, this release of hostility by way of the bodily processes? Sometimes the question is not whether to be sick or well, but how to be sick. Certainly it is unfortunate to die of heart disease at forty, but is it any better to become a criminal, or to spend your adult life in and out of mental hospitals? These are extreme alternatives, but the point is a real one.

One of the sadder stories in medical literature comes from Dr. Flanders Dunbar again, the case of a young woman with a club foot, a deformity certainly not psychosomatic in origin, but psychosomatic in function: although she was born with the club foot, she had used it all her life to explain away anything that went wrong. For instance, she had wanted to be a teacher, but gave up teaching because she felt the children stared at her foot; and she insisted all her problems could be solved by surgery.

Finally the foot was operated on—only to be fractured in a fall as soon as she got on crutches; and after she recovered she soon fell and broke her other leg—"an expression," in Dr. Dunbar's words, "of the patient's unconscious need to keep the deformed extremity as a defense against and cover for her more fundamental personality conflicts." Dr. Dunbar added, "With her recovery, she became increasingly schizophrenic. On discharge psychotherapy was recommended but proved not to be feasible because the patient left town. She returned a year later, the foot and leg in perfect condition but . . . a full-blown psychotic . . ."

Medical men warn against the dangers of "curing" certain patients of the physical symptoms they have come to depend on. Unless this kind of patient receives counseling or unless his life changes for the better, he almost always suffers a recurrence of the old symptoms, or else acquires new ones, or runs into emotional problems. Dr. Silverman did a follow-up in his hospital on thirty ulcer cases corrected by surgical gastrectomy. Of these, seventeen suffered recurrent ulcers, four of them severe; four developed hypertension; five developed asthma; one came down with tuberculosis, and seventeen showed other bodily symptoms of anxiety.

Such patients have reached the point where they can no longer get along without their afflictions, which in the words of Dr. Wolff, "afford relative tranquility and in many instances, a workable and useful life adjustment, becoming a nuisance or menace only when they threaten the goal of survival."

In the words of Erik Erikson, "The individual unconsciously arranges for variations of an original theme which he has not learned either to overcome or to live with; he tries to master a situation which in its original form had been too much for him by meeting it repeatedly and of his own accord."

An original theme which he has not learned either to overcome or to live with: isn't this almost a definition of the power death has in most people's lives? And is sickness, at least in part, an attempt to pose the problem of death and then, by recovering, to seem to solve it?

Anxiety about death, plus a longing to be taken care of: these make a powerful combination. Where are you free to indulge both your deepest fears and your deepest longings? In bed, sick, may be the answer. True, you may hurt, you may feel terrible, you may be afraid. But everyone loves you. You are brought flowers and warm soup. You are encouraged to sleep as much as possible. Otherwise nothing is expected of you. You spend the days catching up on your almost forgotten fantasy life while your doctor shoulders the responsibility of bringing about your recovery.

He bears the responsibility, but you get the credit—for doesn't everyone congratulate you when you are better? And you congratulate yourself. You have come once more through the valley of the shadow; you have confronted death and beaten it again.

Although psychosomatic illness may first crop up in a person's life as a response to some problem he has no other way of dealing with, as the years pass it tends to crop up again, and yet again, and increasingly in situations that are not really all that difficult—in response to problems the person *could* solve, but by now he's so used to responding physiologically that it has become his way of life.

That habit can set in very early. An eight-year-old who is having trouble in school may come down with recurrent stomach upsets. Adolescent acne often occurs in a setting of hostility, strong sexual drive, and guilt. Even colds and flu can be connected with emotional problems. But these are minor ailments which, considering the services they may render, are at least conceivably worth the price they exact. In many people this balance tends to change—and the price to go up—with the onset of middle age. The eight-year-old with the stomach upset becomes the forty-year-old with colitis or ulcers. All these elements—biological, behavioral, and emotional—come together in him at about the same time; and then along comes one more very human complication, rooted in his past, which may be what finally tips the balance toward serious chronic disease.

In order for a girl or boy to grow into an adult, he must break away from his dependency on his parents. This is not easy for him. He has grown accustomed to the comforts of being taken care of and told what to do, and even his parents do not always welcome the change. But change he must, and so about the time of adolescence he sets about it, chiefly by summoning up his latent forces of hostility and turning them against his parents, and against the older generation generally, as part of the renunciation process.

This behavior carries over well into adult life, as the person works to define himself as an independent adult, by establishing his place in the world and founding a family. Even when the worst is over and the crisis past, though he may grow fonder of his parents again, traces of his basic hostility persist for many years, for a part of him continues to wish he were a little child again, with no decisions to make.

But the situation does finally change—chiefly because the possibilities for dependency themselves change. By the time a person reaches his middle forties, his parents are usually into their seventies and in no position to take care of him—it is he who must take care of them. Or they may have died. In either case, they no longer constitute a threat to his independence.

Besides, the years of hostility have bred an accumulation of guilt, which as the threat subsides now comes to bear on the person's behavior. A spirit of atonement takes up residence within him. Old verities turn up in his speech. His politics grow conservative. He may start going to church for the first time in thirty years. His values alter, and kindness may become a more important virtue to him than success, reality more to the point than ideals. He has the sense of relaxing and at last seeing and accepting the truth about life.

Freud called this deferred obedience, and it crops up not only in beliefs and attitudes. At fifty, you may find yourself habitually cracking your knuckles, irritating your wife by the habit just as your father used to irritate your mother. You may also start suffering from shortness of breath and occasional chest pains, and not feel too surprised—after all, it was a heart attack that killed your father.

PART IV

WHAT YOU CAN DO ABOUT IT— PERSONAL SOLUTIONS FOR THE STRESS PROBLEM

So it is stress of a peculiarly subjective sort that is the principal marauder in our society: not the pressure of a gun against the ribs, but a nagging worry about being mugged; not outright competition from a rival stalking the same forest for game, but a cutting memo circulating in a quiet office organization. Our instinctive body responses are of little use against problems such as these. Nevertheless, we go right on responding, with the result that we not only stew in the problems—we stew in the responses too. Can these responses be changed?

In the very long run they change of themselves—which is why people today are taller, smarter and more dexterous than their prehistoric ancestors. Faced with the stress of a new challenge, the species learns to adapt by altering its physical equipment. But it is a slow process, much too slow to help the individual person.

So the individual tries other means. In very early times he tried magic. Then came religion, and for centuries man called his mind his soul. In the present century religion as a therapeutic force has yielded visibly and steadily to science.

The concluding section of this book is an exploration of the techniques of science—both laboratory and folk science—into which people today are putting faith and effort—and money—in attempts to quell their nebulous anxieties, as well as the specific bodily aches that so often accompany them. The simplest of these techniques is physical conditioning: exercise and diet. The most complicated is psychotherapy, a billion-dollar annual business in the United States. A third is pharmacology, the source of all the countless pills and potions that overflow our medicine cabinets, and in particular of the recently developed mood-altering drugs which have changed some people's lives.

But the pressures of twentieth-century stress are severe, and if the clergyman has not always proved adequate to handle them, neither has the family doctor, nor the gym coach, nor the druggist, nor the psychotherapist, not entirely. For additional help Americans are now turning to space age electronics, in the form of biological-feedback machines; and to ancient Vedic rituals like Yoga. They are also turning to one another. Encounter groups and sensitivity-raising groups abound in the land, based on the idea that ordinary people can help other ordinary people break through the pressures and find serenity and meaning.

In America and elsewhere, the 1960's was a decade of stormy mass action, aimed at altering the world, socially, politically, and economically. As we approach the mid-1970's, a new period seems to be shaping itself. This may turn out to be the decade of inner action, of attempts to create a higher, cleaner, healthier—yea, holier—and happier self, person by person, using one method or another. And some of the methods do appear to be effective.

CHAPTER 1

ALTERING YOUR EQUIPMENT
Exercise and diet

Sports and exercise are increasingly important in the twentieth century, as the kind of work people do involves less and less physical exertion. One of the many stresses we suffer from is the stress of our own pent-up aggressive drives. When we express these drives in physical action, we are better off.

Exercise also enables us to bear up better against stress in general. A person who is in good physical condition will withstand the assault of a virus, or a spell of overwork—or even a quarrel with the foreman—better than someone who isn't.

There are many factors that militate against the beginning of any regimen of physical conditioning. On the face of it it seems faintly ridiculous to deliberately work up a sweat in an air-conditioned world. Besides, there is the problem of finding a place and a time to do the damned exercises. Perhaps the biggest deterrent is the suspicion that it will not do you any good anyway.

Also an air of charlatanism clings to the whole idea of conditioning. Series of fads and fetishes have swept the country, from exercise wheels, to the grueling Royal Canadian Air Force routine, back to the great psychological sells of the Adonis-makers, such as Charles Atlas. The exercise masters of the past have been more interested in merchandising than in real conditioning.

This is no longer so true, however. In recent years conditioning has become less of an occasional craze, and more of a crusade. Careers in research started opening up, to be filled by very competent medical men.

Dr. Kenneth H. Cooper, during his early years as an Air Force medical officer, came up with an interesting theory concerning the benefits of regular exercise. He calls it Aerobics, has published a number of medical papers and several popular books on the subject, and, now a civilian, gives it his full time.

What virtually all the professionals in the conditioning field insist, with persuasive cogency, is that the only exercise which really improves the body is a carefully programmed approach to exhaustion. They have nothing against the old bend-and-stretch rituals. They will accept a certain amount of weight lifting, although most of them regard isometrics as useless to health. Pushups and situps they recommend as tonic for certain muscle groups. But what these doctors prescribe most enthusiastically are running, jumping rope, long brisk walks (preferably three miles or more in an hour), swimming, bicycling, and such active sports as strenuous rowing, handball, squash and basketball. These are what they call the endurance activities, and these, they maintain, will fortify the body against stress. Dr. Cooper's Aerobics theory, basically, is that the better condition people are in, the more oxygen they are actually able to use out of the air that they inhale. They may not need this extra oxygen

---

How to Tell When You're Having a Heart Attack— And What to Do About It

KNOW THE SYMPTOMS

These are the usual warnings of heart attack:

- Prolonged, heavy pressure or squeezing pain in the center of the chest, behind the breastbone.
- Pain may spread to the shoulder, arm, neck or jaw.
- Pain or discomfort is often accompanied by sweating. Nausea, vomiting and shortness of breath may also occur.

ACT IMMEDIATELY

- Sometimes these symptoms subside and then return. Don't wait. Minutes count. Act immediately.
- Call your doctor and describe your symptoms.
- If your doctor is not immediately available, get to a hospital emergency room at once.
- The decision to act should not be left to the patient alone. It is also the responsibility of the wife, husband, relative or friend.

SOURCE: AMERICAN HEART ASSOCIATION

---

most of the time, but in stress situations they do, and it can make the difference between health and disease, or even life and death.

Running is Cooper's own favorite workout. The first benefits, according to his regular runners, are emotional repose and untroubled sleep, but Cooper has found considerable evidence that his programs also protect people against a number of common ailments. His reasoning, again, is that developing the lungs so they can get more oxygen into the blood stream—and from there into the body tissues—both increases the supply of blood throughout the body and enlarges the arterial system which carries it. One positive benefit occurs in blood pressure, which usually lowers with physical conditioning. Another occurs in the digestive system. A number of ulcer patients in his program have shown improvement, and Cooper's thesis is that not only does the psychological relaxation of running help by releasing pent-up aggression, but that conditioned people generally produce less acid in their stomachs. For individuals with respiratory problems, he believes greater improvement results from careful exercise than from the old regimens of rest. And in adult diabetes, the amount of insulin required can usually be reduced by a conditioning program.

The organ most drastically affected by exercise is, of course, the heart. This essential muscle suffers when its blood supply is cut down by narrowing arteries. Careful, regular exercise leads to the growth of extra capillary routes which help supply the heart with blood that the clogged main arteries can no longer deliver in sufficient quantity. As a result, people who exercise regularly have fewer heart attacks, and better survive the ones they do suffer.

But unless it is carefully paced, exercise has its hazards too, and many doctors decry the widespread fad today of jogging. The problem is overdoing: too far, too fast, too soon. The result can be a coronary, sometimes fatal.

DIET

One presumed benefit of exercise that you had better not count on, especially if you are over thirty, is loss of weight. Burning off calories through sheer physical exertion is not easy. Skiing across country on a really cold day may help, but you will come back to the lodge with such a raging hunger that your efforts are promptly undone by the solid lunch you eat. In golf, eighteen holes of exercise are easily canceled out by a neat scotch in the locker room afterward.

In short, one's weight depends less on output than on intake: it is not insufficient exercise, but oversufficient food—particularly certain kinds of food—that makes so many Americans overweight.

We tend to think of obesity as a physical condition, or even a personal trait, rather than a form of illness. It remains, nevertheless, a disease, and one that is peculiarly difficult to cure.

It is also a stress disease. First, it creates stress. An obese person is, by the stern standards of our society, unattractive, and this simple fact hampers not only his relations with other people, but also his feelings about himself. In addition, the extra poundage places him under a continuous physical strain. Every time he climbs the stairs or runs for a bus it is as if he were carrying a sack of books with him—all his physical equipment has to work harder to move the load. As a result, obesity in an individual is often eventually joined by other ailments—kidney disease, diabetes, high blood pressure, gall bladder problems, or heart trouble. No direct causative link has yet been established between cardiovascular disease and obesity, but most nutritionists assume that it exists, simply because the two go together so often.

Obesity is not only a cause of stress but, also, very often, a result of it. Certain people react to pressure by overeating, just as certain others react by overworking, and yet others by reaching for a cigarette. Indeed, the dieter and the person who wants to stop smoking face a similar dilemma. The strains that self-denial exerts on them are hideously exacerbated by the fact that the thing they are trying to cut out of their lives happens to be the one thing they have relied on for years to get them through strain of all kinds.

What makes people overeat? Early training may be one answer. Dr. Stanley Schachter, in the anthology *Neurophysiology and Emotion*, edited by David C. Glass (Rockefeller University Press, 1967), describes the plight of the newborn infant in these words:

Wholly at the mercy of its feelings, it screams when it is uncomfortable or in pain or frightened or hungry. Whether it is comforted, soothed, fondled, or fed has little to do with the state of its feelings, but depends entirely on the ability and willingness of its mother or nurse to recognize the proper cues. If she is experienced, she will comfort when the baby is frightened, soothe him when he is chafed, feed him when he is hungry, and so on. If inexperienced, her behavior may be completely inappropriate to the child's state. Most commonly, perhaps, the compassionate but bewildered mother will feed her child at any sign of distress.

It is precisely this state of affairs that the analyst Hilde Bruch suggests is at the heart of chronic obesity. She describes such cases as characterized by confusion between intense emotional states and hunger. During childhood, she presumes, these patients have not been taught to discriminate between hunger and such states as fear, anger, and anxiety. If this is so, the patients may be labeling almost any state of arousal as hunger.

So when obese people say they are hungry, they may not mean the same thing that normal people do when they say they are hungry. The obese may mean simply that they are upset in some fashion—and they respond in the way their mothers taught them to respond, by eating.

Recently researchers have decided that fat people have different kinds of fat cells, and more of them, than thin people, and some have speculated that, again, feeding experiences in infancy may be largely to blame. A normal child possesses some twenty-five billion fat cells in his body, but a baby whose anxious mother regularly overfeeds him may go on to develop two or three times as many as that, all of them ready and waiting to absorb the food he eats in the form of excess poundage. Thus obesity, through training, can become a physiological need as well as a psychological one.

How much *should* people weigh? This is a question that each generation answers a little differently: Lillian Russell had one opinion, Twiggy another. "The simple fact is that some people function at their best with a relatively greater amount of fat tissue, which is normal for them. . . ." wrote Hilde Bruch in 1957. "It is an amazing paradox that our culture, with its great flexibility and liberal ideas, attempts to superimpose *one* form of body build on those whom nature has endowed differently."

The best known expert on natural variations in physique is Dr. William Sheldon. In 1940 he published a study on four thousand college students—all men—and was able to sort them into three categories:

Endomorphs—large stomachs, general softness of body, small bones and muscles.

Mesomorphs—spare, hard, resistant builds, big muscles and bones.

Ectomorphs—thin all around, with small muscles, but large heads.

Sheldon went on to try to relate these physical characteristics to personality traits. He found considerable correlation between endomorphs and the love of comfort. They were given to sociability, gluttony, ample relaxation, slow reactions, even temper, and tolerance. Mesomorphs he found more vigorous and aggressive. They wanted to dominate, and often succeeded. Ectomorphs, by comparison with the other two types, were inhibited, self-conscious, solitary, fearful, and generally reserved.

But does one's body frame dictate one's character, or is it the other way around? "The other way around," is the determined answer of many Americans—with the result that the middle-aged women in this country in a recent twenty-year period willed themselves lighter, by an average of ten pounds. They accomplished this by dieting, in a period when the average middle-age male was gaining six pounds.

Should you join the dieters? is the next question. And if so, how, specifically, should you proceed?

If you are a person with a weight problem, but want to steer clear of fads, your first step is to seek assistance from a reputable general practitioner. He will examine you—and depending on what he finds, he may even advise against dieting. For example a high protein diet can play havoc on anyone with a kidney malfunction; or, in some cases, heart problems, or during pregnancy. The effective diets do, by the very nature of things, upset the balance of nutritional intake, and if your balance is delicate you should know it.

More probably, however, your general health is satisfactory, and the doctor will proceed with somewhat glummer advice: eat a little less, but without disturbing dietary balance. Calories do count, he will tell you. He may point out that the average American intake of calories per day is about three thousand, but that almost anyone who doesn't dig ditches hard all day can get along very well on 2,600. Leave a little on the plate. Don't try to take off more than two pounds a month, but keep at it. Remember that a pound of body fat equals 3500 calories.

Obesity, widespread though it may be, is not the only nutritional problem in America today. In the nation's slums, urban and rural, countless families living below the poverty line are chronically undernourished, trapped in a cruel cycle of economic and dietary deprivation. The children in these families suffer from malnutrition even before they are born. The stunting process begins in the womb, and after birth slowly proceeds to its inevitable end: a human individual, small of stature, weak of body, dull of mind—and thus ill-equipped to break out and change his lot. Malnutrition is a major destructive force in these people's lives.

CHAPTER 2

ALTERING YOUR RESPONSE TO STRESS
Psychotherapy, drugs, encounter groups, meditation,
biological feedback, hypnotism

The subtlest of the sciences is still psychology: the functioning of man's mind, or his psyche. Its most eminent figure, of course, was Sigmund Freud (1859–1939). Today he is widely regarded as a prophet, and deservedly so, but it is important to remember that he arrived at his position not so much by sheer intellectual formulation as through his practical daily work as a physician. It was his mission to substantially improve his patients' emotional condition, and to do this he was willing to venture into forbidden areas. In his youth he even had an interlude of involvement with a mood-altering drug, cocaine, but dropped it in horror when a friend became addicted and died.

Analytical psychiatry in Freud's own time was regarded by most of the public as a form of mental safe-cracking—an invasion of privacy, and anti-Christian to boot. Yet its basic premise is simply that people are individuals, each driven by the intricate motives created by his or her specific experiences back into infancy.

Fundamental to this premise was Freud's concept of the unconscious mind. Under the level of conscious thought and conniving, he taught, lies a vast area of sleeping memory. The unconscious contains the relics of everything that has ever happened to us, original sensations, hopes and fears, infantile worries and adolescent shocks, pleasures, and traumas. From its depths rise strong currents that can stir the surface to storms of depression, even to psychotic typhoons. The only way a person really can understand his own emotional weather is to examine what is down there.

Freudian theory holds that sexual conflicts in infancy and childhood are the basic factors in personality development, and that unless these conflicts are resolved at the time, they perpetuate themselves in later life in elaborate frameworks of neurotic behavior; the patient, in psychoanalysis, attempts to recapture these pivotal early experiences, work them through successfully, and thus cure his neurosis.

Today all psychiatrists acknowledge their debt to Freud's general approach, but many have reservations about the specifics. Is it sexuality that is at the core of our problems, or is it society—our relations with other people? Are our problems innate, part of the emotional and biological structure we are born with, or do we create them, through the tactics we develop to defend ourselves, and which must themselves be defended by still other tactics? Above all, what should we do about it? Should we reach back and relive the long repressed traumas of infancy, or face up to the here and now? Does "insight" really cure? And what is a cure?—What do we want to become?

From orgone therapy to transactional analysis, the various schools of thought today all answer these questions differently. The followers of Wilhelm Reich believe that full genital sexuality is the mark of emotional health, and that neurosis begins when the incestuous longings of early childhood come up against the repressive strictures of society. The Karen Horney group, on the other hand, regards sex as secondary, and holds that the original problem is a clash between feelings of hostility and dependency. In infancy, the future neurotic finds himself at the mercy of his mother, and hates her for it—yet he cannot put his hatred into action because he is so dependent. Threatened in this way by his own conflicting impulses, he proceeds to develop strategies, techniques of behavior that reflect not his natural and spontaneous feelings but his simple need for safety. He may develop into a person who is unduly compliant ("moving toward" others), or unduly aggressive ("moving against" them), or he may, in effect, attempt to evade the whole problem by "moving away"—isolating himself, suppressing his emotions, restricting his wants so he can be independent of others. Normal people also use these three strategies, Dr. Horney said, but use them flexibly and realistically in the service of the self. The neurotic, impelled by his basic fear, is rigid and driven, and his compulsive tactics actually stifle his own development. The purpose of therapy is to change these compulsive patterns and free the personality.

The technique of psychotherapy, as practiced today, varies widely. Classical Freudian analysis remains available—for the average patient, five sessions a week over a period of several years—but it is frighteningly expensive, and there are some patients who cannot afford it emotionally: their inner problems are so severe that plumbing the depths is more than they can stand. Its rate of "cures," most analysts admit, is rather low. Other schools of therapy believe that faster results are achieved by focusing on current problems more than on infantile conflicts, and these therapists are apt to play more active roles in treatment—commenting, interpreting, encouraging. At the far end of the scale is the kind of treatment that omits analysis in favor of what amounts to behavioral conditioning. Dr. Joseph Wolpe of Temple University claims that behavioral therapy improves or cures nine out of ten patients who give it a real chance, compared with maybe six out of ten for psychoanalysis— and he says it does the job a great deal faster.

In any case, the patient will find that talking in the presence of the therapist makes him feel better almost at once—and crying even more so. This is called venting. One doesn't have to be a psychiatrist to qualify as an audience, of course; a tolerant friend may suffice; for centuries clergymen filled the role, and many of them still do. But the impersonality of the psychotherapist, his professionalism, his skilled prompting, his therapeutic intent, give him a great advantage. A disadvantage is his costliness, again, but that enforces the impersonality, and it also makes the process more purposeful for the patient: it gives him, to put it bluntly, a financial motive for recovery.

So far, it is the general value of psychiatry that we have been discussing. What about its value in treating physical stress symptoms? Does it work? The answer is a modified yes.

It works better with some people than with others. Disorders of the digestive tract, such as ulcers and colitis, seem to be particularly responsive. Hyperthyroidism may improve markedly in as few as six sittings. Asthma, on the other hand, can be quite slow to respond, perhaps because it usually starts in childhood and is more deeply ingrained in the patient's behavior.

Even with diseases that develop more rapidly, time is still important and all too often works against the patient. Psychotherapy is seldom the first choice of treatment. Everything else is tried instead—one drug, then another, then maybe a special diet, then surgery—all have their turn, and all may make the patient feel somewhat better, at least for a while. But if he gets worse again, and psychotherapy is resorted to, six or seven years may have passed, and the physiological patterns are firmly rooted.

The same is true of emotional patterns in illness. With the passage of time, a chronic disease changes the mentality of its victims. They get used to it. They learn to live with it. And pretty soon, in many cases, they can no longer live without it. It excuses them from numerous obligations and challenges, and gains them attention and care. It works its way into their emotional economy and becomes a convenient and satisfying mechanism for expressing guilt and achieving expiation.

Therapists who handle a lot of psychosomatic cases emphasize several other points. One is that psychiatric treatment should be combined with standard medical treatment, the therapist and the family doctor collaborating together to solve the patient's physical problem. Therapy can actually aggravate symptoms temporarily, or alter them in other unexpected ways. Another is that therapy for a physical condition, as compared with the treatment of purely emotional problems, is sometimes surprisingly brief. It is not considered necessary or even desirable in most cases to try to recapture the experiences of infancy or the oedipal period. The focus is on the physical affliction itself, on uncovering the emotions that are causing it and then finding a better way of expressing these emotions. This can of course lead to new problems. People undergoing psychiatric treatment are often very hard to live with.

And in fact the therapist must not be in too big a hurry. A patient who expresses his feelings by getting sick does so because the feelings are dangerous to him. If he is pressed to release them fast, before he is ready, the result can be a mental breakdown.

True to Freud, every patient is different, and needs a different course of treatment.

Take the case of a man whose stress symptom is ulcers, for reasons that are almost a cliché. He has a boss who rides roughshod over him, and a wife who is unable or unwilling to comfort him. His children are even less predictable than the boss. The patient is not getting the things he needs out of life, and he resents it bitterly, and knows that he resents it, but what can he do? He is a man, not a child, and his only recourse is to go on struggling—swallow his resentment, go out and seize what fragments and shreds that he can, and play the game according to the established rules. He says to himself, "Naturally I've got ulcers—who wouldn't, in my position?"

Compare him with a second ulcer patient—more or less the same age, same surroundings, in working life as well as personal life. But this one, unlike the first, does *not* understand why his stomach is hurting. The first patient's resentment may be curbed; but this man isn't even aware of his, just of that pain in his gut. In the course of his life to date, what he has learned is how to absorb indignities, perhaps even developing the habit of courting them, without feeling much of anything emotionally.

Psychiatrists, surprisingly, will tell you that the second man may respond more swiftly to treatment than the first. He needs to realize what is really going on inside him, and the shock of recognition may do the rest. If he can only uncover his true emotions—a process involving perhaps ten to twenty hours of therapy—then his stomach can relax, and he will be able to abandon his ulcer diet.

Maybe the trouble with the first patient is that he knows too much about himself, and his knowledge has become enmeshed, so to speak, in the disorder itself, has become a kind of hostage to it—a force that might have worked for his recovery, but instead is working against it.

Then, too, the course of therapy is affected by the nature of the inner feelings involved. If what the patient secretly wants is to be nurtured and cared for, for instance, it makes good sense for him to become aware of these feelings because a place can be found for them in modern society. In the process he may not only shuck his ulcer. He may also part company with his wife, and start getting involved with the affectionate, rather motherly girl in the next office. These may be drastic measures, but they are practical ones because they are capable of improving his life. But what if his repressed feelings are truly unacceptable—homicidal rage, for instance? Then self-awareness isn't enough, and therapy will have to help the patient to change himself, a much more difficult task.

DRUGS

In the early 1950's psychiatrists were presented with a very useful tool, the first psychotropic drugs, chemicals which enabled them to calm down their patients without sedating them. Thanks to chlorpromazine, countless mental patients who would otherwise have to be hospitalized can now live at home and even hold jobs, though they usually do need some out-patient therapy. And meeker, milder variations of these drugs have proved of inestimable help to people who are anxious, depressed, overwrought, suffering the conventional strains and stresses of the culture. For people undergoing psychiatric therapy, judicious doses of the new chemicals diminish tension not only between appointments but also during therapy itself, so that the sessions dig deeper faster. Unlike barbiturates or the even older drug, alcohol, the newer family of chemicals do not turn off the higher functions of the brain, do not dull the sharpness of the patient's insight.

The new drugs quickly turned into a boon for druggists as well, as the word got out. General practitioners began to dispense them almost as antibiotics for the personality and millions of people wanted to try them on for size and style. Some of them quiet you down and some of them pep you up, but what they all do when they work well, from Dexedrine to Quaaludes (methaqualones) is to bring a calm kind of energy to their takers, making it easier to focus on the obtainable in life and to go after it with confidence and pleasure.

In recent years public health officials have worried almost as much about these synthetics as about their poppyseed predecessors, and the remarkable extent to which people in our society have come to rely on mood-altering drugs of all kinds has been documented in many studies. One of these, completed in 1970 for the New York State Addiction Control Commission, and including hard drugs, is particularly interesting because it concerns itself not with addicts, as we think of them, but simply with ordinary users in average American homes. The figures below were projected from interviews with a sizable sample of the 13,690,000 residents of New York State age fourteen or older in the years 1968–70. None of them were derelicts, flop house residents, or patients in hospitals.

Barbiturates. On the basis of its interviews the commission calculated that 377,000 people in the state were depending on Phenobarbital, Seconal, Tuinal, Amytal, and other such depressants of the central nervous system at least six times a month (which in this study was deemed to be "regular use.") These barbiturates, of course, are addictive when overused.

Nonbarbiturate sedatives were in use regularly by about 173,000—such products as Doriden, Noludar, etc. Addiction is possible.

Minor tranquilizers had 525,000 regular users. Some of the brand names: Librium, Valium, Atarax, Miltown, Equanil, Metprotabs, Lobritabel. With extremely high dosage and regular use, addiction is possible.

Major tranquilizers. Intended for psychotic patients, these include such products as Stelazine and Mellaril, and are used regularly by 85,000 seemingly normal people, the commission reported, to reduce panic, fear, hostility and agitation, and to "regularize thinking." There are so many unpleasant side effects that nonpsychotic users' addiction is unlikely.

Antidepressants, only 37,000 regulars. Brand names include Elavil, Tofranil, Marplan, etc. Addiction possibilities are undocumented.

Pep pills, the prescription amphetamines, Dexedrine or Benzedrine, had 110,000 regular users. Addiction is unlikely in pill form but psychic dependency sometimes occurs.

Diet pills, 225,000 regulars. Most of these are amphetamine-like substances, sometimes combined with central nervous system depressants. Addiction is doubtful, but so is long-range effectiveness.

Controlled narcotics (nonheroin), 21,000 regulars. In this classification the natural narcotics include opium; the synthetics, methadone. Addiction is a clear and present danger.

The illegal drugs:

Marijuana, 485,000 regulars.

LSD, 50,000 regular (illegal except for federally approved research projects).

Methedrine, nicknamed "speed," 34,000 regulars. A highly potent stimulant of the central nervous system, taken intravenously to produce euphoria, it creates psychological dependency.

Heroin, 41,000 regulars. Very addictive, craved in constantly increasing doses.

So our society, despite its Calvinist background, has settled out to be a highly pilled one. Yet there are signs today that the situation may at last have reached a turning point.

One is that these pills never really solve anything, they only obscure it. Is it wise, for example, to make yourself feel secure when you're really in danger; or happy when you have reason to grieve; or full of energy when your body is fatigued and needs sleep? Aren't you more likely to correct a situation if you're disturbed by it?

The other trouble with the mood pills is that even when they're not physically addictive, people become dependent on them if they take them for long. If pills help you through a specific crisis, fine. But if you take them day in and day out for several years, you'll gradually come to feel that you can't do without.

The most widely used drug of all in our society is alcohol, the foundation of an immense industry. It brings pleasure and relaxation when used carefully, and misery and destruction when yielded to.

Alcohol is a drug; its value as a food is almost nil. As with injected amphetamines, physical addiction is preceded by that easy psychological dependency. A drink or two before dinner is a reaction to stress, perhaps, but a pleasurable reaction, even a benign one. Compulsive alcoholism is something else—a genuine stress disease that seriously damages the liver and the nervous system, sometimes fatally.

The drugs that improve your state of mind directly, without the diversions of alcohol—the taste, the thirst-gratification, the sociability—are more nakedly habit-forming. For this reason many doctors now refuse to prescribe such mood pills for anyone under the magic age of thirty. As one medical man put it, "You should not start a young person on these pills, but should seek other solutions to his problems. He is still flexible enough to do something about them. And there are physical dangers in a maintenance level of almost any medication over the years. Toxicity builds up. The patient will probably need increasing amounts of the drug, which in time means even more toxicity. Even a high level of aspirin intake can eventually produce a peptic ulcer."

No consideration of pharmaceutical solutions to stress would be complete without a word about placebos—pills that contain no medication but that nevertheless work, because the patient believes they will work. All doctors know how effective they can be, and all doctors know that even "genuine" drugs are capable of curing people in part because of what is called the placebo effect.

Bogus pills, or clinically inappropriate ones, are just the beginning of placebo medicine. Any treatment qualifies which has no definable curative powers but nevertheless improves the patient's health. This goes for the miracles at Lourdes and other examples of verified faith healing. Dr. William Menninger pointed out forty years ago that even conventional surgery can be an effective, if usually temporary, placebo, especially when, as so often is true, the surgeon has a compelling parental personality.

The best placebo of all in a way may well be that old doctor-patient relationship so dear to the American Medical Association. Dr. Albert Cornell, of New York, is a highly successful internist who credits many of his cures to what he simply calls education. After a thorough examination, he sits an ulcer patient, for example, in a comfortable chair and gives him a half hour illustrated lecture, beginning, "It isn't what you eat, but what eats you. Let me tell you about the vagus nerve, which is the brain's telephone line to the stomach. . . ." He explains how anxiety keeps the stomach working overtime until stomach acid finally penetrates the protective mucous membrane.

To the average doctor, half an hour may sound like a lot of time to spend just talking, but if the patient's symptoms improve as a result, without medication, diet or surgery, it is a half hour economically spent.

This is not to say that most, or even many, disorders can be cured simply by talk, or that drugs, rest, diet and surgery, either singly or in combination, do not play an essential part in medical practice. Of course they do, but the physician is the person who must coordinate them all, and first he must understand his patient's true condition, which is seldom exclusively physical. A good doctor spends time on a diagnosis; he then proceeds to search through today's vast medical arsenal for those weapons that will do most to correct the problem, while causing minimal damage on the side. Among these weapons are both drugs and counseling, and a doctor who learns to use the two together is going to get better results.

ENCOUNTER GROUPS

It was on their own initiative, and largely without medical advice, that Americans in the 1960's began flocking into encounter and sensitivity groups, which turn classical psychotherapy inside out in marathon meetings aimed at achieving the quick, sudden—and often explosively emotional—opening up of previously guarded personalities. Encounter groups have been described as treatment for people who are not sick but who are simply seeking fulfillment. Nevertheless, their aims are decidedly therapeutic—to make the individual feel at ease with his own emotions and those of the people around him, despite the depersonalizing industrial society in which he may live. The encounter groups constitute a kind of mass folk therapy, and it is estimated that some two million Americans have so far been moved to join in.

The National Training Laboratories are generally credited with having started the movement, when they began organizing T (for Training) groups for corporation employees shortly after World War II, but the roots go back much farther. It was just after the turn of this century that a Boston doctor named J. H. Pratt began holding classes for tubercular patients who could not afford to go away to a mountain sanitarium, the preferred treatment for TB at the time. Pratt's initial purpose was a modest one: to teach his patients to care for themselves at home—what to eat, how much to rest, how to keep temperature charts, etc. Inevitably, however, the patients raised questions dealing with emotional problems, and the discussions which followed seemed to benefit them both mentally and physically.

It all worked very well, and the camaraderie among the patients in the classes seemed to be part of the reason. Dr. Pratt kept at it for fifty years, and by the middle of the century was referring to the classes frankly as group psychotherapy. Meanwhile in Europe, as early as 1910, Dr. J. L. Moreno, a Viennese psychiatrist, had also begun to deal with patients in groups, and had evolved a technique called psychodrama, the acting out of neuroses in order to dispel them.

Group psychiatry received a big boost as an approved medical method during World War II, when it came into extensive use in the U.S. Army. Then, in the years just after the war, the psychologists began to evolve the encounter groups, and the road forked. Group therapy went one way, and the encounter movement went the other.

Encounter groups—often called sensitivity groups on the West Coast—still are frequently confused with the more orthodox group therapy. The encounter groups are larger—up to eighteen members, as compared with seven to ten in straight therapy. The encounter groups vary in the qualifications they set for leader—in fact sometimes there is no leader, officially—while there must always be a qualified psychiatrist or other approved therapist running the more medical type of group. Encounter groups focus on "personal difficulties," group therapy on the medically identified neuroses. Group therapy is generally much tidier about starts and finishes, meeting once a week for about an hour and a half.

Then, too, encounter groups often specialize in specific problems. The NTL got its start specializing in the problems of specific employee groups in the big corporations—workers in almost any rank who feel trapped in a cocoon of ineffectiveness. From the seeds of NTL sprang the Esalen movement, based in Big Sur, California, and San Francisco, which has gone into personal relationships.

The key to the effective encounter group is not the leader (though certain leaders, particularly on the West Coast, have acquired the status of cult heroes), but the dynamics of the group itself. Most groups start very cautiously and guardedly, before some organizing type—sometimes the leader, sometimes a bold member—decides to propose a set of aims and procedures. When this happens, some others may start protesting, and the game is on. Soon everyone is working on everyone else, first in anger, often, but gradually affection and many other emotions begin to emerge.

When there is a deft leader in charge, he may use physical routines to get things going. People are told to close their eyes and grope, to let themselves fall backward into each other's arms, to hand-wrestle. Sometimes they are put to work painting a mural. In psychodrama, they are told to act out past experiences that gave them distress. The leader becomes the director and puts other members of the group into the cast. Then they rotate roles, so that the person who started acting out his problems gets to see himself from his antagonists' angle. Everyone comments, sometimes cruelly, but always—if the process is operating well—to let the person know just what his personal impact on the group is.

There are limits to what encounter groups can accomplish, and, very occasionally, dangers. Psychotic breakdowns under group pressure, through rare, have happened. Also, the grouper who returns alone into the everyday world can carry with him a certain misconception of reality; he has changed but the world has not.

In fact there are some indications that the encounter movement has peaked, and is headed for a decline. The intellectual vanguard is now rather bored with it, and all the responsible professionals are concerned about the lurid publicity that the more radical groups have engendered.

At the moment, however, the encounter method is ever more available as the movement swells out among middle-class Americans. Many groups these days are sponsored by local YMCA and church clubs. When any group advocate is put on the defensive concerning the real, proven value of the movement, he can bring up the example of Alcoholics Anonymous, one specialized group of long standing that is broadly acknowledged to have accomplished more cures of its particular stress syndrome than any religious, pharmacological, or even strictly psychiatric approach. It is very possible that A.A. demonstrates a truth that Dr. Pratt discovered in Boston, that the greatest benefit from groups is for people caught in the same specific stress problem, be it TB or liquor, ulcers or alienation.

MEDITATION

Another practice coming into widespread use for stress is the polar opposite of encounter groups—meditation.

The most widespread and easily accessible technique is called

Transcendental Meditation. Many Americans first heard of TM in 1967, when the Beatles and Mia Farrow tripped off to the Himalayas to learn about it from Maharishi Mahesh Yogi. The Maharishi, now in his fifties, took a university degree in physics himself, spent the next thirteen years studying the ancient Vedic tradition of India with a scholarly guru, and then retreated to a monastery for two years. He emerged with a benign, but busy, determination to convert the world not to his religion but to a secular method for achieving inner tranquility. By now his teaching evangelists are three thousand strong; they have multiplied the number of transcendental meditators to an estimated 200,000 in the U.S. alone, and the movement seems to be only beginning to accelerate.

The early apostles of TM traveled with rock groups in order to find an audience, but today they deliver most of their lectures before civic clubs and in suburban public libraries. They make it a point to wear reasonable haircuts, neckties and jackets, and many of them are both dedicated and disarmingly skilled as teachers. After two evening lectures, the TM initiate receives an hour of individual instruction. He learns to sit down and close his eyes for two periods of twenty minutes each day, during which time he, in effect, vacates the stress battlefield, willing himself into a state called "restful alertness." He does this by concentrating on the silent repetition of a word called a mantra, a soothing, meaningless sound, secretly assigned by the instructor in an initiation ceremony.

Whether because of the mantra or not, most beginners learn quite readily how to ease off into quietude. Their hands and feet feel heavy and tingling, and their minds idle. Thoughts float. Done twice a day for just twenty minutes each time, the TM prescription is extremely soothing.

The initiation does not complete the course. The learner must then attend three successive question-and-answer meetings with twenty to thirty other new initiates. Here he may learn of some surprising problems in meditation, because first reactions to TM vary widely. Some novices report that they weep or have headaches at first, and some notice that pet animals seem to be strangely attracted to them. Several weeks after initiation, the instructor gives a personal checkup to each initiate, and puts his or her name on a mailing list which soon begins inviting him to come see tapes of the Maharishi's lectures, in color, in evening get-togethers.

In the brief period of time since TM first began to spread across America, it has caught the fascinated attention not only of psychologists but of certain researchers in physiology as well. Dr. Herbert Benson, a cardiologist at Harvard Medical School, has been using transcendental meditators as test subjects for several years, and he is convinced that the technique lowers their likelihood of contracting some common stress disorders. Working with physiologist Robert Keith Wallace, Benson has established that in meditation there is marked reduction of oxygen consumption, the prime measure of metabolic rate. The reduction, he points out, is greater than after six hours of sleep. The arterial concentration of lactate, a chemical sometimes correlated with anxiety, dropped four times faster in meditation than in simple rest. Galvanic skin resistance, another positive key to relaxation, in some cases increased fourfold.

But do the effects persist beyond the twenty-minute meditation period? This is what Dr. Benson is trying to find out, and on the basis of preliminary data he says yes. In particular, he endorses meditation as a medical technique for treating the twenty-two million Americans who suffer from high blood pressure.

TM is not the only Eastern technique on the rise in America. Schools for teaching yoga and other Oriental disciplines abound in the big-city phone books, most of them much more deeply drawn, more intricate, and more demanding than TM.

In these movements derived from the East, diet is often involved, with vegetarian emphasis and much of the Oriental staple, brown rice, as in macrobiotics. Almost always there is also a degree of deliberate detachment from the turmoil of daily urban life, and surrender to a group. The erasure of ego can produce a monkish calm and ease many stresses in living. There is some question, however, how accessible this kind of oasis really is for most Americans, too many of whom may have committed themselves to the urban pace—or been committed to it by their lives. One has to work with what one is, culturally.

Today's spread of Sufi in America and Europe is fairly phenomenal. Sufism has been around for centuries and has a tenuous, all-enveloping fabric. Originating in the Middle East, it has included the whirling dervishes, a sect which reached ecstasy in dance, as well as more moderate, meditative methodologies and a literature, mostly oral. Its most prominent teacher today is Idries Shah from Afghanistan, now dwelling in England, who publishes frequent books translating the folk parables handed down over the centuries by Sufi teachers, adding a few of his own.

In all of these mystical and semi-mystical approaches, much of the point for today's practitioners lies in developing self-awareness. The human personality, these people assert, is not simply a machine for efficient living, and its methods are not purely mechanical. People possess feelings and capacities outside the realm of the intellect, or even the conventional drives, often irrational, often of no practical use, which however need to be expressed and exercised, or the person is not fully human. We need to dream at night, for instance, whether or not we remember the dream the next morning; it has been demonstrated that people who do not dream enough become tense and anxious. Night dreams, daydreams, fantasy, trances more or less hypnotic, hallucinations mild and strong, all are forms of consciousness expansion and all are natural and enriching functions of the human mind, according to these proponents. Dr. Andrew Weill believes that this hunger for irrational inner experience is the real reason behind the rise in drug consumption: drugs (including alcohol) do alter consciousness without effort or training, and thus fill a need that Western civilization cannot fill otherwise—indeed, does not even recognize. Weill points out that many people lose interest in drugs when they take up meditation—because, he says, meditation fills this same need, only better.

Prominent among new organizations in the U.S. is Arica, which in the past three years has come on strong in New York, San Francisco, Boston, Miami, San Diego, Pittsburgh and Los Angeles. It was originated by a Bolivian named Oscar Ichazo in 1970, after he had spent years studying esoteric practices in South America, China, Afghanistan and Tibet. Ichazo claims to have selected the most effective practices of various cults and put them together—the name Arica came from the town in Chile where a group of about fifty people, many from the U.S., spent ten months as Ichazo's first students.

Arica takes much time and effort; the intensive course lasts six weeks, ten hours a day. The Arica students are put in good physical shape by exercise routines. They also participate in many group encounter sessions, and run an extensive gamut of meditation. Typical of the combination of mind-and-body adjusters practiced by Arica students is the posture-correction method called "structural integration." Put very simply, it is that people's bodies are related to the earth through the force of gravity, and that a poor postural adjustment to gravity correlates with both physical and emotional disabilities.

Arica's Manhattan headquarters are off Fifth Avenue just below Central Park, a neighborhood of expensive specialty shops. Outside, numerous stylish people tread the sidewalks, most of them discreetly hostile or, at best, carefully indifferent. But within Arica the faces are different. As you walk down a corridor, you suddenly discover that someone coming the other way is studying your eyes with interest, and his mouth wears a quiet smile. In the middle of New York, the most impersonal city in the world, a total stranger is looking into your face trustfully. It's almost unnerving. A zombie quality? Perhaps a little, but the genuine zombies are downstairs, walking confidently up and down the sidewalks.

BIOLOGICAL FEEDBACK

Behind bio-feedback lies something of a revolution in medical theory. Man's skeletal muscles are obviously at the command of his will. He can force his arms to move up and down, his eyelids to blink fast or slow. But it has been postulated until recently that man cannot consciously control his autonomic nervous system, the unseen regulator of such processes as pulse rate, glandular secretion, and oxygen consumption—the complex mechanisms which, when they go wrong, so frequently trigger the stress diseases.

Dr. Neal E. Miller of Rockefeller University challenged this assumption more than a decade ago with the then outrageous hypothesis that laboratory animals might be taught to control their autonomic systems through a schedule of rewards and punishments. He and his associate, Leo V. Di Cara, then at Yale's Medical School, drugged rats with curare to put their skeletal-muscular systems out of action, and then used electric shock as a teaching tool. Soon they had revised medical dogma.

Taking advantage of the many delicate electronic devices available today, medical doctors and psychologists have set up systems in which patients or study subjects are kept continuously informed of what is going on within certain organs. For example, a tiny sensor is swallowed by a subject trying to control the acid in his stomach. When the acid becomes excessive—perhaps copious enough to burn a hole in the stomach membrane—the sensor registers this fact on a meter in front of the subject. After a time, by concentrating on the meter's signal, the subject may learn to moderate the flow. Nobody yet knows just how he does this, and the theories are abstruse. But the feedback signal is the tool by which he learns. And having learned, the subject can sometimes then go out into the stressful world and control his visceral response without needing the visible feedback signal any longer.

The most dramatic demonstration of feedback benefits to date involves the heart. With two or three days of training, subjects can be taught to slow their heartbeats. Other bio-feedback experts have been able to train hypertense people to lower their systolic readings. These are almost all laboratory demonstrations so far, but the more sanguine feedback advocates are wondering aloud about the possibility of getting down the cost of the very expensive instrumentation and setting up clinics to be run by paramedical aides—not soon, they admit, but some day.

Famous within medical circles is the work done recently by Dr. Elmer E. Green and Dr. Joseph Sargent at the Menninger Foundation, where numerous confirmed migraine sufferers have been trained to anticipate and avoid the terrible headaches that have racked them in the past. After a few weeks' practice, almost 80 percent of the sufferers can be taught to raise their hand temperatures as much as twenty-five degrees by dilating the hand arteries. When this happens, the arteries in the head contract, as a physical corollary, heading off the migraine. The surprising thing is how easy it is to get the knack of willing the hands warmer, simply by recalling other times when they were warm because of the sun, or an open wood fire, or even under a hot-air hand drier in a restaurant washroom. A number of headache specialists are making this feedback treatment available to patients.

At the Langley Porter Neuropsychiatric Institute in San Francisco, Dr. Marjorie Raskin and George Johnson, a social worker, have been replicating such experiments in tension control and migraine to get at the problem of chronic anxiety. Dr. Raskin first became interested in the problem while supervising hard-pressed medical students. She says, "Everyone can cope with a little anxiety, but the person who becomes afraid to do something because he thinks he can't control himself is the person I'm studying. And that represents about five percent of the population. Their fear of failure becomes haunting, and patients become homebound. Headaches are frequent. Insomnia is almost inevitable. Chronic anxiety does not shorten your life. But people who have high intelligence quotients—and most anxiety victims do—don't live up to their potential. Their ability to produce is killed."

Among the more intriguing of the bio-feedback techniques have been those developed for the brain itself. The brain gives off the highest frequency signal when it is under pressure to complete tasks; this signal is called beta. Next down the scale is alpha, reflecting a more relaxed and contemplative mood. Then comes theta, associated with creative thinking; and delta, the lowest frequency, which comes with sleep. An electroencephalograph is used to monitor the activity within the brain.

It has been demonstrated conclusively that people can be trained through feedback to shift their brains from beta to alpha and sometimes even to theta. In the laboratory of psychologist Joe Kamiya at the University of California, for example, the trainee is installed in a quiet room and fitted with two electrodes to the scalp plus a ground wire attached to an ear. At his feet is an electrical indicator that will register the total alpha-wave score he has achieved during each one- or two-minute interval of drilling. During the attempt, his success—or lack of it—will be made evident to him by means of a tone that swells in amplitude when the brain switches to alpha. After the training session, he can also, with technical help, trace the pattern on the read-out from the EEG machine.

No instructions on how to go about achieving alpha are given the subject in Dr. Kamiya's lab. The reason is that directions might make the subject too dependent on the director, and the objective is to train him so that he eventually can summon alpha without using the machine.

Most people begin to find their way into alpha through introspection, summoning up particularly peaceful moments from their past. One subject may recall a lyrical day in a sailboat, or dancing—though he may not have danced, or thought about it, in years. Moments with young children are another staple, as are recollections of sensual repose.

The first hour of striving for alpha, while pleasant in many ways, can be surprisingly tiring. But by the time the second session comes up, the trainee discovers he has already made some progress. His thoughts become less specific, as the inventory of memory is exhausted, and the alpha state becomes more trancelike and self-sustaining, attuned to the signal alone. His scores rise. Almost anyone can learn to attain consistent A, though it may take as many as ten hours of training. The headquarters of McDonald's restaurants, near Chicago, has a brainwave feedback machine for the use of employees. As with other feedback equipment, the cost, around two thousand dollars, so far precludes widespread use.

There is an obvious connection between the attainment of alpha on EEG feedback and the state of meditation. One expert who has tried both meditation and feedback and written papers on them is Durand Kiefer, of Hawaii. He began his research in 1959, and traveled widely for ten years to study various disciplines. His conclusion is that the best solution is a combination of meditation and feedback. The most demanding pure meditation regimen he experienced came during his nine months as a student at Zenshinji monastery at Tassajara in Japan, where he practiced Zen Buddhist zazen, sometimes for as long as twelve hours a day; he achieved stressless bliss for a few moments at a time, he reported in a talk to the Bio-feedback Research Society, but it was very slow work. By contrast, he says, "every hour spent in meditation with EEG alpha feedback has produced some degree of euphoria—the sense of well-being and general serenity of the sort called grace in the Christian terminology. . . ."

On the other side of the fence is Dr. Bernard Glueck, director of research at the Institute of Living, in Hartford. His research indicates to him that although bio-feedback does produce alpha, even as easy a meditation method as TM does it better because it synchronizes all parts of the brain. Glueck told a recent round table on the subject of anxiety that when an experienced meditator begins using his mantra, "it's literally like turning a switch in the brain." He added, "Maybe there is another window into the unconscious. Dreams are one; this could be a second."

HYPNOSIS

Hypnosis, after numberless excursions into the carnival world, has come quietly back to respectability in science. It is used for surgical anesthesia as well as in day-to-day dentistry. Techniques for painless childbirth, whatever their proponents may claim, are essentially hypnotic. More significantly, people can be cured of warts by hypnosis and of certain more serious afflictions, implying an actual change in their immunological responses. And there is little doubt in the minds of some American doctors currently studying the Chinese technique of acupuncture that hypnosis does much of the job there too, although there appear to be neural pathways involved as well.

Dr. Herbert Spiegel, a New York psychiatrist who teaches at Columbia University's College of Physicians and Surgeons, is an outstanding expert on hypnosis. After using it to cure an attack of asthma, for example, he trains the patient to maintain the cure by self-hypnosis, as follows: "Roll your eyes upward, close them, take a deep breath. Let your clenched hand float upward. Imagine your bronchii opening. Tell yourself they will stay open when your eyes are open. Open your fist slowly and then your eyes." Certainly it sounds not unlike meditation and bio-feedback, and Spiegel himself agrees. He says: "Whether you attach electrodes to your head or listen to a priest in a saffron robe, it is all essentially the same. Call it Zen, acupuncture, TM, bio-feedback, or Mesmer, it taps the same kind of attentive, narrowed inner concentration, erasing peripheral distractions—and it can be very useful."

It is easy to dismiss some of the techniques described in this chapter as esoteric entertainments, of little practical value. But there is an important shared significance. The patients are going out after their own cures, sometimes leaving conventional medicine far behind them.

What approach should you try? This has to depend on what kind of person you find yourself to be, perhaps by trying several diverse approaches.

What method of treatment you choose depends also on what you are suffering from. If your condition is a specific physical one—asthma, or arrhythmia, say—a highly specific technique, such as feedback or hypnosis, may be the answer. Meditation, and the encounter groups, on the other hand, aim at improving one's state of mind, and/or way of life, and the physiological side effects, though demonstrable, are more or less incidental. Psychotherapy can go either way. In the end you may find yourself following several of these paths, and getting help from all of them, at least for a time.

But there is something important to understand.

One of the puzzling truths about medical treatment in general—particularly treatment for stress conditions—is the way it often succeeds at first, and then later gradually fails. It particularly occurs with shock treatment for psychotic mental patients. Even today no one knows just how shock treatment works, only that when it does, it makes patients feel dramatically better, and that its effects usually run out after a year or two.

Seemingly the opposite of shock is sleep treatment, widely practiced in Europe to treat emotionally disturbed people, putting them away, back in the cradle, for a week or so, out of the adult world. It can be done chemically, as in France, or electrically, as in the U.S.S.R., although there is some danger of pneumonia in both procedures. There are also two other well-known European methods of treating the stressed, both of them inexplicable medically and both barred in the United States. The first is the injection program at the famous Dr. Ana Aslan's Geriatric Institute of Bucharest, Rumania; her substance is called Gerovital, and is principally novocaine. The other is cellular transplants, originated by a Swiss surgeon, the late Dr. Paul Niehans. In 1927, treating a young human dwarf, Niehans tried intramuscular injection of a pulp made from the pituitary cells of a fetal calf, with, he reported, excellent results in stimulating growth. In subsequent years he developed an entire palette of cell-types, for the treatment of various human afflictions, and today, especially in Germany, many doctors are using freeze-dried cells.

Some doubters—and the majority of physicians fall into the category—propose that if cellular therapy does work it probably does so, again, by administering shock to the human system, stimulating natural rallying. The dangers are numerous, including incalculable allergic responses; medical proof of the merits of the treatment is lacking, apart from empirical reports; and the technique has been callously exploited in some of the places where it is permitted legally. Yet many people hold that they have been helped by it, and patients from all over the world still find their way to the Niehans clinic in Switzerland.

The truth is that shock of some sort is probably a basic ingredient of all medical treatment, from pill, to surgery, to psychotherapy, to "rest cures," as well as in such body-conditioning practices as the sauna, in which you spend an hour in an extremely hot, dry room and then immediately plunge into an icy pool. Challenge the body: change its pace: shake it up: free it of the old patterns: get it moving again, naturally and spontaneously.

A century ago people often found cures for a medical condition in travel, or in religion, or even in love—Elizabeth Barrett was a bed-ridden invalid until she met Robert Browning. From our modern scientific eminence we smile at those Victorians. But theirs were remedies that actually worked, at least for many sufferers, at least for a while. They worked in part through belief—the placebo effect—but probably they also worked in part through shock—the shock of a sudden change in the patient's situation.

Shock, however, is by nature temporary. Gradually its effects fade; normality of some sort ensues; the old responses to stress start building into patterns again that are both mental and physiological. And when they build far enough, the symptoms begin sprouting once more.

The fact that one or another of these regimens fades in its effectiveness for you six months after you undertake it is not unusual, and should not discourage you. Get deeper into it. If, after persistence, it cannot help you, try another. The fight against stress is not a single battle but a very long war of survival, and many campaigns may be necessary.

CHAPTER 3

STRESS AND THE DRIVE FOR SUCCESS

In a thirteenth-century document called *The King's Mirror*, an anonymous Norwegian writer asked himself why certain of his countrymen were willing to undergo the hard, dangerous sea voyage to settle Greenland, and he found the answer in what he called the three-fold character of human nature:

One part thereof is the spirit of rivalry and craving for fame. . . . The second is the thirst for knowledge. . . . The third thing is the hope of wealth; for men look to that wherever they learn that a gain can be expected, regardless that great dangers threaten them on the other side.

In *Tender is the Night,* F. Scott Fitzgerald wrote of his hero, Dick Diver:

. . . he wanted to be good, he wanted to be brave and wise . . . he wanted to be loved, too, if he could fit that in.

A smoldering hope pervades human life. We set up objectives for this hope—money, knowledge, love, recognition, virtue. But what we are really yearning after is something larger: the feeling that we matter; that we make a difference. We must say something with our lives, and what we say must be heard—by history if at all possible; if not, then by our contemporaries, many or few; and if they won't listen we turn toward God. Hope inclines us to believe in God, or something like God.

Despair inclines us to disbelieve, and is the darker force that also drives us, side by side with the bright force of hope. We fight this despair. We try to bury it in dark corners. We rush around and make a commotion to drown out its desolating monotone. But we can never get rid of it for good, this feeling that life is an empty ocean, and we are bubbles that form, and float for a while, and then pop, and that's all there is: we were made to be destroyed.

Hope and despair propel people along a course that often veers sharply from one side of the road to the other. The boss raises your salary: suddenly you matter. He lets you go: suddenly you don't. Your lover leaves you for someone else: you don't. *You* fall in love with someone else: you do again. Your son wins a scholarship: and you both matter. In this way people go through life scoring themselves, and though they sometimes pretend otherwise these scores matter intensely. They also put us under great strain. One practicing psychiatrist was asked what single medicine would most help his average patient, all things possible: self-insight? better relations with the family? The psychiatrist thought for a moment. Then he sighed. Then he smiled—a little ruefully. "Success," he answered at last. "A little ordinary, worldly success."

Another gave the same kind of smile but was even more specific. His answer: "Money."

Money is only one mark of success in our time and place, but it is a hard-edged worldly one, and in its way quite a rational one, and it is what much of our society's struggle revolves around daily. You can count money up. You can hold it in your hand. You can exchange it for something that you value. You can set it aside for a rainy day. You can't do these things with love or with fame, and you can only do some of them with power.

Rich people aren't always happy, but most of them possess quite well-developed egos—a knowledge that they are of importance in the world. They are of importance in their families, where they often remain central figures into old age and even senility.

Money is also capable of freeing. Admittedly, not everyone knows what to do with the freedom: How do you spend your life if you don't have to spend it earning a living? Money can confuse people; it can make problems.

But it can solve them, too.

Say that you lose your job. This is a demoralizing experience for rich and poor alike. The poor man must scramble. But the man with an income has time. He can shop around. He can travel to distant cities. And he can take a month or two to think things out. Maybe he discovers his heart isn't really in advertising, and decides to go back to college again and train to become a teacher. Thus he changes his career and his life. All this he can do because he has money.

There are other ways people assert their value in the world, if none are quite so negotiable as money. One of these is recognition: the name in the newspaper, the prize won, the election to the PTA board, or the union office, or even to government. The jobs are worth doing in themselves but often their greatest personal importance is as badges of success pinned on us by judges around us. Being smiled upon by our peers, or even voted for, feels very good.

Both money and recognition can be comforting things in our society because they say how much you matter. They are not always accurate, of course. Van Gogh had neither during his lifetime, and even the salary of the United States President is modest compared with that of various corporate board chairmen. Perhaps power itself is a more accurate measure. An executive counts the number of employees under him, a violinist the number of listeners at her last recital. How many lives are you affecting? What is your impact on the world?

The other question is, how intense is your impact? A young mechanic on a Detroit assembly line who installs door handles on five hundred automobiles a day theoretically affects the lives of some five hundred people, but none of them really notices so his work seems meaningless. His wife, by contrast, influences only a very few people, mainly her children, but influences them so profoundly that her life is automatically of importance—at least till the children grow up, at which point she may suffer a sudden emptiness.

The strongest impact most people ever have on one another is probably through love. This includes not only love between parent and child but also that quieter version, friendship, plus the flaming version, romantic love.

Exerting personal impact is hard work, of course, and responsibility for what happens to other people, though at first it may feel heady, can be highly stressful, especially in some situations. Nevertheless, people go on pursuing power, just as they pursue money and fame, and with good reason. These ingredients of so-called worldly success are not only reassuring, they are our best practical means for gaining the world's attention. They give us the chance to speak our piece, to say something with our lives. So we struggle hard for them—sometimes so hard that we forget about the second problem.

The second problem is: What have you got to say? What are you going to do with the power? How are you going to spend the money? What's your point? If you don't know, you suffer from the malady known in the pulpits as "mere" worldly success. You have gained the world but lost your own soul. You've got the impact you wanted, but there's no you there to exert it.

The concept of identity—of the sense of self—is much bandied about in psychiatric journals, often quite abstrusely, but there is nothing necessarily mysterious about it. You are the way you are because of a whole list of specifics: what you want out of life; what you believe in; your emotional reactions—what angers or saddens you, or what makes you laugh; what you look like; your bodily responses in various situations; your talents; and so forth. Some of these specifics you are born with, like the shape of your hands; some, like your beliefs, are acquired through experience. Most are at least modified by experience.

From infancy onward, society modifies self—a good thing on the whole. A new-born baby is a squalling megalomaniac. It is society that turns him, twenty-one years later, into a more or less competent and rational adult. But sometimes the process goes too far. The need to get along, to be accepted, to succeed, becomes so important that bit by bit pieces of self are sacrificed until not very much is left. You learn to smile when you are really angry; you get your nose changed; you give up an eccentric hobby; you read the right books and say the right things about them. Pretty soon not much can be seen of you any more but a bundle of correct reactions.

Self is not actually destroyed by this process. But driven underground, it becomes an enemy. One of the ways it attacks you is stress, including physical stress disease.

If your temperament happens to fit the mores of your society, you're lucky: go ahead, enter the corporation, aim for the top job, have the two children and bring them up right, and all the rest. But what if it doesn't? Do you follow the same path anyway, fitting yourself in as best you can? This can sometimes be done, but past a certain point the costs exceed the profits. Skill and intelligence aside, some people aren't equipped for the big managerial jobs—the responsibility erodes them. Some aren't equipped for parenthood—often for the same reason. Some aren't equipped for marriage. People have got to bend to the culture, obviously. But they must also make the culture bend to them, force it to make room for themselves as they really are. Living in society is a reciprocal matter, a constantly shifting relationship between the you and the they. When the balance is right you learn, you grow, you mean something.

Human personality has its bright side and its dark side, and people tend to concentrate on the first while doing their best to ignore the second. You express joy freely; anger you swallow. You welcome hope; you fight down fear. You cultivate your assets; your deficits you conceal as best you can. All this makes sense in a way, particularly in the world of work. You do what you're good at—and what you're good at is of course intimately bound up with your sense of self.

It makes sense, but when it is carried too far life becomes constricted, and again, very stressful. Beauty queens have intellects too. A scholar has muscles. Our equipment is designed for use. If we don't use it, it can rebel and start using us.

This is especially true of the emotions. Like arms and legs, fear and anger are part of the basic human equipment: exercise develops them and makes them useful. A person who is good at solving problems is a person who knows how to be angry. He has learned to use anger to change a situation.

It is when situations refuse to yield that people are most inclined to bury their emotions—the very time, often, when they most need to express them. Not all problems can be solved, but almost all of them can be relieved by the simple strategy of talking about them, with feeling. It is not necessary to scream or to break dishes, but it is vital to phrase your frustrations, to get them out and hear them, even if no one else listens.

Theoretically, life should enlarge as you get older, as your competence and knowledge accumulate. Yet all too often it begins to narrow at what seems a very premature point—in the thirties or forties, sometimes even in the twenties. The vitality is still high, the brain cells all functioning, but the possibilities close down and the personality stops growing. Just a few years ago you were a long-haired blonde who liked the Marx Brothers, hated cold weather, and played a good game of gin rummy. You are still all those things, but you have become a kind of wind-up toy, obediently going through motions. The you is fading out of your life. Habit is fading in.

Perhaps what happens is that the first part of life is mainly occupied by the quest for identity. According to psychologists the individual personality sets very early, and after the age of three no major changes are likely: you are already you. Yet it remains to be discovered what this you is. What am I really like? is a universally fascinating question, and in pursuit of the answer almost any kind of change or challenge becomes welcome. Violin lessons; a hurricane; pneumonia; even war—anything new helps you find out more about yourself.

Gradually the answers trickle in. Some are a pleasant surprise. Most are a little disappointing. Some are painful. But finally a day comes when there don't seem to be any real questions left to ask. You know what you are, for better and for worse. And something very important goes out of life.

Habit is essential to sane living. It gets you to work on time. It helps you keep hold of yourself in emergencies. It is also one way of defining and expressing self: you are the kind of person who takes a shower before breakfast, who reads the *Times* instead of the *News*, watches the Late Show every night. Habits are easy. Habits are reassuring. We all use them.

We use them, and go on using them, and then one day wake up and discover that they have taken over and are using us. We have become a set of mechanical responses, rigid, out of contact with the world, only half alive.

In these circumstances habit, designed to protect us from stress, becomes stressful itself. When a new situation comes along, you must see it as it really is and respond accordingly. Otherwise an opportunity is missed, or a problem goes unsolved. Habit seldom solves problems, and almost never seizes opportunities. It blinds itself to both. It is a substitute for spontaneous, felt action—a way of saying: You can't touch me, world.

But the world has got to touch us, just as we must touch it, if our lives are to say anything. And when we break through the habits, it does touch us and we become human again. A week in San Francisco will do it, away from the routine rounds of office and home. So will a reunion with a childhood friend. So will a confrontation with the eternal—in church, if you like, or perhaps on a mountain or a lonely stretch of beach. Sailing, skiing, ice skating, even a long walk, add the lyric quality to life. Parents with young children especially need to go off by themselves at intervals and rediscover what their marriage is about, besides meals, report cards and home carpentry.

If you know how to make the small changes, the big ones come a little easier. These are the changes that our lives depend on: the showdown with the wife or husband in an ebbing marriage, or with an employer in a job that has gone bad. Both marriages and jobs are sometimes saved by such showdowns. Sometimes they are broken. Sometimes they need to be broken. But the individual himself does not break with them, if he knows how to change.

An important rule is, don't be meek. On the job the meek compete only by working harder, longer, faster, more slavishly. They take care not to evidence dislike of anyone; he may be their boss tomorrow. At home they don't raise their voices for fear of scarring the children's lives. They are meek in the subway, the grocery store, in traffic, with garage mechanics, appliance repairmen and those emperors, the civil servants. Above all the meek are meek in their marriages. They are careful never to place blame. Mentioning anything will only make it worse.

If meekness is unconditional surrender, anger can be a kamikaze tactic. Seemingly the easiest way to control anger is to turn it off, but this is only a short-term solution. Emotions don't go away. They build up slowly, and eventually a day comes when release is necessary. You blow up, yell or scream, perhaps weep, or hit someone. After that you shut it all off again for another long period. What is wrong with this method?

First, anger handled in this fashion changes from a useful, energetic property into a damaging one. A sudden eruption into rage, after months or years of suppression, can devastate the person who experiences it. Maybe in his fury he struck his wife, or the wife walked out on the husband; or either quit a good job; or destroyed an important friendship. Looking about them at the wreckage, they say bleakly to themselves,

"God, I can't afford to do that again.'" The next time around they may release the anger by getting sick, or depressed, or both.

More important, this method of handling anger—long periods of suppression interspersed by occasional outbursts—doesn't accomplish anything. It doesn't go to work on the situations that bring on the anger in the first place.

It is important to remember that anger itself is neither good nor bad for people. The question is not even whether to express it or not; express it you must, one way or another. Aim to use it to improve things. When anger is regarded as a wild animal that must be caged, of course it becomes damaging. Only when you accept it as a natural response to difficult situations of many kinds can it then be developed into a constructive tool. Anger, after all, is what rouses you to challenge a situation, and it is important to be able to act early on this anger, and to make those challenges. If you do so regularly the anger doesn't build up to unmanageable proportions. But even more important, it works *for* you. Often, with its help, you can change things. Sometimes you can't, of course, but even then the challenge is worth making. You have expended the anger, and perhaps you have learned something. Perhaps you have even changed a little yourself.

EPILOGUE

A SECOND CHANCE

Becoming a parent means for most people another try at the world. Not everything works out the way we want in our own lives, but it's going to be different, we decide, for our children: we'll see to that. So it is with hope, but also with a certain anxiety, that we watch them grow and slowly turn into people themselves.

In the process, children gradually develop a way of being sick, as individual as their smile or their way of moving. What influences these patterns of illness, and what can we do about them, given our own patterns that we find so hard to alter?

Naturally, we try to feed them properly, see that they get enough exercise and rest, and administer the proper remedies when they fall ill. But from the beginning, underlying attitudes creep in and complicate the picture. It is when a child gets sick that these inner attitudes really come to the fore. First of all, even if the illness is only a cold the parent becomes somewhat disturbed. Colds can develop into bronchitis, or pneumonia, or rheumatic fever and besides, the household routine is upset. Secondly, the child himself becomes more susceptible. Illness weakens his psychological defenses, and he is suddenly cut off from his customary outlets: school, friends, the dime store, the library, the vacant lot down the street. He is shut in alone with himself and his mother. Suddenly he feels much younger, almost like a baby again. It is quite pleasant but he knows that the whole business of his life is to grow older and more independent. And how his mother reacts to this situation may make matters worse. If she enjoys babying him in his illness, that makes him uncomfortable; but if she is secretly annoyed and treats him like a malingerer, that bothers him too.

This doesn't mean a parent can't be sympathetic, for a sick child is both lonely and vaguely upset. But when you go in to visit with him, don't fall back on stories about how dear he was at the age of two. Talk about how he's going to spend the summer, or what he's accomplishing in school. And see that he has things to do—responsible tasks that will remind him of his basic capability and independence. Perhaps he can organize his baseball cards, or cut up celery and carrots for the soup. If he's old enough he can also help take care of his illness himself. You can teach him to take his own temperature, or maybe to measure out his medicine.

A word about medicine: don't use it unless you have a real reason. Aspirin, for example, reduces pain and fever, but it does so by suppressing the inflammatory reaction, and the inflammatory reaction is one way the body gets rid of disease-causing microbes. Sometimes, of course, the symptoms get out of hand—medicine makes sense for a child with a fever of 103 degrees, or one whose cough keeps him awake at night. But in most illnesses the symptoms indicate that the body is at work fighting its disease, and the best strategy is not to interfere with its efforts.

Medicine is also habit-forming—all medicine, if you take enough of it, regardless of whether it happens to be physically addictive. A person whose childhood was highlighted by frequent dosings of one kind or another, held out for him in a spoon by a loving mother, is the kind of person who in adult life goes in for daily laxatives, nasal decongestants, vitamin pills, sedatives, psychic energizers, and the rest of the vast cornucopia worked up for him by today's drug industry. Medicine, for such a person, has come to mean that somehow Mother is still taking care of him, and he pays for this care not only in cash but often in a derangement of his bodily functions—which leads to yet more medications.

If drugs can make the cycle keep going round, so can that more drastic medical remedy, surgery. Avoid it if you can, where your children are concerned. And if you can't, you must prepare them for it with particular care.

When you talk to your child about the operation he is going to have, it is important to be factual and clear about the procedures involved, as well as calm about the outcome. Tell him he will hurt afterwards, but that he will gradually feel better and when this happens there will be other kids to play with and special things for children to do on his floor.

You should not only prepare the child for his operation, you had better prepare yourself, too—in particular for that moment when he is wheeled back from the recovery room to his bed. Even a twenty-minute tonsillectomy can do it, but the longer he was in surgery the worse he will look. His face will be white, his hair limp with dried sweat; through half-opened lids his eyes will gaze sightlessly ahead without recognizing you. Don't burst into tears. In an hour he will begin to look alive again.

Feelings about sickness are not dictated solely, or even chiefly, by a child's experience with assorted stomach upsets, infections and operations: patterns of health are the result of far wider influences.

Who are the people who get the stress disease?

First, they are afraid of their own feelings, particularly the feeling of anger, which they bury deep within, where it smolders unseen, eventually igniting the body's physical apparatus.

Secondly, they are in one way or another failures in life. When people fail, they try to justify their failures, and many of them do so by getting sick. They also seek compensation—and many find it in being taken care of by their mates, by their local hospital, or by their insurance company. Convinced that they cannot get what they really want from life, they stop trying and aim instead for the next best thing: a salve for their bitter disappointment.

They also, very frequently, reach out for their children—the second-chance syndrome in its fullest and most sinister flower. Perhaps we have not really failed after all; if our children succeed then we will have succeeded, since we produced the children. In this fashion our hopes revive and we go to work, forcing opportunities on them, rousing in them the right ambitions and expectations, molding them, scolding them.

This is very hard on children, particularly when we practice one thing and preach another. You advise them to be aggressive in life—when you yourself can't handle anger. You've got a little drinking problem—so you warn them off alcohol. You tell them how important a college degree is—you don't have one, and look how it's held you back. The message is confusing—and to a child, very disturbing.

It may bother you that your seventeen-year-old daughter dresses drably and has no interest in boys, but you can hardly scold her for that. So instead, when she is late coming home for dinner you chew her out as if she had committed a crime. Or perhaps your son, whom you have envisioned from birth as one day turning into an eminent cardiologist, gets mostly C's on his report card. Maybe his abilities and inclinations all point to a career as a garage mechanic. So what do you do when he gets into trouble? You tell him he can't take that job pumping gas at the Exxon station this summer.

Punishing a child for one thing when you are really angry at him for something else seldom gets results. It also does something to the child at the receiving end. Badness and inadequacy get mixed up in his mind, and both become an established part of his sense of self. The inadequacy he can't do much about, but the badness he can. He can feel guilty. And feeling guilty, he can aim for atonement. Atonement, he knows from experience, comes through punishment; and then reconciliation follows, and he is back where he started from: the cycle is complete, with momentum remaining to begin again. For many people this becomes a lifelong pattern of unproductive behavior. In adulthood, away from his parents, such a person learns to punish himself—often through illness.

Sometimes from the experience of illness we learn to be sick. And from the experience of failure, we learn to fail. And from the experience of being unable to control ourselves, we learn that we are uncontrollable. This is the kind of learning children can do without.

A child's life, including his problems, belongs to him, not to his parents, and their task is to help him learn to control these problems. He will need anxiety, to help him recognize the problems. He will need anger, to help him solve them. He will need grief, to help dispel his failures. But he will need to develop and train these emotions if they are to work for him, just as he develops and trains his body and his intellect. If he succeeds at it, he will turn out to be not a star athlete, perhaps, or a statesman, or a great physician, or whatever his parents' secret or not-so-secret ambitions for him may conjure up, but something better: an adult at home with the world and with his family, physically healthy, able to take failure, able to take success—alive, and glad to be alive.

EDGE OF THE WORLD

ROSS ISLAND, ANTARCTICA

A condensation of the book by

CHARLES NEIDER

Chapter 2, in somewhat different form, was published
in November 1971 by the National Science Foundation
as a booklet entitled *A Historical Guide to Ross Island,
Antarctica*. A condensed version of Chapter 12, "A Walk
in Taylor Valley," appeared in the November-December
1972 issue of the Antarctic Journal of the United States,
published by the National Science Foundation.
The quotation in Chapter 1 from Maurice Herzog's
article in *The New York Times* Magazine of October 4,
1953 is © 1953 by The New York Times Company.
Reprinted by permission. The quotations in Chapter 2 from
Richard E. Byrd's article, "Our Navy Explores Antarctica,"
in the October 1947 issue of the *National Geographic*
magazine are used by permission of the magazine. The
quotations in the same chapter from George Dufek's
Operation Deepfreeze, published in 1957, are used by
permission of Harcourt Brace Jovanovich. The quotations
in Chapter 2 from Apsley Cherry-Garrard's *The Worst
Journey in the World* are used by permission of
Constable & Co., London. The quotations in Chapter 12
from Griffith Taylor's report in the second volume
of Scott's Last Expedition, published in 1913 by
Dodd, Mead & Co., New York, are used by permission
of the publisher.

TITLE PAGE: *Ross Island from the north.*

PHOTOGRAPH BY CHARLES NEIDER

CHAPTER 1

PROLOGUE

The continent of Antarctica and its surrounding seas have been the stage of extraordinary experiences during the last two centuries, eliciting remarkable behavior from men in conditions of extreme stress.

Renewed interest in Antarctica is timely now for several reasons: 1969 marked the tenth anniversary of the Antarctic Treaty and the fortieth of Richard E. Byrd's flight over the South Pole; 1971 the sixtieth anniversary of the attainment of the Pole by Roald Amundsen; 1972 the sixtieth anniversary of the death of the ill-fated Robert Falcon Scott and his four companions on their homeward trek from the Pole, and the fiftieth anniversary of the death of Ernest Shackleton in South Georgia during his fourth Antarctic expedition. The recent discovery of freshwater vertebrate fossils on the continent greatly strengthens the theory of continental drift. American women have recently been introduced into Antarctic life and work. Also, at a time of ecological crisis, the white continent serves as a benchmark of a still relatively undefiled frontier, and readers are perhaps now ready to encounter, if only vicariously, a world of simplicity and purity in which the struggle between man and man must be set aside so that mankind can better understand nature.

My interest in Antarctica goes back to my boyhood in Richmond, Virginia. In 1931, when I was sixteen, I heard Byrd lecture on Antarctica. He became a boyhood hero of mine. I wanted very much to go to the Antarctic, so I wrote letters to the National Geographic Society and the American Geographical Society, asking to be included in an expedition. Naturally I was turned down.

My dream of visiting the continent continued into my adult years but I never thought it would be realized. I have long been interested in man's behavior in conditions of great stress, especially when he is pitted against nature. In 1954 I edited a book titled *Man Against Nature*, published by

Harpers, which included authentic accounts of exploration. In several of these Antarctica was the environment against which man struggled. It later struck me that the time had come for a literary person to go to the Antarctic.

We have had reports from the explorers, and innumerable highly technical papers from the scientists, both emanating from Antarctica, but no one, so far as I know, has brought out a detailed, aesthetic account of the novelistic texture of life as it has been and is lived and worked there. The reason for this lack is that literary persons, like other representatives of the humanities, have rarely been granted a working residence in Antarctica. Such a shortcoming of the United States Antarctic program is unfortunate for the taxpayer, who supports the program and who is culturally impoverished by the current limitations. Hopefully the present book will encourage a congressional broadening of the program to include the humanities. What I am saying about the United States Antarctic program is equally true of the Antarctic programs of other nations, as far as I am aware. There is much in that strange continent (beyond the scope of scientific research) that can enrich the general public.

There are tours that take you by ship from South America to the Antarctic Peninsula but these do not go to the high latitudes. (South of the equator "high latitudes" describes the most southerly ones.) Recently there have been a few, expensive tours by ship from New Zealand to Ross Island. The tourists spend only a brief time on the island but it is far better than no time at all. The usual way for an American to go to the high latitudes is to have the United States Navy fly him from its base in Christchurch, New Zealand, down to Ross Island in the Ross Sea. The main United States base in the Antarctic, McMurdo Station, is on Ross Island, whose latitude is close to 78°.

In November of 1969 I went to the Antarctic as a guest of the Navy, having been invited with three newsmen to observe Operation Deep Freeze, the Navy's logistic support activity on behalf of American scientific research on the continent. The research, which is entirely basic research as contrasted with applied research, is conducted by USARP, the United States Antarctic Research Program, under the supervision and with funds of the National Science Foundation. With us were four science writers who were guests of NSF.

But this is putting it coolly. What actually happened was that from the moment I learned I was a candidate for a trip to Antarctica, however brief, my boyhood hopes and memories welled up and I lived for a period in almost painful suspense. When a letter arrived from an admiral, informing me on behalf of the Navy Department, the Department of Defense and the State Department (I was puzzled by the State Department's being part of the sponsoring group) that I had been selected to go, I reached for the nearest bottle in the liquor cabinet, downed several shots and found my eyes tearful with incredulity and joy. Alone in the house, I waited for my wife Joan to return from an errand so she could be the first to hear the news. I was at the top of the stairs when she entered the door. I said casually, "I'm going to Antarctica." She rushed to the foot of the stairs to see if I was joking, saw my glass in hand and my beatific, bourbonized smile, and, beaming, congratulated me with a kiss.

The lure of Antarctica, that fabulous, awesome and in some ways exquisitely beautiful last frontier, is so great that the long first leg to New Zealand seemed even longer despite the speed of the huge Air Force jet (a C-141) that took us to Christchurch via California, Hawaii and Samoa. You travel with the suspense of a pilgrim eager to reach places sanctified by human and superhuman events. But the chief goal of the Antarctic pilgrim is to reach pure nature itself—from ancient, pre-human time, frozen in an incredible ice cap. Such a pilgrim goes to pay his respects to natural conditions; to take a breath of unpolluted air; and to sense how it all felt in the beginning, before the introduction of man. But he also goes to see how man survives in the world's most hostile place and does so by means of the very gadgetry which increasingly possesses and assails him. He travels, in short, from technological defilement for a glimpse of innocence, hoping to learn along the way a few things about himself.

Innocent he has no doubt the white continent is; because it has so far not been more than superficially degraded by man (although it is not entirely free of nuclear fallout and of traces of air pollution, it's as close to natural purity as one can attain in this world); because nations work there in tranquility and cooperation under the remarkable Antarctic Treaty; because it is largely devoid of life, a fact which in some strange, not easily comprehended way is pleasant to contemplate, as if life itself and not only man is so problematical that it is astringently pleasant to take a vacation from it (perhaps by life the pilgrim tends to mean not those rare mosses and lichens and certain soil organisms which manage to hang on in the Antarctic's inimical climate but pestilential forms which he would gladly do without: cold, flu and pneumonia bugs, which are usually dormant in the extremes of cold and dryness); and because with the exception of a few predatory examples such as the Killer whale and the leopard seal higher forms of life like penguins and seals regard man as a friend, not having had sufficient experience of him to develop inbred suspicion and fear, and because historically they have had no enemies on land—if you exclude the skua's preying on the Adélie penguin.

Read even the early explorers of Antarctica, such as Charles Wilkes and James Clark Ross, and you will understand that Antarctica can become an addiction. Wilkes commanded a United States exploring expedition in the years 1839–42, went very far south and made observations from which he correctly concluded that Antarctica was a continent. He marveled, as did Ross, at the continent's haunting beauty. His name is honored by a vast stretch of Antarctica south of Australia: Wilkes Land. If you read the Antarctic explorers of the early part of our own century you will see that Antarctica is a great proving ground. It tests ships, sledges, dogs, ponies, equipment and above all men. Even while you're there the place sometimes seems like a fantastic dream. After you've left it you want to return to make sure it really happened to you, in all its grandeur, rarity, purity and beauty.

I have sometimes been asked whether one is oppressed by a sense of danger while living and working in Antarctica, or even while making the long flights to the continent that is the windiest, coldest, driest, highest and most remote on earth. The answer, as far as I know it from personal experience and from the experience of some of my Antarctic friends, is that you leave much of your sense of physical danger behind in the temperate zone. You have a long and sometimes rather hazardous flight journey from the United States to Ross Island. In those thousands of miles you seem to take on a new set of values and feelings concerning your physical safety. It's as though you have two Chinese masks, one for the temperate zone, the other for Antarctica. In Antarctica, assuming you like the place (there are those who feel ill at ease in it or even dislike it), you usually wear the mask of euphoria and immortality. You know that accidents, some fatal, do occur, but you do not believe they will happen to you. Any other attitude would make working well there difficult.

The euphoria seems to be caused by a complex of reasons: the extreme dryness of the air; the fact that many places on the continent are high pressure areas; the great beauty of the place; the challenge of danger that so heightens one's sense of being alive. Personally, I also have to reckon with an unusual amount of aggression, which finds a clear and natural outlet against a form of nature that is extremely hostile to life. After my return to Princeton, New Jersey, it occurred to me that with one exception I had not used any medication whatsoever, not even an aspirin tablet, during my second and extended stay in Antarctica. Both mentally and physically I had rarely felt so harmonious and well. The exception was a muscle-relaxant pill prescribed for me because of severe cramps due to dehydration in my left thigh, the result of camping out.

Maurice Herzog, the French mountain climber and author, once wrote:

"The true value of life is never apparent until one has risked losing it. A man who has triumphed over mortal danger is born again. It is a birth without indebtedness to anything on earth. It endows one with a serenity and independence which are truly unutterable.

"Mountain climbers, polar explorers, pioneers in unknown, hostile regions, in the caves of the earth and the sea's depths, are all linked by the same vision. All of them stake their native, human gifts against the unknown. Their reward is to enrich mankind's heritage, and the sense of this is their common bond.

"When all the mountains in the world have been scaled, when the poles hold no more secrets, when the last acre of the last continent has been traversed, when, in short, everything on our planet is known and catalogued, the way will still be open for discovery. The world will never be conquered so long as the zest for conquest, for adventure, is in men's hearts."

During my 1969 visit to Antarctica I was the beneficiary of the usual grand tour: McMurdo Station, Pole Station, Byrd Station, Scott Base, and Capes Evans and Royds, the latter two on Ross Island. I was tremendously moved by what I saw. Awakening in a Jamesway hut early one morning, I felt a desire to write a book about Ross Island and determined that I would do all I could to return to Antarctica to research the book.

Back home in Princeton, I made inquiries by mail regarding the possibility of obtaining a working residence in the Antarctic in connection with the book. I learned from my senators, my congressman and from the legal office of the State Department that such a residence was not available to a person like me. Nevertheless I wrote letters to the Navy and to the National Science Foundation, outlining my project and requesting that I be permitted to return to the ice for a relatively extended stay. Realizing that my chances for success were exceedingly slim, I

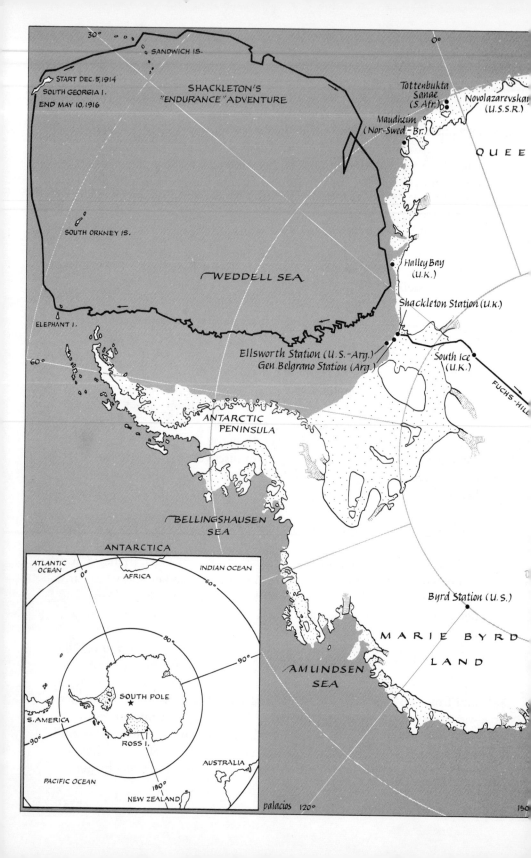

Molodezhnaya (U.S.S.R.)

Syowa (Jap.)

Mawson Station
(Australia)

UD LAND

Davis Station (Australia)

Mirnyy
(U.S.S.R.)

ANTARCTICA

Vostok (U.S.S.R.)

Wilkes
(Australia)

Amundsen - Scott
South Pole Station
(U.S.)

FUCHS-HILLARY

SCOTT

AMUNDSEN

W I L K E S   L A N D

ROSS
ICE
SHELF

Scott Base (N.Z.)

McMurdo Station (U.S.)

Dumont d'Urville (Fr.)

ROSS I.

VICTORIA
LAND

Little
America

Bay of Whales

* SOUTH
MAGNETIC
POLE

ROSS SEA

180°

0   Statute Miles   500

MAP DESIGN: CHARLES NEIDER; CARTOGRAPHY: RAFAEL D. PALACIOS

developed as much leverage as I could by obtaining a grant from the Chapelbrook Foundation of Boston (a philanthropic institution) and contracts with prominent publishers for two books about Antarctica. I was going far out on a limb as more and more of my literary energy was being consumed in difficult and delicate correspondence. If I failed to return to Antarctica I would have nothing to show for the time I had spent.

Both the Navy and the National Science Foundation informed me they were having budgetary problems and that until these were resolved no decision could be made in my case. It seemed to me that the National Science Foundation if not the Navy had something to gain by letting me do my book, for although it had sponsored much important scientific research in the Antarctic, most of its work was unknown to the general public. The Navy, in the form of Operation Deep Freeze, on the other hand, had looked consistently to the broader aspects of its public relations.

There came a time when I sensed that both organizations preferred that I drop the matter. I wrote to the White House, suggesting the desirability of broadening the United States Antarctic program and requesting help for my project. Possibly I would have lacked the temerity to do so had I not had behind me a curious experience of 1959, when I had successfully requested Premier Khrushchev of the Soviet Union to intervene on my behalf in a controversy I was having with *The Literary Gazette* of Moscow. Khrushchev had opened the pages of this magazine to me for a defense against an attack on me in connection with *The Autobiography of Mark Twain,* which I had arranged and edited. As a result of my letter to the President I received a reply, written on behalf of the White House, from an executive of the National Science Foundation informing me that my project would be seriously considered by the Foundation staff.

Some time later, after much silence from the National Science Foundation, I sensed that it was becoming dangerously late in the season for making a decision about my project. Feeling that a desperate move was necessary, I picked up the phone in my home study and called Thomas O. Jones of the National Science Foundation because he was the person who had replied for the White House. I had to deal with two secretaries before I got through to him. He barely remembered my name. I said that it seemed to me extremely important that the humanities had some representation in Antarctica; that the book I had in mind was a unique and good one; and I began to outline the kind of support I had for it. He interrupted by saying stiffly that he knew nothing about this, that he had staffs to handle this sort of thing.

I said, "There is absolutely no hope for my project unless you intervene on my behalf. I can't reasonably expect the Navy to do it. The Navy is not essentially an intellectual organization, as the National Science Foundation is. Only you can help me."

His tone grew more plastic. He said he would speak to his people about my proposal and that someone would be in touch with me about it.

Having taken this last-ditch step, I resolved to put the matter out of mind as much as possible.

Several days later I returned home from an afternoon walk to find a message that a Phil Smith had phoned me from Washington and had said he would either call again before five or in the morning. I had no idea who he was. I phoned NSF, learned that he was Philip M. Smith, Deputy Head of the Office of Polar Programs, and that he had already gone home. His secretary gave me his home telephone number, at which I reached him. He said he was an admirer of my books and that he was very enthusiastic about my Ross Island project. Could I come to Washington for a luncheon meeting?

The meeting, at which Roland Paine and Jack Renirie of the NSF press department were also present, was entirely successful. I knew Renirie from my 1969 trip to Antarctica and had already met Paine. On the Metroliner back to Trenton I studied a booklet called *Survival in Antarctica,* which Smith had given me. It helped me grasp the fact that I had indeed become a member of the USARP team for the upcoming austral season.

During September and October of that year, 1970, I had a residence fellowship at the MacDowell Colony in Peterborough, New Hampshire. MacDowell is an old and honored artists' colony, where I had lived several times previously. I was working on a book but I used part of my time in preparations for my coming trip. During previous stays I had driven daily to Keene, New Hampshire, some twenty-two miles west of Peterborough, to swim a half mile of the crawl nonstop at the Y there. This year I increased the distance to three quarters of a mile. On weekends, when the pool was closed, I cycled long distances in the New Hampshire hills. I had usually been in hard physical condition. Now I meant to toughen myself further, for my work in the Antarctic would be based on a rigorous life, with periods of little sleep and with much physical exertion. My program would be a very varied one. My stay would not be limited to Ross Island. I regarded the island as the hub of United States activities, both scientific and logistic, in Antarctica, and I meant to treat it accordingly. In this view I had the complete support of Phil Smith. Although I had come uncomfortably close to failing in my efforts to return to Antarctica, now that I was a Usarp (pronounced you-sarp) I was to have all the cooperation I could wish for, both from the National Science Foundation and the Navy. I was fifty-five. I hoped my age would not interfere with what I had to do.

There were several things I urgently wished to accomplish on this second visit. I hoped to have the rare experience of camping at Capes Royds and Evans on Ross Island and sleeping in the historic Shackleton and Scott huts there; to live with the New Zealanders at their Scott Base on the island; to observe the operation of the remarkable ice airfield, Williams Field, near the island; to live on an icebreaker as it approached the island and cut a channel to McMurdo; to hike in one of the fascinating Dry Valleys in Victoria Land across McMurdo Sound from the island; to visit Vostok, the Russian station deep in the continent's interior, on the annual diplomatic flight from McMurdo as a witness of the functioning of the Antarctic Treaty; to study McMurdo and its environs at close range; and in general to get to know as much of Ross Island as I could.

Also, I wanted to report as vividly as I was able on what the continent is like, this report being based on both of my visits. The Arctic and the Antarctic are poles apart in more ways than one readily realizes. The North Pole is a frozen, floating point on a sea some ten thousand feet deep. The South Pole is at an elevation of ninety-two hundred feet and is located roughly in the middle of a continent whose average elevation is about seventy-five hundred feet. The Arctic is a sea surrounded by great land masses. The Antarctic is a land mass approximately as large as the United States and Mexico combined, containing great plateaus, vast mountain ranges and an ice cap that in places is almost three miles deep. Its average temperature is some 35°F. lower than that of the Arctic. It is surrounded by the unbroken confluence of the Pacific, Atlantic and Indian Oceans which, with the prevailing westerlies, comprise the world's most savage sea. The lowest temperature ever recorded on earth was noted at Vostok: -126.9°F. Whereas the North Pole is relatively close to places inhabited by man and is not very distant from highly developed forms of life, the South Pole is utterly remote on a continent that holds life at bay, allowing survival only minimally in its interior.

Above all I hoped to bring out a report in language of the awesome beauty of Antarctica; of the mystical spell one becomes addicted to there; and of the unusual persons and morale one is likely to encounter and to get to know in a very special way. The frame of my narrative would be, quite simply, what happened to me: what I did and saw, whom I met, what stories I heard. Within that frame I hoped to include some of the incredible highlights of the island's history. I would not have much time to accomplish all this. Only a bit more than a month had been allotted me on the ice. But still, as a non-scientist I was lucky to be going back at all.

In September I received a notice to appear at the naval base in Kittery, Maine, for a physical examination. I had an early morning appointment. The New Hampshire villages I drove through were still mostly asleep. I encountered fog as I approached the seacoast. The examination was lengthy and thorough. While lying on a table and having a cardiogram taken I fell asleep, to the surprise of the young male attendant. Weird, extremely high and barely audible sounds came through large earphones during the hearing tests. When a male nurse stabbed at my arm to draw blood from a vein it felt like a blow from a hammer. A medical officer was impressed by my low pulse rate: 62. I returned to the Colony with the sense that I was in excellent physical condition.

Shortly afterwards I attended an Antarctic orientation conference, lasting six days, in Skyland, Virginia. The purpose of the conference, sponsored by the National Science Foundation, was to acquaint new Antarctic hands with certain facts and problems and to permit USARP personnel to meet Navy people. Phil Smith had asked me to give a talk at Skyland. I had agreed to speak on some of the psychological aspects of a life of action. I was greatly surprised to learn from a printed brochure that mine was the main talk the first evening of the conference.

As an example of what I mean by the psychological side of action let me mention a repeated revelation I once had at the periscope of a submarine during diving practice. I could see the Atlantic's whitecaps gleaming on a bright sun, and the forward end of the submarine already submerged, and the rest of the craft disappearing rapidly. A part of me still seemed above water while the rest was beneath. I was reminded of Stevenson's imagined split personality as portrayed in *Dr. Jekyll and Mr. Hyde,* and of the equally split protagonist of Dostoyevsky's fictional *Notes from Underground,* and of stories I had read of surgeons performing major operations on themselves.

Some years later I was in the lava zone on Mount Etna in Sicily. The lava patches were hundreds of yards wide and often they were of considerable height, standing like hills. These cold ribbons stretched for miles, flinty, barren. I imagined the molten stuff streaming out of fissures, burying chunks of forest, setting fields afire, then slowly cooling, the gases erupting, the most porous stuff on top, and down beneath, the solidifying lava rock. I had been standing awe-struck when suddenly the place became intolerable, for I was in an entirely inorganic world, without life or souvenir of life: a pitted moon-world. I had a new sense of the awesome loneliness of man in the inorganic universe and felt a close affinity with all forms of life I momentarily remembered, however lowly.

What impelled Byrd to brave the Antarctic winter alone was not only the desire to make accurate and historic meteorological observations but also the opportunity to discover utter, sustained and dangerous solitude and in that solitude to take stock of himself, his future and his relations with the community of men. One of the most fascinating aspects of Jim Corbett's hunting of man-eating Indian tigers was that the man became the beast, with a cunning approximating the tiger's, while the tiger, in its ability to outguess Corbett at times, even to the point of almost hunting him down, assumed the intellectual and instinctual contours of the human being. There is the beast in all of us and there is no sure borderline between the animal and his human brother.

Aside from the feat itself, the most remarkable thing about William Beebe's descent into the deep ocean was its experience of unimaginable darkness, broken by the flashes of phosphorescent fish that suggested the sparks of thought and image in our night dreams. It was beautiful and stunning. That the effect of great darkness is very profound can be attested to by those who have descended into the depths of vast caverns.

What I have been suggesting is that adventure, large or small, excites not only our physical selves but our imaginative ones as well, and that a true adventure is also a psychological and perhaps even a spiritual matter.

Many of the greatest adventures of the present century have occurred in Antarctica, a continent that perhaps more than any other in this period has been the scene of man's prolonged and at times incredibly persistent will to endure in the teeth of nature's hostility. The adventures have not solely involved geographical exploration. There has been interior exploration as well, as evidenced by Scott's and Shackleton's almost complusive need to test the interior limits of man's endurance. Their belief in the nobility of man-hauling sledges was not an expression of masochism (however, it did involve deep national and personal prejudices against the use of dogs in sledging) but at least partly of patriotic concern regarding Englishmen's manliness at a time when there was spreading wonder about the possible decadence of Britain's youth in the face of a rising threat from Germany. While they pushed forward the boundaries of geographical exploration they simultaneously explored the frontiers of their ability to endure severe physical and mental punishment.

At the conclusion of my talk, during the question and answer period, Rear Admiral David F. Welch, commander of Operation Deep Freeze (another name for this operation is Task Force 43), sitting in the front row and eying me steadily, asked, "In your opinion, was Scott's tragedy largely due to the fact he had a narrow Navy mind?"

I thought a moment, smiled, and said softly, "Admiral, I intend to return to McMurdo."

There was laughter, in which the admiral joined.

Then I said it was my view that Scott's greatness and his ability to keep writing up to the end were in some measure due to esprit de corps, to his career in the Royal Navy, his devotion to its tradition, his concern for matters larger than personal ones, his training in the importance of keeping logs. I added that it was no accident that he should have been gifted as a literary stylist. He was steeped in the works of his Royal Navy predecessors such as James Cook, the remarkable navigator, marine surveyor and expedition commander who was also a skilled observer, with an alert prose style. And I said that the partnership between science and naval logistic support, or between naval geographical discovery with the accompaniment and support of science, was a tradition going as far back as Cook of the eighteenth century and continuing through Bellingshausen, Ross and Wilkes of the nineteenth and Scott and Byrd of the twentieth.

I met many interesting people at Skyland. Among them were the British Antarctic explorer Sir Vivian Fuchs; Dale Vance of Boulder, Colorado, who would be spending a year as an American exchange scientist with the Russians at Vostok Station; Roy Cameron, a microbiologist of the Jet Propulsion Laboratory in Pasadena; Bill Cobb of Longmont, Colorado, a meteorologist who would spend about a week at Pole Station; Bob Wood of Johns Hopkins, who had worked several seasons with penguins at Cape Crozier, Ross Island, and who would be returning there; and Chris Shepherd, whom I had met at McMurdo Station in 1969 and who was now the station's USARP representative. I had met Admiral Welch the previous year. I renewed my acquaintance with him in his quarters after my talk. I also spoke at length with Phil Smith.

It was hot and humid at Skyland and the valley below us was obscured by mists except at night, when, looking out over it, you saw the lights of distant farms, cars, a town. We had three large meals daily. The only regular exercise we had was in climbing the trail through woods up to the dining hall. But on occasion a few of us, including Fuchs, who looked handsome and trim, played frisbee.

I heard some interesting anecdotes. Cameron had been the leader of a party camping in Taylor Valley, and one morning a young man, new to Antarctica, was found running and shouting around and around a tent because, as he explained, he could not stand the silence. Cameron had him shipped back to McMurdo. Another young man had been approved for wintering over at Byrd Station, which was underground, or rather undersnow. After a week there he mentioned to some buddies that he felt menaced because there was something above him. They repeated this to the station scientific leader and he was flown out because it was feared he might crack up. I asked several young men who were scheduled to winter over at Byrd Station and Pole Station (the latter was also undersnow) if during their physical examinations they had been asked by a psychiatrist if they had ever had claustrophobia. Their answer was no. They said that both the psychologists and the psychiatrists had behaved in a deliberately aggressive, provocative manner, posing such questions as, "What the hell do you want to winter over at the Pole for?" Their replies had been carefully moderate.

On my return to the MacDowell Colony I found a letter requesting that I appear at Kittery, Maine, for more chest X-rays. It was a long drive for the few minutes it took to take two or three photographs. This time I was treated very specially by the attendants, one of whom was a young woman. There was too much solicitude in their handling of me.

I requested a meeting with the radiologist. He remained seated at his desk. He was about forty and wore Navy khakis. He was studying my films on a lighted screen in front of him.

He said casually, "I'm afraid your right lung is in pretty bad shape. I'm going to have to scratch you from the Antarctic program."

"What do you have in mind—cancer?"

"Frankly, yes."

What struck me most at this moment was not fear that I might have the disease and might require surgery and possibly the removal of the lung or that I might have to face the possibility that the disease had spread fatally, but a horror that after all my efforts I might not make it back to the Antarctic.

He wanted to settle the matter at once; he was already late in sending in the report on me. I explained what my return to Antarctica meant to me and begged him to give me a little time in which to have earlier chest X-rays sent to him by Princeton Hospital for comparison.

Then I asked, "If there is something seriously wrong with my lung wouldn't I feel some pain during the long-distance nonstop swims in which I almost always push myself?"

He thought a moment, said, "Yes, that seems reasonable to assume," and agreed to wait for the Princeton films before reaching a decision.

This was on a Monday morning. He said he should have the Princeton plates by Wednesday if they were sent promptly. He suggested I phone him Wednesday at three.

During Monday and Tuesday nights I kept waking up and imagining that my right lung had collapsed. I went swimming in Keene on Wednesday but couldn't finish even half a mile. I felt my right lung wasn't working at all. When I returned to my MacDowell studio it was ten to two. I downed some scotch and told myself I'd just nap for a quarter of an hour. When I awoke it was almost four. I walked groggily to Colony Hall and got through to the radiologist.

He said coolly, "Oh yes, the plates have come. We're letting you go. Have a good trip."

"You can't imagine what this means to me."

"I think I can," he said. "Stay out of trouble down there."

CHAPTER 2

A HISTORICAL GUIDE TO ROSS ISLAND

Ross Island is one of the most fascinating places in Antarctica. Of volcanic origin, situated at a latitude of almost 78°, roughly triangular in shape and some forty-five miles wide and an equal distance long, it is the site of the continent's largest and most active volcano, Mount Erebus, 12,450 feet high. On its western side, at Cape Royds, it harbors a group of Adélies in the world's southernmost penguin rookery; at Cape Evans, several miles south of Cape Royds, the world's southernmost skua rookery; and on its eastern side, on the ice shelf just off Cape Crozier, the world's southernmost Emperor penguin rookery.

On the southern end of the island, the world's southernmost land accessible by ship, is the continent's largest and most populous station.

McMurdo Station is the United States's prime logistic base for the nation's inland stations and is the center of the nation's scientific research in Antarctica. The station contains the continent's sole nuclear plant and its largest building. Some two miles east of McMurdo Station, on the opposite side of Cape Armitage, is its relatively small but scientifically very active and productive neighbor, New Zealand's Scott Base. Six or seven miles from McMurdo Station is one of the world's most remarkable airfields, Williams Field, built on the floating ice of the Ross Ice Shelf.

Above all, Ross Island is fascinating for the numerous and important historical events which have occurred on or near it and for the remarkable stature of certain of the actors in them. In this respect it surpasses any other place on the continent. The visitor to Ross Island is fortunate to be intimately exposed to a profound sense of the Antarctic past and to the influence of heroic times and men. Both Robert Falcon Scott (1868–1912) and Ernest Shackleton (1874–1922) used the island as the base for their polar explorations. Scott's two huts at Hut Point and Cape Evans and Shackleton's hut at Cape Royds are still intact. All three are protected as historic sites under the Antarctic Treaty.

The island was discovered by James Clark Ross (1800–62), a British explorer who also discovered the Ross Sea and the Ross Ice Shelf and who named many of the most conspicuous features of the island and its vicinity: Mount Erebus, Mount Terror, Cape Crozier, Cape Bird, McMurdo Bay (renamed McMurdo Sound by Scott's first expedition), Victoria Land, Beaufort Island and Franklin Island. On his first expedition (the National Antarctic Expedition) Scott named the island in honor of Ross. The rare Ross seal is also named after him.

Ross entered the Royal Navy at the age of twelve. He was a member of several important Arctic expeditions. At the age of thirty-one he discovered the north magnetic pole. He commanded the *Erebus* and the *Terror* during the Antarctic expedition of 1839–43. On this voyage he conducted experiments in terrestrial magnetism and gathered much important data on the behavior of magnetic compasses in the high southern latitudes. Also, he attempted to reach the south magnetic pole. His hope of being the discoverer of both magnetic poles was frustrated by the fact that the south magnetic pole was not attainable by sea, being located in Victoria Land, and by the dangerous lateness of the season, which made it imperative that he return north without an attempt to winter over on the continent. It was while intrepidly drawing ever closer to the pole that he broke through a wide belt of pack ice into the unsuspected, large and clear sea that was to bear his name.

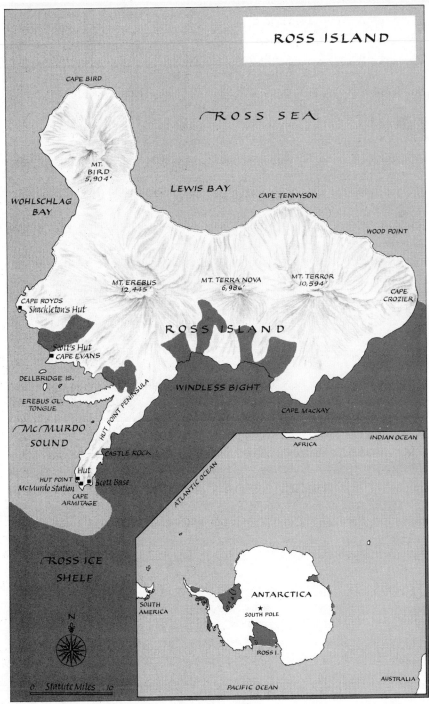

ROSS ISLAND

CAPE BIRD

ROSS SEA

MT. BIRD
5,904'

LEWIS BAY

CAPE TENNYSON

WOHLSCHLAG
BAY

WOOD POINT

MT. EREBUS
12,445'

MT. TERRA NOVA
6,986'

MT. TERROR
10,594'

CAPE ROYDS
Shackleton's Hut

CAPE
CROZIER

ROSS ISLAND

Scott's Hut
CAPE EVANS

DELLBRIDGE IS.

WINDLESS BIGHT

EREBUS GL.
TONGUE

CAPE MACKAY

McMURDO
SOUND

HUT POINT PENINSULA

CASTLE ROCK

AFRICA

INDIAN OCEAN

ATLANTIC OCEAN

HUT POINT
McMurdo Station

Hut
Scott Base

CAPE
ARMITAGE

ATLANTIC OCEAN

ROSS ICE
SHELF

ANTARCTICA

SOUTH POLE

N

SOUTH
AMERICA

ROSS I.

0   Statute Miles   10

AUSTRALIA

PACIFIC OCEAN

MAP DESIGN: CHARLES NEIDER; CARTOGRAPHY: RAFAEL D. PALACIOS

He discovered Ross Island in January 1841. Writing in his book, *A Voyage of Discovery and Research in the Southern and Antarctic Regions,* Ross described the first sighting of the island.

"With a favourable breeze, and very clear weather, we stood to the southward, close to some land which had been in sight since the preceding noon [January 26], and which we then called the 'High Island'; it proved to be a mountain twelve thousand four hundred feet of elevation above the level of the sea, emitting flame and smoke in great profusion; at first the smoke appeared like snow drift, but as we drew nearer, its true character became manifest."

This is still the largest eruption of Mount Erebus to be witnessed and recorded.

Although Ross made landfalls at Possession and Franklin Islands in the Ross Sea, he made none at Ross Island, which remained untouched by man for sixty-one more years. On January 21, 1902, Scott, in the ship *Discovery* (of about 700 tons and specially built for Antarctic work), with a crew of some fifty men, became the first explorer since Ross to make his way into McMurdo Sound. The Sound, which lies between Ross Island and Victoria Land, is forty miles wide at its entrance and is approximately fifty miles long. Its southern terminus is the Ross Ice Shelf and the ice sheet of the Koettlitz Glacier.

Scott's National Antarctic Expedition (1901–4), often referred to as the Discovery Expedition, was sponsored chiefly by the Royal Geographical Society. Like Ross's expedition and numerous Antarctic expeditions both before and after Ross's, it had two main goals: geographical and scientific exploration. During this visit to the Sound, Scott wondered about the possible advantages of setting up winter quarters to the eastward. He was seeking a sheltered place, yet one that would provide him with more than local meteorological data and that would afford him ready access to the south. He planned to explore the Ross Ice Shelf (known as the Ice Barrier or the Barrier at that time), as well as to sledge in the direction of the geographic pole.

Turning north, he sailed around Cape Bird to Cape Crozier, examining the coastline from the ship, then proceeded eastward for several days alongside the imposing cliffs of the ice shelf. Finding no satisfactory harbor, he returned to McMurdo Sound, where on February 8 he decided to winter at Hut Point, the southwestern extremity of Ross Island. The Discovery Hut was constructed during February and the early part of March.

Scott devoted almost his entire life to the service of the Royal Navy. He had become a naval cadet at thirteen, a midshipman at fifteen and a full lieutenant at twenty-three He was reticent, sensitive and moody. His intelligence and admirable personal style marked him as a leader. He was a naval commander when he was selected to head the Discovery Expedition.

During the expedition he introduced a number of Fridtjof Nansen's Arctic techniques into Antarctic work and opened the era of full-scale land exploration of the continent, using sledging traverses. He made many geographical discoveries, among them Edward VII Land, which much later was found to be a peninsula and was renamed accordingly. He also discovered and named Mount Discovery, the Royal Society Range and many important landmarks among the "Western Mountains." The Western Mountains was the name often used by him for the chain of mountains (part of the Transantarctic Mountains), beautifully visible from McMurdo Station, on the western side of McMurdo Sound. He, Ernest Shackleton and Edward A. Wilson sledged to a new farthest south of 82° 17' on December 30, 1902.

It was the Discovery Expedition that named many of the features of Ross Island. Scott wrote in *The Voyage of the "Discovery"*:

"Names have been given to various landmarks in our vicinity. The end of our peninsula is to be called 'Cape Armitage,' after our excellent navigator. The sharp hill above it is to be 'Observation Hill'; it is 750 feet high, and should make an excellent look-out station for observing the going and coming of sledge-parties. Next comes the 'Gap,' through which we can cross the peninsula at a comparatively low level. North of the 'Gap' are 'Crater Heights,' and the higher volcanic peak beyond is to be 'Crater Hill'; it is 1,050 feet in height. Our protecting promontory is to be 'Hut Point,' with 'Arrival Bay' on the north and 'Winter Quarters Bay' on the south; above 'Arrival Bay' are the 'Arrival Heights,' which continue with breaks for about three miles to a long snow-slope, beyond which rises the most conspicuous landmark on our peninsula, a high precipitous-sided rock with a flat top, which has been dubbed 'Castle Rock'; it is 1,350 feet in height."

On the return trek from the new southing Shackleton came down with scurvy complicated by the coughing of blood, and Wilson, a doctor, had fears for his life. Scott seemed to feel that Shackleton had let the party down, even though he realized that Shackleton's illness was as disappointing and disagreeable to Shackleton as to himself. Shackleton was invalided home in March 1903 with a taint of disgrace, as if he had failed to meet the rigors of a polar traverse. After his recovery he mounted his own expedition although he had difficulty in getting it financed. When he asked Scott if he could use the latter's Discovery Hut as his base, Scott declined, explaining that he himself hoped to use it in the not distant future.

Shackleton's British Antarctic Expedition left England on the *Nimrod* in 1907. Shackleton hoped to base himself on the Ross Ice Shelf off the Bay of Whales but on examining the ice there decided it was too dangerous. He thereupon sailed to Ross Island, where he found he could penetrate the sea ice only as far south as Cape Royds, some twenty-two miles north of Hut Point. He settled on this cape, where he built his now famous hut. On January 9, 1909, he and three companions made a southing to within ninety-seven geographical miles (almost 112 statute miles) of the Pole, in the process pioneering the Beardmore Glacier route over the Transantarctic Mountains. The party barely made it back to Ross Island. In his work of laying depots and at the beginning and end of the great traverse Shackleton made use of the Discovery Hut. He first revisited the hut August 14, 1908.

"It was very interesting to me to revisit the old scenes," he wrote in *The Heart of the Antarctic*. "There was the place where, years before, when the *Discovery* was lying fast in the ice close to the shore, we used to dig for the ice that was required for the supply of fresh water. The marks of the picks and shovels were still to be seen. I noticed an old case bedded in the ice, and remembered the day when it had been thrown away. Round the hut was collected a very large amount of *débris,* including seal-skins and the skeletons of seals and penguins. Some of the seal-skins had still blubber attached, though the skuas had evidently been at work on them. . . . The old hut had never been a cheerful place, even when we were camped alongside it in the *Discovery,* and it looked doubly inhospitable now, after having stood empty and neglected for six years. One side was filled with cases of biscuit and tinned meat and the snow that had found its way in was lying in great piles around the walls. There was no stove, for this had been taken away with the *Discovery,* and coal was scattered about the floor with other *débris* and rubbish."

Shackelton's expedition accomplished important work in addition to the new southing. For example, it made the first ascent of Mount Erebus and it reached the south magnetic pole. At that time the latter was some 375 statute air miles northwest of Cape Royds.

Scott's second and last expedition (the British Antarctic Expedition, 1910–13), left England in June 1910 on the *Terra Nova* and reached McMurdo Sound in the first week of January 1911. Unable because of ice conditions that year to base himself again at Hut Point, Scott chose a cape known as "The Skuary," some fifteen miles to the north, for his base. He renamed the cape Cape Evans in honor of his second in command, Lieutenant E. R. G. R. Evans. Like the great eighteenth-century English explorer and navigator James Cook, Scott was much interested in the scientific work of his expeditions, to such an extent that he often tempered the fevers of geographical exploration in order to gather and retain the materials for scientific investigation. But always his and the British nation's prime hope for this expedition was the discovery of the South Pole.

The Discovery Hut was again destined to be used as a staging post for depot-laying parties and as a jumping-off base in an attempt to reach the Pole. Scott revisited it January 15, 1911. He was appalled by its condition. He wrote in his journal:

"Shackelton reported that the door had been forced by the wind, but that he had made an entrance by the window and found shelter inside—other members of his party used it for shelter. But they actually went away and left the window (which they had forced) open; as a result, nearly the whole of the interior of the hut is filled with hard icy snow, and it is now impossible to find shelter inside. . . . There was something too depressing in finding the old hut in such a desolate condition. . . . To camp outside and feel that all the old comfort and cheer had departed, was dreadfully heartrending. I went to bed thoroughly depressed. It seems a fundamental expression of civilised human sentiment that men who come to such places as this should leave what comfort they can to welcome those who follow, and finding that such a simple duty had been neglected by our immediate predecessors oppressed me horribly."

By March 7, after some hard work, the hut had been put into good condition again. On November 3, 1911, Scott and four companions—Edward A. Wilson, Henry R. Bowers, Lawrence E. G. Oates and Edgar Evans—left the hut for the last time. They reached the Pole January 18, 1912, only to find they had been bested by Roald Amundsen, the Norwegian explorer. Their return journey was beset by illness, hunger and blizzards. Evans died February 17 at the foot of the Beardmore Glacier. On March 16 Oates walked out of the tent into a blizzard in the hope of saving those more physically fit. Scott, Wilson and Bowers pitched their final camp only some eleven miles from One Ton Depot on the Ross Ice Shelf (about a hundred and fifty miles from Hut Point) but were hopelessly blizzarded in. In a great naval tradition of keeping logs under the most adverse conditions, Scott kept writing his journal until close to the end. Also, he wrote several letters to friends and colleagues explaining what had gone wrong and crediting his sledging companions with noble behavior under heartbreaking conditions. He referred to himself and his companions as dead men but there was no self-pity and little self-concern in either the journals or the letters. His outlook remained broad to the end.

On November 12, 1912, a search party discovered the tent, containing his body and those of Wilson and Bowers, as well as his records, letters and journals. On the sledge were thirty-five pounds of geological specimens, gathered on the Beardmore Glacier, that the party had declined to abandon despite the fact that for a long time they had been exhausting themselves in manhauling.

The Discovery Hut was to play still other important roles during the heroic era of exploration of the continent. After hearing that Amundsen had reached the Pole, Shackleton concluded that "there remained but one great main object of Antarctic journeyings—the crossing of the South Polar continent from sea to sea." The route he chose was from the Weddell Sea to McMurdo Sound. In 1914 he commanded the British Imperial Trans-Antarctic Expedition in the hope of achieving this goal. He failed to achieve it but as with Scott the failure was in some respects a glorious one: a triumph of the human spirit over great adversities. His ship *Endurance* was trapped by ice in the Weddell Sea, drifted ten months and was eventually crushed. The crew thereupon lived on an ice floe for almost five months, drifting northward. Finally escaping by whaleboats which they had saved from the *Endurance,* they reached deserted Elephant Island. Shackleton and five companions then set out in an open boat to seek help, crossing eight hundred miles of Antarctic waters to South Georgia, where they became the first men to traverse the island's high, dangerous mountains in their journey to the Norwegian whaling station on the opposite side of the island. The men stranded on Elephant Island were rescued, but only on the fourth attempt. One of the extraordinary facts of the Weddell Sea part of the expedition is that not one life was lost.

The McMurdo Sound section, however, lost three men, including its leader, Aeneas L. A. Mackintosh, captain of the *Aurora.* Mackintosh had been charged by Shackleton with the task of laying depots from Ross Island to the foot of the Beardmore Glacier, down which Shackleton planned to make his traverse after reaching the Pole. The depots were duly laid but under terrible conditions and with inexperienced dogs, many of whom died. The Discovery Hut was often used as a base of operations. Ironically, the Mackintosh party, ignorant of Shackleton's plight, did not know that the depots were now useless to him.

The major effort in depot-laying began in September 1915. It was carried out by six men, one of whom, the Reverend A. P. Spencer-Smith, died on the return trek from a combination of scurvy and exhaustion. The others, all suffering from scurvy, holed up in the Discovery Hut on March 18 with inadequate food, fuel and clothes. Their main base was Scott's hut at Cape Evans but they did not dare to venture toward it over the still soft sea ice. (The land route was considered to be even more treacherous than the sea one.) Mackintosh and V. G. Hayward, having grown impatient, set out on May 8 for Cape Evans despite the warnings of other members of the party. Expecting to reach Cape Evans in a matter of hours, they did not carry a tent or sleeping bags with them. Shortly after their departure a blizzard blew up. They were not heard from again. It was presumed that they either fell through the ice or were blown out to sea on a floe.

On July 15 the remaining three men at Hut Point made a safe traverse over the sea ice to Cape Evans, where, together with four other companions already on the cape, they spent the rest of their second winter in the Scott hut. They were all rescued in mid-January 1917 by the *Aurora*.

Shackleton died of angina pectoris in South Georgia at the beginning of his fourth Antarctic expedition. His death, on January 5, 1922, at the early age of forty-eight, may be said to mark the close of the heroic era.

As far as is known, man did not visit either Ross Island or McMurdo Sound for a full thirty years after the *Aurora* sailed in 1917 for New Zealand. Then, late in February 1947, members of the U.S. Navy's Operation High Jump, a task force that had recently established Little America IV at the Bay of Whales, landed at Hut Point to survey the possibility of setting up an auxiliary base there. Although Admiral Richard E. Byrd, accompanying the task force, did not himself land on Ross Island, he described the landing in the October 1947 issue of the *National Geographic* magazine.

"Scott's camp might have been abandoned only a few weeks ago. The prefabricated cabin . . . still stood in perfect condition. The timbers looked as if freshly sawn. Printed directions for putting them together, which were found pasted on one wall, might just have come from the press.

"A hitching rope which Scott had used for his ponies was so completely undeteriorated after 43 years that it was used without hesitation to secure the helicopter in which Admiral Cruzen had flown from ship to shore. A few sealskins scattered about looked new. Cartons of biscuits still were edible, although rather tasteless.

"And there was the 'latest news.' A Russian army was invading the Pamirs, according to the headlines of a British news magazine found in the ice. Paper and print looked as if the publication had come from the press only a few days before. But this journal had been printed in 1892."

Members of the task force also landed at Cape Evans, and Admiral Byrd described the hut there.

"It appeared somewhat disorderly after the buffeting of 35 winters. Snow had drifted through cracks in the planks of the sealed cabin. Straw and debris were strewn over the nearly ice-free volcanic ash.

"The frozen carcass of a dog stood on four legs as if it were alive. Seal carcasses from which fresh steaks might have been cut lay about. Scattered around the cabin were cartons of provisions, still good to eat. A box of matches ignited easily."

A year later members of Operation Windmill toured the huts briefly, after which Ross Island was not visited by man until late in December 1955, when Operation Deep Freeze I established a base in preparation for the extensive and continent-wide scientific activities of the International Geophysical Year of 1957–58. Hut Point was selected as the site in January, and the base was called Naval Air Facility McMurdo, McMurdo being Archibald McMurdo, a lieutenant on the *Terror*, in honor of whom Ross named McMurdo Bay. Ten-man and thirty-two-man tents formed a tent camp until prefabricated buildings could be unloaded and erected. The camp rose in the immediate vicinity of the Discovery Hut. Then Clements huts went up, the chapel was built, a supply dump and a tank farm were constructed, and "downtown" McMurdo, today the western-most part of the station, overlooking the historic hut across the anchorage of Winter Quarters Bay, was born. After the Richard T. Williams tragedy (referred to later), Admiral George J. Dufek, at the chaplain's suggestion, officially named the base Williams Air Operating Facility, McMurdo Sound, Antarctica.

That early form of the station comprised some thirty buildings, including the kennels, a parachute loft, an inflation shelter, VIP quarters and a hut designated as "Aerology." One of the easternmost buildings was the Quonset chapel. The first wintering-over party at the station (1956) consisted of ninety-three men.

The United States scientific program during the IGY was administered by the United States Committee for the International Geophysical Year of the National Academy of Sciences. The Antarctic part of the program was conducted with the logistic support of the United States Navy. At the conclusion of the IGY, the National Science Foundation, an independent federal agency established in 1950, assumed the responsibility for United States Antarctic research.

The great scientific successes of the IGY spurred new and continuous scientific work on the continent, and gradually what was at first envisioned as a temporary central base took on a look of semipermanence. The station began to climb the adjacent volcanic hills and experienced the introduction of metal-frame buildings, a nuclear plant, graded roads, power lines and even waves of "urban renewal." It was renamed McMurdo Station in 1961.

If one were to take a walking tour of the station and its environs, including Scott Base, one might do best to begin at Scott's Discovery Hut (see map) and work back toward the center of the station. In the austral summer there's a bustle as cargo ships unload near the hut but at other times the hut sits silent and remote. It is spacious (some thirty-six feet square) and has a pyramidal roof and overhanging eaves. It was brought from Australia and was the kind of bungalow used by Australian frontier settlers of the time. Inasmuch as the ship *Discovery* was iced in and available as living quarters, the hut was not lived in during Scott's first expedition. It was used for such purposes as drying furs, skinning birds, refitting awnings and for the rehearsal and performance of various theatrical entertainments, complete with scenes and footlights. It was also utilized for gravity observations made by the swinging of pendulums.

Both Hut Point and Hut Point Peninsula derive their names from the famous hut which stands here, overlooking Winter Quarters Bay, McMurdo Station, Observation Hill, Cape Armitage, McMurdo Sound and the Western Mountains. During Scott's first expedition the hut had no formal name but when Scott returned for his second expedition he always referred to the hut as the Discovery Hut. The hut is probably the most important single historic site on the entire continent, and visitors to McMurdo are specially privileged to be able to enter and inspect it. Over the years it became filled with ice and compacted snow. It was restored in 1963 and 1964 by members of the New Zealand Antarctic Society, with the help of the United States Navy.

Scott wrote in *The Voyage of the "Discovery"*:

"It was obvious that some sort of shelter must be made on shore before exploring parties could be sent away with safety, as we felt that at any

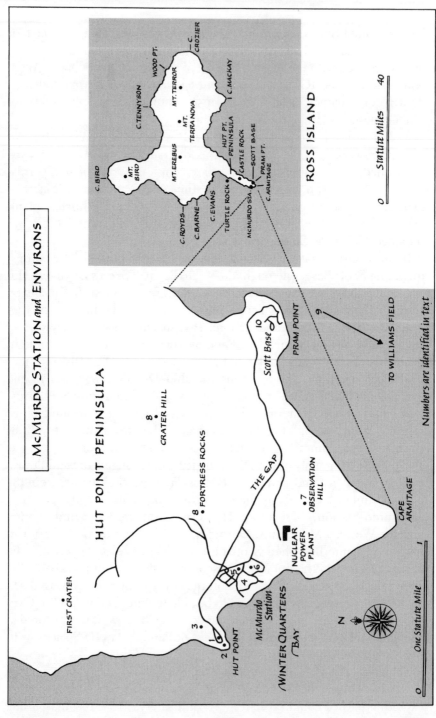

McMurdo STATION and ENVIRONS

HUT POINT PENINSULA

FIRST CRATER

CRATER HILL
8

FORTRESS ROCKS
8

THE GAP

OBSERVATION HILL
7

NUCLEAR POWER PLANT

HUT POINT
2
3

WINTER QUARTERS BAY

McMurdo Station

5
4
6

N

Scott Base
10

PRAM POINT

CAPE ARMITAGE

9

TO WILLIAMS FIELD

Numbers are identified in text

0   One Statute Mile   1

ROSS ISLAND

C. BIRD
MT. BIRD

C. ROYDS

C. BARNE

C. EVANS

MT. EREBUS

TURTLE ROCK

WOOD PT.

MT. TERROR

C. TENNYSON

MT. TERRA NOVA

C. CROZIER

C. MACKAY

HUT PT. PENINSULA

CASTLE ROCK

SCOTT BASE

PRAM PT.

C. ARMITAGE

McMURDO STA.

0   Statute Miles   40

MAP DESIGN: CHARLES NEIDER; CARTOGRAPHY: RAFAEL D. PALACIOS

time a heavy gale might drive the ship off her station for several days, if not altogether. With the hut erected and provisioned, there need be no anxiety for a detached party in such circumstances. . . . We found, however, that its construction was no light task, as all the main and verandah supports were designed to be sunk three or four feet in the ground. We soon found a convenient site close to the ship on a small bare plateau of volcanic rubble, but an inch or two below the surface the soil was frozen hard, and many an hour was spent with pick, shovel, and crowbar before the solid supports were erected and our able carpenter could get to work on the frame.

"In addition to the main hut, and of greater importance, were the two small huts which we had brought for our magnetic instruments. These consisted of a light skeleton framework of wood covered with sheets of asbestos."

The smaller huts are no longer extant.

Approximately ninety yards southwest of the Discovery Hut is Vince's Cross (2), made of wood and erected in 1902 to commemorate Seaman George T. Vince, the first man to lose his life in McMurdo Sound. One of a party of nine that got caught in a blizzard and decided to make their way back to the ship instead of lying low, Vince, unfortunately wearing fur-soled boots, with little traction, slid down what was later to be called Danger Slope and plunged off its cliff into the Sound. His body was never recovered.

Scott wrote: "Tuesday, March 11, was to be one of our blackest days in the Antarctic. . . . From the moment when he joined us at the Cape of Good Hope, Vince had been popular with all; always obliging and always cheerful, I learnt that he had never shown these qualities more markedly than during the short sledge journey which brought him to his untimely end. His pleasant face and ready wit served to dispel the thought of hardship and difficulty to the end. Life was a bright thing to him, and it is something to think that death must have come quickly in the grip of that icy sea."

Almost miraculously, no other member of the group was permanently injured, although a seaman of eighteen named Hare fell asleep and lay under the snow for about thirty-six hours, yet was free of frostbite. He went forty hours without food and sixty without warm food.

Some 330 yards northeast of the Discovery Hut is Our Lady of the Snows Shrine (3), built by United States Navy personnel in 1956. The small rock cairn with the statue of the Virgin Mary honors the memory of Richard T. Williams, a Seabee tractor driver who drowned off Cape

Royds when his Caterpillar D-8 tractor broke through the sea ice on January 6 of that year. Williams went down about two miles west of Royds while he was en route to Cape Evans. His tractor crossed a bridge over a crack in the bay ice and was twenty feet beyond when a section of ice broke and the vehicle fell through. The tractor weighed more than thirty tons. Its escape hatch and side door were locked open, but the machine went down so rapidly Williams was unable to escape. It was after this tragedy that the Navy decided to use a sea-ice runway at Hut Point for its aircraft rather than one that was planned for Cape Evans. When the McMurdo base became known as McMurdo Station, the station's unusual airfield was named Williams Field.

From the Discovery Hut one can make one's way to old McMurdo (4) over Hut Point Road, which flanks the western and northern shores of Winter Quarters Bay. The oldest parts of the station, excluding the chapel, are the western and southern sections. Here stood the original mess hall, the library, the administration building, the medical quarters and the kennels. Standing in front of the Press Hut, one can look out over the anchorage and the historic hut and see the Western Mountains, whose distant peaks and glaciers endlessly fascinate one because, as a result of variations in snowfall, cloud cover, humidity and the position of the sun, they seem to change almost hourly. The Press Hut is an example of one of the old Jamesways, a green, tentlike, round-topped structure of prefabricated wood and insulated canvas, almost windowless, heated by two oil-fired units and containing several tiny semi-private cubicles.

Of The Chapel of the Snows (5), Admiral George J. Dufek wrote in *Operation Deepfreeze,* "It had been planned to hold religious services in the mess hall [in 1956] because there were no plans or materials for a church. But as the construction of the buildings at McMurdo progressed, a mysterious pile of lumber, planks, nails, Quonset hut sections, and assorted materials began to accumulate on a knoll overlooking the camp." The chaplain and some volunteers had begun gathering odds and ends for a church that the chaplain believed to be the first ever to be erected in Antarctica. In that year Father John C. Condit's parish was by far the world's southernmost. The chapel was constructed by volunteer labor. Dufek wrote, "The men, after a hard day's work, would drift over to the church site. Before the main camp was finished a tidy neat church with a steeple was to stand on a ridge overlooking the dump. Later it even had a bell, procured from a small gasoline tanker."

The Richard E. Byrd Memorial (6), standing just south of the chapel, is a bronze bust of Admiral Byrd on a polished black Norwegian marble pedestal. It was donated by the National Geographic Society and erected in October 1965.

As almost everyone knows, Byrd (1888-1957) was one of Antarctica's greatest explorers. More than any other person, he was responsible for the introduction into and wide use of aircraft on the continent. He led five successive Antarctic expeditions, beginning with the expedition of 1928-30. During this expedition he constructed the station Little America on the Ross Ice Shelf near the site of Amundsen's old base off the Bay of Whales, and made numerous geographical discoveries, including the Rockefeller Mountains, Marie Byrd Land (named in honor of his wife), and the Edsel Ford Mountains (now called the Ford Ranges). It was on November 29, 1929, that he first flew over the South Pole and became the first person to fly over both geographic poles.

Returning to Antarctica in 1934, he made other significant geographical discoveries. It was during this second expedition that he wintered over alone at Bolling Advance Weather Station on the ice shelf some 125 miles south of Little America. It appears from his narrative that he not only wanted to take weather readings of the continent's interior but to experience the extreme solitude of a solitary winter over. This was the kind of human exploration reminiscent of Scott's insistent desire to see how far the human body could be pushed short of disaster during manhauled traverses.

An aloof, reserved member of an old Virginia family, Byrd was reluctant to publish the personal details of the near-tragedy that overtook him at Bolling station but was persuaded by friends and colleagues to do so. His narrative is one of the finest to come out of the continent. He belongs to that select group of well-educated, intelligent, gifted and imaginative naval officers (beginning with Cook and including Scott and Shackleton) who produced first-rate narratives out of their Antarctic experiences.

He came close to dying from carbon monoxide poisoning at Bolling station but tried to keep his condition a secret from Little America because he feared that men would risk their lives in a mid-winter rescue attempt if his true state became known. His increasingly erratic and irrational radio messages during the scheduled radio contacts gave him away and a successful rescue attempt was made.

The more athletically inclined visitor to McMurdo will find a climb of Observation Hill (7), about 750 feet high, rewarding for the beautiful panoramic views it affords. Approximately halfway up the hill, reached by a modern road, are the buildings of the nuclear plant (PM-3A), whose construction was authorized by Congress in 1960. The plant arrived at its destination December 12, 1961, and went critical March 3, 1962. It has an electric output of 1,800 kilowatts gross. All nuclear wastes are returned to the continental United States for disposal in conformity with the requirements of the Antarctic Treaty.

On top of the hill stands a great cross, made of Australian jarrah wood, in memory of Scott and his four companions. It was erected by members of Scott's last expedition, who took two days to carry it to the hill's crest. Apsley Cherry-Garrard, a young member of the expedition and the author of the classic account, *The Worst Journey in the World*, wrote of the Polar Party Cross:

"There was some discussion as to the inscription, it being urged that there should be some quotation from the Bible because 'the women think a lot of these things.' But I was glad to see the concluding line of Tennyson's 'Ulysses' adopted: 'To strive, to seek, to find, and not to yield.' . . . We went up Observation Hill and have found a good spot right on the top, and have already dug a hole which will, with the rock alongside, give us three feet. . . . Observation Hill was clearly the place for it, it knew them all so well. Three of them were Discovery men who lived three years under its shadow: they had seen it time after time as they came back from hard journeys on the Barrier: Observation Hill and Castle Rock were the two which always welcomed them in. It commanded McMurdo Sound on one side, where they had lived: and the Barrier on the other, where they had died. No more fitting pedestal, a pedestal which in itself is nearly 1000 feet high, could have been found.

"*Tuesday, January 22.* Rousing out at 6 A.M. we got the large piece of the cross up Observation Hill by 11 A.M. It was a heavy job, and the ice was looking very bad all round, and I for one was glad when we had got it up by 5 o'clock or so. It is really magnificent, and will be a permanent memorial which could be seen from the ship nine miles off with a naked eye. It stands nine feet out of the rocks, and many feet into the ground, and I do not believe it will ever move. When it was up, facing out over the Barrier, we gave three cheers and one more."

From the cross one can see in all directions. Mount Erebus, not visible from McMurdo Station, is the great landmark in the north. One can see Crater Hill, Crater Heights, the Gap, Williams Field, and the green huts of Scott Base at Pram Point.

Even finer views of the environs are provided by the crest of Crater Hill (8), approximately one thousand feet high. On the way to Crater Hill the visitor may wish to pause at Fortress Rocks (8), located in the outlying area behind McMurdo, between the Gap and Middle Crater (Middle Crater is between Ski Slope and Crater Hill). The descriptive name for these rocks was supplied by members of Scott's last expedition. The rocks are now the station's quarry.

Scott climbed Crater Hill numerous times during his first expedition. In *The Voyage of the "Discovery"* he left a detailed description of the views from the hill the fourth week in August.

"With full daylight each detail of our landscape once more stands clear, and the view from Crater Hill is magnificent.

"From Arrival Bay a line of rocky ridges runs towards Castle Rock, facing the north-west and gradually rising in height, with four distinct eminences, of which two are well-formed craters; the fourth is almost on a level with Crater Hill, and therefore nearly touches the sky-line; behind it Castle Rock, rising to 1,350 feet, shows in sharp precipitous outline, a black shadow against the snowy background of Erebus. It is a high, hilly country, this foreground, with many a black mass of rock and many a slope of smooth white snow; in itself it might be called a fine rugged scene, but how dwarfed it all is by that mighty mountain behind, which, in spite of its twenty geographical miles of distance, seems to frown down upon us. Even Castle Rock, with its near bold eminence, is but a pigmy to this giant mass, which from its broad spreading foot-slopes rises, with fold on fold of snowy whiteness, to its crater summit, where, 13,000 feet above the sea [Mount Erebus is actually 12,450 feet high], it is crowned with a golden cloud of rolling vapour.

"The eastern slope of Erebus dips to a high saddle-backed divide, beyond which the snowy outline rises to the summit of Terror, whence a long slope runs gradually down to sea-level far to the east. From point to point these two huge mountains fill up nearly 90° of our horizon, and from this southern side offer almost a complete prospect of snow-covered land. Beyond Castle Rock commences the low isthmus which connects our small peninsula to the main island, and as it bends slightly to the east it can be seen from Crater Hill. In running towards the right slope of Erebus and gradually broadening to its foot-slopes, it sweeps out on either side a huge bay. . . .

"Looking to the eastward from Crater Hill, one has Pram Point almost beneath one's feet, and one gets a good view of the regular parallel ridges that fringe the coast; beyond these ridges stretches the immeasurable barrier surface, limited to the eye by one long clear sweep of perfectly regular horizon stretching from the eastern slopes of Terror through more than 70° of arc to the eastern slope of White Island. . . .

"Meanwhile the eye has passed on to scan that great frowning range of mountains to the west which has looked down on us in such ghostly, weird fashion throughout the winter months. Seen now in the daylight, what a wild confusion of peaks and precipices, foothills, snowfields, and glaciers it presents! How vast it all is! and how magnificent must be those mountains when one is close beneath them! . . .

"Finally, from the vantage point of Crater Hill one can now obtain an excellent bird's-eye view of our own snug winter quarters. Even from this distance the accumulation of snow which has caused us so much trouble can be seen; the ship looks to be half buried, and a white mantle has spread over the signs of our autumn labours and over the masses of refuse ahead of the ship. Hodgson's biological shelters show as faint shadowed spots, and numerous sharp black dots show that our people are abroad and that work is being pushed ahead.

"Over all the magnificent view, the sunlight spreads with gorgeous effect after its long absence; a soft pink envelops the western ranges, a brilliant red gold covers the northern sky; to the north also each crystal of snow sparkles with reflected light. The sky shows every gradation of light and shade; little flakes of golden sunlit cloud float against the pale blue heaven, and seem to hover in the middle heights, whilst far above them a feathery white cirrus shades to grey on its unlit sides."

Williams Field (9) is roughly half a dozen miles from McMurdo by bus. It comprises a large airfield complex that includes a skiway, the adjacent camp (both skiway and camp are on the ice shelf), ice runways for wheeled aircraft on the sea ice and, at a greater distance, also on the ice shelf. It is the focal point of aerial support provided to inland stations. Through it Antarctic Development Squadron Six (VXE-6) maintains air links between the interior of the continent and the outside world.

The site of Scott Base (10), which is about two miles by road from McMurdo Station, was selected by Edmund Hillary, one of the two men (the other was Tenzing Norkay) to make the first ascent of Mount Everest (May 1953). He selected it for two reasons: as a scientific station for the IGY, and as the Ross Island base of the British Commonwealth Transantarctic Expedition, whose goal was Shackleton's old one of traversing the continent from the Weddell Sea to the Ross Sea via the Pole. Hillary led his nation's section of the expedition. His main task was to set up depots from Ross Island to the Pole to support Vivian Fuchs's party, which would make the full traverse. Hillary reached the Pole in a tractor January 4, 1958, becoming, after Scott, the first man to reach the Pole overland.

The station was constructed in 1957. Hillary was a member of its first wintering-over team. During the IGY, Scott Base conducted almost all the scientific research in the McMurdo area. It was not until after the conclusion of the IGY that McMurdo Station began its scientific work.

If Ross Island is indeed one of the most fascinating places in Antarctica, as I hope this chapter has shown, it follows, given the nature of the continent, that the island is also one of the most fascinating places in the world. I was almost painfully impatient to return to it and to experience it as richly and as fully as I was able so I could bring back an authentic account not only of human life and work there but of that awesome extra dimension that goes far beyond man: a sense of the primeval mystery, of unutterable beauty, of unbelievable silence and solitude, of looking out into the universe's spaces while experiencing a humbling regeneration of one's soul.

CHAPTER 3

MCMURDO STATION: ONE

What a contrast there was between my two flights from the vicinity of Washington, D.C., to Christchurch! The first, as I have mentioned, was in an Air Force C-141, called the Starlifter. This giant craft squatted low, its wing almost touching the ground, suggesting the wing of a gull that has just landed. It had a very high tail.

Pipes, tubing, girders overhead; a raw metal floor; two tiers of rudimentary seats, three abreast, facing backwards for safety; very few windows; bright little spotlights everywhere; transparent plastic tubing hanging from the walls, attached to plastic masks in gray plastic cases (these were the auxiliary oxygen supply, to be used in case the craft's pressurization system failed); irregular heating; and a terrific ceaseless noise, a compound of grinding, hissing and bass roaring, rarely varying in pitch or intensity.

At times the noise created a welcome solitude. You became a bit unapproachable when people had to risk hoarseness to converse with you, and they tended to select their words more carefully than usual. Still, some things had to be said even if shouted, such as the claim that Admiral Byrd had once asked, "How do you get a four-inch pecker out of six inches of Antarctic clothing?"

We faced our altar, a mountain of luggage and cargo chained, webbed and plastic-sheeted as though like a maniac it might go berserk and commit unspeakable crimes. At 35,000 feet, mostly on autopilot, we chewed up space in a hurry. Flight time between Dulles Airport and Travis Air Force Base in California: about five hours. A two-hour refuel stop at Travis. Flight time from Travis to Hickam Air Force Base in Hawaii: some six hours. We spent part of the night at Hickam. Flight time between Hickam and Pago Pago: about five and a half hours. Another two-hour refuel stop. Flight time from Pago Pago to Christchurch: approximately four and a half hours.

We mocked the globe's vastness. In doing so we mocked our human nature. Pago Pago had the quality of a dream. We took photographs which we hoped would tell us what we should have experienced.

Our quarters in Christchurch were at the luxurious White Heron Motel near Harewood Airport.

My second flight was in a beat-up C-121, Operation Deep Freeze's last surviving Super Constellation, called *Phoenix 6*. The Connie, which felt small and fragile, looked like a used-up sheep dog. Its triple tail, painted red and outlined in black, like the rest of the craft seemed to be begging for retirement.

A grooved, fluted aluminum floor; bucket seats with dirty orange cloth bags hanging on the backs; an arched, dusty-blue ceiling with a row of shielded lights down the middle; an emergency ladder hanging from the ceiling on one side. When eating (the craft was crowded) you felt on the verge of disaster: one wrong gesture and you could have a lapful of gravy to contend with. Your motions were as cautious as those of a brain surgeon.

We took almost eleven and a half hours to get from Andrews Air Force Base to Alameda Naval Air Station in California. Normal flight time for the Connie was ten hours but the plane bucked headwinds. I spent the night at Alameda, sharing a room with Bill Cobb, whom I knew from Skyland. At breakfast we met Dale Vance, who had flown in from Boulder. Vance was a tall, handsome man with a charming laugh that sometimes broke into a giggle. He said he was eager to begin his long stretch at the Russians' Vostok Station.

We lifted off at 9:15 A.M. It took us ten hours and fifteen minutes to fly to Barber's Point Naval Air Station in Hawaii. We spent twenty-five hours at Barber's Point. Then came the long leg—twenty-two or twenty-three hours—to Christchurch, including a three-hour stopover in bucketing rain at Pago Pago. The Connie, cruising at 8,000 feet, droned on, on.

I noted in my journal:

"One feels impatient, one wants finally to *arrive,* to meet whatever it is that's going to happen. Talk between Sy Richardson and Bill Austin about Tom Berg's death in the helo crash last year. Sy accompanied the remains back to the States. Nobody still seems to know why Berg and Jeremy Sykes died in that crash. . . .

"Saw a circular rainbow seeming to lie upon the ocean. And beautiful coral isles from 8000'. The ocean as usual looks gray, dull, with flecks of bright white that are whitecaps. But the isles show pure pale greens, intensely white circular surf, patches of brown.

"Vance told me a story about a Usarp at Byrd Station. A valuable worker, he got sore over an argument in a poker game, left the station angrily and took a walk. His tracks were followed three miles. The stride was still long, so he was probably still angry. Then they disappeared. He was never found. Vance, who wintered over at Byrd, said there are no crevasses in the area. So the man must have been caught by sudden bad weather."

Landing in Christchurch, we drove downtown to Warner's Hotel on Cathedral Square. This is the old hotel that was known to Scott and Shackleton, the one that now had a huge bar on the ground floor. My room looked out on the back end of Canterbury Cathedral.

Early next morning Vance, Cobb and I went to the USARP warehouse at the airport for the clothing issue, tryout and weigh-in. The warehouse was unheated, the doors were wide open. Together with other Usarps we stripped to our underwear. Much of the clothing was new; tags and straight pins had to be removed and adjustments made—for example in the mukluks: you separated the mukluks, removed in each the double felt inner sole, inserted a plastic sole, inserted the double felt sole, inserted a large felt liner, stuck your foot in, squeezed, banged your heel against the floor to settle everything, laced the boot, walked around. It was very important that clothes fitted properly; they must be neither too loose nor too snug.

We spent three days and four nights in Christchurch. On our last day I walked rapidly to the narrow, winding, willow-shaded Avon and crossed to the Hagley Park side of the river. My gravel trail took me under large trees whose shade was welcome. Thick tan masses of recently cut high grass, dry yet still redolent, called forth childhood memories of Bessarabia, an antediluvian harmony of stable smells, poppy fields and expanses of warm, moist farmland. On my left the park's great fields, empty and virginal-looking, reminded me of days in the Bronx shortly after I arrived in the United States in the early twenties, and a sense of uncrowded park lawns and of a milder time, when our population was a hundred and twenty million. By the time I returned to Warner's I had worked up a good sweat. I took a bath before going downstairs to the bar to drink warmish sweet Kiwi beer in the company of some Kiwi workmen.

Cobb and I dined together and afterwards took a leisurely stroll on sleepy residential streets and in a deserted, very dry park. I did some final packing before turning in.

I awoke at 4:30 A.M. and lay abed until 4:55, thinking how lucky I was to have reached this moment, to have not been frustrated, for example, by some unexpected illness such as the flu currently making the rounds of Christchurch. I was in the lobby by 5:20. Vance, Cobb and I took a cab to the USARP warehouse, where we donned our Antarctic clothes and stored our own clothes. My orange hold bag (a seabag; hold bag because it would go into the plane's "hold"), containing two pairs of mukluks, gloves, heavy socks, extra waffle-weaves and various other items—nothing essential to my survival in case we had an "incident"—was already aboard the Navy C-130. My survival gear was in my hand bag (this too was an orange seabag), which would stay close to me on the craft.

We lifted off at 8 A.M. I was wearing longjohns; a heavy, plaid wool shirt; my own Dacron-cotton trousers under black windpants minus liners; white woolen socks; and my own hiking boots. In my hand bag were the heavy windpants liners, bear paws, black thermal boots, my red USARP parka, gloves, my black pile-lined cap and my own green nylon knapsack with its jammed contents. We sat on canvas seats alongside the raw walls of the plane. There was a long, high stack of green Navy seabags, orange USARP seabags and pale green Scott Base seabags strapped down in front of me. Dirty bunny boots hung here and there. The plane, which had a silvery pylon tank under each wing, was, as usual, terrifically noisy. Pink ear wax was handed out by a crewman. We were flying at 22,000 feet over a great white, cottony world that pained your eyes when you tried to observe it through one of the few portholes. Some people read or slept. Vance and three men played bridge. After a while the bolts on the plane walls iced up, but I got so hot I removed my wool shirt. The pilot didn't chill the craft much on this flight.

Of my previous flight I had written:

"In Christchurch in the austral spring or summer you pick up a United States Navy plane, which in eight hours will take you the twenty-four hundred miles to 'the ice,' as Antarctic hands call the continent. As you board the aircraft the city is warm and it seems mildly funny to be wearing waffle-weave longjohns, Seabee green shirt and trousers, pile-lined cap, cushion-sole socks and huge white rubber thermal boots called bunny boots. (You have acquired Navy-issue dunnage.) You and your fellow passengers sit in two rows on red canvas seats, facing each other across a fence of strapped-down seabags, and wonder what Antarctica will be like and what you will be like in it. The antipodean waters below are so cold that if a person is immersed he can survive only eight to ten minutes. But a plane has never gone down on this flight and everyone is cheerful even as we pass the point of safe return, beyond which the C-130 Hercules, a great ski-equipped four-engine turbo-prop, cannot turn back. There's excitement as the first pack ice is sighted.

"The plane is cool now and you put on two pairs of gloves and a parka with a fur-trimmed flying hood. In your seabag are huge gauntleted furback mittens known as bear paws and lined overpants called many-pocket trousers but these are for places where it's really cold. You will not wear them on your arrival. Meanwhile one can't help but think there's a certain humor in the fact he's approaching the world's quietest place (when the winds aren't blowing) in a craft so noisy one carries on a conversation, if at all, in shouts. The roar is varied by the sound of hissing somewhere and by the screams of wing and tail controls.

"One disembarks, and there is Williams Field. We boarded a bulky, fat-tired orange bus and bounced on a road carved on the annual ice of McMurdo Sound, viewing distant mountains half-veiled by luminous clouds. We reached McMurdo Station, the center of American logistic and scientific activity in Antarctica, whose winter population of two hundred and summer population of almost a thousand makes it the largest station on the continent. Perched on volcanic hills on the southern tip of Ross Island, it has a severe climate, with an all-time recorded low of -59°F. and with winds clocked as high as a hundred and fifty-five miles an hour. Its black hills and roads give it the look of a mining camp."

Yesterday the *Phoenix 6,* heading for Williams Field, had had to turn back because of too strong headwinds. Now there were rumors that we too might have to abort our flight. Bill Heaphy, the soft-voiced, gentle Kiwi who managed the USARP warehouse, had told me that after the other Connie (the *Pegasus*) had crashed at Williams Field in October they had found a man on the plane manifest who wasn't even in New Zealand, much less on the ice. Hearing about this, Admiral Welch had ordered that dog tags be worn in Antarctica from then on, by civilians as well as by the military. So now I was wearing two of them.

When we were over the Ross Sea some handsome, tall Kiwis sitting near me took very seriously the business of preparing to step out onto the ice. They donned huge windpants (orange or pale green); great canvas-covered orange boots made in Japan, with long yellow laces that they tied briskly; parkas; and adjusted snow goggles on their foreheads. They did all this despite the information, given over the intercom, that the current temperature at Williams Field was 25°F. It was funny to watch them.

Suddenly we landed, with a few heavy bumps on the skis. The aft platform was lowered, bluish polar light streamed in, unloading began. We disembarked by the front door and there one was, on the ice of Williams Field, with plow trucks and huts all around, the sun cheery, and Mount Erebus looming like an unbelievable hill, its crest obscured by clouds. Cobb, Vance and I deposited our baggage in one red truck and proceeded to McMurdo Station by another, receiving views of the eastern side of Cape Armitage, of the Gap, Observation Hill, Mount Discovery, the Royal Society Range, and then of Hut Point and the Discovery Hut as we rounded Cape Armitage and saw Winter Quarters Bay and the station.

The station, dark, its background hills dark also despite their patchy mantle of snow, was much uglier than I remembered it to be, for now it lacked a benign covering of snow and ice. Porous volcanic rock was everywhere, crushed to gritty dust in the main roads. There were no streets, only lanes, unpaved, without sidewalks, gray, uneven. Littered as it was with much equipment, some of it on pallets—crates, cases, gas cylinders, sledges, huge fuel tires, generators, bulldozers, reels of heavy wire—the station suggested a wartime supply dump. One saw telephone poles, power lines and large silvery tubing on wooden trestles. The place was not without some color. In addition to the green Jamesway huts there were rust structures, wine-colored ones and crimson boxlike plywood shacks. Towering over the station was the brown-gray heap of Observation Hill, a trail snaking from the nuclear plant to the crest with its Polar Party Cross. At times you wanted to spread something over the hill's embarrassing, ugly nakedness.

I was stunned by the quarters I now moved into. They were Room 104 in the new USARP personnel building, which I dubbed the Lodge. It was a large, blue, two-story prefabricated metal building with buff stripes and was set on heavy wooden timbers so that drift snow wouldn't pile against it but would blow under and past it, and because it was cheaper and quicker to build in this manner than to drill into volcanic permafrost.

There were eighteen separate rooms on the first floor and single rooms and a couple of dormitory rooms on the second. A simple wooden stairway of six steps, with a wooden balustrade, stood at the main entrance. The Lodge was luxurious by comparison with most of the continent's structures.

My room was immediately on the right as you entered the heavy, foyered double doors. It was spacious, had two closets, two single beds, a Formica desk, an overhead light, a floor lamp, bed lamps, two red armchairs, red curtains to match, a coffee table, a linoleum floor, steam heat and—and this was very important to me, for privacy was often hard to come by on the ice—I would not have to share it even though it was designed for double occupancy. One view out of my windows was a row of red Nodwells (a large, heavy, tracked vehicle) parked on the southern side of the USARP garage across the road. Another view, looking slightly to the north, was a couple of the hills behind McMurdo, and of a Jamesway on a rise.

A year earlier I had lived in the Press Hut on the station's western edge. The toilet facilities in the hut consisted of a small metal cone located in the tiny, dark, unheated vestibule between the rear double doors. Waffle-weave longjohns were useful if you had to get up at night, and waffle-weaves were what everyone slept in. Other facilities in the hut were equally simple. There was no water except in a yellowish plastic jug which issued a yellowish liquid to be drunk out of a green ceramic cup.

In the morning you dressed fully before venturing out and you carried your single, small towel, a small bar of yellow soap and your toilet articles up the street to the Officers' Head, where you wrestled with the huge steel door latch both on opening and on shutting the outer door. The head had two rooms, the first of which contained a number of semi-private cubicles. There were no flush toilets. In the inner or basin room you hung your parka, cap and shirt on a high wooden hook, selected a basin and set to work. Some men preferred to wash and shave with their shirt on, for despite the oil-fired stove working noisily nearby, the room was by no means overheated. One night a ceiling leak put out the stove and flowed onto the floor. By morning the floor was ice-covered. Having finished your ablutions, you put on your shirt, parka, cap and gloves and wrestled with the outer latch as you left. Back at the Press Hut you removed the cap, parka and gloves. At times Antarctic life struck you as being largely a matter of donning and shedding clothes and opening and shutting double doors, some of the latter heavy enough to remind you of refrigerator doors.

By contrast, across the corridor from my room in the Lodge was a drinking fountain and the floor's spacious head. In the head were four basins in a row, each with a stainless steel shelf and a single light above a mirror. To the left of these were two urinals. The two toilets, nice modern affairs, with doors, each had a sign reading ONE FLUSH PER SITTING. Some joker had enlarged the last word with a pencil. An adjoining room contained a sauna and two shower stalls. Looking out of one of the head's windows, you saw the station's helicopter pads, usually with one or more H-34's sitting on them. In the distance were the peaks of the Royal Society Range.

The Lodge was situated on the station's eastern extremity. A little way south of it was the new USARP administration building, known as the Chalet. The Chalet was a rare building in Antarctica because it had a bit of style, even though the style was imitation-Swiss. It sat on a hill above the helo pads and hangar. As you approached it from the Lodge you saw beyond it the sea ice of McMurdo Sound and the beautiful white cone of Mount Discovery. The structure, whose A-shaped roof was a lighter shade of brown than its sides, contained a foyer, three office rooms overlooking the Royal Society Range, a small auditorium, a lounge, a small kitchen, a bathroom and a mezzanine. To the right of the entrance door, in silver letters, was the legend: NATIONAL SCIENCE FOUNDATION.

Immediately after depositing our luggage in our rooms—Vance had a similar room on the second floor; Cobb, because he would be at the station only overnight, had been assigned to a dormitory—Vance, Cobb and I went to the wardroom for a couple of drinks, then to the chow hall for dinner. The chow hall was in the Navy personnel building, the largest on the continent. Work on the building had begun in October 1966 and had been completed in February 1970. It was a steel, insulated, panel structure, half single-story, half two-story, and contained a laundry, a library, a barber shop, the ship's store and had a berthing capacity of two hundred and fifty and a feeding capacity of a thousand. All ranks ate the same food but dined separately. There were two cafeterias, one for the enlisted men and one for the chiefs and officers. Civilians ate in the officers' section. I ate a great deal more than was usual for me: sardines, green beans, roast beef, hominy and foods I no longer remember. I kept feeling thirsty and drank much cold water.

I turned in early. During the night I had my shade and curtains drawn to darken the room but enough light seeped through for one to see easily by. Going to the head once, I frowned at the brilliant outdoor light.

Lights burned in the head at all times and the humidifier across the corridor from my room never stopped. Apparently there was no shortage of electric power, thanks to the nuclear plant. There was such a degree of comfort in the Lodge and increasingly in the station that at times it was difficult to realize that nothing lived or grew here that we readily recognized. There were no mosquitoes or flies; no spiders spinning webs; no scratching sounds of mice.

On the way to the chow hall next morning I ran into a friend, Bob Mullins, who was delayed on an early-morning flight to Byrd Station (as was Cobb on a flight to the Pole) by ice fog over Williams Field. The fog was only some five hundred feet thick; a C-130 could easily take off through it; but if for some reason the craft got into trouble it might be in for a dangerous landing; so Mullins, Cobb and others were standing by. I led Mullins to the station's western edge to point out the Discovery Hut across the horseshoe-shaped anchorage. Hut Point was barren, dark; the hut was sharp in the morning light. Heading back toward the chow hall, we saw fog mists slipping over the crest of Observation Hill and lying like smog to the right over the sea ice, the tip of Mount Discovery showing gleaming white above it. The Royal Society Range was majestic with snow. I experienced a thrill each time I stared at its mountains—peaceful, remote, grand, unspoiled, with clean whites and pale blues. The range was a striking visual relief from gritty, dark-gray McMurdo. Meltwater rivulets, running down the hills, crossed the station. Crusts of ice lay on some of the roadside pools.

After breakfast I dusted and swept away the volcanic grit that was everywhere in my room and that, as I soon learned, was the price of leaving a window open. The grit, a summer phenomenon, was caused by the vehicular traffic on the dry roads and by the frequent and variable winds. I lunched with Dale Vance and his friend Frank Merrem. The latter was just in from the Pole, where he had wintered over. He had gone to the Pole Station in November 1969, when I was first on the ice. He was rather slightly built, had graying hair, wore glasses and had a very pale forehead. He was leaving on the first plane out for Christchurch and planned to tour New Zealand a bit before returning home to Boulder, Colorado. At the Pole he had worked in atmospheric physics. His little laboratory had been situated about a quarter of a mile from the main station. He had walked every day for at least twenty minutes, even when the temperature was a hundred below. He had been frostbitten a few times and once his plastic spectacle frames had suddenly snapped but it hadn't been painful or even difficult to breathe at that temperature. He had felt he was "burning up" when he arrived at Williams Field at 28°F. No one at the Pole Station had had a cold during the wintering over, but two weeks before he departed he had started packing boxes he had brought and he had developed a whopper. There had been no significant medical problems except those of a petty officer who seemed to have some sort of lung trouble.

In the afternoon I met with Chris Shepherd (the station USARP representative) in the Chalet, where, overheated and spending much time working a 3M #209 photocopier, I felt fretful and a fool to be operating a machine when outdoors was glorious Antarctica. But insurance against the loss of my journal was necessary to the security of my work in progress; I had determined to mail out pages periodically. Vance picked me up and we went to the wardroom for beer. The bar was out of ice; all three ice machines had broken down. Some Navy officers joked that with all the ice in the world down here, they couldn't get any for their drinks. Vance got caught up in rolling dice with the enlisted-man bartender and a Navy officer. They played Korean Threes. I went to my room, wrote some cards and met Vance for dinner, which consisted of tough steak, tiny shrimp in a bitter sauce, creamy pepper soup, prunes and mixed-fruit pie.

Afterwards I went to the chapel, where Chaplain John Q. Lesher (Protestant), a lieutenant commander, was practicing hymns on a little organ. He was the McMurdo custodian of the Dicovery Hut key. I borrowed the key from him and walked down the long, cindery, curving road that flanked the anchorage on its way to Hut Point. A solitary skua circled above me and swooped at me several times before flying away. The hut's exterior wood was pale, bleached, but it had not rotted. I unlocked the door and let myself in, smelling an acrid odor like that of a stable. It was dark inside; the few windows were small. Black slabs of gleaming seal meat lay in a pile against a wall. There were splotches of milky ice on the floor. Not much if anything remained of the original contents. Some day the place would probably be cleaned up and made into a museum that would falsify with brightness and clarity.

A howling wind came up and rattled the lock and door. Standing there alone, I found myself tending to underrate the place because Scott and his companions hadn't actually lived in it. I didn't visualize him in it readily, as I had in the Cape Evans hut last year. I reminded myself that this Discovery Hut was of the greatest importance in the human history of Antarctica.

The east wind blew harder. I stepped out to glance at the sky, then climbed the black hill to Vince's Cross. The wind was so strong I feared it might blow me off the soft ridge leading to the cross. On the station side the hill sloped gently; on the western side it fell like a cliff to the sea. The footing was loose. I saw the Sound, the tidal cracks, and skuas skimming over the sea ice. The wind began to bite. I decided not to linger at this time.

Returning to the chapel and seeing some flag markers moving in the wind, I had the illusion of the presence of ducks or chickens before remembering that there were no domestic animals here. No sound of a cat, a dog. No children's voices or women's voices either. I slipped the key under the door of the chaplain's office and visited the Biology Laboratory, where Beethoven's Ninth was being played on an expensive tape machine and where I ran into Robert Feeney, a bearded professor in biochemical research at the University of California, Davis, who was currently senior scientist at the Biolab.

This was Feeney's sixth working residence and the seventh year of his program in the Antarctic. At fifty-seven he was remarkably youthful in demeanor, interests, curiosity, friendliness and laughter, and he looked in fine physical condition. I had met him at McMurdo the previous year and at Skyland, Virginia, this year. When he asked me now if I cared to go fishing through the ice next morning out at the fish shack, which was located on the Sound about two and a quarter miles from Hut Point, I accepted with alacrity, for I had never fished through ice and had not visited the shack. We agreed to have breakfast together.

CHAPTER 4

FISHING THROUGH THE ICE

It was a very pleasant meal, for Feeney was a jolly companion, and I was full of keen anticipation regarding the imminent new experience. At first we planned to walk to the shack, and Feeney and I wore windpants and mukluks for the purpose, but the wind proved too strong, so we went by Nodwell instead, riding with his post-doctoral colleague, Gary Means, and his three assistants, who were Feeney's graduate students. Feeney told me that the Navy people did not enjoy his habit of walking out to the shack alone but tolerated it because he had been here so often. Nor were they happy about the Nodwell's being driven to the shack so late in the season. The sea ice had softened and thinned, the tidal cracks had split wide, and just the other day a truck's front wheels had gone through the ice, and the truck had had to be pulled out by another truck. The Nodwell, which had metal tracks on eight tired wheels, was a heavy vehicle and the Navy people feared it would sink through a soft patch. Feeney told me that at the shack the ice was still fairly thick—6.9 feet—and that midway between the shack and the station it was 6.6 feet. Motor toboggans would have been the thing but they were all out in the field.

Means, who had gotten his Ph.D. degree in biochemistry at Davis under Feeney, was endlessly cheerful, had remarkably kind eyes and wore a beautiful, grandfatherly, reddish-gold beard. Before we went to the shack he and I drove up a hill behind McMurdo to a gas-storage depot, where he filled the Nodwell's tank. A large sign urged him to be sure to ground the fuel line before using it. This was designed to avoid accidents due to the considerable Antarctic static electricity.

As we descended from McMurdo to the ice, Feeney walked ahead and guided Means, who was driving. He pointed the way across the tidal cracks (bridged by heavy boards) and onto the firmer ice. The rear door of the vehicle was left open as an escape hatch. The assistants were Ahmed I. Ahmed, Jack R. Vandenheede and Charles Y. Ho. All five men were bearded. The Nodwell was full of gear—survival packs, a sled, metal equipment—and was smoky due to an oil leak (the engine was housed inside the cabin). It was a cloudy day, with an east wind that blew in gusts and brought the frigid air of the ice shelf. The Western Mountains looked somber; the glaciers there gleamed dully under long cloud banks. The sea ice, with patches of discoloration like eczema, was rough enough to throw us about. The Nodwell growled, whined and clanked. A couple of ice-scraping machines stood on the ice north of us. Feeney remarked that they looked like tanks abandoned on a desert of white snow.

The fish shack was a squat red plywood structure. A couple of small red flags stuck up out of the ice to the right of the door. North of the shack were the black features of Observation Hill, the Gap, Crater Hill and some of the slopes of McMurdo Station. The day was too overcast for one to see the Royal Society Range, but I could make out the lower part of Mount Discovery and a portion of Brown Peninsula. Some skuas, having seen us coming, flew to the shack and stood around waiting for odds and ends of fish to be thrown to them.

As you entered the shack you saw on the left a couple of bunks and an oil stove. On the right were a work table and some shelves. The shack was equipped with rations, sleeping bags, chemicals, retorts, test tubes, microscopes and dissection equipment. Its most prominent feature—this was near the door—was an uncovered hole, about four feet square, cut in the wooden floor and through the ice below. Looking down, you saw the irregular sides of the ice hole and the large, beautiful, many-faceted and seemingly phosphorescent crystals jutting out toward the center. The ice was luminescent with light refracted under the shack. Normally the stove was fired day and night to keep the hole from freezing over. It had gone out, so now there was a heavy ice skim on the water, which had to be broken up, scooped up with a long-handled net and dumped outside. After this was done, smaller nets were used to scoop up the finer stuff, which tinkled and which shone with rainbow colors. Then plastic buckets were lowered and water hauled up and poured into a large plastic tub that would hold the day's catch. When the skim was removed the water looked darkly clear, a brownish gray. I was told that the Sound here was about 1,500 feet deep. Meanwhile the stove was lit, and soon it was grunting heavily, and I wondered if it was working itself up to an explosion.

Feeney, Means and I sat on metal folding chairs and fished without bait, using light lines with multiple hooks. A school of silvery fish appeared: *Trematomus borchgrevinki,* named after C. E. Borchgrevink, an Antarctic explorer who built a hut, still extant, at Cape Adare, Victoria Land, at the end of the last century. The fish were divided into "keepers" (large enough to keep) and "leavers" (too small for efficient biological use). To avoid splashes that might frighten the school, "leavers" were placed on a little pale green ice shelf, from which they wriggled into the water. You could see the school hovering, or swimming as though in slow motion, their silver flashes outlined against the depths like the tracings of nuclear particles in a cloud chamber. They had very little experience with hooks; few persons had ever fished so far south. They didn't fight. The "keepers" were rather small this day, some eight to ten inches long. We handled them without gloves. They were slippery, felt scaleless and were very cold.

One marveled at the scene's strangeness: three men luring small exotic fish through pale green and pale blue ice almost seven feet thick, in water three degrees below the freezing point of fresh water, a couple of thousand miles from civilization and some 850 miles from the Pole; and three other men sitting at a long table and busily dissecting the freshly caught specimens and collecting blood, eyes, brains, muscles, livers and hearts. Part of the fish material would be studied at the Biolab and part would be frozen and shipped to the States for more leisurely study with more sophisticated equipment.

The Feeney team's chief interest was in the effect of temperature on biochemical reactions. They were looking for adaptive changes that occurred in cold-water fish but didn't take place in warm-water ones. They had already studied four of the enzymes involved in muscle energy and had made a detailed study of one of the critical respiratory enzymes in the heart muscle. They were currently studying blood clotting; brain enzymes; a red-cell enzyme that converted carbon dioxide to bicarbonate and vice versa; they were obtaining the mitochondria of hearts by differential separation; were working with respirometers; were collecting liver to use the liver enzymes on some of the blood proteins; and were gathering brains to study a brain enzyme involved in neural transfer.

They also had a major blood program going: they were studying the anti-freeze in the serum. This remarkable fish anti-freeze, which kept the blood from freezing in waters at a temperature of 29°F., worked about as glycerol did but was some hundred to three hundred times more efficient, and about a thousand times more efficient than the theory of colligative action called for. The freezing and boiling points of water were affected by materials through a process called colligative action.

The team was also interested in comparative biochemistry as a tool for studying molecular engineering, and in understanding how large polymers, particularly proteins, worked. They were looking for changes in protein structure caused by evolution, in the hope of better understanding function. One of the good places for obtaining proteins in significantly large quantities was egg white. Feeney had started the penguin egg-white program at McMurdo during his first visit to Antarctica seven years ago. He had begun with the Adélie, whose egg was about twice the size of a chicken egg and weighed an average of 120 grams. As for the huge Emperor penguin eggs, the drawback there was that you couldn't obtain fresh ones inasmuch as they were laid in midwinter, when conditions were too severe for human existence at Cape Crozier, at any rate for such a relatively minor purpose as collecting fresh eggs. So Feeney and his various colleagues and aides had collected frozen Emperor eggs in the austral summers and had made approximate corrections for changes they knew would be induced in the properties of the egg-white proteins by freezing. They had chopped the frozen eggs out of the ice with ice axes. These were eggs that the penguins had lost, presumably because of severe storms. The Biolab teams had also done much work in penguin taxonomy.

The Emperors, whose rookery was on the sea ice off Crozier, lived a very hazardous life. They had had a catastrophe earlier this year when a combination land and ice slide had fallen on the rookery and killed many birds. About four years ago the ice had gone out early from Crozier and had taken the rookery with it. The young birds hadn't molted yet and couldn't swim. When the ice melted as it traveled north they drowned.

No Weddell seals had come up through the ice hole in the shack this season. In some past seasons they had suddenly appeared, occasionally bringing with them from the great depths a large fish weighing from seventy-five to a hundred pounds. This was the *Dissostichus mawsoni*, known at McMurdo only because the Weddell would bring it to light. Waiting around the hole would be a rapper and a gaffer. The former would rap the seal on the head with a poker; the latter would gaff the fish when the seal opened its mouth to turn on its attacker. Some three dozen specimens had been obtained in this manner.

There are several kinds of seals in Antarctica, among them the rare Ross, the vicious leopard, the homely crabeater and the remarkable Weddell. The Weddell can dive two thousand feet in search of food and can stay submerged up to forty minutes. How does it withstand the pressure? How does it detect its prey in the blackness of the depths? How does it find its way back to a hole in the ice that it itself had cut with its teeth? Why doesn't it get the bends on coming up? These are some of the questions scientists studying Weddells are trying to answer. Studies of Weddells may, among other things, reveal how our bodies use oxygen.

I was reminded of the time last year when I had gone from McMurdo by Nodwell over the ice northward to Hutton Cliffs, whose ice colors at midnight were startling: aquamarine, turquoise, sapphire, cobalt. I had visited the hut there that was used as a seal station. It contained three beds in a tier, a desk and scientific equipment. A TV camera had been lowered through a hole in the ice and could be aimed by remote control. Standing in front of a small screen, I had observed Weddells in the water and heard their sounds with hydrophones: clucking, whistles, grunts, glottal clicks and pops. Outside, some mothers and pups basked on the ice. A large seal lay alone on her back, making coughing noises. Sometimes she blew air hard through her nostrils before closing them tightly with what sounded like a sigh. Or she took a deep, seemingly painful breath and made laughing motions with her throat. But the sounds that issued were comically inappropriate to her mass: they were parakeet whistles. When I drew close she mooed and showed her teeth.

As we fished in the red shack, suddenly, as if something in the water had struck a note or a scent, the school of *borchgrevinki* disappeared; and although we sat patiently, hoping to catch more, and tried fishing deeper to arouse new interest, the hole remained empty. One felt the movement of cold, heavy air from the hole like the exhalation of a giant refrigerator. Ahmed brought me an excellent cup of hot chocolate. There was a long, pleasant silence during which one stared into the beautiful hole and wondered how it would feel to fall in. It would probably be impossible to climb out without help. Yet Fenney had fallen in once while alone and had managed to save himself.

That was at a time when the Biolab had a shack smaller and a good deal more cramped than the present one. While waiting hopefully for a seal to surface with a large fish in its mouth, he attempted to go across the side of the hole, slipped and fell in. He had a fish trap on the bottom of the sea, and this was attached to a wire hanging from a nearby winch, and he was able to throw one knee onto an ice ledge, catch hold of the wire and pull himself out. He turned the stove up, took off his clothes and got into a sleeping bag. He often stayed at the shack alone at night. He loved going outside and observing the remarkable scenes all around him.

The worst scare he ever had on the ice was at Crozier while studying penguins. He was still new to Antarctica then.

"When you're green, you're cautious about things you don't need to be cautious about, and not cautious about things you should be. One of the things you don't do is walk the penguin trails at the edge of the ice. The ice sometimes overhangs, and you weigh a lot more than a penguin, and if the ice breaks off you may have had it, for often there will be a drop and you won't be able to get out, and the leopard seals patrol there. I was out there in between our work periods, and I was trying to get some movies of a leopard seal eating an Adélie. The seal throws the penguin up in the air, catches it and slaps it on the water. He removes its skin in this way and blood shoots all over. Well, I saw a leopard seal come up right next to the ice, and I saw him start off, and I took after him on the trail. I was running. Then I got to this one spot and paused. I don't remember why. Maybe I had to climb over something. At that moment, when I was about two feet from the sea, a leopard seal threw his head and upper part of his body onto the ice and snapped at me. He missed me by a matter of inches. I was able to throw myself backwards after he slid back in, but not right at the moment. I got back about three feet from the edge and just lay there, sweating heavily, before I had the strength to get myself back another ten feet. All I could see were that great face and those jaws. It just scared the dickens out of me."

I sat there hoping for the fish to bite again, for I had many things to do while in Antarctica and would probably not have the time to return to the shack. I hoped in vain. We headed back for the station.

CHAPTER 5

MCMURDO STATION: TWO

O n returning from the fish shack I lunched with Dale Vance, after which I went to the chapel, borrowed the key to the Discovery Hut and headed for the road that swung around the bend of Winter Quarters Bay. There was a bitter wind on this gray afternoon. The dry "streets" of the station looked particularly ugly and the black hills felt ominous. Seabees were erecting a large metal building. Occasionally a huge truck or bulldozer raised a cloud of dust that gritted between one's teeth. As you descended the bend you saw equipment stacked on the shore below: large vehicles, fuels lines, a Jamesway, a roaring generator making electricity for a welding arc. Seabees were bulldozing and grading, preparing the offloading area for the ships that would soon be coming. The gray-green tidal crack here was now some six feet wide. The rotten sea ice along the shore had been shoved up by pressure.

The Royal Society Range was under cloud cover, but I could see a number of the slate-blue planes of the craggy foothills, as well as the cradles of small glaciers glinting in a source of light not visible to me. I could make out Hobbs Peak (the northernmost part of the Range), Hobbs Glacier and the outlet of the Blue Glacier. The combination of overcast in the west, together with the spotlighted, white-cradled glaciers among blue hills that seemed to be in motion, was quite dramatic.

Reaching the hut, I removed my gloves and struggled to unlock the small, seemingly frozen padlock that secured the lockless, latchless door. The wind, sweeping off the ice shelf and through the Gap and over the station, made my hands cry out in pain. It was this wind with which members of Scott's first expedition were so familiar. When I was inside it gave the impression of being demonically intent on destroying the door: it kept exploding the latter open so violently I feared it would rip it off its hinges. I could pull the door shut by a rawhide thong but I could not fasten it. I found a bit of ancient rope near the blubber stove, tied one end to the thong and knotted the other to a rusty nail above the door frame. This managed to hold the door shut. Sounds of howling; of rattling of the padlock against dry wood; of creaking, banging.

A Weather Bureau thermometer that I had brought with me registered 18°F. on the floor and 19° about twenty inches above it. I poked a flashlight beam into rafter corners in the absent-minded expectation of finding spider webs. On shelves were boxes of oatmeal; cans of marmalade, sardines, damson jam, biscuit; an empty old bottle of

Courvoisier cognac. Here and there were sledge-hauling harness; long wooden arcs that had probably been used in gravity experiments; the slabs of seal meat I had seen yesterday; and sticky blubber in the blubber pot near the stove, the skin black, the blubber orange.

On returning the key to the chaplain I saw two enlisted men on their knees in the chapel corridor, scraping old wax off the linoleum with razor blades in preparation for Christmas. One of them was going to the Pole tomorrow for the rest of the austral summer. The chaplain dropped to his knees and scraped away too. Walking towards the Lodge and passing piles of equipment that looked abandoned, I felt a sense of release in living in a place so casual about neatness.

At the Lodge I sought out David Elliot, a geologist who had made a spectacular fossil find the previous austral summer season, and made an appointment with him to be interviewed in my quarters two days later in connection with my book. I had read about the discovery in *The New York Times*. The find had a very important bearing on the validity of the theory of continental drift, the increasing proof for which I had been following with keen interest for years. Long ago, for my amusement, I had made plaster of Paris templates of the continents from a globe, had arranged them like the pieces of a jigsaw puzzle until they seemed to form a super-continent, and had photographed the result. At McMurdo I had heard many fine things concerning Elliot's competence as a scientist, his high intelligence, his articulateness, and his attractive English personality, so I was understandably eager to chat with him in private in the hope of learning from the most authoritative source the details of the discovery and what it had been like to make it.

At first, as I sensed, he was cool to my proposal, possibly because he was very busy. He asked probing questions about my project. I was relieved when, after I explained the purpose of my book, he consented to be interviewed. Still, I feared he would not be sufficiently communicative for a good interview. To my surprise and pleasure, he was to stay in my quarters for a long time and we were to chat on and on about matters unrelated to the discovery. He had an excellent grasp of the works of Scott and Shackleton and it was delightful to discuss the relative merits of the two men with him, although we disagreed strongly at times.

Vance was in his room, looking damp and tired from hard work. He showed me a package he had received from an uncle today: a six-pack of bloody-mary mix he would take to Vostok. We drank beer together in the wardroom, where we learned that the Connie had lost an engine yesterday on returning to Christchurch. The popcorn and mixed nuts were free; the drinks were very inexpensive. There was a huge photograph of a beautiful pinup girl on the wall facing the customers. She was lying on her back, breasts standing, one leg raised, her lips smiling sensually, her eyes staring at one. In one hand she held a back scratcher.

I got up late next morning (7:15), skipped breakfast and went to the radio-communications building on a hill behind the station, where a Lieutenant Parker asked me if I'd be willing to be the first to try out some new radio gear when I camped at Capes Royds and Evans. This was a compact radio with a whip antenna and was designed to operate on batteries. The question was if it would perform faithfully at a range of fifteen to twenty-five miles of McMurdo. I said I'd be glad to, although it struck me as funny that a novice at Antarctic camping should be asked to try out a new rig on his very first time out. I was given a course in radio communications and was presented with a unit called a Patrolfine H.F. Single Sideband Transceiver, known more simply as a Southcom 120, which was manufactured in Escondido, California. The unit had two extra sets of nickel-cadmium batteries. If all three sets failed to work I was to switch to a generator, which was good for 1,800 watts. If I couldn't get through to McMurdo directly I was to try an aircraft channel and ask that my messages be relayed. My call number would be McMurdo Three Two (S-32 being my USARP project number). Calling time would be 0800-1000 daily.

Judging by the degree of indoctrination I received on the use of the generator, I gathered that the lieutenant did not have his hopes up about the ability of the batteries to withstand Antarctic temperatures. I must be sure to open the fuel line first, then set the lever to CHOKE, and then crank with the rope. After three or four cranks I must set the lever to RUN. When I wanted to shut the generator off I must close the fuel line to empty the carburetor; this would prevent freezing in the latter. I must let the generator run about fifteen minutes so it could warm up thoroughly before I drew power from it. It was best to run it with the tank almost full; the more fuel, the more gravity would help to move the fuel through the line. Fuel, a mixture of gasoline and oil, would be provided by USARP.

Later in the day I attended a scientific briefing, which reminded me of briefings given during my first visit to the ice, after which I had written:

"The equipment is frostily sedate even when it contains tiny colored lights, but at the cosmic ray station in a long red hut between McMurdo Station and Scott Base it goes into an antic dance. It does this every two minutes when the digital readout (an automatic counter) whirls lighted numerals faster than the eye can catch them and punches its findings on a roll of narrow tape to be sent to the States for analysis. The new Antarctica is accustomed to complex control and instrument panels. One sees them in the cockpits of aircraft, in the small nuclear plant at McMurdo where seawater is desalinated and electricity produced, in some of the scientific stations and at Williams Field. We heard discussions of the next logical step: unmanned automated stations that will radio their findings to polar satellites. Meanwhile, manned American research on the continent continues in numerous fields: glaciology, oceanography, biology, cartography, meteorology, geomagnetism, seismology, aurora, upper atmosphere physics (including cosmic ray and ionosphere opacity studies), paleontology and others.

"Why has Antarctica been chosen as the site upon which to conduct basic · research? There are a number of reasons, among them the following: the continent comprises one-tenth of the earth's land mass; it contains significant clues to the earth's past; it greatly influences the weather patterns of the Southern Hemisphere; it is relatively free of radio static; and it is ideally suited to upper atmosphere studies.

"The scientists we encountered were young, eager, personable and very competent. We often saw them as a different breed from the Antarctic hands who wintered over in the old days. The tall, fit-looking young man at the cosmic ray station was about to return to the States after a stay on the ice of thirteen months, much of it in the hut. One remembered how winter-over personnel in the past felt the prolonged absence of sunlight, some growing morose, irritable, and a few breaking down. The young man had wintered over alone, had walked now and then to McMurdo on an errand and had received supplies and an occasional visitor. Had he ever been lonely or depressed? On the contrary, he asserted, he had enjoyed the winter. There had been fewer distractions, and being without mail had its advantages; there was no mail to upset him and no cause to be disappointed because someone hadn't written. Did he smoke, drink, play cards? No. 'I'm a straight arrow,' he said with an ironic smile. Then how had he spent his free time? Well, he had faced and stained the walls of his bedroom with veneered plywood, had kept a diary, had taken photographs. Occasionally he had spoken with his folks by ham radio. He was not only a different breed from his predecessors; he also lived under very different conditions. In the Antarctic, solitude has perhaps a less deleterious effect than the old condition of extreme crowding in tiny, primitive huts. He had electric light, a telephone, and the medical facilities at McMurdo."

The rest of the day was consumed by conversations and chores. At around nine o'clock, after drinking with Vance in the wardroom, I walked alone to a point quite close to Scott Base. The evening was extraordinarily warm. I removed my cap and left my parka unzipped. The road through the Gap, gravelly, gray, in spots soft, was well-traveled now that the sea-ice route was too rotten to be trusted. It was the main way to Williams Field: over the Gap; a brief distance northward of Scott Base; east past pressure ice and onto the ice shelf; and several miles east on the shelf to the field. A truck, coming downhill toward McMurdo, stirred a cloud of dust resembling steam. On my left the southern slope of Crater Heights still held much snow. Pools of meltwater marked the road shoulders. Those in the shadow of Observation Hill had ice skim forming on them. In the sun my ungloved hands were warm; in the shadow of the hill they turned painfully cold. A rivulet was scurrying across the road on its way to the Sound. The road was pockmarked as if by small explosives. Each hole contained milky water.

I reached the Gap's crest. Pressure ice on the left of silhouetted Cape Armitage rose in jagged masses, its crevices showing cobalt blue. On my right the lower portion of Observation Hill swooped down in a black plane. Beyond the hill lay the mottled, pale blue annual or sea ice, which, in the evening sun, had a faint, lilac, pearly cast. Directly ahead of me, some miles away on the ice shelf, the gray of White Island's cliffs and hilltops peeped through embayments of creamy snow. The little island looked almost idyllic, it rose so gently out of the shelf. I made out a faint, ribbon-like white line on the icescape, running approximately north and south. This was where the shelf and the sea ice met. At this point the shelf was barely ten feet higher than the Sound. The low-hanging sun illumined hills, ice and snow in a subtly dramatic, at times beautifully nostalgic way with a gentle ivory light. The sky was smoky except at the zenith, where it was azure.

I heard hillside snow and ice melting and occasionally a tinkle as of metal when a piece of ice broke loose and skittered down. The sun was lower at night than by day, so there was more glare during the night hours. At night it was painful to observe the Royal Society Range without sunglasses. My hands were atingle with warmth, yet earlier in the day they had felt like frozen claws, and the fingertips and nails had been very white.

I spotted Scott Base below me, with its handful of pale green huts on Pram Point. It seemed very strange to find a human settlement there. The sudden green of the base struck me as extraordinary, suggesting as it did young grass or spring leaves. For I was surrounded by a black wasteland that seemed to have been blasted into infertility. All around me were porous volcanic rocks, most of them black but some with a reddish hue. Yet the visual beauty was what one was chiefly aware of: the terrific contrasts between sweeping black shapes with the faintly blue ice; or between the rose-tinted powder puff clouds with the sky's azure.

In the south Mount Discovery was tall, large, majestic, its cone suggesting a bald white head. In the north, beyond the great white stretch of Windless Bay, Mount Terror, a contemplative-looking mountain sweeping eastwardly into a cape—or so it seemed from where I stood, its bayside cliffs resembling chalk cliffs because of the way the snow was catching the light directly opposite them, its luminous gentle shadows the palest blue-grays—was thrillingly opalescent. It was a fairy world over there of pale blues, dappled grays and gleaming, glowing nacres. In the bay itself—this was the bay well known to Wilson, Bowers and Cherry-Garrard from their midwinter traverse between Capes Evans and Crozier—the shelf ice looked subdued, a twilight blue; but nothing was flat or dead there; everything was textured, even if only faintly, and was therefore alive.

When one turned one's head one experienced a tremendous sweep of space, and within the framework of this relatively monochromatic world there was the excitement of color: the sweet blue of the zenith, the lime above the horizon, the lavender, lilac and prune in the ice shelf, the slate blues of islands and mountains. The sea ice was a fiery mirror. The water rushing down the hillside gleamed like a stream of mercury. The unspoiled silence, the uncluttered views, the aloofness of the Royal Society Range, and the scene's incredible expanse worked profoundly on me. I felt in love with something or someone. Also, I felt loved, blessed, graced. "Lord, Lord," I kept saying to myself, "how lucky I am to be here," and my eyes filled with tears.

CHAPTER 6

MCMURDO STATION: THREE

The morning of December 17 I climbed Observation Hill, going from the Lodge by road up to the nuclear plant, then following the steep trail over volcanic gravel, soil and rock. It was not an easy climb for someone about to turn fifty-six but for one reason or another I was driven to go rapidly. My heart pounded; I sweated heavily. I had been indiscreet in coming alone and in not telling anyone where I was going. If I broke an ankle or had a heart attack I'd be in serious trouble, for I had climbed beyond shouting range of the station; and I would be invisible to the station in a sitting or prone position. Several times I felt like quitting. To look directly up or down raised questions better not asked and only drove me to climb more rapidly. Then quite suddenly I felt the steady, shockingly cold wind blowing off the ice shelf and realized I could be badly frostbitten or even frozen if I became immobilized. I put my cap back on and zipped up my parka. The sweat was rapidly chilling my body.

Near the summit of the hill was a visitors' register consisting of a lectern with a drawer containing two chained ballpoint pens that didn't work, a pencil and a ledger. Some of the comments written in the ledger intrigued me.

"Mountain climbing ain't my bag."

"November 25, 1970. I have come to the summit of Ob Hill this day with the help of God and rum cokes and a cold. This historic occasion marks the first accession of this hill by a graduate of Sacred Heart University, Bridgeport, Conn., 1968. Hurrah etc. for the Alma Mater and for all those who follow. Private [name illegible], Westport, Conn."

"November 26, 1970. My name is Ahmed I. Ahmed and I am from U.A.R., Egypt. Actually it is the first time for me to climb such high mountain. I am so tired, especially after this heavy Turkey Thanksgiving dinner. Thank you. Ahmed I. Ahmed."

"Thanks God who has done a lot of wonderful things to me. Thanksgiving Day, 1970."

"November 26, 1970. Today may be Thanksgiving but there is nothing to be thankful for on this shitty mountain or at this shitty base. I dedicate this climb to all the poor souls who will be here for Thanksgiving of '71. Carl Ruffer." Someone had written above this, "Your a dumb shit. Your writing speaks for you."

"Nov. 26, 1970. To whom it may concern. I left that bottle up there. Good headaches to you. I climbed this hill for my wife Debby, whom I love very much."

"Nov. 26, 1970. I'm a civilian at heart. I climbed this hill for my wife Millie, whom I love very much, and for Ralph, who will be born soon, whom I also love very much. Neither of them like the Navy and I don't blame them."

From the crest of the hill, beside the Polar Party Cross, I had a view in all directions and saw at a glance almost the entire station and could gauge how much of McMurdo's stores were stacked outside and could hear the sounds of heavy truck and bulldozer engines. The nuclear plant halfway up the hill seemed far below me. Directly below me were gray, brownish and umber volcanic chunks, sharp, flinty, lying on a series of dead hillsides that were part of the hill. I could see four silver fuel tanks beside the Gap road, and Crater Heights, whose westernmost section was a concave ice sheet gleaming at the edges. The sun was directly above Erebus, which was beautifully visible and sported a plume of steam rising diaphanous and uncharacteristically straight. Clad as if in ermine, its pockets of blue-gray shadow resembling ermine tails, the volcano looked like a female breast, the kind that is still shapely even when a woman is on her back.

When I returned to the Lodge and went to the head I found to my astonishment that someone had left a faucet freely running. In Antarctica you use water as sparingly as possible. Despite the fact that the continent contains some 95 percent of the world's permanent ice—if the ice were to melt, the oceans would rise an estimated two hundred or two hundred and fifty feet—there is little natural water during most of the year at McMurdo and none at all at the inland stations. As a consequence fire is probably the greatest single danger on the continent. Potable water is even scarcer than seawater and is expensive to make by the usual method: melting snow or ice. As for showers, everyone is honor-bound not to take more than one a week and a "Navy" shower at that: a quick dousing, a soaping with the water turned off, and a quick rinse. Because of the cold and the extreme dryness one isn't aware of inadequate hygiene.

Three Hawaiian repairmen entered the head, wearing only longjohns. They quartered in the Jamesway on the rise across the road from the Lodge. The Antarctic is an informal place. The waffle-weave longjohns are widely used as pajamas not only because the huts can be cold at night but because switching from one to the other is time-consuming and awkward in the extremely narrow, crowded and sometimes dim confines of a cubicle. The use of names is also informal. You hear Willy Field or Willy for Williams Field, helo for helicopter, Herc for Hercules, Connie for Constellation, O Head for Officers' Head, Ob Hill for Observation Hill, Cheechee for Christchurch, Kiwi for New Zealander, Hono for Honolulu.

The Navy tends to downgrade formality in such a place, although it continues the tradition of the wardroom and of separate dining quarters for enlisted men, chiefs and officers. In the officers' section of the chow hall one receives a very pleasant impression of diversity within uniformity. People dress alike and eat the same food at the same informal tables but they may be sitting in Navy groups or scientist groups or visitor groups and discussing strikingly dissimilar matters in dissimilar language. But there is a certain formality too, as well as a university air because of the presence of numerous university-affiliated scientists.

Despite its primitive setting and still fairly primitive facilities, McMurdo is a sophisticated, intellectual and cosmopolitan outpost, where you see and hear foreigners, for example, as a matter of course in the spring and summer. What everybody seems to have in common are excellent morale and a sense of the ready and rather unreserved acceptance of each other. The latter is probably a result of a lively awareness of how hostile the environment can be and of how important therefore free cooperation is. There are many reasons why men become addicted to Antarctica—the adventure, the unspoiled freshness of it, the beauty, the excitement of scientific research—but ranked high among them, certainly, are the informal way of life, the acceptance of each other and the high morale.

Rear Admiral David F. Welch's quarters at McMurdo looked modest on a little knoll. The outside of the hut was rough but the inside was graced by touches, on the day I had visited in November 1969, uncommon in the Antarctic: a linen table cloth, place cards with names carefully hand-printed on them, and an unobtrusive servant. On the center of the table was a vase with plastic flowers. I had asked the admiral what problems kept him awake at night. He said there were two: the uncertain legal jurisdiction on the continent, and tourism. The admiral had complete criminal jurisdiction over the men in his command, but none over the civilians.

"If you shot one of my men I doubt that you could be tried for it," he said. "The U.S. has no sovereignty here. Nor would the laws of the high seas apply. Technically we're guests of the New Zealanders, who claim the Ross Dependency, which was turned over to them by Great Britain in the twenties. But all territorial claims were frozen for thirty years by the Antarctic Treaty. Also, the U.S. has never recognized any nation's claims in the Antarctic and has never made any. Of course, I'd fly you out of here even if I had to manhandle you, but that's all I'd do."

As for tourism, he had no doubt it would come to the Antarctic. The only question was how soon.

"I just hope it won't happen during *my* watch. I'm responsible for the safety of all Americans in the Antarctic, yet I can't tell tourists what they can or can't do. What if they started wandering around on the ice? There's a tourist agency which wants to bring a ship down here and use it as quarters for tourists whom they'd fly down in a chartered plane. This is completely open territory—anybody can come down here if he has the means of getting here and staying here. But if they start flying a plane down I'd have to be prepared for a rescue mission in case it got into trouble. What if somebody decides to fly across the continent alone, in a private plane? I couldn't stop him, yet I'd have to be ready to help if he needed help or to find him if he went down."

There was a discussion of the Antarctic Treaty. Signed originally by the United States, the Soviet Union and ten other nations, it provides for the free exchange of scientific information and for international inspection, and bans military bases and maneuvers, weapons testing, nuclear explosions and the disposal of radioactive wastes. The military role is restricted to logistic support efforts. This treaty is a relatively new but very important factor in Antarctic morale.

After climbing Observation Hill I phoned Jim Brandau, the helo pilot of Gentle 5 (an H-34) when it crashed in November 1969, and arranged to meet him in the wardroom at eight. Then Dale Vance, three other scientists, Jim Elder and I bounced and careened in a red USARP pickup truck over rutted, clogged, iced lava roads into the hills northwest of the station to a radio shack, called Pogo, near Arrival Heights. Elder, in charge of the Field Party Processing Center, drove crazily. I shared the cab with him. The others rode outside. Pogo was alone among black hills. From its doorway you saw Observation Hill: a brown pyramid beyond a black, pitted islandscape; and the Royal Society Range in the west; and glaciers gleaming over there on the seaward edge of Victoria Land. A great white plume seemed to stand like an ice shaft in Erebus's crater to the north of us.

In the shack, which was electrically heated, was Vance's ham radio rig that he planned to take to Vostok Station and to use to call his family during his year at the Russian base. He meant to test it now and to try for some phone patches for the rest of us as well as for himself. After warming up the rig he roused a friend at Byrd Station, then his good friend Steve Barnes in Boulder, Colorado. He spoke with his wife and two children in Boulder, then got me through via Barnes to my wife Joan in Princeton. It was 4:20 P.M. at McMurdo and 11:20 P.M. of the previous day in New Jersey. Barnes explained to Joan that it was a one-way call: when you temporarily finished speaking you said "Over" to notify your interlocutor it was his turn to talk. Joan sounded greatly surprised and excited.

Feeling like a nervous virgin, I sensed I wasn't being affectionate enough. I sounded too businesslike and too much a part of an exclusively male world. I kept saying how much I loved Antarctica and how my expectations of the ice, aroused by my first visit, had all proved true, and how much I admired the men I had met and how much I looked forward to camping in the field and how terrifically good I felt physically. Joan responded as I hoped she would: she stretched her imagination for me and understood my boyish enthusiasm and my great remoteness physically. Vance remained in Pogo with me, monitoring the equipment. The others had gone to a smaller, unheated shack to give me privacy.

I suggested to Joan that she wake Susy, which she did. Susy, almost thirteen, came on cool, affectionate and an instant master of "Over," to Vance's delight. I was tremendously elated all evening and into the next day as a result of the phone patch.

Everyone got a patch, which made Vance very proud. Jim Elder, grinning, said after his patch, "There's nothing like that to give you an ego boost."

After dinner Vance and I had a few drinks in the small, dim wardroom, which was in an old Jamesway near the Officers' Head and near another Jamesway for Distinguished Visitors named the Ross Hilton. Outside the wardroom was a dim, long corridor where you could hang your parka and cap. The wardroom was always warm, smoky and cozy, the drinks generous and cheap. A large bronze bell hung over the bar. If you pulled the clapper cord and sounded the bell, either deliberately or accidentally, you were obliged to buy drinks for all present. There were ruses to cause a novice to ring the bell. For example, a man at the bar's end might ask the novice to please pass the clapper cord over to him, giving the impression that the man meant to sound the bell and treat. The novice might oblige, causing the bell to ring to the general merriment and his cost. Also, it was a rule that anyone who entered the wardroom with his hat on had to buy drinks for the house. The wardroom was where you could mix freely with anyone, including the admiral. At one end of the room, near a dart game, was a door leading to a small movie theater, where movies were frequently shown. Admission was free.

Brandau did not show up at eight. At about eight-thirty Dave Murphy, a young friend of mine who was in the wardroom, phoned Air Ops (Air Operations) and learned that Brandau was out on a mission. At about nine-thirty Vance and I went to Vance's room and drank from a bottle of bourbon, then I went downstairs with the intention of turning in at once, for I was very tired. There was a knock at my door. When I opened the door I saw an odd but interesting figure in a dirty, rumpled, khaki flight suit and heavy khaki boots. Bowing slightly as though nervously, he shyly said in an uncertain but deep voice that he was Jim Brandau. Dave Murphy had described him to me as resembling Burl Ives, the folk singer and actor, but Brandau was shorter and by no means as stout. As a matter of fact, he looked unusually powerful and fit. I was attracted to him at once and flattered he had come.

As I invited him into my room he said quietly, "I'd like you to have these," and handed me a large piece of Antarctic petrified wood and a piece of Antarctic coal, both of which he had picked up about a hundred and fifty miles from McMurdo. This generous and touching gesture was typical of the man, as I soon discovered. Remembering that Susy had asked me to bring back some interesting rocks, I gratefully accepted. He apologized for not having met me in the wardroom, explaining where he had been, and asked if I cared to go on a helo flight to Cape Evans in the morning to drop off two Kiwis from Scott Base and then stop off at Erebus Glacier Tongue to see an ice cave. I said I'd be delighted.

Then he said that Chris Shepherd wanted to see me now in the Chalet. It being after eleven, I wondered about the request but was glad to go. A party was in progress in the Chalet's mezzanine, with both USARP and Navy people present. Shepherd seemed quite relaxed and very different from the up-tight man he had been the last several days, when he had had to play host to a number of DV's. The clue to the party's meaning was scrawled on the blackboard near the lectern downstairs: two chalk drawings of a raised middle finger, one in full view, the other in profile. Above the drawings was the caption "DV's." Below them a sign read FUCK YOU.

Someone shouted, "Shall we sing a hymn for the DV's?"

There were cries of approval and everyone sang out, "Him! Him! Fuck him!"

Then somebody cried, "How about a folk song?"

And everybody sang loudly, "Folk! Folk! Folk him!"

Shepherd asked Brandau to fetch Vance, who soon joined us. Bottles of booze stood on the long conference table. The VXE-6 people had brought a red wine, served out of a Jim Beam bottle, that Brandau told me had been brewed at Willy Field. I got a shock when I took a large swallow. It tasted exactly like vinegar.

Some 8mm stag films were projected. The first reel was too dark in places. There were boos. The sex act was shown very explicitly. There were groans and comments. When this reel was concluded, at about 1:15, Vance, Brandau and I left. Vance too had been invited to see the ice cave and the three of us were in for a short night.

We breakfasted together next morning, helicoptered to Scott Base to pick up the two Kiwis Brandau had mentioned, dropped them off at Cape Evans, then flew close to the entrance of an ice cave inside Erebus Glacier Tongue, causing some basking Weddells to writhe and hump away in alarm as we descended, hovered and landed. The Tongue cliffs, massive although from the air they seemed insignificant, resembled chalk. The Tongue, afloat but attached to Ross Island, thrust into the Sound with the appearance of a serrated knife from above. From our landing spot we could see white Hut Point Peninsula, Castle Rock jutting black out of it, black islands on the white snow-ice expanse of the Sound, the crisp Royal Society Range, and lovely, thin cloud formations in an azure sky. The day was utterly brilliant: cold if you were in shadow, warm if you weren't. We walked on patches of thick snow in which we descended to our shanks, and on gleaming, hard, uneven, treacherous, beautiful bluish and greenish ice.

The cave entrance was like a pelvic slit, gorgeously and startlingly blue. We climbed and clambered into the cave. The glowing light inside was an eerie, electric lavender. Strange ice formations clung like frozen whipped cream to the ceiling, and glistening ice crystals were encrusted high on the walls. I was the only member of the party not wearing gloves. Occasionally, in a narrow passageway on the rolling, slippery floor, I had to lean a hand against an ice hummock to avoid falling. My hand screamed immediately as though burned. The ice inside the cave was probably at close to mean temperature, many degrees below zero. The view toward the cave entrance showed patches of light, burning through long, thick icicles, that made both walls and ceiling dance.

On returning to McMurdo I went to the Chalet, where I decided with Chris Shepherd that I would go camping at Cape Royds in the morning, taking as my field assistant Dave Murphy of Holmes & Narver, the private contractors. I would stay two nights and be picked up at 1600 on December 21. Later in the day I met with Brian Porter (the Scott Base leader), Shepherd and a Navy commander with a thin face and flaming jug ears. Porter, very cordial, granted me permission to sleep in the historic Ross Island huts and asked me to act as their honorary custodian during my stay. After dinner with the chaplain I spent much time with Dave Murphy, preparing for our outing.

That night I awoke at 3 A.M., dressed, and walked down to the Discovery Hut, the key to which I had borrowed from the chaplain during the evening. I carried with me the first volume of Scott's *The Voyage of the "Discovery"*, which, along with a number of other valuable first editions, the Firestone Library of Princeton University had kindly let me ship to the ice. The hut is about thirty-six feet square and has a pyramidal roof and overhanging eaves. Scott described the eaves as resting "on supports some four feet beyond the sides, surrounding the hut with a covered verandah."

"The interior space," he wrote, "was curtailed by the complete double lining, and numerous partitions were provided to suit the requirements of the occupants. But of these partitions only one was erected, to cut off a small portion of one side, and the larger part which remained formed a really spacious apartment.

"It had been originally intended that the 'Discovery' should not attempt to winter in the Antarctic, but should land a small party and turn northward before the season closed; the hut had been provided for this party and carried south under the impression that circumstances might yet force the adopting of such a plan. Having discovered a spot in which we felt confident the 'Discovery' could winter with safety, the living-hut was no longer of vital importance; but, even retaining the ship as a home, there were still many useful purposes to which a large hut might be adapted."

Later in the volume he wrote again about the hut, this time drawing directly upon his diaries.

"'The main hut is of most imposing dimensions and would accommodate a very large party, but on account of its size and the necessity of economising coal it is very difficult to keep a working temperature inside; consequently it has not been available for some of the purposes for which we had hoped to use it. One of the most important of these was the drying of clothes; for a long time the interior was hung with undergarments which had been washed on board, but all these water-sodden articles became sheets of ice, which only dried as the ice slowly evaporated. When it was found that this process took a fortnight or three weeks the idea was abandoned, and the drying of clothes is now done in the livingspaces on board. . . . But although the hut has not fulfilled expectation in this respect, it is in constant use for other purposes. After the sledging it came in handy for drying the furs, tents, etc.; then it was devoted to the skinning of birds for a month or more, a canvas screen being placed close around the stove, whereby a reasonable temperature was maintained in a small space; then various sailorising jobs, such as the refitting of the awnings and the making of sword matting, were carried on in it; and finally it has been used both for the rehearsal and performance of such entertainments as have served to lighten the monotony of our routine, and in this capacity, when fitted with a stage and decked with scenery, footlights, etc., it probably forms the most pretentious theatre that has ever been seen in polar regions. Of late a solid pedestal of firebricks has been built in the small compartment and on this Bernacchi will shortly be swinging his pendulums for gravity observations; while in the spring I hope that we may be able to use the larger apartment as a centre for collecting, weighing, and distributing the food and equipment of the various sledge parties.

"'On the whole, therefore, our large hut has been and will be of use to us, but its uses are never likely to be of such importance as to render it indispensable, nor cause it to be said that circumstances have justified the outlay made on it or the expenditure of space and trouble in bringing it to its final home. It is here now, however, and here it will stand for many a long year with such supplies as will afford the necessaries of life to any less fortunate party who may follow in our footsteps and be forced to search for food and shelter.'"

Still later in his volume Scott described in some detail two of the theatrical performances produced in the hut, activities that greatly brightened the winter.

"The idea of requisitioning our large hut as a place of entertainment had occurred to us early in the winter, and in this connection it was first used for a concert given during the first week in May [1902]. Royds, who took such pains in getting up this function, arranged a long programme in order to bring forth all the available talent; but although we were not inclined to be critical of our amusements, one was fain to confess that our company had not been chosen for their musical attainments. However, there were exceptions to the mediocrity, and some exhibition of dramatic talent, which prompted the conception of a modified entertainment for a future occasion; so Barne was entrusted with the task of producing a play, and after much casting about succeeded in getting his company together. All became very diligent with rehearsals, and as these were conducted in the hut with all due secrecy, the audience remained in ignorance of even the name of the play until the night of its production. It was decided that this should be immediately after our mid-winter celebrations, and my diary for June 25 gives some account of this great night:

"'At seven to-night we all journey across to the hut, forcing our way through a rather keen wind and light snowdrift. The theatre within looks bright and cheerful, but as there are no heating arrangements other than the lamps, one conquers the natural instinct to take off one's overcoat and head covering, and decides that it will be wise to retain these garments throughout the performance. On one side of the large compartment a fair-sized stage has been erected, raised some two feet above the floor; the edge is decorated with a goodly row of footlights, immediately behind which hangs a drop-curtain depicting the ship and Mount Erebus in glowing colours, and boldly informing one that this is the "Royal Terror Theatre." The remainder of the compartment forms an auditorium of ample size to accommodate all who are not performing, with a stray dog or two brought in to enliven the proceedings.

"'In front stands a row of chairs for the officers, and behind several rows of benches for the men; the apartment is lighted by a large oil lamp, and when all are seated one must own to having seen theatricals under far less realistic conditions. When all are seated also, and when pipes are lit, there is a perceptible improvement in the temperature, a condition that one feels will be very welcome to the lightly clad actors.

"'In due course programmes are passed round, informing us that Part I will consist of several songs rendered by popular singers, and that for Part II we shall have the "Ticket of Leave," "a screaming comedy in one act." These programmes, I may remark, are correct at least in one respect, in that there is some difficulty in picking out the information from amongst the mass of advertisements. Presently the curtain rolls up and discloses Royds at the piano and the first singers in true concert attitude. We have a duet, followed by several solos, and occasionally a rousing chorus, when one rather fears that the roof of the Royal Terror Theatre will rise. On the whole the first part passes decorously, and we come to the interval, when the wags advertise oranges and nuts.

"'Then we have Part II, which is what we are here for; the "screaming comedy" commences and proves to be fully up to its title. There is no need for the actors to speak—their appearance is quite enough to secure the applause of the audience; and when the representatives of the lady parts step on to the stage it is useless for them to attempt speech for several minutes, the audience is so hugely delighted. Thanks to Mr. Clarkson and his make-up box, the disguises are excellent, and it soon becomes evident that the actors have regarded them as by far the most important part of the proceedings, and hold the view that it is rather a waste of time to learn a part when one has a good loud-voiced prompter. As the play progresses one supposes there is a plot, but it is a little difficult to unravel. Presently, however, we are obviously working up to a situation; the hero, or perhaps I should say one of the heroes (for each actor at least attacks his part with heroism) unexpectedly sees through the window the lady on whom he has fixed his affections, and whom, I gather, he has not seen for a long and weary time. He is evidently a little uncertain as to her identity, and at this stirring moment he sits very carefully on a chair—he almost dusts the seat before he does so. Seated and barely glancing at the window, he says with great deliberation and in the most matter-of-fact tones, "It is—no, it isn't—yes, it is—it is my long-lost Mary Jane." The sentiment—or the rendering of it—is greeted with shouts of applause. Later on we work up to a climax, when it is evident that the services of the police force will be required. This part is much more to the taste of the players; somebody has to be chucked out; both he and the "chuckers-out" determine to make their parts quite realistic, and for several minutes there is practically a free fight with imminent risk to the furniture. And so at last the curtain falls amidst vociferous cheering, and I for one have to acknowledge that I have rarely been so gorgeously entertained. With renewed cheers we break up and wander back to the ship, after having witnessed what the "S.P.T." ["South Polar Times," the ship's paper, edited by Shackleton] may veraciously describe as "one of the most successful entertainments ever given within the Polar Circle"—and indeed they might with some truth add "or anywhere else." ' "

As I stood alone in the hut, feeling remote from the rest of the station, possibly because it was the middle of the night and the station had looked completely deserted, I opened Scott's volume and read the above pages. Then I read a paragraph that has always moved me:

" 'Beyond the large hut stand the smaller magnetic huts, and from the eminence on that point the little cluster of buildings looks quite imposing. In the midst of these vast ice-solitudes and under the frowning desolation of the hills, the ship, the huts, the busy figures passing to and fro, and the various other evidences of human activity are extraordinarily impressive. How strange it all seems! For countless ages the great sombre mountains about us have loomed through the gloomy polar night with never an eye to mark their grandeur, and for countless ages the wind-swept snow has drifted over these great deserts with never a footprint to break its white surface; for one brief moment the eternal solitude is broken by a hive of human insects; for one brief moment they settle, eat, sleep, trample, and gaze, then they must be gone, and all must be surrendered again to the desolation of the ages.' "

CHAPTER 7

CAMPING AT CAPE ROYDS

Cape Royds, a dark volcanic mass, the westernmost part of Ross Island, located approximately midway between the island's northern and southern extremities, is noteworthy for at least two reasons. It was the base of Shackleton's British Antarctic Expedition, the Terra Nova Expedition of 1907-9; and it is the site of the world's southernmost penquin (Adélie) rookery. In addition, it is fascinating because of its eerie, moonlike beauty.

A friend of mine recently asked me, "What's special about the fact that Royds is the home of the *southernmost* penguin rookery?"

The answer is that the farther south you go in these latitudes, in general the more extreme are the weather conditions you encounter. The Adélies feed in the sea; there is nothing on land to sustain them. They return to their old nests. Each October the Royds Adélies leave the pack ice and the open sea and walk and toboggan southward over the frozen Sound to their rookery. There is a certain raw courage, even though based on ancient habit, in their being the southernmost of their kind, and not only of *their* kind but of all penguins as well.

The prospect of returning to Royds excited me. (I had spent part of a day there the previous year.) I wanted to check my memory with respect to the cape's beauty as well as to learn if the place was as lovely late in December, when much of the snow would have melted, as it was in November, when it sported a thick mantle of snow. And I looked forward to observing the Adélies again, this time at leisure. But above all I was eager to live in the field.

Few people have the opportunity to camp out in Antarctica who do not have either scientific or logistic work to do there. Yet it is only in the field, away from the comforts of stations, that you can hope to get an authentic feel for the continent. Also, I wanted to go over the terrain until I no longer felt a stranger to it. The reason I planned to sleep in the historic hut was that I hoped thereby to lessen the awe I had for it, and the sense of distance I felt between me and its early residents, who had dared and endured so much. It seemed to me that awe and a sense of distance would not be conducive to sober and hopefully illuminating writing about such a place.

I knew of three kinds of previous residents at Royds: the original ones—indigenous so far as one can be indigenous in a place so hostile to land life; scientists in modern times; and the huts restoration parties (New

Zealanders), who lived and worked there about a decade ago with the logistic support of the United States Navy. All had one element in common: functional work. Dave Murphy and I were to be something new to the place: extended visitors. If before we went to Royds we had notions of ourselves, as some of our friends had, as being idle vacationers we soon became disabused of them. We learned that camping at Royds was bone-tiring. When, having lost weight and been badly sunburned, we returned to McMurdo, the heated buildings came as a bodily shock.

The gap between visitors and residents at Cape Royds as well as at Cape Evans is considerable. Visitors stop by for an hour or two to tour the rookery and the hut. Few people have resided for a substantial time at Cape Royds since Shackleton's day. All in modern times have been scientists, studying the penguins, skuas and the cape's geology. In Shackleton's time the cape meant home. To modern residents home is McMurdo Station or Scott Base, with which, normally, they are in daily touch by radio. The early residents wintered over. No one in modern times winters over at any of the capes of Ross Island.

Neither Murphy nor I had camped out in Antarctica before. We asked many questions about what camping at Royds would be like but rarely received firm replies. For a while we could not elicit so simple a fact as whether the cape contained a wanigan (refuge hut). At last the deputy leader of Scott Base, Jim Barker, assured me there was one there, although he hadn't seen it. What did it contain? What was the temperature inside it and inside the Shackleton hut likely to be this time of year? What steps ought I to take to keep my cameras, tape recorder and batteries from freezing? We encountered a surprising ignorance regarding these and similar questions. Part of the reason was the lack of continuity of personnel. People came and went, and many failed to leave records.

One day at dinner three microbiologists from California asked me if it was true that I planned to sleep in the historic huts. When I said it was, they professed to be concerned about me. The huts, they asserted, were loaded with viable fungi, bacteria and viruses in conditions capable of supporting good cultures. Blubber decayed into energy and water; the water could keep certain microorganisms alive. In addition to blubber the huts contained old unwrapped biscuits, pony fodder, dead penguins, seal meat. The microbiologists named a fungal lung disease, aspergillosis, that you could contract by breathing spores. The chances of my becoming infected were probably slight but I should not discount them, I was told.

I heard some lively anecdotes about the viability of microorganisms.

For example, there was a house in California that sixty years ago had been occupied by a tubercular family. Recently some bedroom baseboards had been ripped out and had been found to be harboring live bacilli. Viable bacteria had been discovered in feces deposited during the Scott and Shackleton expeditions. A group of graduate students had rummaged around in old Indian sites in the San Joaquin Valley in California. Twenty had come down with Valley Fever and one had almost died of it. One of the microbiologists expressed the strong suspicion that the population decline of the Royds rookery since Shackleton's time was largely due to the presence of the hut, which in his opinion was probably a source of infection. He counseled me not to sleep in the huts; if I insisted on doing so I should spend a minimum of time in them and avoid stirring up dust and touching things.

I 'had never thought of the huts as a form of man's pollution of Antarctica. I had conceived of them only as historic shrines. The microbiologists were experts at obtaining and analyzing air samples. When I asked them to analyze samples of air from the Discovery Hut they said they were too busy, which probably was true but which alerted me to the possibility they were pulling my leg out of its socket.

One other bit of intellectual-emotional baggage accompanied us to Royds. This was the matter of the untried radio. Would the rig operate successfully on batteries? Or would the latter be too weak for the distance, or fail because of the cold? Would the radio work on the generator if necessary? The rule for field parties was that they check in daily with McMurdo by radio. If a party was not heard from for seventy-two hours McMurdo would send a plane to seek the reason. If your radio went bad you were advised to exercise special caution in anything unusual you did, for a minor accident could be serious if it occurred relatively far from shelter and was followed by bad weather. We knew this but paid little attention to it. Also, we were told unofficially that as long as the weather was bad enough to cause risk to pilots' lives we would not be rescued in case we were in trouble. We didn't bother to ask ourselves if this was hyperbole, for we really didn't care if it was or not. There is something about Antarctica that gives you a feeling akin to the self-confidence of the punchy boxer about to enter the ring for the victory he knows he so richly deserves.

On Saturday, December 19, after an early breakfast, Murphy and I walked up to the Field Center, loaded our gear onto a pickup truck and drove down to the helo pads, where some enlisted men were warming helo engines with huge pre-heater hoses. A strong wind was blowing. Murphy inquired if the helos would fly in it this morning. The men thought not, but when one of them asked Murphy who his pilot was and Murphy replied, "Brandau," the man said, "Oh, *he'll* fly in anything."

A little later Brandau, wearing a rumpled flight suit and a tan woolen hat like a skull cap, and with an old sheath knife strapped to his left leg, walked up from the helo hangar and said, "Mr. Neider, you'll sit in the cockpit."

He told the crewman to show me how to climb up to the cockpit on the port side. The crewman warned me not to touch a small yellow handle, which was designed to eject part of the canopy in an emergency, and to avoid another handle, which would do something else I wouldn't enjoy at the moment. It felt like more of a climb than I had expected. I slipped my right leg into the cockpit, got my torso to follow it, then drew my left leg in and sat down. My toes rested on a small platform but my heels were in the space of the cabin below me. The crewman, having climbed up behind me, cautioned me not to interfere with the motion of the control stick between my knees and not to touch the pedals or any of the levers. He showed me how to harness and belt myself in and how to don the communications helmet and plug it into the intercom system.

Brandau flew inland to show me black Castle Rock, that historic landmark, at close range. Passing to the right or east of it, we got shoved about by strong gusts. His sun vizor was always pulled down. Inasmuch as mine interfered with the use of my cameras, I utilized it only rarely. Whenever the heading of the craft brought the sun to my eyes I was instantly blinded and had to slip the vizor out of the helmet's forward compartment. Mostly I was shooting through my open hatch in the direction away from the sun. Brandau had told me I was free to slide the hatch open or shut as I pleased. Usually, in the Navy H-34, I had marvelously unobscured views when the hatch was open, even when I looked down. But when we were too close to the ice, the rotor blast caused the air directly below us to vibrate and shimmy, and scenes there were distorted as if by heat waves. The open hatch let in a raw, cold airstream, which pained my naked hands and immediately chilled the cockpit, but Brandau never complained. On rare occasions I leaned far out and into the stream; it was difficult to catch one's breath then, and tears ran copiously.

We flew over Erebus Glacier Tongue, over Cape Evans, then out over the Sound off Cape Royds, where he hoped to show me some whales in the pack ice. This was as far south as the pack went at this time. No whales were visible. We saw slices of green or oil-brown water. We flew over Backdoor Bay (so named because it's behind Shackleton's hut) and landed on a hilltop pad marked by a circle of red-painted volcanic rocks. This prescribed route for helicopters avoided the rookery. Adélies are terrified by helos that fly low over them. They scatter in a panic, leaving eggs and chicks as easy prey for the always waiting skuas.

Brandau shut down the engine and descended to the rookery while Murphy and I off-loaded our gear with the crewman's help. We carted the lighter things to a lower area behind a ridge, thus sheltering them from the rotors, which on take-off would make a wind of some thirty or thirty-five knots. The heavier ones we placed on the plateau near the pad. Brandau returned and then, as we waved good-by, the helo lifted off.

Some of our gear, such as the 1,800-watt generator, the five-gallon plastic jugs of water, the five-gallon fuel drum, the cartons of food, was quite heavy. With the exception of the generator, which we left near the pad, we carried the gear over uneven terrain down a long, curving black slope to the door of the Nimrod (Shackleton) Hut. From the hut the way sloped gently downward to the thawed eastern shore of Pony Lake, then northward and upward some two hundred feet to the wanigan. Securing ourselves against the possibility of the weather's souring, we moved water, food and survival gear into the wanigan and staked down a heavy handline between the two structures, hammering short black metal stakes into the black volcanic soil. I had promised Brian Porter, the Scott Base leader, that only I would sleep in the hut and that I would bring nothing into it that might endanger it. The historic huts, being located in the Ross Dependency, were technically under the jurisdiction of New Zealand. I had visions of a New Zealand headline: Yank's Carelessness Destroys Shackleton's Antarctic Hut.

If, while I was asleep in the hut, a long-lasting blizzard blew up, I might be trapped without food, heat and water. In that case it would be uncomfortable to crawl alongside the yellow line to the wanigan, but without the line I might conceivably not survive. At the moment, the sky being cloudless, I felt a bit foolish to be hammering at the stakes. I hoped Murphy did not think I was unduly cautious. But I knew from reading that men had come close to dying within feet of a door or a handline during Antarctic blizzards. An Antarctic blizzard had the capacity not merely of animalizing you; it could make a vegetable of you; it could disorient you to the point where you behaved in a manner that seemed suicidal. The winds could bowl you over and over, and the particles they blew about might have more of the consistency of sand than snow.

We spent much of that first day in tiring chores. By leaving some of our sweat at Royds we came to feel we had earned the right to call the place home. The work, sapping us physically, thereby set a sober or at least a non-superficial tone to our stay. We both were ready for a greater physical price than we had been paying at McMurdo and for the deeper experience we hoped would accompany it. Also, we got to know each other during those long hours. I felt very lucky in my choice of Dave Murphy as a field assistant and companion. I had gotten to know him almost accidentally. On the day of my arrival at McMurdo he and Vance had helped me lug my cartons of gear, shipped ahead of me from Davisville, Rhode Island, down the cindery hill to my room in the Lodge. I had encountered him casually here and there and had invariably been impressed by his good humor, modesty, brightness and by the aura of quiet competence which emanated from him. Twenty-four, he was strong, had a fine if somewhat raucous laugh, and was keenly aware of and sympathetic to the work I had to do.

Turning to the radio, we tested it from inside the wanigan, for an icy wind was now blowing. We heard scientific data and various comments being exchanged. All had in common the fact that the purveyors and receivers were oblivious of our battery existence. We could receive but not transmit. Had the batteries so soon been drained by the cold? Or was the trouble perhaps in the whip antenna, that long, rapier-like appendage that threatened one's eyes, especially in the confined space of the shack?

We tried to transmit from outside the wanigan but still without success. We were without communication with the world but this seemed fine to us, for it left us free after the encroachments on one's privacy and freedom inherent in the life of an Antarctic station. On the other hand, as long as we were without radio contact we could not leave Royds ahead of schedule should we find it urgent to do so. An escape on foot was not possible, even in the best of weather.

As for the weather, if we got socked in we could hold out in the wanigan a long time. In addition to our own food we had the emergency supplies on the shelves, in the form mainly of dehydrated foodstuffs packaged in New Zealand and Australia. There were also such items as canned goods, sugar, flour, biscuits and lots of hard candy. The weather was still good although a wind from the direction of Erebus was bringing heavy clouds.

We carried the radio to the helo pad and tried it up there, hoping the hilltop position would get us through. No dice. We hooked up and started the generator, letting it warm up for the required fifteen minutes before drawing power from it. Over and over I said, "McMurdo Station. McMurdo Station. This is McMurdo Three Two requesting a radio check. This is McMurdo Three Two at Cape Royds, trying out some experimental gear. Do you read me? Over."

At last we heard McMurdo—he came in booming and clear, startling us—telling us we were extremely weak.

But dependence on the generator wouldn't do. Our task was to try to get the radio to work on batteries alone. We carried the radio to the crest of a black hill just south of the hut, in the lee of which the hut had been built so it would be sheltered from the biting southeasterlies. McMurdo could receive us, but again he said we were very weak.

It was time now for lunch. Carrying the rig, we returned to the wanigan. Standing, completely dressed except for gloves, we wolfed salt crackers and unlabeled canned butter; tea with Pream; and unlabeled canned strawberry jam with the consistency and appearance of pink axle grease. Meanwhile Murphy fried some frozen steaks on a bed of salt and heated some vegetable soup, but only after much fussing with the Coleman stove, which refused at first to throw a blue flame, giving us instead a long yellow one that threatened to blacken the inside of the shack. For dessert we sucked frozen peaches. There was nothing to heat the shack with except the cooking stove, and we had to keep the door ajar as a precaution against monoxide fumes. We could have sat on the double bunks or on the crates visible beneath them. It was simpler and warmer to stand and shift about.

The wanigan was a plywood box which I judged to be 8′×12′×8′. It was secured against winds by a staked-down wire hawser looped over it. The side farthest from the door had the two bunks. Murphy now chose the upper one for sleeping in, generously leaving me the lower for a work space. The southern wall (on the door's right as you entered) contained the shelves of foodstuffs; the northern had a work table for preparing food. The quarters were cramped but cozy and snowtight. There were no pinups. Instead, there were little pinned pieces of paper telling you who had lived here and when.

We washed dishes and utensils in warm water, then set up a dipole antenna behind the wanigan, failed to get through with it, found a break in a connection, mended it with adhesive tape and failed again. We brought the antenna with its poles and long wire to the vicinity of the Nimrod Hut, lugged the generator downhill to the south of the hut and tried the radio with both dipole and generator, working outdoors so the generator's power line was at a safe distance from the historic structure.

At last we roused McMurdo but so weakly he said he would see if he couldn't improve things for us. He asked us to call him next at 6 P.M.

Free now to visit the rookery, we headed for it along the feather-strewn north shore of Pony Lake, passing dead Adélie chicks whose stomachs had been pierced by skua beaks; a few dead adult penguins; some dead skuas; and some skeletons of both. The shore's rocks and soil were thinly crusted over in places by a whitish substance that we took to be salt from evaporated spume and scud blown inland from the Sound when the latter was ice-free. The lake, about the size of a pond, contained bird debris as well as algae in the shallower, thawed parts we were able to observe.

At one point, to the right or north of the rookery, the cape plunged from a height into the Sound. The dark terrain was not forbidding, for it was brightened by the pure sky and the Sound's whiteness. The Sound looked marbled at close range because of contrasts between the sea ice and the latter's thin mantle of snow. The ragged snow splotches were whiter than the ice, which was tinged with a faint wash of bluing. The tidal crack, reflecting the sky's blue, was some ten to fifteen feet wide. Half a dozen Weddells lay just beyond it, and a group of some twenty Adélies were waddling far out, heading north.

The penguins in the rookery paid little or no attention to us. Their eyes looked unreal, jewels stuck in black velvet. Their beaks were mottled brown, like tortoise shell, and were flesh-colored inside. From places in the rookery you could see the birds backgrounded by Erebus, a white plume flying from the volcano's crest. In the rookery were hard, guano-crusted trails between boulders. Some of the birds were nesting high up on boulder conglomerate that looked like giant loaves of black bread mashed upon each other. A lone skua stood placidly within the rookery, now and again making a little quacking sound. The penguins dozed on their nests. When they occasionally shifted they revealed one or two pale blue eggs, or a pair of very young gray chicks with spindly necks, whose heads wobbled uncertainly as the beaks opened wide for a meal of regurgitated food. The parents kept looking down to make certain the eggs and chicks were securely in place. When a skua flew low over the rookery or landed in it, angry grunting was elicited from the nearest Adélies.

I had written earlier about this rookery:

"The Adélie is about eighteen inches high and weighs some fourteen pounds. (The Emperor is much larger, being about three feet high and weighing about sixty pounds). Penguins are marvelous navigators. They navigate by the sun, but exactly how is not yet understood. They have been known to attack men (comically) and dogs (tragically), with the manner of a person strong on moral indignation. Everyone has read about their comical behavior, their curiosity about man's doings, their innocence in the presence of huskies, their being preyed upon by leopard seals and skuas.

"There were hundreds of them already egg-sitting but there was a great bustle as individuals sought little gray pumice-textured stones for their nest, picking them up earnestly and waddling proudly away, their flippers working like primitive arms. If a nest is temporarily vacant a neighbor doesn't hesitate to steal stones from it. The occupant on returning seems blissfully unaware of the loss. When a bird wanders too close to an occupied nest the nester squawks furiously and makes threatening gestures, causing the trespasser to retreat in haste. There is a great quacking and squawking but with no suggestion of chaos, rather of the patient, endless bustle of a flea market. Their food is in the unfrozen sea miles to the north and they wait unfed until their mate returns from the sea to spell them. I had expected to visit immaculate citizens in formal dress but this was not an immaculate time. The white breasts were stained brown, tan and green and the areas around the nests were colored by guano. I had read in the accounts of the early explorers how strong the guano smell is but it seemed mild today, hardly more pungent than that of cormorants at their hangouts on Point Lobos in California.

"Occasionally a bird points its beak at the zenith, stretches its neck to the utmost, flaps its flippers and makes a clucking, chattering sound which begins slowly and softly and rises to considerable speed and volume before dying out. Sometimes as it fades it ends with sounds of choking or gargling, reminding one of a death rattle. This exercise, moving from individual to individual, is almost continuous in the group. When several birds display simultaneously the effect is cacophonous."

A year earlier I had headed from the hut towards the rookery. The way then was over thick snow and across Pony Lake with its treacherously hidden green ice. After that first visit to Royds I had written, "Both Scott and Cherry-Garrard have commented on the great beauty of Cape Evans, with its western views of glaciers and snow-capped mountains and with its proximity to the striking snout of the Barne Glacier."

But Royds too looks out on the Western Mountains. And when Scott wrote in his journal so enthusiastically about Evans he had not had a chance to live at Royds. It's true that the Royds hut is not elementally close to the shore, as the Evans one is, and lacks the proximity to something so dazzlingly raw as the Barne Glacier, and is humanized by the humanoid Adélies, but these facts only place it in a tamer setting than that of Evans, not a less beautiful one.

Heading north along shore rocks to have a closer view of some pressure ice, we broke through crusted ice into fish-stinking muddy water almost to our ankles, Murphy in his mukluks, I in my hiking boots. Then I slid and almost fell into thawed guano on a small hillside. We gave up trying to go further along the shore in that direction, for we might break through into the sea itself. We returned to the rookery.

While Murphy, fascinated, lingered there, I went to the Nimrod Hut to prepare my sleeping accommodations, which consisted of a green canvas cot with an aluminum frame, a striped cot mattress and a green Bauer sleeping bag. The temperature in the hut was 29°F. on the floor and 30° on the large table near the stove on the hut's eastern side. I set up the cot between the table and a pewlike bench south of it. The bench was covered with dusty burlap and held four and a half pairs of battered old shoes. Above it were photographs of Edward VII and Queen Alexandra, the sovereigns who had given Shackleton's expedition their public blessing by visiting the *Nimrod* just before it left England in 1907. I thought of Shackleton's bitter disappointment in being invalided home; of the great difficulties he had experienced in obtaining financial support for an expedition of his own; and of his persistence, persistence and unsinkable optimism.

The hut was more substantial than I remembered it to be from my visit of a year ago. It was about nine of my paces wide and, excluding the porch, about fifteen of them long. The floor, of neatly joined boards, showed much wear, discoloration and the marks of hobnailed boots, yet it was still so solid it didn't creak. Many of the original bunks, as indicated in the hut plan in Shackleton's *The Heart of the Antarctic,* were no longer extant, so the interior was more spacious than it had been. In Shackleton's time some of the bunks had been set at right angles to the walls. Now there were two cots and a cratelike bunk parallel to the northern wall, and a similar bunk parallel to the southern one.

When new, the structure had had two southern and two northern windows. The southwestern window had been boarded up long ago. From the remaining southern window you saw, as Shackleton and his companions had seen and as Scott had later seen, a small, more or less free land area, past which, some fifty feet away, was a falling crest of lava rock. From the northern windows you looked out over the remains of the pony stable: bales of fodder, piles of corn kernels, rusted tin cans, sacks of wheat and flour. Past the stable was a wasteland of black hills suggesting a moonscape. The hut was well illuminated. It looked neat. And although it had the inevitable odors of such a place—of dankness, of a stable, of fishy rot—they were not strong enough to be overly offensive.

On the north side were a pair of finneskoes; white canvas sacks; socks worn through at the heels. On a cot were two large dark reindeer-skin sleeping bags. Here and there were a book on a shelf, its covers gone; a hobnailed boot hanging from a nail; bits of netting; canvas shoes; jackets and trousers; a great pair of navy blue trousers. Hanging from a shelf was something resembling a white prayer shawl, dirty, red-striped, with tassels. Harness hung everywhere. A ski leaned against a wall. Patches of dirty white canvas lay on crates or on the floor. Suspended from a beam above the table was an old Nansen sledge as well as heavy iron bars from which gear could be hung. The stove and its pots were deeply rusted but bits of the original black paint still clung to the oven doors. Beyond the stove (that is, east of it), was a tiny cubicle, originally a darkroom, separated from the rest of the place by a sheet of striped burlap. In it were dusty jars and test tubes. On a shelf to the right of the cubicle were enameled metal plates and trays as well as some crockery. There was no photograph of Shackleton visible but his presence seemed to me to linger strongly in the hut.

I was fascinated by the foods still intact in their unopened cans and jars; foods that brought one's thoughts to an earlier, simpler time, that of his first expedition, before the First World War. Bird's Concentrated Egg Powder, "a complete substitute for though not made from eggs." Colman's Mustard. Heinz Preserved Sweet Midget Gherkins. Arrowroot. Ox tongues. Ham loaf. Kippered mackerel. Chicken and veal pâté. Consolidated pea soup. Pure preserved beet roots. Pure preserved scarlet runners (no soaking required). Preserved carrots. Pure preserved celery. Cabbage. Scotch kale. Chicken and ham pâté. Gravy soup. Ox tails. Kidney soup. Cloves. Calavances. Valencia raisins. Split peas. Marrow-fat peas. Flaked tapioca. Hops. Mixed pickles. Gooseberries. Parsnips. Cocoa. Apple jelly. Red plum marmalade. Tripe. Boiled mutton. Minced steak. Bacon rations. Stewed kidneys. Irish Brawn. Boiled mutton. Roasted veal. Mutton cutlets. Cod roes. Many foods, such as Huntley & Palmer's Digestive Plain Biscuits, were still in their sealed crates. Three unopened hams hung from hooks.

All these foods reminded me forcefully of Shackleton's personality, his trials, and above all his great achievement, the incredible farthest southing made with this hut as its base. It was wonderful to be alone in the hut—I had lacked the privilege the previous year—and to feel, slowly, the place changing for me from a shrine to a structure that was, temporarily and in a tiny sense, my home, which would shelter me for the night.

From my journal:

"When the penguins aren't quack-squawking and the wind is down the silence is miraculous. The air is superb and very dry. You are alternately very cold or comfortable, depending on the wind and on where you are. The floors of both huts are very cold. Dave put on mukluks for this reason. I brought along black thermal boots but prefer to use my own hiking boots. We eat standing. I could carry in the brand-new collapsible plastic crapper with its aluminum legs, or drag out a small crate from under the bunks, but one is fed up with chores, one is lazy, very tired, one's back literally aches from bending, squatting, stooping, *carrying*— and one doesn't give a damn whether one sits or stands, the main thing is that one is *here,* in all this incredibly photogenic landscape."

For dinner we had dehydrated shrimp that tasted like softly compacted sawdust. After downing some of it we threw the rest out in front of the wanigan. Two skuas came and gorged themselves. Always hungry, we filled up on beef stew, canned bread, more frozen peaches and on some of the wanigan's hard candy, then sat silent in the shelter of the front of the refuge hut (the wind was still blowing behind us, from the east), resting in the warmth of the evening sun.

We turned in early. Undressing in the Nimrod Hut, I was momentarily shy about the windows being uncovered, then realized how sensational it would be if a stranger peeked in. The uncertain radio communications added to the sense of our autonomy. I hoped no visitors would descend upon us tomorrow to spoil our splendid isolation and our proprietary sense of the place. On an impulse I shone my flashlight beam into some of the dark upper corners, expecting to see cobwebs. Then I remembered. "No webs down here. No spiders. No insects. This is Antarctica."

I crawled into my sleeping bag, bunched my wool shirt into a pillow, and zipped myself in. I fell quickly asleep. I awoke twice during the night and lay awake a bit and thought of all the chores I had to do and about the microbiologists' warnings and about whether I was breathing in the spores which might give me aspergillosis and whether Murphy and I would ever find the contact lens he had lost in front of the hut and I realized that the bright light, shifting with the unsetting sun's circular motion, had been bothering me, and I looked around for ghosts but there were none.

CHAPTER 8

CAPE ROYDS CONCLUDED

My alarm clock awoke me at six. The night had had an unexpected effect: the hut's foodstuffs no longer seemed strange, and the skis and sledges seemed to beckon as if I had once used them. I went outside. The sun was over Erebus.

Two guy wires had been looped over the hut to secure it against blizzards. On the right of the door an old sledge leaned against a wall. The door, originally hinged on the right or southern side, had been blown off in a storm long ago and was now hinged on the left side. It had been painted a brilliant orange, I presumed in modern times.

On the hut's northern side, where the stables had been, were bales of browned, weatherworn, still-wired fodder; venesta cases neatly stacked to form a wall; harness hanging from nails; rusty tin cans; a wooden puppy house; a large metal funnel; and a toilet seat made by cutting a round hole in the top of a crate. I wondered what the Shackleton expedition had done with feces, which do not decay readily at that latitude. We had found modern feces north of the wanigan, very dry, looking like plastic, and I had shoveled as many as I could find into latrine sacks to be taken back to McMurdo. Later today Murphy would roll three large empty fuel drums up to the helo pad for removal. This was Brandau's idea. Brandau had a passion about keeping Antarctica clean. There was old litter on the southern side of the hut too, including glass jars and many rusted cans.

I went inside the hut, where I picked up my copy of the second volume of *The Heart of the Antarctic,* in which Shackleton had set down some fascinating notes on the effects of severe hunger during the southern journey. I read:

"When we were living on meat our desire for cereals and farinaceous foods became stronger; indeed any particular sort of food of which we were deprived seemed to us to be the food for which nature craved. When we were short of sugar we would dream of sweet-stuffs, and when biscuits were in short supply our thoughts were concerned with crisp loaves and all the other good things displayed in the windows of the bakers' shops. During the last weeks of the journey outwards, and the long march back, when our allowance of food had been reduced to twenty ounces per man a day, we really thought of little but food. The glory of the great mountains that towered high on either side, the majesty of the enormous glacier up which we travelled so painfully, did not appeal to our emotions to any great extent. Man becomes very primitive when he is hungry and short of food, and we learned to know what it is to be desperately hungry. I used to wonder sometimes whether the people who suffer from hunger in the big cities of civilisation felt as we were feeling, and I arrived at the conclusion that they did not, for no barrier of law and order would have been allowed to stand between us and any food that had been available. The man who starves in a city is weakened, hopeless, spiritless, and we were vigorous and keen. Until January 9 the desire for food was made the more intense by our knowledge of the fact that we were steadily marching away from the stores of plenty.

"We could not joke about food, in the way that is possible for the man who is hungry in the ordinary sense. We thought about it most of the time, and on the way back we used to talk about it, but always in the most serious manner possible. We used to plan out the enormous meals that we proposed to have when we got back to the ship and, later, to civilisation. On the outward march we did not experience really severe hunger until we got on the great glacier, and then we were too much occupied with the heavy and dangerous climbing over the rough ice and crevasses to be able to talk much. We had to keep some distance apart in case one man fell into a crevasse. Then on the plateau our faces were generally coated with ice, and the blizzard wind blowing from the south made unnecessary conversation out of the question. Those were silent days, and our remarks to one another were brief and infrequent. It was on the march back that we talked freely of food, after we had got down the glacier and were marching over the barrier surface. The wind was behind us, so that the pulling was not very heavy, and as there were no crevasses to fear we were able to keep close together. We would get up at 5 A.M. in order to make a start at 7 A.M., and after we had eaten our scanty breakfast, that seemed only to accentuate hunger, and had begun the day's march, we could take turns in describing things we would eat in the good days to come. We were each going to give a dinner to the others in turn, and there was to be an anniversary dinner every year, at which we would be able to eat and eat and eat. No French chef ever devoted more thought to the invention of new dishes than we did.

"On a typical day during this backward march we would leave camp at about 6.40 A.M., and half an hour later would have recovered our frost-bitten fingers, while the moisture on our clothes, melted in the sleeping-bags, would have begun to ablate, after having first frozen hard. We would be beginning to march with some degree of comfort, and one of us would remark, 'Well, boys, what are we going to have for breakfast to-day?' We had just finished our breakfast as a matter of fact, consisting of half a pannikin of semi-raw horse-meat, one biscuit and a half and a pannikin of tea, but the meal had not taken the keenness from our appetites. We used to try to persuade ourselves that our half-biscuit was not quite a half, and sometimes we managed to get a little bit more that way. The question would receive our most serious and careful consideration at once, and we would proceed to weave from our hungry imaginations a tale of a day spent in eating. 'Now we are on board ship,' one man would say. 'We wake up in a bunk, and the first thing we do is to stretch out our hands to the side of the bunk and get some chocolate, some Garibaldi biscuits and some apples. We eat those in the bunk, and then we get up for breakfast. Breakfast will be at eight o'clock, and we will have porridge, fish, bacon and eggs, cold ham, plum pudding, sweets, fresh roll and butter, marmalade and coffee. At eleven o'clock we will have hot cocoa, open jam tarts, fried cods' roe and slices of heavy plum cake. That will be all until lunch at one o'clock. For lunch we will have Wild roll, shepherd's pie, fresh soda-bread, hot milk, treacle pudding, nuts, raisins and cake. After that we will turn in for a sleep, and we will be called at 3.45, when we will reach out again from the bunks and have doughnuts and sweets. We will get up then and have big cups of hot tea and fresh cake and chocolate creams. Dinner will be at six, and we will have thick soup, roast beef and Yorkshire pudding, cauliflower, peas, asparagus, plum pudding, fruit, apple-pie with thick cream, scones and butter, port wine, nuts, and almonds and raisins. Then at midnight we will have a really big meal, just before we go to bed. There will be melon, grilled trout and butter-sauce, roast chicken with plenty of livers, a proper salad with eggs and very thick dressing, green peas and new potatoes, a saddle of mutton, fried suet pudding, peaches à la Melba, egg curry, plum pudding and sauce, Welsh rarebit, Queen's pudding, angels on horse-back, cream cheese and celery, fruit, nuts, port wine, milk and cocoa. Then we will go to bed and sleep till breakfast time. We will have chocolate and biscuits under our pillows, and if we want anything to eat in the night we will just have to get it.' Three of us would listen to this programme and perhaps suggest amendments and improvements, generally in the direction of additional dishes, and then another one of us would take up the running and sketch another glorious day of feeding and sleeping.

"I daresay that all this sounds very greedy and uncivilised to the reader who has never been on the verge of starvation, but as I have said before, hunger makes a man primitive. We did not smile at ourselves or at each other as we planned wonderful feats of over-eating. We were perfectly serious about the matter, and we noted down in the back pages of our diaries details of the meals that we had decided to have as soon as we got back to the places where food was plentiful. All the morning we would allow our imaginations to run riot in this fashion. Then would come one o'clock, and I would look at my watch and say, 'Camp!' We would drop the harness from our tired bodies and pitch the tent on the smoothest place available, and three of us would get inside to wait for the thin and scanty meal, while the other man filled the cooker with snow and fragments of frozen meat. An hour later we would be on the march again, once more thinking and talking of food, and this would go on until the camp in the evening. We would have another scanty meal, and turn into the sleeping-bags, to dream wildly of food that somehow we could never manage to eat."

Reading these pages, it seemed both strange and marvelous to be standing in Shackleton's hut.

Murphy was still asleep when I reached the wanigan. I heated water before waking him. He prepared a steak breakfast. Afterwards we hiked northward, intending to reach the southern limit of the pack ice. In a niche of the hills we came upon an old, rusty dump heap. Sometimes, when we climbed black hills with the consistency of sand dunes, our heels smoked with volcanic dust. Much of the terrain looked burned out. We crossed solid black rock. In the hill shelves and cups it could be almost oppressively warm but if you came within range of a wind you might get rapidly chilled. Standing on a hilltop, we saw the wanigan, the hut, the rookery, Flagstaff Point. The rookery seemed to be bathed by dappled poetic light even though the sky was cloudless. Its guano-tan was the sole warm color in the entire cape scene. The shore of Pony Lake nearest the rookery looked gentle. Although the sky was a pale blue, the color reflected in the lake was a gorgeous royal. Beyond the rookery we saw the dome of Mount Discovery, far to the south.

It was extremely pleasant to wander in this landscape. Erebus showed bare veined ribs. Its second crater looked quite clear of snow. There was a fascinating contrast between the black foreground—huge, strong, sweeping—and Erebus's delicacy, with its gentle slopes and sensuous, snowy sides. The black mass had been vomited out of Erebus's throat. We saw vistas of loaf-studded black terrain petering out toward the volcano's glacial slopes. We came to a pond in which skuas were bathing. The pond's shores were thick with coarse red algae; its waters were reddish. This was Shackleton's Green Lake. I could not understand why it had been so named. (Next day, coming upon it from a different angle, I saw a green cast to it.)

The skua is a powerfully built, gull-like, bipolar bird with a strong arched neck, a large, curved bill, and capable talons. The Antarctic skua has been described as resembling a small eagle. It has no hesitation in attacking man. Seeing us, the birds set up cries of alarm, cries somehow pathetic, like those of primitive women keening. Then they attacked, diving low in an effort to strike us with the leading edge of their powerful wings. One bird kept coming in at chest level, wing edges uplifted, tail fanned out, beak open. Some flew above us, hovered, and tried to defecate on us. When we passed beyond the lake they ceased attacking us en masse, but it was not possible to avoid being attacked from time to time as we moved northward, for they nested in the hills, and their nests were mere depressions in the lee of a rock.

It was exciting to encounter an erratic boulder occasionally—granite, gneiss, schist, porphyry, sandstone—brought by glaciers from the Western Mountains. They were a relief from the volcanic forms all around us. We gathered some rocks. Most were porous and dark gray or black but a few were the hue of old red brick. Some were heavy and contained feldspar crystals.

Encountering streams of noisy meltwater, we went as far north as Blacksand Beach, one of the few beaches in the McMurdo Sound area. There was pack ice abreast of it, hummocked and shredded by pressure. A long snow slope ran down like a road to it from the height on which we stood. It would have been fun to go down there but the snow was deep and looked soft. We might have disappeared in it.

We visited the rookery again and again; climbed to the end of Flagstaff Point; hiked to Green Lake a second time; studied the hut's interior at greater length; fiddled endlessly with the radio, which worked only off the generator and not well even then. And we hiked, hiked, eager to get a feel for the strange terrain that had become so familiar to Shackleton. On the third day, when our fingers showed deep cracks because of extremely low humidity, a lone Adélie wandered up to the wanigan to peer inside and to study us at length, first with one eye, then the other. When he departed he cast several suspicious glances back at us.

The first night my legs had *taken* me to the Nimrod Hut. The second I had to direct them to it. The thrill was gone, and the smells in the structure were really not pleasant. Also, I had failed to encounter ghosts, nightmares or even just interesting dreams. I do not remember dreaming during either night.

McMurdo Station from Observation Hill
A run on the ice shelf

Right: The Suess Glacier, Taylor Valley

Below: Shackleton's Nimrod hut at Cape Royds and the author camping in the hut

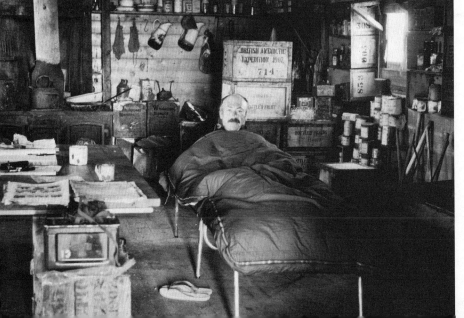

The crash scene
Mount Erebus

CHAPTER 9

CAMPING AT CAPE EVANS

E vans is a minor cape, a mere volcanic protuberance, of Ross Island, and if it had not served as the base of Scott's last expedition and as the base also of the Ross Island section of Shackleton's Endurance Expedition it would be interesting, probably, only because its skuary is the world's southernmost rookery. The remarkable characters and events of the two expeditions have lent to Cape Evans a depth of history, a tragedy and a nobility unmatched by any other single place on the continent. It was for obvious reasons that I wanted to camp there, again with Dave Murphy as my field assistant.

We were originally scheduled to lift off for the cape at 8 A.M. on Saturday, December 26, but the time was changed to 1 P.M. because the pilots, like everyone else, had been partying at McMurdo on Christmas Eve and Christmas Day. Our lift-off was delayed by fog until 1:30. We arrived at Evans a few minutes after two. Circling above the cape, which is some fifteen miles north of McMurdo, we saw the Scott hut below, on the beach of North Bay, and the small wanigan about 250 feet west of it. Evans is a shallow cape, blunt-nosed, pointing westward, and is full of cuplike depressions (at that time meltwater ponds) and great black boulders. It was much easier to set up camp there than it had been at Royds. The landing pad was on the beach, midway between the hut and the wanigan, and so we had to haul our gear only a short, level distance from the pad to our camp side. We staked down a handline between the wanigan and the hut and tested the experimental radio on batteries by calling McMurdo Station. The radio was not completely reliable even at this shorter distance from McMurdo but it worked much better than it had at Royds.

Murphy napped for several hours after we set up camp, using the single bunk on the seaward wall of the wanigan and putting his head in a crate to keep out the light. The wanigan, situated close to the beach and catching the light reflected from the sea ice and the Barne Glacier, was almost always brilliantly illuminated, even when the door was shut, for it had two windows, one on the north and the other on the east side. The northern window overlooked the Sound and the Glacier, the eastern one the Terra Nova Hut and its beach. Murphy had sprained a leg while skiing at Scott Base the day before and was now on a muscle-relaxing medication that made him sleepy. Also, he was using a chemical heating pad that turned very hot when you added a couple of tablespoons of water to it. While he slept I wandered around the environs, climbed a couple of ridges, then climbed Windvane Hill for its excellent views to the south and north. The hill was so named by the Scott expedition because an anemometer was established on it. Scott and his men often climbed the hill, and it was well known to the men of the *Aurora* section of Shackleton's Endurance Expedition.

On the hill, visible from many points on the cape, was a large, pale, rocked-down wooden cross, the base of which was a plaque with a printed inscription: SACRED TO THE MEMORY OF CAPT. A. L. A. MacKINTOSH, RNR, AND V. G. HAYWARD, WHO PERISHED ON THE SEA ICE IN A BLIZZARD ABOUT MAY 8, 1916, AND OF THE REVEREND A. P. SPENCER-SMITH, BA, WHO DIED ON THE ROSS BARRIER ON MARCH 6, 1916. A PAPER BEARING THIS INSCRIPTION, WRITTEN BY THEIR COMRADE A. K. JACK, WAS FOUND IN THE ICE-FILLED HUT BY THE NEW ZEALAND HUTS RESTORATION PARTY, 1960. JACK AND JOYCE, WHO MADE AND ERECTED THIS CROSS, HAD NOT ENOUGH TIME TO CARVE THE INSCRIPTION ON IT. THIS PLAQUE WAS ERECTED BY ANTARCTIC DIVISION, D.S.I.R., N.Z., 1962–1963. (The death of Mackintosh and Hayward was discussed in Chapter 2.)

From the hill I observed Skua Lake beyond the hut and the morainic ridge east of the hut that Scott had named the Ramp, then I walked along the beach toward the hut, which is very close to the Sound. The sea ice was still intact but the tidal crack was four or five feet wide and the ice nearby looked rotten in places, darker, wetter. There was still plenty of thick snow on the beach edge, in which meltwater had formed caves and tunnels whose icicles sparkled. From the beach one could see that a large chunk of the Barne Glacier had collapsed, forming a small embayment.

I was surprised by the amount of junk the warm summer had revealed around the outside of the hut and that the snow and ice had hidden from me during my visit of the previous year. Even the front of the hut was littered with broken bottles, rusty wire, wooden splinters, burlap and various odds and ends which were not only an eyesore but a foot hazard, and in the vicinity were foul, fishy smells of decaying ancient birds and seals. It seemed to me that this might be a case of carrying scholarly respect too far, to the point where it approached desecration. It would be an easy matter to deposit the litter in a shack built in the hills, where it could be saved for interested scholars, if any. Scott was a sensitive, orderly, aesthetically inclined man, and I imagined he would be distressed to know that so much offensive stuff lay around his last home.

Aesthetically there's a marked contrast between this hut and the Shackleton one. The Shackleton one also has litter but not in the front, and it is mild—packing cases, fodder, some rusty tin cans—and there are no smells of putrefaction in its vicinity. The Shackleton hut leaves a very pleasant impression, which tends to inspire visitors with respect, whereas the ugly appearance of the immediate environs of the Scott hut may encourage visitors to take a casual attitude towards its contents. The poor impression was strengthened by a large pool of meltwater on the hut's southern side (the side away from the beach), in which junk was richly decaying.

I walked around the hut before entering it, and saw pony fodder, ropes, rags, boards, two outhouses, harness, rusty large cans, pieces of tubing, and a mummified tan dog curled in a fetal position, its skin intact, almost no skeleton showing, its excellent teeth exposed as if in a snarl. The dog was still wearing a broad, dark leather collar. The hut was not only much larger than the Royds one, it was also much darker and gloomier inside. I set up my cot, mattress and sleeping bag beside the old galley, which was close to the door. The cot ran parallel to the hut's length.

When Murphy awoke I said we ought to have a look at Skua Lake and at the strikingly conspicuous, light-brown conical mound halfway up the Ramp. The color of this mound was not in itself vivid but the contrast between it and the black hills was strong. He agreed. As we neared the lake our presence caused scores of skuas to leave its whitish, feather- and guano-strewn shores and soar above us like pearly leaves, wheeling against the cloudless sky in groups as though wind-scattered, and at times seeming to hang as still as kites. Occasionally a bird would dart at another and there would ensue a flurry of disagreement. The water, its crisping surface thick with feathers, appeared to be thoroughly polluted, but one was always thrilled to come upon a pond-sized body of fresh water in so high a latitude. We had not seen skuas in such profusion before. At Cape Royds we had at most encountered two dozen at a time. At Skua Lake there were several hundred. We wondered where they obtained food. At the Royds rookery seven miles to the north? At the McMurdo garbage dump fifteen miles to the south? The Sound was still frozen, and there was nothing at Evans to sustain them.

Then, as though realizing belatedly that we were committing lese majesty, they stopped our further progress toward the conical mound by hurling themselves, screaming in alarm and anger, at us from all directions in a maneuver we called dive-bombing, for they occasionally ejected excreta at us. They kept us busy ducking.

It was exciting to stand your ground and let them come at you; to wait until the last moment, trying to frame a bird, to focus and to hold your camera steady, before dodging. Most of them gave the impression of bluffing, but a few flew so low and intensely they convinced us they had every intention of colliding. They swooped up at the last possible instant and at an altitude lower than where your neck had been, as photographs subsequently showed. Skuas are well known to be fierce, particularly when their nesting grounds are trespassed on. Although they gave the impression of being muscle-bound they were marvelous fliers. Their flight has been described as being more like that of a small eagle than a gull. We delighted in their beautiful maneuvers, their sudden climbs, dartings, peelings off, swoops, wheelings and bullet-like attack dives.

Rarely do skuas show their talons when diving, but one came at me chest high with talons extended. A cold pulse of fear swept over me as I imagined my eyes being raked. Being attacked by skuas had seemed at Royds a harmless sport provided your timing was adequate when ducking, although I remembered how Herbert Ponting, the gifted photographer of Scott's last expedition, had once received an unexpected strike across the eyes that had caused them to water for hours. It was his belief that the brim of his heavy felt hat, softening the blow, had saved his eyes from permanent injury. The skua that made the unusual pass at me seemed angrier than the others and more determined. Also, he flew lower, and there was something menacingly loose in the way his legs dangled. (When the other birds attacked, their legs were tucked under them.) His legs gave the impression not that he was crippled but rather that he was half demented.

Murphy, wearing a red stocking cap, his face taut with excitement, had just finished dodging when a bird, having swooped on him from behind, struck him in the head. I heard as well as saw the blow, administered with the leading edge of the wing. Frightened, he threw himself prone. I ran over and stood cover for him as he rose. He rubbed his head thoughtfully, then we both laughed. Deciding we would return tomorrow armed with the two bamboo poles we had noticed leaning against the wanigan's southern exterior, we returned to the wanigan.

Murphy was justly proud of the tiny cave he had dug in the side of a nearby snowbank, from which he now extricated some food for dinner. We had tomato soup, steak, salt crackers with butter, frozen peaches, tea and a chocolate bar. Then we hiked over small black hills and ridges and across miniature black valleys in which colorless meltwater streams flowed noisily. We almost always had surpassingly beautiful views but despite them our eyes were often cast downward in a search for interesting rocks, ostensibly to bring back souvenirs for our friends but probably in an unconscious effort to find relief from the very grandeur around us. At Royds your eye was fascinated by the variety of sculptured forms. At Evans you felt more exposed to the great elements, and possibly for this reason it was a comfort to lose yourself in the little world on the ground.

What a thrill it was to find a colored rock! The rocks were never large; the large ones invariably were the common black basalt. Nor were they to be seen in quantity. A thrifty hand had scattered them on those parts of the cape farthest from Erebus. Westward from the wanigan and on the tiny plateaus above it if you looked carefully and persevered you came upon a bit of precious color now and then in that black scape. There were brick reds, browns from coffee to rotten plum, umbers, and occasionally a bit of yellow scoria. The rocks contained tiny caves, and scalloped beaches, and tubes and tunnels, some of the last beautifully fluted.

We came upon the black beach named West Beach by the Scott expedition. Here we found three tiny dried starfish, a sea urchin and a translucent brown coin shell, and almost stumbled on some dead Weddell seals, some fully skeletonized. Others were intact on the bottom and were skeletons only on top.

We were attacked by four skuas. While two would come at you frontally the other two would disappear beyond the brow of a hill, gain altitude, then dive at you from behind or against your flank. They seemed to have an endless store of energy and determination. We looked around for signs of an egg or a fledgling. I was struck heavily across the left temple and ear by a skua I hadn't detected. It was a powerful blow, causing me to cry out instinctively. For a moment I wondered if I was going to pass out. It occurred to me then that it wouldn't do to be struck while standing on a cliff edge. Murphy, alerted by the sounds of the blow and my cry, ran frowning towards me. I assured him I was all right. A little later I was struck again, this time behind my right ear. Several skuas joined the first four. I decided to try to record on film just how low the birds dove. Murphy, standing out of range of their attacks and using one of my cameras and a 135mm lens, took a series of photographs of me ducking. In one I am shown almost squatting while a bird apparently attempts to rake my back. The birds were relentless, so, with my ears still ringing, we returned to the wanigan, took up the bamboo poles, then went back to West Beach, where the skuas promptly attacked us again, as though they had been waiting for us. Occasionally they hit the poles, which we held above our heads, but they were effectively prevented from striking our bodies.

Wandering closer to the sea ice, we discovered why the birds were so proprietary about the area. Nestled on the bare sand in the lee of a rib cage and thus more or less protected from the predominant southeasterlies, was a brown egg, beside which huddled a lovely, furry, pearl-gray chick with black eyes and a black beak, blending neatly with the skeleton and with the deep-gray or blackish beach sand. Having been alarmed by the cries of the adult birds, the chick stared uncertainly at us with alternate eyes. The tiny thing, surviving without real shelter in this, the world's southernmost bird breeding ground, stirred one's paternal feelings. We went quite close to it; and now the birds, having realized that we had outfoxed them, landed at a distance and grew very still, possibly out of fatalism, because they counted the chick and egg as already lost to us (as many an Adélie egg and chick had probably been lost to them), or because they cunningly hoped, in their fierce bird brains, that their sudden silence, calming us, would divert us from our murderous intent.

Afraid the chick might freeze when deprived for long of its parents' warmth, we hurried away, continuing westward to some other seal carcasses, from one of which Murphy managed to pry loose a canine tooth with a sheath knife despite the stench and despite the powerful grip of the mummified gums and the still strong, gleaming jawbone. We also climbed some capelike cliffs, from whose height we saw oil-green tidal cracks, blue patches of rapidly decaying sea ice, the light-bristling, chalk-textured snout of the Barne Glacier, and, serene above everything, the gently sloping sides of Erebus. Unlike Cape Royds, where the penguins make their various sounds and where the skuas cry plaintively as they scout above the rookery, Cape Evans has silence in which one listens, rapt, to the ringing of blood in one's ears and is aware of the mysterious purification of one's soul that seems to take place in them.

Some Weddells, basking on the sea ice just beyond the tidal crack near the wanigan, were making their weird noises when we returned from our hike. I felt I was too far from them to hear them clearly, so I went alone out onto a spit, but a meltwater stream gurgled so loudly it confused what I had come to listen to. However, it was fascinating to stand still beside the stream and observe the green algae waving in the current. Bits of plant life in this wasteland!

From my journal:

"We have not yet examined the interior of Scott's hut, which is a bit strange inasmuch as the hut is our chief reason for coming here. But we're surfeited with McMurdo and its artificiality—the hum of generators, the hot water, the abundance of food, the drinking in the wardroom every evening, and especially the round of holiday parties—and are exhilarating in the quiet, the birds, the seals, the sea, the mountain, the glacier, the ice, the volcanic land, the terrific sky. Tomorrow we'll turn to the hut, after we've had a brief respite from man.

"The razor sun on my cheek as I write near the wanigan door. No flies, insects. You expect them in this warm sun, with the brooks running. Find myself thinking of Cheechee nostalgically: of the trees, the summer sun, the green lawns, the pretty girls, Warner's bar, the buildings. This wanigan has two *Playboy* pinups. They're distracting, almost objectionable. Looking out the windows, you see the frozen Sound, the glacier, ice-covered Erebus, and you know that nakedness doesn't fit in here. The two girls are spendidly built and very pretty but they don't belong in this ice-land. You want to concentrate on what you have—the beauty, the historical perspective—not on what you lack: women."

When I left the wanigan after writing up my notes Murphy was already long and deeply asleep. As I walked beside the handline and approached the smelly litter heap that felt like a barrier between the hut (and Scott) and me I felt at moments a positive distaste, but once I was inside the structure I was brought back forcefully to the men who had lived in it and to their great stories, and although the place was very cold I had a brief look around before turning in.

I went to Scott's cubicle at the eastern end and observed the grimy remnants of what had once been there. His bunk. A reindeer-skin sleeping bag, dark, heavy, the leather dried out. A pair of worn-out shoes hanging from a nail. The sheath of a knife. A pair of very large hand-knitted gray socks. Leather mittens on a chair. The folding table on which Scott had written in his diary and on which he had carefully figured sledging rations, studied maps. On a shelf above the bunk was a copy of *The Green Flat and Other Stories of War and Sport*, by A. Conan Doyle.

I opened volume one of *Scott's Last Expedition*, a first edition of which I had with me, and read what Scott had written about the hut. On January 10, 1911, he wrote, "The hut is progressing apace, and all agree that it should be the most perfectly comfortable habitation. The sides have double boarding inside and outside the frames, with a layer of our excellent quilted seaweed insulation between each pair of boardings. The roof has a single matchboarding inside, but on the outside is a matchboarding, then a layer of 2-ply 'ruberoid,' then a layer of quilted seaweed, then a second matchboarding, and finally a cover of 3-ply 'ruberoid.' The first floor is laid, but over this there will be a quilting, a felt layer, a second boarding, and finally linoleum; as the plenteous volcanic sand can be piled well up on every side it is impossible to imagine that draughts can penetrate into the hut from beneath, and it is equally impossible to imagine great loss of heat by contact or radiation in that direction. To add to the wall insulation the south and east sides of the hut are piled high with compressed-forage bales, whilst the north side is being prepared as a winter stable for the ponies. The stable will stand between the wall of the hut and a wall built of forage bales, six bales high and two bales thick. This will be roofed with rafters and tarpaulin, as we cannot find enough boarding. We shall have to take care that too much snow does not collect on the roof, otherwise the place should do excellently well."

On the nineteenth he wrote, "The hut is becoming the most comfortable dwelling-place imaginable. We have made unto ourselves a truly seductive home, within the walls of which peace, quiet, and comfort reign supreme."

He stated in a letter written at this time, "Our residence is really a house of considerable size, in every respect the finest that has ever been erected in the Polar regions; 50 ft. long by 25 wide and 9 ft. to the eaves.

"If you can picture our house nestling below this small hill on a long stretch of black sand [the hut was some dozen feet above the sea], with many tons of provision cases ranged in neat blocks in front of it and the sea lapping the ice-foot below, you will have some idea of our immediate vicinity."

I undressed rapidly, slipped into my bag and immediately became aware of powerful and unpleasant odors. However, there was no other place in the hut that I could move my cot to, presuming that a change would be helpful. The hut was crowded and I felt crowded in it. My head was close to two cases of Fry's Pure Concentrated Cocoa and to a case of Heinz Baked Beans. Lying on my side, I stared at rows of enameled metalware hanging from hooks; at many chipped pitchers; at the galley stove and chimney, which had rusted badly. All the colors blended: mahogany, mauve, rust. I felt neither here nor there: not far enough from the door or close enough to the middle; up against a Nansen sledge on the door's left and close to the galley on the door's right. I assured myself that it made no difference where in the hut I slept.

I heard sounds as of distant thunder. I knew the sky was still cloudless, so I wondered, as I fell off to sleep, if the imitation cannonading was caused by some shifting of the Barne Glacier, or by snowslides on the great Erebus slopes.

CHAPTER 10

CAPE EVANS CONCLUDED

O n the two or three occasions when I awoke during the night in Scott's hut I thought of Scott and of his companions on the tragic journey and of what they had had to endure before death released them; and my realization of what they and Shackleton and the latter's farthest-southing companions had managed to accomplish in an almost incredibly hostile country was buttressed by vivid recollections of my own trip to the Pole in November 1969 and by a remarkably low flight over the Beardmore Glacier on the return to McMurdo. Of my visit I had written:

"Early one morning my press companions and I headed for the Pole, where only the Americans have a station. To paraphrase a current politician, once you've seen one undersnow station you've seen them all, with this proviso: that you see the Pole Station first. Because of its historical signficance, its remoteness, its hostility to life of every kind and degree, or if for no better reason than that, like Mount Everest, it's there, the Pole is the Mecca of all imaginative Antarctic residents and visitors, only a handful of whom get to visit it.

"It is still a difficult and hazardous traverse to the Pole from any Antarctic station. By the ski-equipped Hercules departing from McMurdo the trip takes three hours. The eight hundred and forty miles are covered pleasantly if noisily but perhaps with a certain apprehension if one is making the trip for the first time. How cold will it be? Will the altitude affect you after the sudden change from sea level? Will you be blinded by the light?

"Although my flight as a flight was routine, it was unique in one respect. It was carrying the first women ever to visit the Pole: five Americans and a New Zealander. Five were scientists and one was a science writer. The Navy was nervously determined that no one of them should have the unfair if accidental distinction of being the *first* woman to step down at the Pole. After some discussion among high-ranking officers the solution to the problem was found: lower the cargo ramp in the rear of the plane, disembark all passengers with the exception of Admiral Welch and the ladies, and have the latter descend the ramp arm in arm, the admiral in the middle. Navy photographers would record the historic event.

"As we neared the Pole we donned our waddle pants, lowered and secured our ear and neck flaps, closed the air valves in our bunny boots and checked our bear paws and fur-trimmed hoods. I glanced through one of the aft portholes and saw the vast, arid, blinding polar plateau. Warnings came over the intercom. The parka hood would eliminate our side vision, and the cap ear flaps and hood would dull our hearing, so it was best to exercise caution in one's movements. Several visitors in recent years, becoming confused, had wandered forward and had nearly been chewed up by the still-turning props. We were warned to be on guard against frostbite. The temperature at the Pole now was –49°F., the wind ten knots, making the effective temperature somewhat lower than –80°F. Unless we didn't mind losing skin we had better not touch metal with our bare hands, and if we had a range-finder camera it was wise not to touch the finder's metal rim with our cheek. Because of the Pole's considerable altitude we were advised to move slowly and to breathe often.

"But all went smoothly despite this last-minute counsel, much of which was a reiteration of earlier briefings. When we left the plane we waited for the cold to hit us but it didn't. What hit us was the light, for we had exited facing the sun. We were on a great flat desert plain and wherever we turned, there was the same glaring white featureless northern horizon. The sun hung low in the sky like a terrible spotlight. The snow was thick and extremely dry, the sky fantastically blue. Only man lent visual interest to the barrenness: vehicle and boot tracks, communications antennas, a khaki instrument dome, black fuel drums on a huge sled, a red cleated vehicle, a khaki rubber storage bladder for fuel. Some hundred feet away was the famous "barber" pole with its red and black stripes surmounted by a gleaming chromium-plated globe. We walked toward it and felt the effects of the altitude. Our breath issued in white streamers, frosting our glasses. Diaphanous steam rose and billowed from people and machines. My companions made me think of walking tea kettles. The red beard of one of the men had turned a brilliant white.

"I removed my bear paws, unzipped my parka and fumbled for the light meter and camera hanging from my neck. And now, as I shot the scenes, I at last felt the cold. My hands, even though covered by two pairs of gloves, ached and rapidly grew numb. I felt a strange satisfaction. After all, I told myself, I hadn't come more than thirteen thousand miles to experience warmth.

"We were photographed individually at the barber pole by official Navy photographers. Statistics on a sign were photographed with us. The ice cap in the Pole's vicinity is over nine thousand feet thick. The average temperature is –57°F. The population is twenty-one. I remembered other statistics—the highest temperature recorded at the Pole is 5.5 F., the lowest -113.3°F. The annual precipitation (in terms of water equivalent) is less than 2″, as compared with Phoenix, Arizona's 7.2″. I thought of the tragic contrast between Amundsen's and Scott's arrival at the Pole and remembered Scott's words from his journal: 'Great God! this is an awful place and terrible enough for us to have laboured to it without the reward of priority.'

"A Navy journalist, peering at my face, said the end of my nose was very white and advised that I go inside the station temporarily. I went to a wooden door and down a precipitous flight of wooden stairs, at the foot of which stood the station's medical officer, with whom I chatted while I warmed my nose with my hand. The tunnel extending from the stairs was encrusted with ice crystals. Its temperature was thirty or forty below. Other frostbite cases descended the stairs to be advised by the officer. This same pleasant young man doubled as the station's postmaster and later cacheted the group's envelopes and led some of its members on a tour of the station, showing them the tiny infirmary (one bed, rarely occupied), the communications room, the ham radio room, the food storage area, the snow melter, and his own tight quarters, all under the ice. The station had originally been constructed on the surface of the snow (during the International Geophysical Year, 1957) but drift snow had covered it, compacted into ice and was slowly crushing it. The station would soon have to be abandoned. This was just as well in one sense, for the station had drifted with the ice cap away from the Pole. A new station, of superior design, would be built at the Pole itself in the early Seventies.

"We lunched in a small mess room, one wall of which was crowded with huge-breasted pinups. It was interesting to see the confrontation of these ladies of men's dreams with the real ladies casually consuming spaghetti with meat sauce, buttered bread chunks, mincemeat pie and coffee. The bread and pie were fresh out of the station's oven. We left on schedule after a visit of two hours, hearing that the ladies had been persuaded to leave souvenirs of their visit: a bobby pin, a comb, a pair of earrings and a lipstick.

"If the flight to the Pole was dull because it occurred at too high an altitude for interesting sights, the return flight to McMurdo decidedly was not. It offered those few of us lucky enough to have access to a porthole a series of spectacular views of the Beardmore Glacier, which the pilot flew over at low altitudes, descending during one sequence to three hundred feet. The Beardmore is a landmark familiar to students of Antarctic exploration because it provided first Shackleton and then Scott with access to the polar plateau through the Transantarctic Mountains. Both the Shackleton and the Scott parties were in great danger on the glacier due to exhaustion, hunger and cold as they made their way back to Ross Island. The Shackleton party survived by a hair. The Scott group was trapped and destroyed by a blizzard on the Ross Ice Shelf not long after leaving the Beardmore.

"At first, after the wastes of the seemingly endless plateau, with its dead flatness except for occasional nunataks (mountain peaks visible above the ice cap), we saw delicate scenes such as the pale grays and gray-blues of a mountain range peeping out of snow. But soon we came on naked, barren, slate-gray mountains, vast, sprawled, showing the ribs of cliff edges. From a height the glacier looked like a bluish plain, behind which were serene mountains of a deeper blue, at whose foothills were the congregated gleaming points of something resembling a town. But actually these points were an array of sastrugi, crevasses and crumbling buttes reflecting the low-hanging sun and suggesting the vast forces involved in the ice cap's movement to the Ross Ice Shelf and eventually to the Southern Ocean. As we flew over long, parallel ice ridges the ice river's width seemed immense, the distant part looking smooth, level, fit for traverses, the foreground giving the impression of having been chewed up by a thousand half-tracks. Far away was a lesser glacier, tonguing down between mountains to add to the Beardmore's mass. A mountain range, pale slate with a hint of violet, crests capped by snow, rose out of a creamy sea. Now the plane descended rapidly and one saw pale-green, veined splotches of bare ice or splotches resembling ragged circles of boiling white metal. There were huge upward-curling flakes among wildly mixed-up tremendous crevasses, and gleaming wild waves, a frozen surf, great buttes, and immense sections resembling crumbling blue cheese."

Lying in my sleeping bag in Scott's hut, the one to which he had been fated never to return, it seemed to me almost beyond belief that he and his companions had accomplished so much in such a life-threatening country, not only in terms of geographical exploration and scientific discovery but in the refusal to lower their dignity under the most desperate of physical circumstances. It was inevitable, spending the night alone in his hut, with many of its original contents ranged around me, that I should feel a special closeness to him.

From my Cape Evans journal entries:
"3:20 P.M. Have just awakened from a nap on the wanigan cot. Dave still asleep in his bunk. We walked to the conical mound and far beyond,

were gone more than three hours, returned, had lunch of steak, frozen peaches and tea, were exhausted, so went to sleep. Am now sitting near the door. Cold wind out, fierce desert sun in a blue sky. Had a terrific time walking across a moonscape, but interspersed with brooks, rills, creeks, ponds, some with beautiful green or blue ice, one with pea-green ice. . . . A wild scape, utterly enchanting, and it helps to know you're the only humans within miles. We hiked to Erebus's ice skirts and along them southward on a land ridge toward the great ice cape projecting into the Sound with its visible crevasses. The incredible light there near Land's End, had to wear sunglasses, and my beach glasses felt insufficient. Dave has a pair of mirrored glasses with a horizontal slit across the middle of the lens, and I think the lenses are double-gradient density. The exhilaration of climbing, of looking. During the hike we kept an eye peeled on the fog bank building up near the Western Mountains. It would not have been pleasant to have to make our way back to the wanigan in fog." ·

We climbed a good deal (but sometimes came to soft, furry hills down which we glissaded in our boots) over the extreme unevenness of the volcanic terrain, which was a dump heap of moraines, rocks, boulders, scoria and dust. Sometimes we made our way from boulder-crest to boulder-crest, or climbed over boulders that barred our way. The bamboo poles were very useful in this work. Wearing a red ski cap, a red parka, blue dungarees and mukluks, handsome in his thin blond mustache and struggling goatee, Murphy was as fine a camping companion as I could imagine: youthful, humorous, athletic, discreet, taciturn if need be, intelligent, and appreciative of Antarctica's wonders.

Looking down from the height of the Ramp, we saw a great deal of water running off Erebus's slopes: rivulets, creeks, fingers, ribbons, sheets, all racing toward the opalescent tidal cracks. We also saw numerous cuplike hollows that had become pools. Here and there we viewed ponds partially frozen over: pale blues, pale greens and a few lavenders, all marbled, a wondrous surprise after the monotony of the cape's cinder mass. In places the snowbanks showed plum colors or gentle lilacs. The contrast between the darkness of lava rock and the paleness of the snow, or between the boulders and the sky's purity, was not only extremely pleasing, it was also awe-inspiring. Life was largely absent here but this did not make the place depressing for us. We had much open sky and the regal blues and purples of the ponds to cheer us.

The fact that Ross Island is of volcanic origin greatly adds to its interest and beauty. A more ordinary island would not be so extreme, so lunar in its scapes and so varied in its tiny forms. Far from feeling life-poor because of the lack of what recognizably looked like temperate earth, we were increasingly aware of the aesthetic realities, source and chief of which was Mount Erebus, stark, beautiful, a pennant of steam and smoke flying northward from its crater. Erebus is a shield volcano; that is, it is broadly rounded, with gently sloping sides, not conical like Mount Fuji. In size it is one of the world's major volcanoes, with an elevation greater than that of Fuji or Etna or Vesuvius.

We visited the Terra Nova Hut before and after dinner. I had had enough of the hut's penetrating, unpleasant odors, which had caused me to wake up with a throbbing nose and head, so I decided to sleep in the wanigan that night. The southeast wind roared all night, shaking the little structure badly. At about 12:30 A.M. I went outside in longjohns to look at the weather. We had a lot of cloud cover now and the sun was not visible. Erebus too was obscured. I returned to my bag shivering, my hands numb. I awoke at five, went out briefly to look around (the cover had spread), lay in my bag till six, then got dressed.

At breakfast it was 18° outside and the temperature was falling. When I checked in with McMurdo he said it was 7° there and requested hourly weather reports. He wanted to know the wind's direction, its estimated velocity, including gusts, the surface conditions, the horizon visibility, the state of the cloud cover and whether any particles were blowing about.

From my journal:

"When one becomes cold one grows awkward, careless, one starts injuring oneself, mainly in small ways, bruising one's fingers, tearing nails from flesh, bumping into things, stumbling."

But when the wind swept down over the crest of the dark, boulder-studded hill behind us; when a hot drink was welcome; when we stamped our feet to sense life in them; when the two pairs of gloves each of us wore were inadequate outdoors; when our eyes flooded with tears in the wind—when this was the state of affairs we were pleased, for it countered some of our embarrassment of yesterday when we had sweated in the hills while climbing.

The cloud cover cleared a couple of hours after breakfast. Shortly afterwards a red helo brought four Navy cameramen to photograph the interior of Scott's hut with movie gear. We helped them to unload, served them coffee and later made lunch for them.

In the late afternoon we were taken out by helo and returned to McMurdo.

448

CHAPTER 11

BRIEF STAY AT SCOTT BASE

The morning after my return to McMurdo from Cape Evans I did some of those inevitable chores that help deplete one's precious Antarctic time: duplicated pages of my journal at the Chalet, airmailed the photocopied pages to Joan, bought odds and ends at the ship's store in the personnel building, spoke at length about my program with Chris Shepherd at lunch, made arrangements to move to Scott Base at four, and selected the gear I wanted to take with me. I was no stranger to the Kiwi base but now my plan was to obtain a more intimate feel of it by spending two nights there. I remembered well the first time I had hiked there alone, some thirteen months previously, after which I had written:

"One morning I received permission to walk the two miles from McMurdo to Scott Base on condition that I was to phone the MAC (McMurdo) duty officer when I left McMurdo, when I reached Scott Base, when I departed from Scott and when I returned to McMurdo. Although the walk was safe enough, the weather in Antarctica is very uncertain and I could be caught in a blizzard or a whiteout, the latter a polar phenomenon in which the sky and the snow or ice reflect each other so completely that one loses orientation and feels as if he were in a bottle of milk. If caught in a whiteout one should sit it out until it passes. It may last an hour or two or a couple of days, depending on your luck. I suspected that the real reason for the calls was that I was a member of the tenderfoot press group and therefore a prime candidate for getting into trouble through ignorance and an excited imagination.

"I left McMurdo after an early breakfast, taking outlying lanes and seeing a fuel tank farm, crates stacked outside of warehouses, and fork trucks and bulldozers. As I climbed the Gap between Crater Heights and Observation Hill I came upon men constructing a tank which would hold more than two million gallons of fuel. The temperature was 4°, the wind velocity at McMurdo ten knots. But in the Gap were head winds of twenty knots and more, which brought the effective temperature down to −35° F. or lower. The winds made the going slow. Also, my Navy gear was heavy, the thermal boots caused my feet to drag and the way was still surprisingly steep. I had the neck and ear flaps of my cap down but side gusts burned my eyes, causing them to run copiously.

"On my right the island sloped away, black rock and white snow, to the bluish ice shelf which stretched out flat and immense to the horizon. On my left was a mottled, flinty, dark, volcanic hill of pumice-like stuff swept clean of snow and marked by regular vertical ridges that appeared to have been made by bulldozers. A hill further along on my left was furry with snow and on my right and somewhat ahead of me, far below on the white shore, was Scott Base, looking tiny with its antennas and green huts. I descended the steep road, slippery with brittle shards of volcanic rock, and became aware of the pressure ice at the coast's edge, its angular, uplifted, helter-skelter and vaguely frightening forms tinted with delicate blues and greens. Skuas were wheeling above the shoreline. Far out on the ice, almost indiscernible, was a cluster of specks that was Williams Field.

"A Kiwi led me past pressure ridges and over minor crevasses onto the ice to see some Weddells and their pups. The seals were massive, and the ice and snow in their vicinity were stained yellow, red and brown by the afterbirth. In this world of blacks, whites, greens and blues the warm afterbirth colors were very conspicuous. A seal observed us across her wiry whiskers, bawling cries of alarm if we drew closer than some six feet. Her pup's eyes were large, dark and soulful looking. When my companion, squatting, reached out a glove the pup suddenly snapped at it, just missing it. We threaded our way back among the pressure ridges with their jewel blues and cobalt shadows."

Named in honor of Scott, the base is located on Pram Point, a low rocky projection on the eastern side of Hut Point Peninsula. In 1971 it consisted chiefly of nine prefabricated huts linked by corrugated iron tunnels or ways. The ways permit movement around the station regardless of the weather and without the loss of time that would be involved in changing clothes. Auxiliary buildings included two magnetic huts, two seismology huts and a large former hangar, now a garage and work space. The main reason for the present existence of the station was its scientific work. In 1971 Scott Base conducted experiments in seismology, geomagnetism, ionospheric physics, auroral and air glow, VLF (very low frequency) radio propagation, satellite tracking and meteorology. Its post office was the world's most southerly one to provide all postal and communications facilities, and it had its own set of stamps.

I was driven to the base in a Nodwell and taken in tow by Jim Barker, the deputy leader, a hearty, booming-voiced, sunburned, smiling, bright-toothed man whom I had met in the McMurdo wardroom. He led me to my quarters, the tiny hospital room in D Hut. (The station handled minor medical problems; more serious ones were treated at McMurdo.) The room had a speckled green linoleum floor and two small square windows that you opened and closed by a screw arrangement. It felt like a freighter cabin and was cold during the time I worked in it, even though I wore thermal underwear and a heavy wool shirt.

To save on laundry (water was made by melting ice cut and transported from the ice shelf's pressure ridges) Barker asked me to use a sleeping bag instead of sheets. To my amusement the thin, zipperless khaki bag on the bed was narrower than a mummy bag. It was tricky to slip into it. You mounted the bed, braced your behind against the wall, set your feet into the bag and slowly snaked your way inside. Once you were inside it was difficult to move about. The bag had a pale blue liner and was provided with a pillow in a fresh case.

Barker, showing me around the station, introduced me to a number of friendly, attractive men. On the whole they were a youngish lot. They looked as if they had spent much of their lives outdoors in clean air; had keen eyes on the alert for humor; and smelled good in their heavy beards and rough, tweedy clothes.

I had some New Zealand beer with Barker in the mess hall before dinner. Barker liked to use Maori words, such as potai (poe-tie) for head covering and smoko (smoe-koe) for tea break. The hall contained two long tables, each made up of three smaller, squarish ones. There were two table maps under glass, one of Antarctica, the other of New Zealand. The dinner, prepared by Frank Bonn, who was originally from England and was now a resident of Auckland, consisted of rare roast beef, broad beans, roast potato, Yorkshire pudding and a piece of fresh fruit. You picked up a plate, went to the kitchen and served yourself. You sat where you liked. You knifed up communal butter or jam without bothering to clean your knife of previous food; or at best you cleaned it on your slice of bread. When you finished eating you scraped your leavings into a container, placed the plate on a kitchen counter and dropped your utensils into a tin box half-full of soapy water. It was the duty of the house-mouse detail to wash the dishes and clean the hall. Food wasn't offered you in explosive quantities as it was at McMurdo.

There were twenty-two men at the base at present, excluding me. Two more residents were due to arrive that evening from the Pole. A few others were in the field. Eleven, including Brian Porter, Jim Barker and Frank Bonn, would winter over. The rest would return to New Zealand in February. All the current base personnel were on the ice for the first time. The personnel were selected by the station leader with the approval of the Antarctic Division of the Department of Scientific and Industrial Research.

At eight there was a movie in the mess hall: *Midnight Lace,* with Doris

Day and Rex Harrison, borrowed from the Navy at McMurdo. The mess hall was cool; you wanted to keep your hands wrapped in something. As soon as the film was over, men huddled close to the diesel-fired stove. The casual conversation was sprinkled with four-letter words, as it often was at McMurdo, and there were the usual sexual allusions.

One man asked Frank Bonn, "How are you?"

Bonn replied, "Still hanging. How's yours?"

Some of the men read Christchurch papers, snacked on bread, jam, tea, fruit, coffee. I spoke with Graham, the radio man, who told me that the base made regular phone calls to the States, Europe and elsewhere by short wave to New Zealand, then by cable. Unlike the phone patches from McMurdo these were two-way commercial calls. A call to the States cost $3NZ per minute. Graham said that quite a few people came from McMurdo on a regular basis to make calls.

I slept deeply and awoke very hungry. Out of overpoliteness I hadn't eaten enough at dinner. For breakfast I had two poached eggs, bacon, homemade bread, butter, black-currant jam, gooseberry jam and tea. Also available were smoked cod warmed in water, fried eggs, marmalade and coffee. An American rock singer was being played on the Philips stereo machine. The mess hall was warm and cozy now.

During the morning I wandered around the base's vicinity, fascinated by the razorbacked slabs of pressure ice, yellowish in places, that had been pushed up by the ice shelf. The Ross Ice Shelf has its northwestern terminus at Ross Island. Its northern side, facing the Ross Sea and stretching eastward from Cape Crozier, is some four hundred nautical miles or roughly four hundred and seventy statute miles long. The shelf is approximately the size of France; this gives one some idea of the continent's vastness. The shelf is believed to be afloat although attached to the continent, and its thickness has been judged to be between eight hundred and a thousand feet. It is the largest in the world, is in slow motion, moving generally in a northerly direction, and presses against the eastern shore of Ross Island, a shore much of whose outline is conjectured only. It is this pressure that causes the chaotic upheavals known as pressure ice. Antarctica's uniquely tabular bergs are tabular because they are formed by ice calving off the ice shelves. On occasion immense tabular bergs have been encountered by ships. An iceberg approximately the size of Connecticut was reported some years ago.

Now I saw blocks of ice, huge shapes jutting out of the shelf's flatness (the shelf had a pale, bluish-lilac tint), that looked as if they had been tossed about at random. The pressure ice was no place for a novice to explore: it contained crevasses, some of them hidden because they were snowbridged. Beyond it were several basking Weddells.

Near the base's entrance was a sign listing air distances to some major cities. Wellington: 2536. London: 10588. Moscow: 10501. Buenos Aires: 4449. Paris: 10382. Washington: 9214. Capetown: 4603. Brussels: 10520. Oslo: 11085.

After attending the morning tea break at ten, I went to my room, where my hands turned very cold as I wrote in my journal. Glancing at them, I realized it was not a smart idea to cut your nails short if you went camping in the high southern latitudes. When your nails were short, flesh tended to separate from them, and the dirt under them was difficult and painful to remove. At lunch I was invited to go sledging with the huskies and to join an ice party afterwards.

Few nations nowadays keep dogs. The trend for some time has been all to motor toboggans, which don't run off without you, don't fight each other and aren't carnivorous. Scott Base legitimately feeds its dogs seals under the Antarctic Treaty, but occasionally I heard grumbling at McMurdo about the misuse of Weddells in order to hold to a tradition now anachronistic. Whether the Kiwis continue to use dogs in addition to motor toboggans more out of a sense of tradition and romance than for other reasons, I do not know. No doubt they get good work out of the dogs in the field. Sometimes the dogs and sledges are airlifted to distant work sites by the United States Navy. But it seems to me in keeping with New Zealand's slower and more nostalgic pace in the world for Scott Base to continue to use dogs.

Shortly after 1 P.M. I walked with two dog handlers northward along the coast to where the huskies were staked out. The handlers were young, strong and bearded. One I knew only as Ken; the other's name was Mac Riding. Riding had a magnificent, brown, patriarchal beard, a fine nose and clean, engaging, sharp eyes, but he cut a strange figure in his mechanic's coveralls streaked and spotted with grease, in his filthy, broken-vizored cap (the vizor hung limply on his forehead, making the cap remind one of the little fatigue article worn by the Japanese Army in World War II), and greasy white thermal boots. I wondered where these affable Kiwis, newcomers to the ice, had learned to handle huskies.

The dogs had been born in Antarctica and would die there. As they sensed our coming they began to howl, bark and whine, at first gently and in fits and starts, as if unsure we were heading their way; then, as we came in sight, loudly and continuously; and from their compound rose an uproar of wild sounds that to the handlers were by now probably ordinary but that to me were electrifying, for they not only vividly stirred thoughts of Scott, Shackleton and Amundsen but told of harnessed energy, runs on the ice shelf and potential savagery.

Siberians and Greenlanders with eyes suggesting an oriental look, the dogs were spaced on chains attached to a long wire to prevent their getting at each other. Like their counterparts of the old days, these charming, friendly-looking animals, who bounded against you and licked your face, sometimes had murder in their hearts for their fellows. They were work dogs, used to and needing to work, and they lived a dog's life. Their compound was urine-stained, and spotted with dark feces that had sunk deep in the snow, and they themselves were stained with urine and seemed to smell of it. They were half-wild creatures who endured extreme cold for much of the year, subsisted on fishy seal meat and occasional human caresses, and probably daydreamed of coupling, running and fighting.

Only nine dogs would be taken out for the day's run. The pack howled, barked and pranced to get the handlers' attention in the hope of being chosen. There were twenty-one dogs at the base. Riding said that tomorrow there would be twenty. One, a nine-year-old bitch who still hadn't shed all her winter coat, who no longer pulled well in the traces and was no longer worth what it took to feed her, would be killed. Riding would shoot her.

After each dog was harnessed he was lifted by the collar so his forelegs were in the air and was brought to the sledge in this manner to keep him from taking off and disappearing in his frenzy of activity. Snorting, grunting, heaving, pulling, whining, barking and lunging, he was led to the traces. Ken, Riding's assistant, wore a white woolen ski cap over long brown hair, blue coveralls over heavy clothing, and orange mukluks. Like Riding he was sunglassed and barehanded.

By the time Osman, the leader and the last of the dogs to be harnessed (an Osman was a leader on Scott's last expedition), was brought to the head of the double line of dogs, I was seated on my parka at the end of the Nansen sledge, my back wedged against the sturdy sledge back, my heels propped against a long weighted cardboard box covered by a green canvas and well roped down. I had been told to dress warmly. Hatless and gloveless, I was sweating, for the sun was sharp and the compound was protected from the winds by hills and pressure ice. Riding warned me to hold on: the dogs would take off like a shot and go flying over the shelf ice until the steam was out of them.

However, they were slow getting started, the sledge was on wet deep ruts, and suddenly they tangled and were a great furry mass of contorted, snarling, slashing bodies. Possibly certain personal grudges were being settled. The impression I received was that the dogs were biting at random, with those on the bottom getting the worst of the fray. The guttural snarling was intense and moving. The handlers, carrying heavy rope knouts, rushed silently to the heap and flailed at it. Despite their fury the huskies made no passes at the men. But it was some time before they responded to the blows.

We made another start (Ken was sitting in front of the cardboard box) and almost overturned on a sharp slope. The snow shone with diamonds and rainbows as we tore across fresh surfaces, over old ruts and came close to spilling as we crossed narrow crevasses. I saw bloody ears and legs. One dog limped and whined and was pulled and dragged during the entire run. Riding remarked in a disturbed voice that there was no help for it, the dog would have to learn the hard way. On the flying snow I saw drops of bright blood. When the pack showed signs of slackening, Riding, clinging to the end of the bouncing sledge (the shelf's surface was rougher than it looked, as I knew from my trips on it in Nodwells) and breathing heavily just behind me, and occasionally and accidentally rapping my bare head with the handle of his ice ax, shouted, "Ready, dogs! Ready, dogs! Ready, ready, ready, dogs!" Or "Osman, you dirty bastard!" Or "You bloody cunt!" Or "Come on, you fucking bastards!" "Ready, dogs! Ready ready *ready*, dogs!" Soon he was hoarse.

We were sledging at what felt like great speed over patches of sastrugi, over deep, rough-textured, virginal snow and over stretches of pale blue glacial ice. On our left was Erebus; on our right were Black and White Islands; receding behind us were Pram Point and Cape Armitage. The dogs, silent, were running as though for their lives.

Suddenly we were following vehicle tracks and Riding cried, "Look at the bloody fuckers! They're too used to roads! Koo-woo-woo! Koo-woo-woo-woo!"

Koo-woo-woo was the signal to Osman to turn to the right. Osman blandly ignored it.

Then Riding ran as fast as he could to the right of Osman and ahead of him, a flying bearded broken-vizored figure, hoping Osman would follow him, shouting, "Osman! Osman! Osman you bloody stupid bastard! Koo-woo-woo! Osman! Koo-woo-woo-Osman! Osman you fucker! Koo-woo-woo-woo!"

But for a long time Osman didn't respond. When he did, Riding cried,

"Good Osman! Good dog! Ready, dogs! Ready, dogs! Ready ready ready ready, dogs!" and away they flew, and Riding had to run with all his might across soft snow in his huge bunny boots to catch up.

Once Riding cried out, possibly for my benefit, "Every dog handler has to swear at his dogs!" Another time, when Osman was lagging and Riding had to run to the head of the line to urge Osman to follow him, Riding cried, "A dog handler has to set an example!"

I thought of Amundsen's highly trained dogs, who, if they had disobeyed, would have immediately felt the whip. Not that Amundsen had been insensitive to dogs; he had loved them. It was that his mission and his life had depended on them.

When we came to a snow cairn with a little red flag on a pole they ran over the cairn and broke the pole. They tried now to turn right to head for the base, which was no longer visible to the naked eye. Riding shouted several times, "Osman! Uh-rrr-uh!" (He rolled the "r" on the tip of his tongue.) This was the signal for Osman to turn left. Osman took his time before complying. The dogs broke into another fight and again the handlers had to knout them to stop it.

The Nansen sledge was comfortable; it felt as if it had built-in shock absorbers.

Returning to the base, we crossed several crevasses, into one of which a dog disappeared. But he quickly emerged, being yanked out by the others, and Riding shouted, "Tighten the traces, you bloody fuckers!"

I was on the sledge for more than two hours. It was a marvelously interesting, exhilarating and profane ride.

I was let off near the ice party, which was in a tiny valley, a trough between hummocks in the pressure. There was a great deal of glare. The five bearded men wore sunglasses. The group was cutting ice from the top of a pressure ridge north of the base and loading it in great milky cubes onto two huge yellow sledges in tandem, with high, fencelike sides. Two men were using power saws that sent steamlike smoke against the blue sky and were so noisy one of the loaders, a blond young scientist, covered his ears with his hands. It was hot, heavy work and the three loaders strained under the loads. Full of dynamic, extreme motion, they reminded me of figures, say of smiths at a forge, in certain of Goya's paintings. The loaders had removed parkas, hats and shirts and were laboring in white or navy wide-mesh net undershirts of the kind I had seen in Christchurch shop windows.

I waited until the sledges were filled, then rode back toward the base on the tail of one. They were pulled by an orange Caterpillar bulldozer with NZARP painted on it. When the bulldozer got stuck on a steep slope a Nodwell had to be fetched to pull it free with winch and cable. The bulldozer then tried to winch up the sledges, which were on the edge of a deep crevasse about two feet wide. The cable harness broke and the sledges were temporarily abandoned. I continued to the base on foot in the company of the ice party.

During dinner I asked some of the men how they had learned about positions being available at the base. Without exception they had answered advertisements in the New Zealand papers. Later I hitched a ride to McMurdo by Navy truck, picked up my mail and hitched one back to Scott Base in time for the evening smoko. In the communications room I drank a couple of cans of Piel's Real Draft Beer with two Kiwis while some Americans waited in the tiny post office next door to make calls to New Zealand and the States. The sun was deliciously warm this evening and pellucid as it poured through windows, luring you into believing there was still plenty of time before nightfall: take it easy, mate, have another beer, another chat. I got chilled working in my room before turning in in the very light but thermally adequate bag atop the white hospital bed.

I arose at 6:30. After breakfast I wandered around the area north of the base for close views of pressure ice and a chance to stare at serene, smoking Erebus. My left thigh was troubling me. Its underside had been sore for almost a week, making it painful for me to sit in certain positions and impossible to touch my toes. When I returned to my room and tried touching them for ten minutes the consequence was twofold: I failed, and the thigh was in considerable pain for a couple of hours afterwards. It was depressing to have to consider one's body in Antarctica while one still had much urgent work to do that required one to be fit and on the move.

The Candy Wagon (USARP power wagon) picked me up at 1:30 and took me back to McMurdo Station, where I reported to the Dispensary across the fast-running, silvery meltwater stream from the chow hall. Examining the thigh, a medical corpsman declared that a muscle was in spasm as a result of dehydration, adding that dehydration was a fairly common human ailment on the ice. I checked my memory but could not recall that it had been a problem mentioned by either Scott or Shackleton. He urged me to drink lots of water and gave the thigh a heat treatment on a hospital bed, during which I fell into a deep sleep lasting more than an hour. The other beds were vacant. When I awoke, the plastic Christmas tree in the room looked friendly with its illuminated, colored little lights. I listened awhile to the pleasant murmuring of the voices of two corpsmen in a nearby office. Before releasing me, the corpsman handed me a box of light green pills called parafon forte, saying they would relax the muscle and warning they might make me sleepy. I had a hunch it was the same kind of pill that had caused Dave Murphy to sleep so much in the Cape Evans wanigan.

I went to my room in the Lodge. While plodding through chores (cleaning gear, unpacking, packing, finding places for new acquisitions, duplicating pages of my journal, writing and mailing letters, doing some laundry), I realized suddenly, with a sense of something like horror, that I had only ten days left on the ice and that I still had many impressions to receive and much data to mine and record. I wished I could stay on longer but I knew my chances of receiving an extension were slim. Even scientists had difficulty in obtaining an extension. From the scientific point of view, the view that my sponsor, the National Science Foundation, naturally took, my program was marginal. When I considered this fact together with the condition of my thigh it was hardly surprising that I grew a bit depressed.

CHAPTER 12

A WALK IN TAYLOR VALLEY

The continuation of the Transantarctic Mountains that fringes the coast of Victoria Land on the western side of McMurdo Sound and that Scott unofficially called the Western Mountains contains mountain ranges, foothills, and scores of glaciers and valleys. Some of the names in this region are colorful: Killer Ridge, Purgatory Peak, The Pimple, Mount Dromedary, Obelisk Mountain. Many of the valleys, large and small, are free of ice as a result of deglaciation and are therefore known as the Dry Valleys, although in the austral summer they may be rich in meltwater flowing from the receding glaciers. They are strange, rare and rather sterile oases in a continent of ice and have fascinated explorers and scientists since their discovery by Scott's first expedition.

They reveal extensive outcrops of bedrock; consequently they offer scientists an opportunity to glimpse the geology of the continental margins. In a number of instances their surface-frozen lakes act as solar heat traps; the waters of the lake bottoms may be as warm as the middle seventies Fahrenheit. Such lakes provide material for wonder as well as study. The valleys are characterized by low mean temperatures, very low humidity and frequent and high winds. They are earth deserts within the vast ice desert of the continent, and contain ventifacts, sand dunes and mushroom rocks. Evidence that post-glacial processes have begun is not lacking; soils have started to form, and algae, mosses and lichens are to be found. It is not surprising that since the International Geophysical Year the Dry Valleys of the so-called McMurdo Oasis—there are several other, lesser oases in Antarctica—have received the special attention of geologists, geomorphologists, glaciologists and botanists. The deglaciation of the McMurdo Oasis is not fully understood. It does not necessarily suggest an ebbing of the Antarctic ice cap in general. The question of whether the cap is increasing or decreasing, known as the Antarctic budget, is still unresolved.

The most famous and one of the largest of the Dry Valleys is Taylor Valley, first explored by Scott during the Discovery Expedition. In *The Voyage of the "Discovery"* Scott used the plural form, referring to the valleys. But Shackleton, in *The Heart of the Antarctic,* referred only to "the Dry Valley," meaning the still unnamed valley that Scott had found. And Griffith Taylor, the geologist on Scott's last, Terra Nova Expedition, who was the first to understand that the Ferrar Glacier is really two glaciers in apposition (that is, that the two are Siamese twins, in a sense), adhered to Shackleton's usage. Scott later named both the Taylor Glacier, formerly the northern arm of the Ferrar, and Taylor Valley in honor of the geologist. Historically, Taylor Valley was the original Dry Valley. Extending from the Antarctic ice plateau on the west to McMurdo Sound on the east, and lying just north of the Kukri Hills, it was once entirely occupied by the Taylor Glacier. The glacier has receded toward the plateau from much of the valley and has diminished both in depth and width, but what is left of it still constitutes a mighty ice river, more than sufficient to plug up the valley's western end.

At Scott's request Taylor explored the valley in January 1911. He wrote enthusiastically about it in a chapter of *Scott's Last Expedition:*

"A strong keen wind was blowing up the valley, but the most remarkable feature of this region prevented it from becoming obnoxious. There was no drift-snow! Imagine a valley 4 miles wide, 3000 feet deep, and 25 miles long without a patch of snow—and this in the Antarctic in latitude 77½°S. . . . Between the serrated crests of the giant cliffs towering five or six thousand feet above us were cascading rivers of ice. These hanging glaciers spread out in great white lobes over the lower slopes of dark rock, and in some cases the cliffs were so steep that the lower portion of the tributary glacier was fed purely by avalanches falling from the ice fields above. And, most amazing of all, not a snow-drift in sight. It was warm weather most of the time we spent in Dry Valley—rising sometimes above freezing-point—and everywhere streams were tinkling among the black boulders, so much so that this valley, in spite of its name, was certainly the wettest area I saw in Antarctica!"

I had been scheduled to camp in Taylor Valley with Roy E. Cameron and three of his colleagues so I could observe the work of scientists in the field while I was experiencing a Dry Valley. Cameron, of the Bioscience Section, Jet Propulsion Laboratory, California Institute of Technology, was interested, among other matters, in developing a life detection system that might be used on the forthcoming Mars probes and that might illuminate the problem of planetary quarantine of materials brought back from extraterrestrial environments. In his words, "Although Antarctica does not possess a Martian environment, it can serve as a useful model of ecology for design, testing, and extrapolation. The naturally harsh environmental conditions of the Antarctic provide a valuable testing ground for space exploration and manned bases."

But the Cameron party changed its plans and camped in the Mount Howe region near the Pole during the time I was available for a stay in Taylor Valley. As a consequence I visited the valley on my own on January 7, 1971, spending a long and wonderful day in the excursion. I took with me as my field assistant ("buddy") David Dreffin, the personable, tall, heavily bearded, blue-eyed and sensitive man in his early twenties who monitored the equipment in the red cosmic ray shack on the road between McMurdo Station and Scott Base.

Dreffin and I breakfasted together the morning of the seventh and reported to the helo hangar at 8:45. I was happy to learn that Jim Brandau would be our pilot, and was delighted when he invited me to fly in the cockpit. As I swung myself through the cockpit port hatch the crewman, standing below me, remarked, "Most people try to go in body first." It was nice to realize I had learned how to swing my right thigh over the seat while the rest of me still clung outside. I eased myself down and reached for my harness. Brandau, entering from the starboard side, said, "You've become more agile."

Brandau could have flown directly across the Sound to the mouth of Taylor Valley and up the valley to Lake Bonney, our destination. This would have entailed a trip of approximately seventy-five miles. Instead, he went by a roundabout way in order, as he later casually mentioned, to expose me to some unusual sights. The length of our outward flight was roughly one hundred and seventy-five miles.

As we drew near to Brown Peninsula—the tip of the peninsula is about twenty miles southwest of Hut Point—we flew low over vast fields of chaotic ice, much of which, mixed with morainic deposits, resembled mudflats. Dark silt lay between the morainic ridges. We encountered a few patches of dirty snow. Water was visible in the form of pools and rivulets but none was blue. We had a cloud cover now and the water, failing to catch a blue sky, showed black. It was a black-and-white scene, for both ice and snow were entirely and unusually white, although a dirty, messy white. I was totally unprepared for such a wild wasteland, which was unlike anything I had ever seen. At times we crossed great furrows and ridges, like plowed black land that had been snowed upon long ago. At others we viewed mazes of ruts and crisscrosses that suggested an alluvial delta. It was impossible, from the helicopter, to judge the depths of the streams, or whether the ice surface would support a human body, but the area looked thoroughly untraversable. Everything was a stark black and white except for a bit of thin blue sky far, far to the west.

We swung north and crossed the mouth of the Koettlitz Glacier, which is some twelve miles wide. The Koettlitz, about forty miles long, flows between Brown Peninsula and the mainland to the Ross Ice Shelf at the head of McMurdo Sound. With the exception of the piedmont glaciers it is the largest glacier west of the Sound. Its eastern side is full of ridges, icefalls, gullies, and undulations; its western half is marked by deep thaw streams, bastions of pinnacled ice, silt, and ridges of moraine materials. Discovered by Scott's first expedition, it was named by Scott for Dr. Reginald Koettlitz, physician and botanist of the expedition.

In the glacier's mouth we saw fantastic blue ice forms, some of which must have been a hundred feet high. Blue? Not the subtle glacial pastel. I mean a blue bluer than the desert sky; a riotous candy blue. What we saw was as unbelievable and pleasurable as fairy tales: snow and ice forms looming out of fields of ice: teahouse kiosks, turrets, battlements, cliffed islands, Swiss lake dwellings. And blue ice streams snaking along in a stupendous nightmare of slow motion. The blue showed despite the cloud cover, so I assumed it was in the ice itself. What a scene it was: the glacier so spacious, we flying quite low, and all these varied shapes against the powder blues of the basic glacial ice. The exotic formations were caused by erosion, by sublimation of ice, and by variations in the tempo of melting, the latter being due to the debris the glacier was carrying, the darker portions, absorbing more heat, melting more rapidly than the lighter ones. The ice river was moving and depositing a vast amount of material and was exerting pressure against the land and against the sea ice. It caused the sea ice adjacent to its mouth to look utterly chaotic. Meltwater ponds were as fascinating as the ice shapes. Observing them, I imagined I was seeing non-objective paintings, or cross-sections of agate, moonstone, coral, pearl.

All the while, as if for the first time, I kept experiencing that special kinaesthetic thrill that comes from flying in a helicopter cockpit. And I imagined I was a bird: fluttering, hovering, suddenly darting. The experience was rhapsodic, and was marked by a stroboscopic-like flicker that the whirring rotors made across the instrument panel and my eyes. I was working with my two 35mm cameras close to the limit of my intensity and I felt marvelously well. Brandau, as usual, was an inspiration to me. He handled the craft with art. And it was astonishing how conscious he was: he seemed to observe everything: the helicopter, the scenes, my actions, even my moods.

We caught glimpses of the inland, white plateau. There, in the west, the sky was clear, a deep blue near the zenith. Heading for Marshall Valley, we approached the strange, denuded brown land with its mountains, glaciers and valleys that I had wanted for so long to visit. The tops of hills and mountains were often obscured by clouds. At times we flew through clouds that felt like fog. We crossed Marshall Valley and went up Miers Valley, seeing the Miers Glacier and Miers Lake, then came to the Blue Glacier with its many icefalls. The Blue Glacier is rather short and is not fed directly by the plateau ice cap. Smaller glaciers, spilling down hills, pour from the plateau into it. In places we saw splotches of textured ice in many vivid hues of green and blue. Brandau flew to the glacier's head, where we had close views of the frozen, broken falls. We were at quite a height now, around 5,000 feet. I leaned out of my hatch into the windstream and glanced back. Along the horizon, right to left, tiny yet still recognizable, were Cape Armitage, Observation Hill, the Gap, Crater Hill, Castle Rock, Hut Point Peninsula and the Turks Head Ridge. The Ridge was the Erebus icefalls back of Cape Evans. Erebus was hidden by clouds.

We flew above Overflow Glacier to the Ferrar Glacier, then headed west along the Ferrar's southern side. The Ferrar Glacier, some thirty-five miles long and from three to six miles wide, lies between the Royal Society Range and the Kukri Hills. It was named after Hartley T. Ferrar, geologist of the Discovery Expedition. The Kukris, named by the same expedition, are so called because of their supposed resemblance to a Ghurka knife. Serrated, dark brown, in places tan, their crests now laced, cottoned and curtained by pearly clouds, with glaciers hanging down the crests and meeting the great highway of the Ferrar, they were very beautiful. The Ferrar is rather a rotten glacier, chopped up, highly textured, with many meltwater courses and numerous dirty areas due to silt material. It has long dark lines running down its length.

"I have a feeling I'm satiating you," Brandau said.

But if my eyes and brain were satiated—*could* I be satiated who was due to leave this continent so soon, possibly never to return?—my will and fingers were not, they were as eager as ever to bring back a report of a world beyond belief.

Hugging the golden, barren mass of Briggs Hill, with its gray cottony clouds that seemed to be falling down its slopes—the hill met the Ferrar sharply—we approached Cathedral Rocks, those massive, brown, spired mountains so well known to Scott and Shackleton that are the northern terminus of the Royal Society Range. The tops were now brilliantly sunlit and etched with snow.

"I get a shiver up my spine every time I see them," Brandau said.

We saw areas of pure white snow, some on glaciers subsidiary to the Ferrar, others on mountain sides; naked brown or tan hills that gave the impression of being made of brass; jagged mountain tops; crumbling icefalls. On our left we passed first Table Mountain, whose top was swathed in clouds, then the Knobhead, the latter, showing slabs of dark brown dolerite interspersed with strata of tan sandstone, resembling a terra cotta pyramid. Glancing westward up Windy Gully with its icefalls and crevasses, we had glimpses of the great, high, bleak plateau and of nunataks on it, and, in the foreground, saw New Mountain on the right or northern side of the Gully and Terra Cotta Mountain on the left of it. We flew low over some Windy Gully icefalls that suggested a mass of whipped cream that had suddenly been frozen while being frothed.

"Let me have some smoke," Brandau said.

Windy Gully is famous for its katabatic (gravity-caused) winds that sweep from the plateau down to McMurdo Sound.

The crewman tossed a bomb out through the cabin hatch. The craft banked, swiveled, turned to the direction from which it had come.

"The wind usually blows forty knots here," Brandau said.

Seeing the purple smoke column wanly rising, he cried, "My God, it's absolutely calm!"

We touched down on New Mountain close to the Windy Gully ice river. New Mountain, not far from the plateau, is the easternmost spur of a group of mountains and valleys that includes Pyramid, Finger, Maya and Aztec Mountains and Turnabout, Beacon, Furnell and Arena Valleys. There were patches of snow on New Mountain but most of the mountain was bare. Looking eastward at the bad weather we had left behind, we saw a world boiling and steaming in a huge cauldron. The Ferrar Glacier seemed to be emitting volumes of steam.

We left the helicopter briefly to hunt for "ashtray" rocks. They are of sandstone and resemble beautifully formed ashtrays of various sizes and depths. Most of them have a single concavity but some have two or even three. They are formed by chemical weathering and by the winds. The rims are sometimes so highly polished you think they're coated with a film of oil until you touch them. An ashtray rock is not easy to come by unless you happen to have helicopter time at your disposal and a pilot like Brandau who knows where New Mountain is and is willing to fly roundabout to take you to it. He once said to me, apropos of Antarctica, "There are people here who don't like this place. They travel in a straight line between two points." He knew several such rare and out-of-the-way places as New Mountain. As I had myself learned, he gathered things not for their possession but for the pleasure of giving them away, and of stimulating interest in the continent. But he was careful not to broadcast his special knowledge, for he disliked the thought of a general hunt for souvenirs, and of the latter's depletion.

We took off again and flew west briefly over Windy Gully, then northwest over the land mass of which New Mountain is a part, crossing a rich, brown, denuded sterile land of peaks, crags, valleys, and of large amphitheaters composed of bands of sandstone alternating with ribbons of dolerite. Bad weather, moving in from the east and north, was filling the amphitheaters with smoke-colored clouds. The Lashly Glacier was part of the distant background, as were the Lashly Mountains. Tabular Mountain, in the middle ground, looked remarkably fine: pale, gray, a suggestive thin wash setting off the spectacular brilliance of the terra cotta areas. Coming around east of Pyramid Mountain—both Pyramid and Finger Mountains had a terra cotta appearance and the area between them formed an amphitheater full of creamy snow—we had views of the head of the Taylor Glacier, which resembled a steaming cauldron: the weather was thick there. The icefalls there gave the impression of being in great motion. Beyond the Taylor, the Asgard Range rose out of agitated clouds. Finger Mountain, well known to the early explorers, swung in a tight arc, the fingertip pointing southeast. The Taylor moves down from the north side of New Mountain. At Cavendish Rocks it is apposite to the Ferrar Glacier. It is some thirty-five miles long, from two to ten miles wide and flows from the Victoria Land plateau into the west end of Taylor Valley, north of the Kukri Hills.

We crossed its upper reaches, then swung eastward over Pearse Valley, in which we saw a small, lovely blue and green lake. As we left the valley we picked up the Taylor Glacier again, whose cliffs appeared to be several hundred feet high. The glacier's surface was a pale, dusty blue, with patches of white; occasionally it was daubed with circular tan spots indicating rock and boulder debris. Flying eastward alongside the Taylor's northern edge, we caught sight of the Kukris with their glaciers that hung like loose tongues. The Catspaw Glacier sprawled over two or three hills opposite the Kukris. The valley's hills were a fine, dark gray. When illumined directly by the sun they looked almost tan. The Taylor receded from us like a triangle down the valley. Its surface as we moved eastward began to show crevasses and rotten low spots. At times we flew beside its eroded cliffs with their embedded boulders and soil. One large place in the cliffside was splotched by what looked like egg yolk. Reaching the glacier's easternmost snout, we came to Lake Bonney, which stems from it. We landed at Bonney Hut on the shore of the lake.

The green, A-frame hut was more substantial and better-equipped than I had expected. At one time it had been used by scientists for prolonged stays. There was a smaller, storage shack nearby. The hut contained provisions, a large stove, a large generator, ceiling lights, a sink, cots, chairs, cooking utensils and, in case one had forgotten what naked women looked like, many pinups in color. It lacked blankets and sleeping bags. Brandau, showing us how to operate the stove, said we would be picked up at about eight. We accompanied him to the helo pad, near which were several empty fuel drums and a rock cairn, and watched him take off. It was now almost noon.

In the vicinity of the hut there was no way to cross over to the north shore of the lake. We wanted to approach the snout of the Matterhorn Glacier, so we hiked eastward until we reached an isthmus separating Lake Bonney from a smaller lake. Here we moved to the valley's northern side. It was a boulder-strewn valley with a gray pebbly floor and with numerous glaciers tonguing down from above. The very dry hills were brilliantly sunlit. We came to the shores of a pond. Our boots sank in the porous soil. Proceeding along the pond's northern shore, occasionally we leaped across meltwater streams, Dreffin flying through the air with stilt-like legs.

We reached higher, firmer ground. The hills rose on both sides of us to a naked, dazzling sky. I recalled the grays and blacks of Royds and Evans, the volcanic darknesses of McMurdo. When I turned around to look back, I saw the Taylor Glacier filling the valley floor thickly. There was something hauntingly strange here. Then I realized what it was: the absence of birds over dry land.

No life stirred that the naked eye could discern. The world seemed purely inorganic. No leaves or weeds to rustle in a breeze; no treetops to sough or sigh. There was no wind. If and when we left the sound of meltwaters we would encounter the great Antarctic silence.

We came upon what I thought of as "mysterious" tracks, of about four persons, heading eastward and going persistently and intelligently, selecting the middle ground to avoid unnecessary climbing over debris hills, finding the best way among boulders, moraines and across streams, and often following little trails that I suspected were old meltwater courses. Occasionally, when the ground was very hard, almost bony, we lost the tracks. Then we hunted for them, for our "friends," as we called them, or for our predecessors and trailmasters, as I thought them. Given the facts of life in Antarctica, I was fairly certain that the makers of these tracks were no longer in the valley. I would have been informed of the fact at McMurdo if they were. So who were they and how long ago had they been here? And had they been just legging it along like ourselves, going as far as the spirit moved them?

When we came abreast of the Matterhorn we stared up at its rotten, vertically striated snout suspended on the northern hillside above us, and at the ice boulders strewn in a helter-skelter mass directly below the snout. We listened to the sounds of a brook rushing westward past us, and to the noises of waters flowing from the dying glaciers and trickling over the dry earth and being sponged by the earth. I stared in wonder at the brook. There were freshets aplenty in the McMurdo environs this summer, but those were volcanic-milky, whereas this one at my feet was limpid, crystal, inviting us to drink. We drank and moved on.

The valley at times doubled and tripled because of long morainic hills. The glacial debris made this place a rock hunter's paradise. Then we found that the valley had subtly turned; we were no longer able to look back and see Lake Bonney. Sometimes the footing was soft, laborious; we slid, lost ground. Near the Lacroix Glacier we heard meltwater rushing among boulders and under giant slabs of fallen glacial ice. At times the valley floor bristled with light glancing off rocks, many of them erratics. We found numerous interesting stones: granites, marbles, chalks, conglomerites; others suggesting coke or cinders; some pink with gray veins, or plum flecked with bits of ivory, or rose and resembling glazed clay; others burnt coffee, angelic white. Many had been sculptured by the winds in such a way as to be lovely to gaze at and to handle. A grapefruit-size piece of marble, cracked, irregular in shape, whitish in places, yellowish and glazed in others, contained deep, grainy, burnt-rust little holes. One long stone, heavy, gray, had been streamlined and polished to an especially pleasing result. We came to moraines like earthworks. Occasionally the valley floor looked dunelike in its freedom from morainic clutter.

We reached a mummified crabeater seal, one of some half dozen, including pups, we had encountered on our way. We studied this phenomenon, reported as long ago as Scott's first expedition, and wondered, as Scott's people and no doubt the makers of the tracks had, how the seals, whose habitat is salt water, had gotten so far up the valley.

When we were close to the Nussbaum Riegel (rock bar), which protrudes northward from the Kukri Hills and almost cuts the valley in two, we turned back. But before doing so we climbed to the top of a hill of shards and rocks and viewed the Suess Glacier to the east of us, with its sensuous, gentle fall down the north slope on our left. A small, ice-covered lake, with patches of snow, beautiful with pale greens, blues and touches of lavender, lay between us and the glacier. Clouds were by now moving into the valley's western end, causing us to wonder if the helicopter would be able to pick us up on schedule. If it wouldn't, we could make do for the night by firing up the stove in Bonney Hut. On our way back we ascended the slope to the Matterhorn's high, massive, clifflike snout, under which we rested. Looking across the valley from this shadowed vantage point, I had the feeling I was viewing two large Egyptian pyramids atop the sunlit Kukri Hills, whose dryness and color reminded me of the Sahara near El Gîza.

Moving now into the last lap back, and doing it by a more southerly route, on the opposite side of the valley from which we had come, we reached what looked like an alluvial delta. On the shore of a little lake as green as jade were the remains of another crabeater seal. The lake rippled in a wind, its surface aflame with whitecaps. Waves of gratitude to all those who had made my being here possible swept over me. In this mood I reached Bonney Hut.

The stove, the generator, the cots, chairs, a sink that emptied into a tub; shelves with canned rations; our gear flung about; and Dreffin gulping a long time from his canteen, then leaning back on a cot in a corner, wild-eyed with fatigue, without his large sunglasses, his long brown hair askew, his long legs lying as if broken at the knees, observing me, wondering perhaps what my next move would be. I left that look and that huge beard and went outside to gaze at the lake's frozen cap and at the glacier beyond, then re-entered the hut and prepared a supper of K rations. Afterwards I cleaned up and looked through a window at the brilliance, the radiance. Dreffin still sat asprawl.

I went outside again, walked along the shore, then stood very still, listening to Antarctica's silence (the wind had died down), now exquisitely broken as bits of floating, iridescent ice flakes, colliding with icicles, tinkled like tiny musical glasses. Some three billion human beings were teeming on the surface of the earth. I was one of a handful who had been lucky enough to walk at the world's very edge.

CHAPTER 13

CRASHING ON MOUNT EREBUS

I was scheduled to fly in a Navy helicopter, an H-34, from McMurdo Station to Cape Bird at 1 or 1:30 P.M. on January 9. My mission was to become acquainted with the layout of the cape while camping there; to observe if possible some predation activities of leopard seals against Adélie penguins; to observe Killer whales if to my good fortune any showed themselves; and to witness the life of scientists in the field.

The Kiwis at Cape Bird were irritated by the unexpected descent on January 5 of what in their view was an unconscionably large number of American visitors. It should be emphasized that this was not the first unscheduled appearance of Americans during the season—at least that was what Brian Porter later told me—and that the Cape Bird Kiwis believed such visits were serious interruptions of their scientific work. They made their feelings known to Porter at Scott Base during a scheduled radio contact. Porter communicated their displeasure to Chris Shepherd, who informed me the morning of January 8, the day after my walk in Taylor Valley, that both Porter and the cape Kiwis were now doubtful whether I, as an American, a non-scientist and one of the January 5 visitors, was welcome to camp at the cape, considered both by New Zealand and American authorities to be New Zealand territory.

I immediately looked up Porter at Scott Base and underscored my innocence in the episode. When I asked if he had lodged a complaint with the Operation Deep Freeze people he replied he did not wish to create an "incident." I said I could understand this desire to underplay the affair but that I took no pleasure in being a scapegoat. I asserted that I did not consider my mission to the cape a light matter in my program of gathering material for my book, that I was sorry the Kiwis at Bird, whom I liked, felt affronted, and that I would do everything I could to mollify them, not only for my mission's sake but because I was sure there had been a misunderstanding concerning the attitude of McMurdo regarding the unfortunate visit. I promised to bring the cape Kiwis whole cartons of foods, such as fresh fruits and vegetables, that they were in very short supply of.

Porter, now sympathetic to my cause and probably influenced by the fact I had recently been a happy member of the Scott Base community, convinced the cape Kiwis to let me camp there. But he was told by them, or so he informed me, that I must come alone and bring a tent: I would not be welcome to share the wanigan; I would have to live alone and apart from them. They indicated they would cooperate minimally with me, that I would have to look after my own safety and that I would have no need of a field assistant, who would only serve to clutter the scene.

I was obviously in for an interesting time at Bird. I wished I wasn't quite as tired and as short on sleep as I was, but I was not seriously troubled. The Bird people were young and pleasant; their irritation would wear off; and I had no doubt they would eventually accept me as their friend. However, their insistence on my bringing a tent gave me something to think about. Living in a small unheated tent in Antarctica is one thing; trying to write in one is quite another. The wanigan at Bird had four bunks, all currently occupied. But it also had a fair amount of floor space, as I had seen, and I had hoped to sleep on the floor and to use the structure's facilities at least for the physical part of writing in my journal.

As it turned out, the matter of the tent was crucial. If I hadn't brought the tent along on the flight toward Cape Bird on January 9 my three companions and I probably would not have survived the crash experience, at least not without permanent injury. Also, because I expected both to live and to work in the tent, I brought along two cot mattresses rather than one. I intended to use one under my sleeping bag; the other I planned to employ as a work surface on the tent's floor. The extra mattress too proved important to our safety. During my conference with Porter the latter asked me to do Scott Base two favors: to deliver an ice ax and a packet of mail to the cape Kiwis. The ice ax played a role in the crash story.

As for the tent itself, I selected an Air Force survival tent because, never having used this type, I wanted to familiarize myself with it. It is not a tent one person can easily load gear into. It has two entrances, which are tubelike, wormlike and double-layered. You crawl in order to reach the interior. Such entrances help keep wind out and body heat in but because they create a potential trap it's a good idea to have a sheath knife on you or very handy, for in case of fire you would need to cut your way out rapidly. I wanted to set up the tent quickly and efficiently. Also, I had no intention of hauling my considerable gear alone from the beach up to the cliffside plateau on which I was to camp. So I requested the services of a field assistant on a turnaround flight.

The assistant, with whom I was acquainted superficially, was Van Enderby, twenty years old and from Arizona. A tallish, lean man in excellent physical condition, he was reserved, reticent and always quietly eager to be of help. From the look of his legs in jeans and his feet in boots and from the way he carried himself I took him to be a strong hiker. I had rarely encountered him except when I had had occasion to visit the field party processing center. Like Dave Murphy, he was a Holmes & Narver employee there. I selected him under urging from his boss (this was not Jim Elder), who, when I indicated that I wished to take Dave Murphy because I knew, liked and trusted Murphy, protested that I had already "done more than enough" for Murphy and that, in all fairness, I ought to consider the needs of other deserving young men. His boss informed me that Enderby hoped to become a geologist; that he would be very grateful for any opportunity to get away from McMurdo and see some other part of the island, even if only on a turnaround flight to Bird; and that he was entirely capable of preparing me to camp at the cape.

As I have already suggested, few persons working in Antarctica today have the chance to see the place extensively; most have the feeling, I suspect, of being marooned. Young non-scientist civilians like Enderby would put in long work weeks in the warehouse-like Field Center, and on their days off had only McMurdo, Scott Base and a few hikes in their vicinity to vary a quite monotonous life. It was understandable that Murphy was envied by his fellow employees for having camped at Capes Evans and Royds.

Murphy told me *he* wanted very much to accompany me to Bird, for he had never seen the island's terrain north of Royds. I had the unhappy task of explaining that although I much preferred to have him with me on the turnaround flight, the pressure was on me to stop "favoring" him on my field trips; and that because I felt harassed by lack of time I had decided not to buck the pressure and had accepted Enderby.

Now, as to who was to fly me to Bird: Brandau was out of the picture, for he was scheduled to depart from McMurdo for Christchurch at 12:30 or 1 A.M. of the ninth in connection with a planning conference, along with some DV's and Shepherd and Putzke, the skipper of the icebreaker *Staten Island.* In the wardroom the evening of the eighth Billy Blackwelder told me he would fly me. At breakfast on the ninth, however, Dan Biggerstaff, known as Biggee, informed me that *he* would fly me, adding that Brandau had asked him and Blackwelder to look out for me during his absence and that they meant to do it.

I headed for the helo hangar at a bit before 1 P.M. of the ninth, leaving Enderby at one of the lower helo pads to handle my gear, which he was offloading from a truck and which he had prepared and gathered at my instructions but not under my personal supervision, for, as I had told Murphy, I was greatly pressed for time. I had turned over to him the key to my Field Center cage, in which my camping gear was stored, with both verbal and written instructions regarding my needs, including the special foods I wished to present to the cape Kiwis and which he would have to obtain from the Navy commissary, and had helped him load my stuff onto the truck. I was not carrying a radio; the Kiwi radio contacts with Scott Base would suffice to keep McMurdo Station informed of my whereabouts and safety.

Biggerstaff emerged from the hangar to inform me there was too much cloud cover today over the McMurdo-Bird route—or, at any rate, too much for the H-34. The McMurdo-Bird route fringed the island's western coast; I had flown over it when I had gone up to Bird. By contrast, flying in a helo over the island's deep interior was considered to be extremely dangerous for several reasons, a major one being the fact that Mount Erebus, with its ice-sloped, crevassed and ice-falled sides, occupied so much of the island's mass, and a forced landing might be hazardous. I make this point now because of its considerable relevance to the crash tale. Not that the coastal route was viewed as safe by VXE-6 helo pilots; on the contrary, they referred to it half jokingly as "the suicide route."

Biggerstaff said some of the flight to Bird would have to be made under the cover—the cover, massive, was both low and high—and at times probably over water instead of ice: it was well known the sea ice was rapidly breaking up north of Royds. If an H-34, with only tricycle landing gear, had to ditch in water it would sink with the certain and quick death of all on board because of the water's temperature. He said actually it was illegal for an H-34 to fly over water in Antarctica. But a Coast Guard helo, the H-52, with its hull fuselage and pontoons, could fly over water with a fair degree of safety, for unless it hit the deck too hard it would remain afloat, certainly long enough for a rescue attempt. If I still wanted to fly to Bird today a Coast Guard helo, the one on the upper pad below the Chalet, was prepared to take me.

Biggerstaff said maybe I ought to consider postponing the flight.

I said no, I was fast running out of time and preferred to fly now.

And so the decision was made. Later, during the massive search for us, he convinced himself he should have scratched the flight—he had the authority to do so—and felt very bad when, for a time, my companions and I were given up for dead. He and I were very fond of each other. In addition, he had Brandau's request that he and Blackwelder look out for me to add to his burden of guilt and sadness.

I regretted having to switch from the H-34 to the H-52, for I had hoped Biggerstaff would ask me to fly in the cockpit. I had no reason to think the Coast Guard pilot, whose identity I did not yet know, would invite me to do so. I would not ask him to share it. I had never asked a pilot for a favor and I had resolved I never would. The pilots had enough to do without my imposing on them.

Biggerstaff said the Coast Guard pilot was Stu Palmer (of the *Staten Island*), now in the hangar. I went inside the hangar, greeted Palmer and told him I would fly with him to Cape Bird. Palmer delayed the flight some ten or fifteen minutes while he had a leisurely cup of coffee.

He was a quiet, reserved man whom I took to be about thirty-two or thirty-three, with straight brown hair, a long and wispy brown mustache, a soft-skinned face that gave you the impression he had the lightest of beards, a soft-voiced drawl (he was from Georgia) and with dark eyes lidded in a manner that suggested an owl's. I didn't know if he was a family man and don't know now. I never felt a desire to lessen the distance between us, possibly because I sensed a dark side in him that I didn't feel in the other Coast Guard pilots I knew. He was remote not only with me and other civilians but with military men as well. He often sat alone in one of the wardrooms, aloof from the singing or hilarity around him. At least this is how I remember him. Perhaps I'm confusing his behavior after the crash episode with his behavior before it. He was rather handsome and of good height. I imagined he was popular with women. But he didn't give the impression of being vain; this I liked in him. I sensed he might be soft physically by my standards, that he disliked being in Antarctica, that he hadn't chosen to come here, and that he felt much more comfortable in semi-tropical places. I sometimes even wondered if he hated the continent I loved so much.

We climbed to the upper pad, where I found that my gear was already aboard. The crewman walked to the front of the craft while Enderby and I climbed aboard and began strapping ourselves in. Palmer, boarding the craft, said he had to fuel up at Williams Field. In the H-52 the pilot enters the cockpit via the cabin; cabin and cockpit are on the same level.

Then Palmer surprised me by asking, "Chuck, would you like to sit in the cockpit?"

"Yes, sir!" I replied in delight.

I went to the copilot's seat, harnessed myself in, squeezed the spherical helmet onto my head and plugged it into the intercom system. The helmet was so tight I wondered if I'd be able to endure it all the way to Bird. The direct flight from McMurdo to Bird takes about forty-five minutes but we would be stopping en route at Scott Base as well as Williams Field. We lifted off and headed down and around the tip of Cape Armitage, then north. From a distance and a height the exotic airfield, a dark, speckled mass on the huge white sheet of the ice shelf, with three rows of JameswAys, the latter resembling dashes, seemed like a tiny, otherwordly settlement. It was fascinating to watch the place, including its runway to the right of the control tower, and the dark line of the old bus route leading off to the left, looming to meet us. Vehicle tracks ran southward; almost none went north. Mount Terror was dappled with light. Mount Erebus rose on the left, its crest clear, but cloud cover was already halfway up its western slopes. More cover was moving in from the west.

We touched down, shut off the engine, took on fuel and flew briefly over the shelf to the New Zealand base to pick up the packet of mail I had promised Porter I'd deliver to Bird. I already had the ice ax. Palmer did not shut down the engine at the Kiwi base. We were on deck just long enough for my friend Paul, who managed the Kiwi post office and who was standing by for our arrival, to run out, ducking under the spinning rotors, and hand me the packet through my open hatch.

We lifted off and proceeded toward Bird but with, for me, this significant difference: whereas I had automatically expected us to retrace our way around Cape Armitage and go briefly westward past McMurdo, then north along the western coast, we crossed gleaming, low-lying Hut Point Peninsula itself and headed for black Castle Rock, which we soon passed. Still frozen McMurdo Sound, an expanse of whites, lilacs and pale blues, was speckled with cloud shadows, in the midst of which one of the icebreakers, too tiny for identification without binoculars, looked very vulnerable. Some blue sky was still visible directly above us but the western ranges were rapidly dimming behind curtains of weather. In the northwest, that is, in the direction of Cape Bird, there was a great deal of thick, ominous-looking cover.

We took to hugging the glaring crevassed slopes of Erebus. Wondering why Palmer was going so far and so dangerously inland, why in other words he wasn't following the traditional route as our flight plan required, I told myself vaguely that that was his business, not mine, and continued with my own, which was the use of my two cameras, but shot without my usual enthusiasm, for one reason because the scenes were no longer fresh for me and for another because my hatch views were badly obstructed by the H-52's port pontoon. I felt myself resisting a growing irritability, which was not aided by the pressure the helmet was exerting on my temples and by Palmer's silence, broken once when he asked me if I knew the way to Cape Bird. I replied that I did, at which he looked relieved.

In retrospect I realize I should have wondered at that look, which possibly suggested he would do well to return to McMurdo and not encounter, in a state of doubt as to where he was, that northwestern terrain and that cover which in conjunction threatened to be a hazard to our safety. It occurred to me he might have heard of Brandau's feat in taking an H-34 over Erebus and that he meant to emulate him with the H-52. If that was his intention I hoped he was a damn good pilot, for despite the H-52's greater maximum altitude capability than the H-34's (by some 4,000 feet), I had about three hundred pounds of stuff on board and a field assistant whom I judged to weigh, clothed, in the neighborhood of a hundred and seventy-five pounds. I also trusted he had asked VXE-6 helo pilots lots of intelligent questions about what was involved in climbing the atmosphere close to Erebus and had elicited informed replies.

We now began to climb, not fitfully but steadily. Both pilot and copilot had two altimeters: a barometric one indicating elevation above sea level, and a radar one showing elevation above the ground. I observed my barometric altimeter with fascination.

At 8,000 feet we were inland from Cape Royds. Looking down at the cape, I made out portions of its seaward side. Its upper slopes were covered by massive clouds resembling vast steam explosions. As we continued to climb I saw many crevasses—curved machete slashes —some of them snowbridged, and many clifflike rock slopes. The sky was still blue but beyond the large second crater, that is, north of it, hung a great white cloud bank. We were hugging the precipitous slope of the second crater and encountering more and more naked rock. Looking down and immediately westward, I saw little more than a sea of clouds. But far, far to the west, above the cover, was serene blue sky.

At around 11,500 feet we saw Erebus's crest clearly. Light smoke, probably mixed with steam, was issuing from the crater. We were on the volcano's northwest side and close to the top of the clifflike second crater. Erebus has three craters, the third being the topmost. We saw many rock outcrops, for here the mountain was exposed to the warming effects of the summer sun, which, as we know, slowly dips as it rounds the sky counterclockwise, reaching its nadir at midnight, when it is above the Pole.

Palmer said calmly, "I'd like to clear it but we've got too much weight."

At about 12,000 feet he said, "It's as high as she'll go," yet he seemed to be pushing the craft to go still higher.

Erebus's crest felt very close to us. At moments we seemed to be heading directly for it. During my current visit to Antarctica I had several times imagined Erebus to be Ross Island's godhead, and its crest to be the mountain's face, remote from mortals, a legendary place where great prophecies were pronounced. This despite my knowledge of the meaning of the name. In Greek mythology Erebus is a son of Chaos and also the dark nether place through which souls pass on their way to Hades. At times I had thought of the mountain as a symbol of Antarctica, a continent both extraordinarily beautiful and dangerous. I had seen the mountain from many sides, always at normal distances. What I was now experiencing were abnormally intimate views of the northwestern side of that face.

I made out Beaufort Island on our left and some open sea to our right. It occurred to me I should ask Palmer to abandon this madness and take me immediately to Cape Bird as scheduled. But I was not about to cry chicken.

"If he wants to keep climbing that's his business," I thought.

What an idea: as if my life were not my business.

The craft was straining; it seemed to be trembling. My altimeter registered more than 12,500 feet. The reader will recall that the elevation of Mount Erebus as indicated on current official maps is 12,450 feet and he will no doubt wonder if, since we were higher than this, we could see into the crater itself. I should like to remind him that the figure of 12,450 feet represents elevation based on triangulation at sea level, and that my readings were in barometric terms, that Mount Erebus is in a low-pressure area, and that in such terms its elevation is approximately 13,300 feet. I saw some open sea, a lot of pack ice, and the watery horizon in the north, where there was still a good deal of lovely blue sky. Cape Bird was under thick cover.

We were approaching the crest from the northwest now. It rose to a mildly sloping peak, at the top of which was some dark stuff with the hue and texture of an ash heap. I was shooting through the windshield and through a strange apparition: a distorted reflection of a helmet surrounding a mongoloid face. At the crest, in addition to the ash heaps—the central one was the largest and darkest—were some snow and some precipitous rocky areas; the gullies of the latter were snow-filled. There was a moment when we seemed to be almost on a level with the top of the mountain. I was shooting out of my hatch now. We were spiraling very slowly clockwise. Beyond the heaps was the smoking crater itself.

I was both willing and ready to take advantage of the situation if we cleared Erebus, yet I kept silent, whether because I had something to gain by Palmer's overflying the crater or because I was determined not to cry chicken I shall probably never know. Technically the pilot is solely responsible for his craft, and nothing I said or failed to say could mitigate this fact. But I *might* have succeeded in persuading him to descend if I had tried. Possibly he had gone too far out on a limb and needed me to save his face. Perhaps if I had felt less distance between us I would have been kinder and have given him, presuming he needed and wanted it, the overt excuse to lose altitude voluntarily.

I am not unaware of the fact he may have taken a great risk in a desire to do me a service, as he had already done me one by inviting me to sit in the cockpit with him, and that I was responding meanly. Or, knowing that I was gathering material for a book about Ross Island, he may have tried to impress me in the hope of playing a role in it. On the other hand, inasmuch as I would have been much safer in the cabin than in the cockpit during a crash, and inasmuch as he was inviting a crash by his rashness, he may have done me a disservice by inviting me to share the cockpit. These are subtle and painful matters and have puzzled and troubled me ever since.

Suddenly we seemed to hang still. Then we descended quickly, not flying but falling. Yet it was not a vertical fall but a forward one, as if we were trying to land too rapidly.

Palmer cried in a brittle, bitter tone, "We've got a downdraft! We're going down!"

For an instant I thought he meant we had merely failed to clear Erebus. Then I realized that our single, turbine-powered engine had air-starved in the too-thin air. This was bad enough. In addition we were being shoved down by a powerful downdraft.

And so Palmer had made the mistake of flying around to the opposite side of the updraft. The updraft, on the southeast side of Erebus, was due to the prevailing southeasterly, that bitter, life-endangering wind that swept down from the polar plateau and across the Ross Ice Shelf. The downdraft was on the northwest side. Until this moment, and during the other helo flights I had been fortunate enough to experience in a cockpit, I had enjoyed the feeling of having nothing between me and the outside world but a thin Plexiglas shell. Now I felt I was in a free fall, with not even the shell to protect me, and that on impact the back of the craft would slam against me.

The wild, desolate, rocky landscape rose up to greet us. Strangely, I thought for a moment that Palmer was possibly trying to land somewhere—anywhere—in order to have a look around or to think things through. I hoped he retained enough control of the craft to be autorotating but I could not really believe he had sufficient altitude for an autorotation or that an autorotation was possible in such a downdraft.

A white mass of snow came at us, magnifying with great speed and intensity. There were gray and black boulders and rock aprons and shoulders everywhere. There was insufficient time to experience fear, yet there was time for fascination, for observation and above all for acute experience.

Palmer, shouting "Mayday! Mayday! Mayday! Any station! Any station!" desperately flipped toggle switches.

The snow and ice masses rose up and slammed us. We bumped, buckled, spun around, skidded. I wondered if I was about to be killed. Suddenly we were motionless. There was a terrific silence. I unfastened my harness, removed my helmet, realized I was in one piece and that my cameras, which hung from my neck, hadn't been damaged. The engine had quit. The rotors were still. We weren't on fire.

Palmer, having unharnessed himself, jumped up, his face contorted, and shouted, "Fuck! Fuck!" in disgust and exasperation, flipping some overhead switches.

"Take it easy, Stu," I said.

I went outside for a look around. The crest looked unbelievably close, and bad weather was moving in from the west and north. It was obvious the latter would soon engulf us. We had dropped down onto a colorless world: nothing but blacks, grays and whites. The blue of the sky was so rapidly being transfigured into a milky gray it hardly counted as a color; in any event it would not be a color for long. The only colors were those we had brought with us: for example, the brilliant red of my USARP parka. The helo's tail pointed in the direction of the crest. The cockpit faced rock aprons, huge black and gray boulders and two large ice fumaroles just beyond the boulders. In the crest's direction was a series of parallel-like and horizontal rock ridges, rising one above the other, interspersed with boulders and patches of snow and ice. The smoke issuing from the crater beyond the ash heaps was blowing away from us. On the craft's starboard side were more rock aprons and boulders. On its port side was a long stretch of naked and fairly level rock; but there too were many boulders the helo had miraculously missed. We had come down on the upper portion of the plateau of the second crater, whose great cliff was not too distant in the direction of the ice fumaroles. I wondered how it would have felt if we had gone spilling down that cliffside.

It struck me as being about the worst place for a ditching imaginable: difficult for single-engine helos, the only kind available in Operation Deep Freeze then, to ascend to for a rescue; almost impossible for them to start an engine at if it conked out; death to walk down from past the rock and ice cliffs and ice slopes and ice falls and crevasses I knew about from extensive reading, from studies of high-altitude photographs and from having observed some of them at first hand from helicopters. Doubting that my companions suspected what a man-killer Erebus could be, I resolved to keep such knowledge to myself as long as possible.

An examination of the craft revealed that the landing gear had been badly damaged. We had hit the deck on the port side. The port tire had blown. The port wheel had been slammed out of position on its axle. The struts connecting the port pontoon with the fuselage had been telescoped and their covering shredded. The pontoon was almost vertical instead of horizontal. The small tail wheel had been partially rammed into the fuselage. The starboard wheel had been bent out of shape. Its tire was almost flat. But the pontoon looked all right. The helo was resting on its hull and tipping strongly to port. One of the rotor blades was almost only head-high.

We were now all outside and greatly relieved to be uninjured. It seemed a miracle that we had found a bit of level, snow-covered ground among all the rocks and boulders. Also miraculous was the fact we hadn't come down in straightforward, tricycle fashion. If we had, we would have had sufficient momentum to pile up on the boulders and burst into flames. Coming down on one side had caused us to swivel around and skid sideways; this had given us sufficient traction to brake us short of disaster. And fortunately the snow had been soft and deep enough to act as a shock absorber. If we had hit down on ice or flat rock we would have pancaked.

Studying the damage, once again Palmer cried "Fuck!" in despair, his face showing anguish. It was inevitable that such behavior, coming from the leader of our group, would be infectious. The crewman's face trembled, he worked to control his emotions, he said "Fuck" in a low voice, bit his nether lip and swung his head from side to side. But Enderby looked stolid although pale. I learned from him later, at McMurdo, that he had thought Palmer had landed deliberately.

Palmer said as if to himself but very clearly, "I'm going to be shipped out."

He remarked several times how lucky we were one of the rotor blades hadn't hit the snow; if it had, we would have been flipped over. He entered the cockpit and tried to start the engine. The crewman stood by outside with a fire extinguisher. We had plenty of battery power but the engine could not grab hold. I had heard a story about a Coast Guard helo going too high somewhere on Erebus, landing, shutting down its engine and being unable to start it without the help of other helos, special batteries and special equipment. And that hadn't been near as high as we now were. Palmer called out to the crewman that he had a red warning light indicating fire.

"Look for a fire!" he shouted.

The crewman replied he didn't see any sign of a fire but that smoke was pouring out of the exhaust. The smell of fire in the cabin was too strong to be ignored. I asked Enderby to remove my survival tent and gear from the craft and to set the tent up as best and as quickly as he could at a sufficient distance from the helo to protect it if the helo burned. Whether the craft burned or not, we would need the tent if the temperature kept dropping. I told him not to bother staking the tent down thoroughly.

"Just secure it against a possible gust of wind. Then give me a hand with the food."

I started lugging cartons out of the craft. The effects of the altitude, which became apparent the moment one moved about or worked, were unpleasant now: breathlessness, a pounding of the heart, dizziness, quick fatigue, the possibility of blacking out. But they were mild for me as compared with my companions. I was surprised when, quite early, the

crewman complained of a vicious headache. Then Enderby and Palmer
said they had very bad headaches too. I explained my lack of a headache
to myself as being the result of all the swimming I had done and the
oxygen hunger I had deliberately endured.

After a while the smoke stopped and the smell of fire disappeared. We
were still warm from the craft's heating system. Things could be worse.
They could also be somewhat better: for example if the HF (high
frequency) radio was functioning. But the HF radio required a lot of
juice, and we had lost the radio with the engine's failure. You lose your
single engine and go down, and to help along your morale you also lose
your HF radio.

Palmer fetched a line-of-sight hand radio and walked around the craft,
saying, "Mayday! Mayday! McMurdo! McMurdo! Any station! Any
station! This is copter one four zero four down on the northern slope of
Mount Erebus!"

He handed me the radio—it was small, with a flexible, tubelike
antenna—and asked me to keep calling. So I walked around outside and
pressed the transmission button and said over and over, "McMurdo
Station, McMurdo Station! Mayday, Mayday, Mayday! McMurdo
Station, this is helo one four zero four down on the northern slope of
Mount Erebus!"

But I felt very dubious about the effort, for Erebus was between us and
McMurdo.

Again Palmer tried to start the engine and again he received a fire
signal. Coming outside, he told me he believed the engine was all right
but that the air was too thin to permit the engine to take hold.

He said, "We'll have to walk to a ridge overlooking McMurdo and use
the hand radio from there. Chuck, you know Ross Island best. Can we
walk to the top?"

I said it would be foolhardy to try it. Visibility was poor and getting
worse. We were going to be socked in very shortly. The temperature was
rapidly dropping. We might have to contend with bad ice slopes, even
crevasses. And we had no crampons, no rope and only one ice ax.
Furthermore, we had the altitude effects to contend with.

Palmer walked around examining the craft, uttered a few more
"Fucks," then turned to me and said, "Chuck, I'm sorry to have gotten
you into this place."

"Forget it, Stu, it's okay."

"We'll *have* to get to a ridge," he said. "If not up there, then a lower
one, maybe lower than here. Van and I will look for a ridge."

He said,' "Hell, let's walk down the mountain and get away from this altitude."

I said, "You wouldn't get three hundred yards before you'd be dead. There are snowbridged crevasses. You could fall through and go down thirty or forty feet. Even if you survived the fall and we had rope and gear and know-how to rescue you with, there'd be little time. Down there, below the surface, you'd be at mean temperature, probably fifty or sixty below. And there are icefalls and ice slopes. We have no belaying equipment, only one ice ax, and no knowledge of the safest way down. The best way down I know about is at Royds, but we're too far north of that. And how would we see in that mass of clouds? We wouldn't stand a chance."

He looked startled.

"We're trapped," I said. "We'd better stay close to the craft. It's our best chance of being found."

I wanted to say more. I wanted to ask, "Why don't you drain the helo's fuel and lubricant while they're still warm, so we can use them for heat and for smudge pots?"

But I could sense that he still hadn't accepted the fact the craft was here to stay, that he was hoping the engine would somehow fire, catch hold and extricate us from our most unusual predicament; and clearly I was eager to share his hopes even though I wondered vaguely if the engine system had been damaged in the crash, for otherwise I would have said what was on my mind; or wouldn't I?

And so Palmer and Enderby headed southwestward, Enderby probing the way and Palmer looking unearthly in his huge helmet. If they remained as much as possible on the plateau on which we found ourselves, which contained a substantial amount of outcrop, and if they used the ice ax responsibly they would be reasonably safe. Soon they disappeared below a nearby ridge, leaving me alone with the crewman.

CHAPTER 14

THE HELICOPTER

I walked to an outcrop to study the crash scene from a distance and to view the helo, this poor kitelike box that through mismanagement had fallen out of the sky; this outpost of civilization in a bleak and savage wilderness; this comfortable "home"; but a home which, because it was a metal fuselage, was a heat sink, beautifully capable of dissipating our body heat into space; therefore a home that could destroy us if we depended overmuch on it; this representative of high technology, costing half a million dollars, but a technology, as for example in the case of the HF radio, that had failed us; or that we had significantly failed.

The cloud cover that had been steadily moving in on us had by now engulfed us like a thick fog. Who would have dreamed it had the audacity to climb so high? At times one had to resist the notion it was malevolent. For weeks Erebus had been clear. Now, in the increasing warmth of the austral summer, more and more seawater was free of its frozen state and creating massive fogs and clouds. The cover made the largest, blackest boulders appear to be faint gray shadows in a vast milky stuff. Visibility was seventy-five to a hundred feet. Beyond that range, in every direction, including overhead, was a potentially murderous white wall. What a thing to happen at a time when we had strayed grossly from our flight plan! We might as well be underground for all the good it would do to set off flares and smoke bombs.

The crewman, wearing a white spherical helmet, a khaki flight suit, light khaki flight gloves and beat-up desert boots, was standing uncertainly in front of the open hatch. He was a gracefully tall man with a pleasant, easy-smiling, longish face. Little brown hairs sprouted from his bony chin in what, hopefully, was the beginning of a beard. I had paid little attention to him. One saw helo crewmen but looked through them. What did we have in common? Usually very little. But this present crewman and I had a good deal, despite the fact that we had been born greatly apart, he in Illinois in 1950, I in Russia in 1915. We might well die together; or, if not together, in tandem. And I believe we also felt the uncommon bond of representing life in a mostly inorganic world. I thought "mostly" in the faith there must be little outposts, faint strains, of life here, even though none were presently visible.

Realizing that I didn't know his name, I walked over and asked what it was. It felt odd to be making such a request inasmuch as we had crashed and worked together and he had been addressing me as Doc. But I had been uncertain as to whether we would lift off and remain strangers to each other. Now I knew we were not going to take off—not in one four zero four, which had found its last resting place. We were going to get to know each other before we were out of this.

"Jack Eights," he replied.

I gave him my name but he called me Doc throughout the episode although Palmer and Enderby called me Chuck. He looked unhappy. I suspected he felt very lonely. I knew I did, yet I had relished the feeling of loneliness, or rather of being alone, in Taylor Valley and at Capes Evans and Royds. Four had been diminished to two; temporarily it was only he and I against raw nature here in the form of Erebus.

I asked him to help me secure the tent. We were lucky the wind was mild, but would it continue to be? Our lives might depend on the tent. He worked at the ropes and poles while I hammered at the rock pegs with a fire extinguisher. We had thin cylindrical metal pegs, meant for Cape Bird, instead of square wooden ones. In snow and ice and in a steady, grinding wind the metal pegs, providing less friction, would work loose more readily. The sound of metal on metal ricocheted around us. The temperature was dropping steadily.

Occasionally Eights looked on the verge of panic. Once he said harshly to himself, "Fuck! What am I doing here?"

He was, as we know, only twenty. When I saw him like this something paternal stirred inside me.

"We'll be all right," I said.

Glancing up, he asked hopefully, "Think so, Doc?"

"Yes. I wouldn't miss this for anything."

He smiled. He seemed more relaxed after that. Possibly I represented for him the responsibility and reliability of middle age. And perhaps he had already begun to doubt Palmer's ability to bring him intact out of the situation and had begun to look to me to do it. Maybe he was impressed by my relative calmness, which resulted, I believe, from my being acquainted with the facts of life in Antarctica. Also, I was fascinated by everything and was trying to observe and remember acutely. What must have seemed a naked disaster to him seemed to me at times, in addition, a remarkable opportunity.

There was more work to be done, but his head was splitting and I was breathing very heavily and rapidly. We rested awhile, watching the weather. He drew out his sheath knife, saying, "Doc, I've always wanted to stick this into a helo and now I can."

I laughed. But, not wanting to witness the sticking, I turned away and walked to a distant outcrop to take a few shots of the boulders showing in the cover. It occurred to me that if he was temporarily mad enough to tilt with a dead helo he might also be sufficiently unhinged to stick a knife into a man. I went back to him. He said his feet were numb. His boots could be called boots only by extravagant courtesy. I suggested he stand on rock because rock, being dark, had absorbed the sun's heat better than snow and ice, which had reflected it back. We made our way across hard, squeaky snow to an outcrop near the ice fumaroles, going on the path we had probed earlier with the ice ax. His feet felt better on the rock.

If our luck had been bad before, it became rotten now: the cover got so thick it approached the dreaded whiteout condition. In response, the outcrop grew bitterly cold. Soon it made little difference to our feet whether we stood on rock or snow. We glanced skyward longingly, hoping the cover would break up and permit the sun to give us back our body heat. I judged our present temperature to be about five below.

Eights entered the cockpit and said through the open starboard hatch he thought the engine would start if we had some sunlight to warm it and a head wind to blow air into the turbine intake. There was still plenty of battery power. The engine made lots of noise, spewed smoke out of the exhaust and emitted a strong smell of fire. A red warning light flashed on the instrument panel.

Emerging from the craft, Eights murmured, "Christ, Christ, we're fucked," his lean face showing despair.

He asked me to spray a long fire extinguisher's contents into the turbine intake as he again tried to start the engine. The carbon dioxide in the extinguisher was depleted; only air was coming out; hopefully the latter would help the engine to grab hold. I climbed onto the fuselage and did what he requested. The effort was useless. Without a thicker air mixture the engine was dead.

I wandered off in the direction Palmer and Enderby had taken, going farther from the helo than before, intending to shoot the scene so I would be able to convince myself, in the event we were rescued, that the weather had been as bad as it now looked. I saw narrow, long, green crevasses. Although it seemed unlikely, judging by the terrain, that I would encounter wider ones, I could not be sure, so I made my way with some caution. The mostly white craft would not easily be visible from the air. The bottom of the hull was white, as were the cabin and the engine housing. A red stripe ran down the back of the cabin. The front exterior of the cockpit as well as the tail were red. The rotors were black, with orange tips. Up on the turbine housing were the numerals 1404.

I had stopped at a large deep cleft in some rock. Glancing into the cleft, I saw a patch of pink lichen: the non-human life I had hoped was here.

"Doc?" Eights called anxiously.

I headed toward him to see what he wanted. He left the helo to meet me.

"We'd better not get separated," he said, handing me a khaki plastic whistle with a braided black cord.

I didn't blame him for not wanting to be left alone in a place where everything was so unfamiliar and threatening. He had recently arrived on the ice for the first time. He had been living on the warm, crowded *Staten Island*. He had visited warm, crowded McMurdo. And now he was near the top of Mount Erebus, with his life's supply of heat steadily diminishing.

He was such a nice-looking boy, and possibly he had been thinking of his parents, or of a girl friend, or of places in Illinois he especially liked, or of some chore he had meant to do on the icebreaker, or was wondering by what sour luck he had been chosen for this flight, *my* flight, designed solely to deliver me to Cape Bird, and probably he realized I might have decided, had I felt less pressed for time, to scratch it, considering the state of the cover. Was the cover as thick along the coastal route as it was up here? It struck me, from the little I knew of such things, as being capable of lasting many days. If it stayed a long time would we handle ourselves badly or well? I was still ignorant of facts I would soon acquire. I believed then that we possessed the means to fight the cover and the mountain with a sporting chance of coming through, even if we had to hold out for weeks. I wonder now how much of my reaction to Eights was guilt for my having had a share, such as it was, in causing his predicament.

It seemed to me that Palmer and Enderby had been gone too long. We had crashed at approximately 2:30. It was now past a quarter to four. Where were they? Would they find their way back in this white stuff? What if one or both had fallen into a crevasse? What if they were lost?—they were without shelter or food. And they were lightly clad. Palmer, as we know, had on his helmet, his flight suit, his flight gloves, flight boots. And Enderby had on a USARP parka, whose hood he had pulled over his head—I didn't know what kind of shirt he was wearing under it, but I assumed it was the standard heavy woolen one—blue jeans, hiking boots and black gloves. I knew how cold they must feel: I myself was lightly clad for this temperature. I wore thermals, a black cap, a wool shirt, threadbare tan cotton corduroy trousers, a USARP parka, black double gloves and my own hiking boots, and I had begun to experience fits of shivering, as had Eights. The cold that was penetrating our bodies was sending alarm signals to our brains, crying as if in panic, "Beware! Beware! Parts of you are in danger of freezing!" Adrenalin flowed accordingly, whether you wished it to or not. If Palmer and Enderby died it would be a poor beginning to a tragedy that might have the added horror of being long drawn out, with Eights and me following them but more slowly because we had the tent, food and the helo. We ought to have decïded how long they would be away. How stupid it had been of us not to have formed a plan. We had had no right to improvise so casually.

Warning Eights I intended to use the whistle, I walked a fair distance in the direction in which I had last seen them and blew a long blast, hoping I would hear a cry in return. I heard nothing human. It was not easy to blow hard at this altitude. You got dizzy; you wondered for a moment if you were going to black out. Between blasts you listened to the eerie Antarctic silence, interrupted now only by the hum of the wind as it caressed jagged volcanic boulders and your ears. I blew half a dozen times at intervals of about five minutes, becoming increasingly alarmed, for I knew that our best chance for survival was to stick together, to remain near the helicopter and to keep up our morale.

I returned to the craft, where Eights had broken out smoke bombs, flares and a Very pistol with shells. I asked him to fire the pistol at the cover overhead. The flare rocketed up, burst, divided into two brilliant red mushrooms and fell, dying. It came nowhere near reaching the cover. Taking inventory of our signaling devices, we resolved not to use them unless the cover lifted and we heard a plane.

Not long afterwards Enderby and Palmer appeared slowly out of the mists southwest of us, looking very tired, Enderby still carrying the ice ax. I was relieved to see them. We were all together again; we hadn't done anything irreversibly stupid. Palmer was shivering; he was obviously unwell for some reason. He said the hand radio was useless; its battery was too cold. Enderby's face was red and drawn. He reported that his feet had gotten wet and were very numb. By questioning Enderby, who gave me the impression of being more stolid than stoical, I learned that they hadn't heard the whistle—what had muffled it? ridges? the cover? the thin air?—and that they had had no trouble following their tracks on their way back. They had not found the ridge they had been seeking, one overlooking McMurdo. They had reached several ridges but each had given way to another. Feeling the cold badly, with the altitude fatiguing them, and having trouble with altitude headaches, they had decided to go no further. What Enderby and Palmer did not reveal then for some reason (I learned it from Enderby back in McMurdo after our rescue) was that Palmer had taken two spills, slamming down on his back so suddenly and hard as to cause Enderby to be seriously alarmed.

Palmer was silent now and his glances tended to be averted. Was it because he suspected he had already said too much by declaring, "I'm going to be shipped out?" Why had he taken Enderby instead of Eights on his search for a ridge? Because he wanted to avoid the sense he had abandoned the passengers? Probably he was still stunned by the falls. I wish now I had known about them. Such knowledge might have lessened my resentment of him. I caught myself thinking, "Going over Erebus is a game in which there can be no sympathy for failure."

Yet there were crucial questions, such as whether he had autorotated—I doubted he had—that I failed to put to him in order to spare him possible embarrassment. His mental state was important to our safety; he was still our leader, who would pull us through. I failed utterly at this time to grasp our true condition, for example to take stock of our survival gear. Much later, on reviewing the episode, I was astonished it had taken me so long to grasp the real situation.

A strong north wind came up and whipped the tent flaps, strings and openings. Enderby pounded at the tent stakes and checked the poles and ropes. I thought, "Prepare yourself for a long stay and prepare the others." We gathered in the tilted helo cabin, which still felt warmer than the outside, and shut the hatch. I told Palmer what I had already explained to Eights about the metal fuselage being a heat sink. He was skeptical. He said the cabin was a good place to remain in; it was more roomy and more comfortable than the tent. I said that the tent, being much smaller than the cabin, was easier to warm with our bodies. He remained dubious even when our feet began to freeze from contact with the floor.

It slowly became clear to me that there was a failure of leadership on his part. He seemed unwilling or unable to take command, and was understandably reluctant to hand it over to me. However, it became increasingly unnecessary for him to relinquish it formally. As he turned more and more inward the two young men looked to me for suggestions and orders and I found myself having with painful embarrassment to take over his role out of necessity.

He asked me—I was closest to the cockpit—to see what the windshield thermometer read. I reported it was at $-25°$C., or about $-15°$F. The two scales begin to merge at low temperatures. At forty below there is no difference between them. They diverge again below that figure. The wind had a permanent feel to it.

And now, quite suddenly, certain unpleasant facts came to light. Enderby stood up, looked at me with a pale face full of embarrassment, and said in a small voice, "Chuck, I forgot to bring my survival gear."

It struck me as especially ironic that he, who worked in the Field Center, which was supposed to know something of the hazards of

Antarctica, should be guilty of this lapse. Perhaps he had thought, "It's only a turnaround flight. We're in the middle of a heat wave. Why bother to drag my survival bag along?" But probably he hadn't. The history of Antarctica was dotted by people who had taken the continent for granted, sometimes to their sorrow. Now his sorrow was mine also, for I would have to share my survival gear with him. Of course, he had not known the weather was foul on the McMurdo-Bird route. Still, that route was as long a flight as you could make on Ross Island, and he ought to have taken survival gear along on even a short flight: it was the rule, designed to save limbs and possibly lives.

Then Eights told me that the helicopter's four survival packs, each weighing about fifty pounds, were not on board. They had been removed for the shuttle flights between McMurdo and Willy Field and, through some confusion, had not been replaced. Furthermore, he said, he had brought no personal survival gear; nor had Palmer. Palmer, staring at the floor, remained remote and silent.

The harsh facts of our situation were now beginning to take full hold of me. My companions had trifled with Antarctica. They had been lulled by the heat wave at McMurdo; by the comforts provided by the nuclear plant; by the security suggested by all the aircraft and heavy equipment and men. I was by far the oldest of the group, with the least chance of coming through, despite my good physical condition. When I considered that my ability to survive would be greatly lessened by my having to spread my gear thin to help my companions a bitterness rose temporarily to my palate. My careful habits had proved insufficient to my safety. The lesson was simple: it was not enough to provide for yourself unless you were traveling alone.

An intuition caused me to ask Enderby suddenly, "Did you pack matches in my gear?"

Enderby paled, looked stunned.

"No. I forgot."

I turned to Eights.

"Are there matches on board?"

"No, sir."

"Anybody got any matches?" I asked.

There was no reply.

We were losing moisture with some rapidity. When one of us spoke, clouds of steam escaped him. The continent was notoriously dry; its air was like a sponge. But now we had the added complication of the special dryness of high altitude. It seemed obvious to me—a thought that I expressed to my companions—that our lives would first be threatened by severe dehydration, which would cause certain organs to collapse, and that somehow we would have to make a fire and heat snow to make water. The snow outside was already too cold to put in one's mouth safely, and the temperature was steadily falling.

By now the engine's lubricant had no doubt congealed and could not be drained; it should have been drained within a half to three quarters of an hour after the crash. With the lubricant and using wicks we could have made flares as well as smudge pots. But the helo's fuel was still fluid at this temperature. We could drain it, using a section of the canopy or some other article as the container. We could improvise a stove out of a large can or whatever else was handy and, using bits of gravel or small rocks as a base, pour fuel on them and burn the fuel for heat, for making water, for thawing food and for cooking. The helo's fuel, if carefully conserved, could last us quite awhile. But it was useless without matches. If the sun were out and we had a magnifying glass—perhaps one of my camera lenses could be used as one—we might make a fire, for the sun was strong in this dry air, especially at our altitude, despite the fact that it hung low over the horizon. However, given our cloud cover, I did not think we had a right to be optimistic about its reappearing soon. I wondered if the helo's battery could be used to make sparks and then a fire, and wondered also how long the battery would hold up at this low temperature. Possibly it was already dead.

Eights's feet were the first to go. I pulled my mukluks out of my orange seabag—they were rated to forty below, I had been told in Christchurch—and gave them to him. He had no headgear aside from his helmet, and only his flight suit and flight gloves. I gave him my khaki woolen balaclava and a pair of heavy gray mittens. To Enderby I handed fresh woolen socks to replace his wet ones. Palmer had no headgear other than his helmet. I had no headgear to give him. I handed him a double pair of gloves to be used in addition to his thin flight gloves. Luckily he was wearing sturdy leather boots, as was Enderby. My own boots were inadequate: the soles had been ripped by my climbing around the volcanic terrain of Royds and Evans. My feet felt frozen, especially the left one, which had been run over by a car and which, ever since, had been the weak one. My legs were turning numb. After considering the matter a moment I asked if it was all right if I put on my windpants, explaining that I was losing sensation in my legs.

"Hell yes!" Palmer said loudly out of his silence.

I said, "This gear belongs to all of us."

Then—I hated myself for doing it, for I had only one pair of windpants—I pulled them out of the survival bag, removed my boots, laboriously donned the black pants, then put the boots on again, my head spinning with the effort of bending over, my hands thick, clumsy, my thoughts murky. I felt guilty, nasty for wearing the windpants when no one else had windpants. On the other hand, only Eights had mukluks and he was delighted to have them and to know he was not going to risk the loss of his feet. Then I thought that, after all, the pants were mine and that I was the oldest of the group and presumably the least able to take the thing that might be coming: a tremendous test of our ability to cling to life. A second thought came forcefully: at what price was it worth hanging on? At the cost of one's honor? Then I thought that if we had all brought our survival gear and the helo's four survival packs we wouldn't be in a very bad way unless a long-lasting blizzard blew up. We could set up a couple of tents and be comfortable in our sleeping bags. We could rest and sleep the time away until we were found, even if it took a couple of weeks.

Well, we were in for it and it would take a few miracles to get us out. I was convinced we must soon move into the tent. I could say simply, "I'm moving into the tent" and let whoever wanted to follow me follow. But that would humiliate Palmer and lower his morale still further. If it continued to decline, his will to survive would fall with it; with a weak will his chances of survival would greatly lessen and he might do something to decrease them further: for example, he might take a serious fall. If one of us suffered badly the others would have to minister to him. In the process we would lose our own narrow margin of safety and we might all go down into irreversible damage or death. So I refrained from saying, "I'm moving into the tent" not out of altruism but out of self-interest. For the clear fact was that our lives depended on each other.

CHAPTER 15

THE TENT

It was now about four forty-five, two and a quarter hours after the crash. Our mayday signals had obviously not gotten through, for if they had we would have heard C-130 engines overhead long since. We should have reached Cape Bird at about two-thirty or two-forty and notified McMurdo Station of our arrival. By an hour later McMurdo had no doubt become thoroughly alarmed. I expected that the coastal route between McMurdo and Bird was being completely although hazardously searched. Cape Bird had probably already been visited. We wondered if an SAR (search and rescue) Condition was in full operation.

We took stock of our means of survival. We had one Air Force survival tent, designed for single or double occupancy, one Bauer sleeping bag, two cot mattresses, one ice ax, one canteen of water (already frozen), a good deal of food, much of which would need thawing out, and no apparent means of making a fire. We also had the helo's insulation and a lightweight brown blanket that I assumed belonged to the helo but whose ownership I have not been able to establish with certainty. Enderby later told me it may have been part of my camping gear; he wasn't sure. In addition we had the clothes we were now wearing and a pair of bear paws in my seabag that no one, I think out of delicacy, used because it was the only pair among us.

Our situation was not good but it could have been much worse. No one had been injured in the crash. We had a tent and therefore were not obliged to stay in the helo. Without a tent we would have been forced to remain in the craft, for we lacked the tools for digging body trenches in the hard snow. We had the sleeping bag, which, when unzipped, could serve as a blanket. We had the brown blanket. We had the survival gear I had brought along.

The cold began to feel savage. The temperature was steadily falling and the wind was still rising. The metal fuselage was rapidly draining us of body heat even though we tried to avoid metal contact. When I repeated forcefully that we would freeze in the cabin, Palmer said, "Maybe we'd better move to the tent."

I asked Eights to strip the cabin of its insulation and told Enderby to crawl inside the tent and prepare a flooring with the stuff we would hand him. Palmer and Eights stripped the helo of everything that looked useful, including the seats, and handed it to me. I carried the stuff to the tent about twenty or twenty-five feet away and gave it piecemeal to Enderby through the complicated, wormlike entrance. All I saw of Enderby during this operation was his hands. I also passed to him the two cot mattresses, the canteen and the sleeping bag. When I crawled in to examine his handiwork I made my way through a billowing red tube of light material, then through some white, gauzelike stuff that served as a curtain-door, and fouled myself at times as though in a shroud—I felt like a crawling blind man—and even the extra little exertion of getting down on all fours made itself felt by a wild beating of my heart. I was surprised to see how neatly he had arranged things. He had spread the helo insulation on the tent floor, the mattresses side by side on the top of the insulation, and had made a blanket of the sleeping bag. It all looked unexpectedly cozy.

"What a fine boy he is!" I thought.

We gathered together our necessaries and set them down near the tent entrance, that is, the one facing the summit. The opposite one Enderby had tied into a great knot as a protection against the wind. We had a Very pistol and shells, flares, smoke bombs, dye markers, and cartons and crates of food: fruit, vegetables, bread, frozen steaks, frozen rock lobsters, even milk chocolate.

Palmer and I agreed on a plan: to huddle in the tent and to try to ward off permanent damage while we got used to the altitude. Each man's thermal margin was so small, even in the tent, as we were soon to discover, that if one of us had reached an irreversible stage, with the psychological consequences this would have entailed, and required ministering to, the others would probably have gone down in domino fashion. Eights asked me how long it would take to get used to the altitude. I replied that the effects would probably increase before they diminished. My friend Dale Vance, now at Vostok Station, had felt fairly good there the first day but for the next ten had had headaches, insomnia and some nausea. We were approximately as high as Vostok.

You sensed that the altitude was like an animal, lurking to assail you, and although you were cautious, being by now aware of its potency, it worked on you suddenly: when you were walking or working or even just standing still and talking. It made you breathless, caused your speech to be fuzzy, disarranged your thoughts. Your words came out too slowly or mixed up. It was easy to do something stupid or dangerous. In addition, the altitude prevented you from warming up by jogging in place. To try jogging was to invite blacking out or vomiting. However, the altitude effects were inconstant and fortunately they were infrequent. But my companions were plagued by intense headaches which I took to be as bad as migraines. In addition to the altitude, always you sensed the power and personality of Erebus. This domineering, remote volcano now had an intimate place in our minds, our lives and perhaps in our death.

Glancing at my companions—we were still outside—I found myself wondering who would outlast whom. I thought of my age. In nine days I would be fifty-six. How long would my heart endure the demands being put on it? It beat very rapidly and pounded even when I did not exert myself. I told myself I must not think about my age: I must put all negative thoughts aside if I meant to survive. I must keep up my morale and the morale of the others. Above all I must behave well. For this, in the end, was what it was about, my having come to Antarctica. It was the subject that had intrigued me so long and intensely: getting at the heart of a magnificent, wild continent. Whenever I remembered my wife and daughter and thought of what my death would mean to them I put them quickly out of mind. I could not afford to let myself be softened by sentiment. Anyhow—and this struck me as very odd—I felt that my truest loyalty was to my present companions, strangers to me. It was with and for them I must behave well; but primarily it was for myself.

And then there was the cold: that thief of one's life's warmth. We kept glancing hopefully at the sky, and when the scud showed patches that seemed thinner than usual our hearts sang, and we grinned, cracked jokes. If the sun were to come out we'd be *warm*. My left foot was worrying me; it had begun to lose all feeling.

Palmer entered the tent. Enderby was outside somewhere, Eights was in the helo cabin. We needed rocks with which to secure the tent flaps in order to minimize the seepage of wind in the tent. I took the ice ax to some boulders and tried to break chunks off. The volcanic stuff was unbelievably hard. All I managed to achieve was to stimulate my hands with the shock of the blows. One would need a pickax to dent such material. Eights, having emerged from the cabin, suggested inflating the helo's one-man life rafts and placing them against the sides of the tent; this would to some extent hold down the flaps. We inflated the rafts but not to much effect. Later, when we were huddling in the tent, we would feel minutely the variations in the wind's strength. When the wind subsided, the tent grew noticeably warmer. When it rose, we immediately felt threatened, and involuntary alarm signals went off throughout our bodies, various appendages crying out that they were in imminent danger of dying.

I walked to a distant outcrop to take some photographs. Returning to the helo, I found Eights standing in front of the cabin hatch, munching on a chunk of cabbage. In one gloved hand he held a whole head, from which he had cut a hunk with his sheath knife. He had thrown the outer leaves onto the snow. Picking them up and tossing them into the cabin, I said, "Our lives may depend on these. There's no telling how long we may have to hang on. Don't throw *anything* away."

He stopped eating.

I thought, "Stu has made no move to inventory the food and to prepare to ration it. What's he thinking of? Is he positive we'll be rescued? Doesn't he realize this cover can hang on for days, during which fatigue will worsen, causing irritation, illness, accidents? But first will come the dehydration."

As if reading my mind, Eights asked, "Why can't we eat snow, Doc?"

I said the temperature of the snow was now probably twenty or twenty-five below; that the temperature of a freezer compartment in a house refrigerator was about five above; that the snow would injure lips, tongue and palate.

He said, "We've got lots of fruit."

"Which will be like billiard balls soon."

I went to the cockpit to read the thermometer. It registered $-35°C.$, the equivalent of $-31°F.$ The wind was blowing steadily. What was the effective temperature? Fifty, sixty, seventy below?

Eights and Enderby crawled into the tent. I followed them. We lay on our backs under the sleeping-bag blanket at right angles to the entrance and would continue to lie like that, without the luxury of lying on our sides. Any motion on the part of one of us disturbed the others and robbed them of body heat. I was nearest the entrance. Farthest from me was Palmer, lying parallel to me; next to him was Eights, lying opposite him; and next to Eights was Enderby, lying opposite me.

The unzipped sleeping bag wasn't large enough to cover us adequately. We shifted the brown blanket from time to time on an emergency basis. My right side and thigh, only partially covered, grew very cold. I asked Enderby how his feet were. He said he had lost feeling in them. I invited him to place them under my parka, which he did. I felt like crying about him. He had come on a simple turnaround flight and now he might die here. He and Eights aroused painful fatherly feelings in me. Of the four of us they had the most to lose by dying now; it was right that they were in the middle, where it was warmest. I had the least to lose. I had lived a long and complex life, containing its share of tragedy, and I did not discover a strong desire to cling to it.

My own feet were a problem, especially the left one. For a while I hoped they would recover under the blanket—we had removed our boots—but I realized slowly it was not responding. I tried wiggling the toes. I rubbed it against my right foot. I curled the right foot over it. Finally I handed Enderby my two left gloves and asked him to put them on my left foot. Slowly the foot came around but then my right foot began to go. At the same time I felt sleepy; I wanted to sleep in order to conserve strength. But if I slept I would fail to stay on guard for my foot's sake. How would it be to return to the world footless? So I determined not to sleep unless my whole body was secured. Meanwhile it became plain that it wasn't just my right foot that was in trouble but my right side from the hip down.

Palmer said, "I'm not going to make it if my left leg doesn't get more cover," and Eights rearranged himself, in the process unavoidably rearranging Enderby and me, and the brown blanket was passed to Palmer temporarily.

We huddled close together, shivering fitfully. It was remarkable how small our margins of body heat were. We would all have to be on a constant alert if we were to succeed in warding off permanent damage.

We were struck by what the red tent did to colors. The green sleeping bag had become a deep navy blue, my red parka a pale yellow-orange. Eights kept commenting on this transmutation of colors. He seemed more relaxed now, although once I overheard him saying to Enderby, "Every once in a while I feel panicky." He cracked jokes and exhibited a comic, mugging side. He could not seem to let go of the subject of colors.

Then we heard C-130 engines in the north for a while; in the south; in the west. So there was no doubt the search was on. One wanted to shout, "Here we are!" and to send up flares. We took turns crawling out of the tent to see if there was a break in the cover. Each exhausting effort dissipated some of our body heat. Each shivering returning man brought in more cold.

Invariably the report was, "It's the same."

I thought, "If only there was a tiny Plexiglas window in the top of the tent, through which we could observe the weather. What a lot of body heat it would save!"

For a while all we wanted was for the cover to break up. That would signify *the next step,* without which there could be no help for us. The long hours passed.

Then, to my great astonishment, Palmer asked casually, "Would anybody mind if I smoked?" and broke out a little lighter.

And Eights, asking the same question, withdrew from a pocket an identical lighter.

"Great Christ!" I thought. "I'm dealing with children!"

One charitable explanation I could put on their having failed earlier to reveal the existence of the lighters was that they were positive we were not in a genuine survival situation; we could carry on our lives in normal fashion; we were sure to be rescued. But if that was the case why had they shown signs of panic? Were their minds, then, dissonant with their bodies? Did their minds say, "There's nothing to worry about. I'll be taken care of."? Or did they say, "There's too much to worry about, and I'll just smoke to comfort myself."? Another charitable explanation was that they had misunderstood, or had failed to grasp, or had disagreed with, or had discounted, my warnings of the dangers of dehydration. A less charitable one was that it graveled them to be helped by a middle-aged civilian, a writer at that, somebody who typically spent much time on his behind.

At any rate, we could make a fire after all! I, a non-smoker, did not enjoy the prospect of the small tent's being filled with smoke. Apparently an abstainer could not escape cigarette smoke even near the crater of Mount Erebus. But if smoking was good for Palmer's and Eights's morale, I was for it—for the moment. So I did not raise an objection. Enderby didn't either. Nor did I ask why the lighters hadn't been mentioned previously. Anyhow, I hoped they would not enjoy smoking at this altitude and would quickly give it up. I was wrong. They seemed to find comfort in it.

We were all sitting up now. The tent felt very crowded but not as much as when we were prone on our backs, our heads against the tent walls or helo seats, our chins thrust down, cricks developing in our napes and in our throat muscles. The narrow tent was not meant for use by persons lying at a right angle to the entrances. How long would it take before such crowding made us exceedingly irritable, debasing the quality of our social behavior, lowering our will to survive and causing a proneness to accidents?

The problem arose of where to put the cigarette ashes. Palmer offered his helmet. I suggested to Eights he use some tinfoil from one of the milk chocolate bars we had with us. He did. He was greatly intrigued by the vivid, electric green of the cigarette flame. He had begun to expand. He was very charming now, I thought. Often, happening to glance his way, I discovered him staring intently at me. He and Palmer finished their cigarettes and we lay down again.

The time slipped by. At one point I focused sharply on Joan, my wife. I felt I was communicating with her. I imagined saying intensely to her, "Lift the cloud cover. It's an urgent matter. If you wish for it hard enough it may go away." Then it struck me that if there *was* anything to ESP I might alert her to my situation, which would be terrible, for it would make her aware of her inability to help me. So I quit this game.

I thought I was a bit old for my heart to be beating as hard, as fast and as strangely as it was. It hammered against my chest cavity like a live, wild thing: jumping, twisting, bouncing in a way I had never experienced. When I had swum hard my lungs had worked hard in rhythm with my heart. Now they worked heavily but quietly while my heart, like some wild caged bird, beat so powerfully I experienced it as a unique, alien entity, some small but mad bit of life that had gotten trapped inside me and was frantically trying to escape. I think it was the altitude that caused it to behave like that. If it was fear, it was for me an entirely new kind, without overtones in my mind and in other parts of my body, as far as I knew. I do not recall feeling fear during the episode, not fear in the very personal sense; certainly at times I was alarmed for us as a group. Quietism seemed to have possessed me. I felt ready to die peacefully; I knew that freezing was a peaceful death. It did not seem at all like a big deal to take off. It felt, as a matter of fact, like a pretty good moment for me to go, and I was comforted by the fact I was well and specially insured. It occurred to me more than once that, financially speaking, I was probably worth more dead than alive. I wondered how long this little bird in my chest could keep beating its wings in such a mad way and I thought what a messy situation it would be for all of us if I had a heart attack.

My bare left hand was in a parka pocket with a furlike lining. My double-gloved right hand lay on my chest. Now and then I was aware that the middle finger of my right hand was slowly assuming a hook shape and that the knuckle was extremely sore. Once, when I removed the gloves and glanced at the hand, I saw that the tendon was taut and whitish under the palm flesh. It was very difficult for me to straighten the finger.

There were hours of silence, during which I asked myself what my resources for hanging on were. It seemed to me that Erebus could be personified as cunning and that if I was to survive I must be more cunning than it. I must be more cunning than I had ever been in my life. Above all I must not fight the mountain head on. I noticed that if I kept my face beneath the blanket my face became warm from my breath, and that the energy conserved in not having to warm my face as much as when it was exposed went into warming my right thigh and foot, making their temperature bearable. This was not something I imagined; I tested it. With my face exposed, my right thigh and foot felt achy, numb. With my face covered they began to relax with more heat. It was an example of being cunning, I thought. I reported this minor discovery to my companions, although without using the idea of cunning; they soon confirmed it. I also noticed that whenever I sat up I had strong abdominal cramps and felt on the verge of vomiting. To vomit would mean to leave the tent and lost much body heat. So I took to sitting up very slowly, calming the cramps with an effort of mind and not mentioning them in order to keep the group's morale as high as possible.

Palmer announced that he needed "to take a dump" but would try to hold it in. Defecation meant leaving the tent and exposing yourself to cold and wind. A trifle, perhaps; but by their sum a series of trifles could determine if you survived or not.

I resolved I would try to survive. But for whom? My wife? My daughter? Myself? It seemed redundant, self-serving, meaningless to survive for oneself. Although it was clear to me that I ought to try to survive for my daughter's sake because of her youth (she was thirteen), I felt the need to survive for my wife, who, I told myself, needed me more than she knew. And so when I felt very tired—I hadn't had a good night's sleep in days and last night I had slept for four hours—and on the verge of not caring any longer what happened to me, of drifting off somewhere—to sleep or gangrene or death—I thought of her needing me, and then my eyes opened wide beneath the sleeping-bag blanket, and that popping open roused me with a lunge to full consciousness, or to superconsciousness, as it seemed to me then. Over and over, thinking of her needing me, I came wide awake and determined I would *live*. If I didn't have the will to live for myself there was no doubt I had it for her. Perhaps this exercise in determining to live for someone else was also a part of being cunning.

Occasionally I realized how silent it was when the wind died down. This was the great Antarctic silence: a ringing of blood in one's ears. But mostly I didn't hear it because my breathing was heavy: my chest rose and fell with force to provide me with sufficient oxygen, and if I started to drift off toward sleep I would awake with the feeling I was out of breath.

Cunning: I warned my companions not to eat bread because bread was gas-forming and because the expansion of gases at twelve thousand feet was considerable as compared with that at sea level. Dale Vance had overeaten at one of his first meals at Vostok and had lain on his back for hours, gasping. Sea level? By air miles we were so close to it, and to McMurdo, and to warmth and security.

I wondered at times why Palmer didn't try to use the HF radio on battery power. I knew I was ignorant on the subject and so I didn't mention it to him. I assumed the HF radio required more juice than the battery could provide. About a year later I happened to be talking with Jim Brandau about this matter. Brandau asked me if we had heard planes while we were on Erebus. I said yes, often. He looked surprised. He said it took a lot of power to send HF signals that would bounce off the ionosphere and go beyond the horizon, more power, probably, than could be obtained from a battery, but that Palmer should have tried the HF radio on battery in an effort to contact the planes within sound of us.

Palmer was perhaps at least partially in a state of shock. He had taken two bad falls, as we know. They had occurred because he had failed to notice that certain patches of snow were a lighter shade than others and had not avoided them. Such patches often indicate a thinner layer of snow over ice and can be treacherous to walk on. Enderby had stayed clear of them. He had either failed to warn Palmer or Palmer had ignored the warning. As Enderby described the falls to me when we were back at McMurdo, Palmer's legs had flown from under him; he had landed heavily on his back; and he had reacted with great surprise and a good deal of bewilderment. Probably the two falls influenced his subsequent abandonment of any serious effort to provide leadership for our group. Such falls were what could come of ignorance. They were also the result to some extent, I suspect, of hubris. A more modest man would have walked in Enderby's tracks, especially inasmuch as Enderby carried the ice ax and occasionally probed the snow with it.

Some months after the crash episode it occurred to me that the state of one's conscience during a crisis can determine whether one behaves badly or well. Thus the fact that I was the only one of the group with survival gear placed me in the position of the giver rather than the receiver and left me with a fairly clear state of mind. Palmer was in the worst position of us all: he had brought us onto Erebus and was now technically responsible for our welfare. Affecting his behavior must have been the realization that his career if not his life had abruptly reached a turning point.

The extraordinary thing is that not once during the long hours when we waited for a rescue did any of us ask him, at least so far as I know, any direct, pertinent questions which might have revealed his motives, his intentions or what precisely had happened; nor did he offer such information. I suppose we had better things to think and talk about than what was now in the past. We were concerned with our future, or rather with the question of whether we had one. I suppose too that a sense of delicacy prevented us from raising questions that might have injured his morale. He turned inward almost from the start and psychologically moved increasingly away from the rest of us. From time to time he coughed, and once he said he believed he had pneumonia.

There were various practical aspects of the question of being cunning. For example, when I lay with my face exposed and opened my eyes now and then, I didn't mind the pink, dappled light of the red tent—how misleading that light was! how it always tricked us into thinking the cloud cover was lifting!—but when my face was under the blanket and I then had to uncover my eyes and look around the tent, the light was atrocious, it assaulted my eyeballs violently, causing nerves to throb madly all the way from my eyes deep into my head, and I knew I could not sustain many such seizures without becoming snow-blind. So I developed a little strategy to minimize the assault. I covered my eyes with my fingers, slowly opened my eyes, then tentatively, carefully, spread my fingers until the light was bearable. It was strange that the light was so intense while the cloud cover was so thick.

Cloud cover: that was mostly what I thought about, wondering when it would lift and asking myself how to be patient, even if I had to wait for days. Patience too was a way of being cunning. Unless you were patient Erebus would surely defeat you. You must be as simple-minded, in some ways, as a penguin. At Cape Evans in the nasty, bone-destroying southeast wind that had come off the polar plateau and the ice shelf, I had observed Adélies lying on their breasts out on the sea ice, seemingly asleep, waiting for the bad weather to pass. This was what I too must do. And it was what we were doing: lying low, waiting for that momentous time when we would be able to use our flares and smoke bombs. The cover was endlessly on my mind and endlessly the subject of tent conversation when there *was* conversation. Mostly there was none; there were vast silences when it was easy to assume my companions were asleep. The silences conserved energy. They allowed us to animalize in this primitive moment, to sink somewhere inside ourselves to a secret place where we could concentrate entirely on clinging to what strength each of us had. But what if the cover hung on day after day? Would there come a time when we would crack?

There were also less pleasant aspects of being cunning. Palmer was snoring, which meant he was asleep and regaining strength; he would be in better shape than I in the morning. In a crisis—as if this in the tent was not enough to justify the name of crisis—he would outlast me. So I began to think what I could do to be more cunning than he.

Hours passed, passed. He and Eights lit up again.

I said half jokingly, "Easy on those lighters. Our lives may depend on them."

Neither Eights nor Palmer responded to the remark. I was profoundly irritated by Palmer's failure to requisition the lighters for the common good. When they lit up a third time, I resolved that at the fourth I would ask them to stop smoking and make the lighters common property. I hoped the confrontation would not be ugly. Fortunately it never came.

Palmer finally couldn't hold it in any longer; he crawled outside to "take a dump," returning with a rueful expression and reporting, "It froze while I was wiping it."

I suggested it wasn't necessary to move our bowels in the open. We could defecate in the cabin's large metal cabinet that contained cans of lubricant. It would be a simple matter to line the cabinet's bottom with a helo seat cover. This would permit us to dispose of the feces from time to time. One could shut the hatch and keep out the wind, and one would have the cabinet's side to sit on. My companions agreed, so I removed my gloves, withdrew a Swiss army knife from a parka pocket and cut away a seat cover. To my surprise, although the cover was very cold the foam rubber inside it was much warmer, and the styrofoam was even warmer. These materials were not as efficient heat conductors as the plastic cover. So this too was an aspect of being cunning: saving body heat by using as pillows foam rubber and styrofoam instead of whole seats.

At times my abdominal cramps rose to a pitch and I too felt I might need to defecate. I held on, hoping I wouldn't vomit. I thought how disastrous violent indigestion could be in our circumstances.

At one point, to make sure I hadn't been mistaken, I made a special trip to the cleft in the outcrop where I had seen the lichen. There the bit of life was, a striking pink suggesting the warmth of human blood. What a lonely, dreary place the lichen lived in, yet its existence deeply comforted me by suggesting that even here there were fascinating things to occupy one's mind, however little of one's life might be left.

Occasionally we heard planes. They always sounded far away. How long would they keep looking for us? Palmer said they'd never quit; this was no civilian matter; the search would continue until the mystery was solved. It was comforting to hear it but was it a reasonable view? I doubted it. We might have fallen into the open sea without a trace, or into a giant crevasse. The search could not go on indefinitely. If it stopped, *then* what would we do?

Unlikely though it may seem, at times I was glad to be in this spot, for if I survived, what a tale I would have to tell! Over and over a gear slipped in my thinking as I projected myself into the future and found myself a rare bird, one who had crashed on Erebus and lived. It was pleasant and perhaps necessary for me to dream like this; it lessened the burden of waiting; but the dreams always ended abruptly when, with a thud, I recalled I was in the present and that my future might never come.

Several times I donned my boots and left the tent to observe and to take photographs. It was very pleasant to be alone. What a beautifully subtle if menacing scene it was! In my mind I threw my life away on each of these solitary excursions. If one died now one would have the satisfaction of knowing one had died fairly well. The glow that one could not be robbed of and that sustained one again and again was the knowledge that one was behaving decently, as far as one knew. This knowledge was the best gift one had, and the best one could hope to bring down off Erebus.

Saying his headache was killing him, Eights went to the helo and fetched a first-aid kit, which contained morphine but no aspirin.

"Shall I take some morphine, Doc?" he asked.

I said if he did he would fall into a deep sleep and wouldn't know if he got badly frostbitten. I told him where in the cabin he could find my toilet kit and get aspirin from it. He swallowed two or three tablets of aspirin without water, but his headache did not respond. Enderby said *his* headache was going away.

A little later Eights sat up, broke out a bar of milk chocolate and ate some of it. Palmer said nothing, so I said, "Stu, I don't think we have a right to eat at will. We should ration everything we've got. There's no telling how long it will be before we're found. We may have to hold out for weeks."

Palmer said, "I thought it was the other way around, that we eat as much as we want while we're still in good shape."

"Stu," I said, "you're still fresh from McMurdo, from the ship. You're well fed. The time may come when we'll desperately need food and water to survive."

He thought a moment, then suggested we all eat a bit of chocolate and an apple to stave off hunger. My companions each placed a small apple in an armpit, meanwhile munching chocolate.

Later, lying with my eyes closed, I found myself thinking, "You son of a bitch. You threw my life away."

But I knew I must stop resenting him, for if I didn't I would soon hate him, and his knowledge of the hatred might lower his morale even lower than it was. Without high morale we could not show the volcano what human beings were capable of. No, in this place Palmer and I were one, bound together like Siamese twins. To hate him, or just to resent him, was to threaten my own morale and survival as well as that of the two young men.

The hours passed: in silence. Always, except for the wind and the sound of engines, there was silence. Then the engines faded out. Did this mean the search had stopped temporarily? If so, when would it be resumed? If we were not found in time when *would* we be found? *We* knew we were all right but those searching for us were no doubt wondering in what condition they would find us, if find us they did. Occasionally I saw myself with their eyes, for I had come so close to not being all right that it was as if I had tasted the experience of being smashed, frozen. *If* we were found, how would it happen? And if we were *not* found?

The ceasing of the engines brought apathy. There was no longer an urgent need to check on the cloud cover, for even if the cover lifted now, what good would it do us if there were no planes in our vicinity? The hours were passing without signposts. On eternity's edge time itself grew apathetic.

CHAPTER 16

FOUND

After a time we heard engines again. They sounded quite low and seemed to be helos. I scrambled out of the tent. An engine approached, dimmed. Another seemed to draw close but faded. The cover was too thick for me to see planes. I returned to the tent.

Lying half-conscious, I thought I heard a helo coming close and *above* us. The sound was very faint but I was sure it belonged to a helo. I alerted Eights, who, after listening a moment, agreed with me. I shouted to Enderby to take a look. He was more agile than I. He rushed out in stockinged feet. The engine sounded louder.

Then we heard his electrifying cry: "I *see* it!"

We had left the loaded Very gun in an open carton beside the entrance shroud.

I shouted, "Fire the Very pistol directly at him!"

I heard the gun go off. Eights was tearing outside.

"They *see* us!" Enderby cried.

In that twinkling everything changed for us.

"Wave him off! Don't let him land!" Palmer shouted.

This was sound advice, for we had not selected and marked a landing pad, nor indicated by smoke bomb the wind direction.

A moment later Eights cried that the helo was dropping two survival packs. Palmer and I were fumbling with our boots. My hands were not cooperating. I crawled through the shroud, belly cramping, head swimming. Palmer was behind me, coughing heavily.

A Coast Guard helicopter was departing beyond a high ridge just to the right of the crater. On that side of the crest the sky had cleared a bit and the sun was showing milkily. My watch read precisely midnight, which meant it was due south where the sun was. We didn't realize then that the helo would not return until about 2:30.

Eights and Enderby retrieved the survival kits, which contained no headgear and footgear but which did have matches and fat white candles and lots of mosquito netting. We laughed. We felt wonderfully refreshed.

I went to the helo cabin, where my two caseless cameras were white with frost, removed the lens covers and began shooting the damage to the helo, knowing the Navy would want close-up shots for the investigation that was sure to come. It was not easy to keep one's mind clear at the altitude while portions of one's body kept sending signals warning of the danger of irreversible frostbite. One had to caution oneself to do everything in slow motion. It was now as well as earlier that one's practice with cameras in the temperate zone became crucial. While I was photographing the telescoped strut that ran from the fuselage to the port pontoon, Eights stripped metal from it, commenting on how easily it came away. Later he amused himself by lobbing red flares into the mouths of the two ice fumaroles. The red glow was very conspicuous in the fuzzy gray world.

When the cameras ran out of film I carried them into the tent and rewound the cassettes as slowly as I was able. I was still wearing the double gloves. I could feel from the tension of the rewind knob that the film remained intact. Back at McMurdo, trying to reload cameras while wearing the gloves, I had failed in the experiment, as I had failed when wearing only the large, bulky shell. I had no alternative now but to reload the cameras with naked hands. I had not brought along anti-contact gloves but in any case they would have prevented only adhesion of skin to metal, not frostbite. I remembered what had happened to the fingers of my right hand when, earlier in the crash episode, frustrated by a Very pistol shell that was stuck in its casing, I had removed the gloves from that hand and freed the shell. It had been strange to the point of fascination to observe the fingers rapidly turn a dead white almost to the knuckles. Since metal and skin had been extremely dry there had been no adhesion.

The frost on the cameras had by now seemingly ablated. I touched the cameras tentatively and found that my fingers did not stick to them. As I reloaded, my fingers burned, and turned very white, and then I lost feeling in them but they kept responding to my commands. Going outside to continue shooting, I discovered that the lenses were frosted over by condensation of moisture from the tent's interior. I set the cameras on the floor of the open helo cabin, where they cleared by ablation, then shot skid marks, pontoons, wheels, struts.

Before we were found—and it was still by no means certain we would be rescued: the cloud cover was playing tricks over the summit—it had seemed to me that there was really a simple equation inherent in our situation. I had been fairly sure our lives had been forfeited. The only relevant question was, it had struck me, would one die well or badly. If by some miracle we were rescued, I had thought, the sole thing of lasting value one could hope to bring off this mountain was the knowledge one had behaved well. Frankly, I had not relished the prospect of having to deal, for the rest of my life, with the memory that I had behaved otherwise.

Failure to do one's duty, duty being for example work one had committed onself to, in my case to bring back data gathered during my visit to the continent, was an element in behaving badly. If I failed to take pictures during such an episode what could I tell myself later? That I had been too cold, tired, sleepy, numbed, frightened? But such excuses, if they didn't wash now, and they didn't, would hardly wash later. I would have to deal with the fact I had let myself down, and I wasn't ready to pay so considerable a price. As a result, I had few qualms about risking parts of my body by leaving the tent periodically to take photographs. Besides, it was fruitful to confront oneself alone from time to time; and keeping busy helped one to be mentally resilient. In addition, I had thought, if we died on the mountain, the photographs, when found, would be a partial record of what had happened to us as well as a suggestion that I had died while at work rather than in a state of funk. And if we should be rescued they would be a record of what had occurred.

At about 12:30 a Herc appeared and flew under the high cover in huge circles over us. He never let go of us, and once he made a low pass and I gathered he was shooting us. It was a tremendous morale boost to have him up there.

Still shooting, in a while I realized I had better warm my left foot. And my hands had gone strangely very bad despite the double gloves. So I crawled into the tent to work on the foot.

Palmer, sitting under the brown blanket, was warming a stockinged foot with a lighted candle. The candle's green flame was close to his foot and the blanket.

I thought, "He's showing the same poor judgment he showed when he tried to overfly Erebus. If this tent goes up in flames, and presuming we escape, all our gear will go with it and we may well go under even though we've been found, for there's no telling how long it will be before they come for us, or *can* come for us."

I said, "Take it easy with the candle, Stu," but he didn't respond.

I asked Eights where the hand radio was. He said he had tried to communicate with the rescue helo both by beep and by voice but had failed even to pick up the craft, and had got so disgusted he had thrown the radio into the crashed helo's cabin.

"They should have dropped us a radio so they could tell us their plans," he said. "Or at least they could have dropped us a note."

When Palmer tired of the candle Eights asked for it and warmed his naked right hand over it, staring at the flame, and the flame singed the elbow of Enderby's parka and came close to the tent wall. Then, after I warned him, Eights set the candle down on a small piece of styrofoam and studied it, fascinated by the flame's unbelievably pure and intense green.

He and Enderby wondered aloud when the rescue attempt would be made and how. Would Coast Guard helos hazard an attempt? Or would a Herc try to skylift us out one at a time?

Palmer said, "They're not going to skylift *me*. You get a hell of a jerk when they do that. And you'd freeze to death before they pulled you inside."

The speculation between Enderby and Eights continued awhile.

Palmer said, "They can't take us out all together. We'll probably go out two at a time. We ought to decide who's going out first."

For myself, I didn't care whether I went out first or last. We had been found, and if I were the last to be scheduled to go, and got socked in by weather for days, my position was known, I'd have the sleeping bag to myself, and matches and candles, and I could lie low, and drink enough water to keep from getting seriously dehydrated, and I'd be fine.

I said, "I volunteer to go last."

After an awkward silence he said, "I'll go out with you."

"Take it easy," I told myself. "He did behave well in looking for the ridge. He did wave the helo off. He did invite you to fly in the cockpit with him. And possibly he did autorotate, select the landing spot, save our limbs if not our lives."

But later, when I returned to the tent after shooting some more while my companions were under the sleeping bag, Eights said, "You and I will go out last, Doc."

I said, "I thought Stu and I were going last."

"Stu's not feeling too good," Eights said.

Palmer said nothing.

As I slid beneath the blanket I expected to resent or even to hate him. I was wrong. My resentment seemed to have burned itself out at the time when I had told myself I couldn't afford it. Actually, I felt paternal toward him now, as I did toward the two young men, and discovered, on looking back on the long hours of hoping, that at times I had already felt that way toward him. I discovered also that I *had* been afraid at times, in little bursts, but that the essential thing was not whether one was afraid but whether one's fear could be controlled.

Then suddenly we heard a helo approaching—with that beautiful familiar chopping sound—and we were lacing our boots and crawling outside, and we spotted not one but two Coast Guard helicopters circling over Erebus, and the scene was unreal, for here we were on this ice and snow and rock shelf, and there was the red tent, well staked down, its rope taut, the cloth brilliant, and the stricken helo leaning to port, heavy on its hull, and Eights setting off violet smoke bombs, and up there was the volcano's summit, obscured by scud and smoke, and beyond the summit was a milky, wan sun, the summer sun that for months never set, the sun that had burned me badly at Royds, and up there in that fairyland the two helos were circling, feeling their way carefully, and I thought, "My God, that's hairy," and I wondered if they too would air-starve, and meanwhile the Herc watched over all of us, and I tried with all my might to observe and remember everything.

We had selected a landing pad—an apron of sloping, almost naked rock not too far from the tent—and Eights and Enderby now marked it with my green rucksack and some food cartons, and Eights signaled the first rescue helo (1377, from the *Staten Island*) to a landing. I naïvely stood nearby and watched the helo touch down. The blizzard caused by the rotors hit me full in the face, and my eyes were blasted by ice and snow particles. Blinded, I whirled to give the blizzard my back. After a moment, glancing at my frosted cameras sitting on the cabin floor, I saw that the lenses, or rather the UV filters, were white with snow. I wiped them clean with a gloved finger.

The pilot of 1377, Neil Nicholson, whom I knew, dressed lightly but looking confident and warm, left the craft and walked rapidly to 1404, his helmet making him look like a megacephalic Martian out of a science fiction tale. He came up beside me. I was studying my gear on the cabin floor, deciding what I had to take out with me. He touched my arm and asked with a glance of concern, "Are you all right?"

It struck me suddenly as extremely remarkable that the eerie, immense and in some ways marvelous silence of Mount Erebus was being shattered by 1377's barbaric sounds; yet I was grateful for those sounds; they were made by a *live* engine; and I found myself responding with a new and special intimacy to the noises a helo made as against those made by a C-130 like the one circling, circling above us.

I shook my head affirmatively.

Again he asked, "Are you all right?"

Again I shook my head.

"We've got to get out of here fast," he said. "The weather is very bad and may close in again. Leave everything behind except maybe a camera."

"I'm not leaving without my professional gear," I said.

He glanced at my face, shrugged, and walked away.

Enderby fetched the Kiwi mail from the cockpit and handed it to Palmer, who ran to 1377 and boarded it. Meanwhile the second rescue helo had disappeared. I hoped it hadn't crashed. It would be terrible if someone got killed while trying to save us. Taking my cameras, I went to an outcrop near 1377 and observed what Nicholson, his crewman (who was wearing a brilliant red flight suit) and Eights were doing to mark the pad for the second helo. A vivid red line was drawn on the outcrop to indicate the position of the front of the cockpit. Smoke bombs marked the position of the rear wheel. Nicholson had hung my blue towel from a tent pole as a wind sock and was now marking the pad with flares, dye markers and smoke bombs. The preparations were very colorful in the gauzelike, black-and-white terrain: red, orange and purple smoke poured along the base of the pad, was caught by the rotor blasts and sent northward, southward and then directly at me, choking me. Feeling tremendously lucky to be there with cameras that seemed to be functioning well, I believed this was my best moment on the ice. I kept warning myself to remember to check light meters, to advance frames slowly, to double-check focus, to compose carefully, and above all to work in slow motion, being mindful of the effects of high altitude on one's judgment.

Then I realized that my double-gloved hands had been screaming for some time, as if they were being crushed by giant pincers, and I wondered vaguely why they were making such a fuss—my face felt fine—and I wondered if reloading the cameras barehanded had something to do with it. The fact was that the double gloves were not sufficient protection for hand work at that temperature. One needed to wear bear paws to be comfortable. As we know, I had brought a pair in my survival bag but one of my companions was now using them.

And then Neil Nicholson stripped to the waist and replaced the towel with his undershirt because the towel was too heavy to flutter in the current breeze, and I thought, "It's thirty below and he has a small, very white paunch. He has a great deal of body heat from the warm helo to be able to do that."

I intended to photograph him like that but my hands failed to respond to my orders. All feeling had left them. I was not to regain full sensation in the finger ends for from six to eight months, and at this writing a certain amount of circulatory and neural damage seems to be permanent. I let my cameras hang from my neck while I clapped my gloved hands together. It was like clapping boards, for all the feeling there was in it. Enderby ran over to me and handed me the bear paws he had been wearing, and he ran to the helo and boarded it, and I kept slamming my hands together in the bear paws.

Suddenly Nicholson, now in the cockpit with his copilot who had never left the helo and who had not shut down the engine, raced the rotors for liftoff, and I stood there idiotically, having already forgotten what had happened when 1377 had hit the deck. My face felt as if it were hit by a metal curtain, and pellets of ice stung my eyeballs. I wheeled, and hung on to the outcrop, digging with my toes and bracing to be kept from being blown off. The helo's liftoff caused such a whiteout that for whole minutes nothing could be seen. The whiteout cleared, and, by God, there was the second helo, descending, and Eights ran to the pad and signaled it in.

"Let's go!" he shouted to me, and boarded the craft.

With gear hanging from my shoulders and cameras from my neck, I ran to the hatch and fumbled to climb aboard, but my knees were weak, my hands couldn't clutch, and my gear was pulling me backwards toward the pad. It was a high step to the cabin floor. The bearded crewman, warm, fresh, reached out above me, grabbed my armpits and with a tremendous jerk hauled me aboard.

I removed my gloves and fumbled with my seat belt. The crewman, noticing I was having trouble, belted me in. My hands were dead white, especially from the knuckles to the nails. To the left of my seat I felt a current of warm air. I hung my left hand down in it. The crewman bent over to increase the air flow. I warmed my hands in it alternately until they hurt very badly and I knew they would be all right. Eights slouched back in his seat, his long legs outstretched, his arms limp. His eyes were closed. The crewman offered us coffee. I had given up drinking coffee about a year ago, so I declined it.

"Gee, Doc, take it," Eights said. "At least it's warm to hold."

I accepted a cup.

The bearded crewman with his large blue eyes and foreign-sounding name—he was older than the usual crewman and looked mellower, wiser, perhaps also sadder—stared at us with a gentle, pensive, fatherly smile, now and then glancing almost lovingly at us. Eights, grinning, showed me a raised thumb.

"We're on our way down, Doc," he said. "I'll get the gear back to you."

I patted his knee and said, "You're a good boy, Jack. You behaved well."

His eyes filled with tears.

A little later he leaned toward me and in the roar of the engine and rotors said, "He said an admiral is going to greet us," by *he* meaning the bearded crewman.

I thought, "The admiral's in Cheechee, and no admiral is going to greet us in the middle of the night," but I let him have his pipe dream.

I sat staring at the floor and feeling the warmth slowly returning to my body.

Stepping down at the helo pad at McMurdo, where it was startlingly warm and bright, I glanced at my watch. The wheel had come full circle. We had crashed at about 2:30 P.M. It was now several minutes past three in the morning.

I remember the extraordinary emotion I felt at that moment when I expected McMurdo to be the ghost town it usually was at that hour. What seemed like a wave of human bodies slowly, methodically moved towards us, surrounding us, not speaking much, just smiling. Many people had been unable to sleep, apparently. They wanted to be at the pad when we got back.

While on the mountain I was convinced the crash episode didn't really get to me. A phone patch I had with my wife the day after I was rescued will give the reader some idea of what the experience did to me and how painful it was to recall it.

I was a bit reluctant to talk with her but I had been told that news releases had already gone out, and if she must learn about what had happened it was best she learn it from me and in advance. Would I behave well with her? Would I keep up my guard? For I must reassure her of my safety and well-being and must not let anything in my voice betray the emotions which I seemed to believe I had never had on Erebus. The distance between us was great, phone patches hard to come by, I must make my point casually and well. If I wasn't up to it it was better not to phone her at all.

The phone near my room in the corridor of the Lodge rang. It was the ham operator, asking if I was Charles Neider and how long I was going to talk. I explained that this was a high-priority patch approved by the x.o., that I was one of the guys who had crashed on Erebus and that as far as I knew there was no time limit on the patch.

"Yes, sir," he said.

I hung up, went to my room, drank some more scotch, lay down on my bed and stared at the ceiling, my heart pumping fast and hard.

The phone rang again. It was the same voice, this time saying, "Stand by, please. Don't hang up."

While my hands that had experienced a frost change went cold with nerves and suspense, I waited, feeling naked in the corridor and hoping no one would come along during the call.

Then she was on: that voice I knew so well, with a lilt and a gaiety, and I said, "There's something I want to tell you. If you read or hear about a helicopter accident down here and my name is mentioned don't be concerned. I'm fine, as you can hear from my telling you. I was involved in a crash. We crashed near the summit of Mount Erebus but were rescued after twelve hours and are all in good condition. So you're not to be concerned."

She asked for details. I provided them.

She said, "I'm flabbergasted."

Now and then, for example when I told her about my hands and glanced at them, my heart grew cold, I felt I was melting away, my voice dropped in pitch, it sounded unlike itself, my throat trembled, I did not dare to speak, I struggled to regain control, my jaws clamped shut, my eyes threatened to grow moist, something threatened to babble out of my voice box, and I grew icy with fear, for I must above all, above all carry it off well and not let her suspect there were unresolved forces fighting inside me, trying to overwhelm me, unman me. I kept thinking with horror that the sole purpose of this call was to spare her anxiety and that I was in great danger of doing precisely what I wanted to avoid. There were moments of hard silence when I lost my voice and when something terrible seemed to be threatening me. The silences terrified me. They must not be allowed to give me away. She must not realize that I was wrestling with something tremendously powerful, that one moment I was calm, objective, serene, then suddenly I was beset, especially when I spoke about myself in some detailed way. She must not be permitted to realize the horror of the wrestling match I was so unexpectedly going through. I fought, fought, rescued some semblance of a voice, managed a bit of humor and perspective.

"Is there anything the matter? Are you all right?" she asked.

"I've been drinking scotch. I guess I've drunk a fair amount," I said, relieved to have an excuse.

Then she said, perhaps glad to change the subject because of what she probably suspected, "Aren't we going over our time?"

I explained that this was a high-priority patch.

My feelings about continuing the patch were mixed. I was glad to be speaking with her but I obviously couldn't trust myself, and just as my heart on Erebus had seemed to be throbbing wildly in a rhythm all its own, so now my voice and jaws seemed to have deserted me for very urgent tasks and messages, they seemed to need to cry out something with enormous strength, something of highest priority, but also something which I was convinced would shame me. I knew my task if they didn't: it was to handle this call gracefully and with only one objective: my wife's peace of mind. If I flubbed it she would be badly upset, would decide I was covering up a serious injury, and I would not get another patch for some time, and a letter to her trying to set things right could take a long while reaching her.

Some merciful force appeared from nowhere to help me through. I steadied myself, and at last I managed to sign off decently. Once I hung up, that terrifying wrestling match ceased. I walked like a half-dead person to my room, lay down, closed my eyes and listened to echoes of the conversation, hearing significant parts of it and feeling I had made it by the skin of my teeth.

Exhausted, gathering my forces as best as I knew how, I was no longer prepared to believe I had been emotionless on Mount Erebus.